Reagents in the minerals industry

*Papers presented at the Reagents in the minerals industry conference, organized by
The Institution of Mining and Metallurgy in association with the
Consiglio Nazionale delle Ricerche, Istituto per il Trattamento dei Minerali,
and held in Rome, Italy, from 18 to 21 September, 1984*

Edited by Michael J. Jones and R. Oblatt

THE INSTITUTION OF MINING AND METALLURGY

Published by The Institution of Mining and Metallurgy
44 Portland Place
London W1
England

ISBN 0 900488 78 6

UDC 661.1:622.7

Printed in England by Stephen Austin/Hertford

Reagents in the minerals industry

Foreword

In October, 1980, the Institution of Mining and Metallurgy, in association with the Istituto per il Trattamento dei Minerali of the Consiglio Nazionale delle Ricerche, organized a very successful conference in Rome on the topic 'complex sulphide ores'. Two years later our Italian colleagues suggested that a second conference, based on some aspect of mineral processing, might be held in Rome in 1984. Informal discussions, initially in Toronto between Michael Jones and Professor Anna Marabini and subsequently in London and Rome, showed that there would be an interest in a meeting devoted to the study of reagents that are used in the minerals industry.

The Organizing Committee was established and papers from industry and the academic world were requested. A large number of abstracts were offered and the present volume is the result of an extensive reviewing procedure. The committee is hopeful that the selected papers, together with the discussion that will follow their presentation, will add to our knowledge of the chemicals that are used in mineral treatment and bring out valuable information on new developments.

As in 1980, a more agreeable venue than Rome in autumn can hardly be imagined, and the Organizing Committee is most grateful to Professor Marabini and her colleagues for their help in arranging the venue of the conference, the various social functions and the technical visits that are part of the programme.

The minerals industry has, as always, given generous support, as has the European Commission as part of its policy of aiding meetings that serve to improve the effectiveness of industry throughout the Community. The financial assistance of the European Commission, Farmitalia Carlo Erba, Interox Chimica S.p.A., Stazione Sperimentale del Vetro, Wemco-Unitec Europe and Wemco (UK), Ltd., is gratefully acknowledged.

The support of the following in regard to the conference technical tours is also much appreciated: Istituto Donegani—Società Montedison, Farmitalia Carlo Erba, Samim, Pertusola, Centro Ricerche Venete Samim, Bariosarda, Eurallumina, Silius and Progemisa.

K. A. Fern
Co-Chairman, Organizing Committee
August, 1984

Organizing Committee

K. A. Fern (*Co-Chairman*) (*Company Director and Consultant, Carshalton, Surrey, England*)

Anna M. Marabini (*Co-Chairman*) (*Professor and Director, Istituto per il Trattamento dei Minerali, Consiglio Nazionale delle Ricerche, Rome, Italy*)

C. Abbruzzese (*Istituto per il Trattamento dei Minerali, Consiglio Nazionale delle Ricerche, Rome, Italy*)

G. Bottaccio (*Istituto Guido Donegani, Novara, Italy*)

P. Bourdeau (*European Economic Community, Brussels, Belgium*)

J. V. Bramley (*Laporte Minerals, Eyam, Derbyshire, England*)

H. E. Cohen (*Department of Mineral Resources Engineering, Imperial College, London, England*)

M. Donato (*European Economic Community, Brussels, Belgium*)

M. Ghiani (*Istituto di Arte Mineraria e Trattamento dei Minerali, University of Cagliari, Sardinia*)

P. M. J. Gray (*Metallurgical Consultant, London, England*)

M. J. Jones (*Secretary, Institution of Mining and Metallurgy, London, England*)

P. Massacci (*Istituto di Arte Mineraria, Università degli Studi di Roma 'La Sapienza', Rome, Italy*)

E. Occella (*Istituto di Arte Mineraria del Politecnico, Turin, Italy*)

M. J. Pearse (*Allied Colloids, Ltd., Bradford, England*)

G. Rinelli (*Istituto per il Trattamento dei Minerali, Consiglio Nazionale delle Ricerche, Rome, Italy*)

D. Watson (*Warren Spring Laboratory, Stevenage, Hertfordshire, England*)

P. Gill (*Organizing Committee Secretary*)

List of authors

Ackerman P. K. Mineral Processing Section, The Pennsylvania State University, University Park, Pennsylvania, U.S.A.

Alesse V. Istituto per il Trattamento dei Minerali, CNR, Rome, Italy

Alfano G. Dipartimento di Ingegneraria Mineraria e Mineralurgica e Centro Studi Geominerari e Mineralurgici del CNR, Università di Cagliari, Italy

Alferiev I. S. Institute of Chemical Kinetics and Combustion, Siberian Department of the Academy of Sciences of the U.S.S.R., Novosibirsk, U.S.S.R.

Antti Britt-Marie Division of Mineral Processing, Luleå University of Technology, Luleå, Sweden

Aplan F. F. Mineral Processing Section, The Pennsylvania State University, University Park, Pennsylvania, U.S.A.

Barbaro M. Istituto per il Trattamento dei Minerali, CNR, Rome, Italy

Barbucci R. Dipartimento di Chimica, Siena, Italy

Barino L. Istituto Guido Donegani S.p.A., Novara, Italy

Belardi G. Dipartimento di Ingegneraria Chimica, dei materiali, della materie prime e metalurgia, Università di Roma La Sapienza, Rome, Italy

Bernasconi P. Laboratoire de Chimie et Electrochimie Analytique, Université de Nancy, Vandoeuvre-lès-Nancy, France

Bessière J. Laboratoire de Chimie et Electrochimie Analytique, Université de Nancy, Vandoeuvre-lès-Nancy, France

Bonifazi G. Istituto per il Trattamento dei Minerali, CNR, Rome, Italy

Bornengo G. Istituto Guido Donegani S.p.A., Novara, Italy

Bottacio G. Istituto Guido Donegani S.p.A., Novara, Italy

Burneau A. Laboratoire de Spectrométrie des Vibrations, Université de Nancy I, Vandoeuvre Cédex, France

Buttinelli D. Department of Chemical Engineering, University of Rome, Rome, Italy

Carlini F. M. Istituto Guido Donegani S.p.A., Novara, Italy

Cases J. M. Centre de Recherche sur la Valorisation des Minerais de l'E.N.S.G. et L.A. 235 du CNRS 'Minéralurgie', Vandoeuvre Cédex, France

Chen Jingqing Guangzhou Institute of Non-Ferrous Metals, Guangdong Province, China

Clerici C. Dipartimento di Georisorse e Territorio, Politecnico di Torino e Centro di Studio per i Problemi Minerari del C.N.R., Turin, Italy

Collins D. N. Warren Spring Laboratory, Stevenage, Hertfordshire, England

Corezzi S. Dipartimento di Chimica, Siena, Italy

Dalton R. F. Imperial Chemical Industries PLC, Organics Division, Blackley, Manchester, England

Dautzenberg Horst Institute of Polymer Chemistry, Teltow-Seehof, German Democratic Republic

Del Fà C. Dipartimento di Ingegneraria Mineraria e Mineralurgica e Centro Studi Geominerari e Mineralurgici del CNR, Università di Cagliari, Italy

Dietzel Wolfgang Institute of Polymer Chemistry, Teltow-Seehof, German Democratic Republic

Dobiás B. University of Regensburg, Regensburg, Federal Republic of Germany

Egorov N. V. Central Research Institute of the Tin Industry, Ministry of Non-Ferrous Metals, Novosibirsk, U.S.S.R.

Forssberg K. S. E. Division of Mineral Processing, Luleå University of Technology, Luleå, Sweden

Frisa Morandini A. Dipartimento di Georisorse e Territorio, Politecnico di Torino e Centro di Studio per i Problemi Minerari del C.N.R., Turin, Italy

Fuerstenau D. W. Department of Materials Science and Mineral Engineering, University of California, Berkeley, California, U.S.A.

Garbassi F. Istituto Guido Donegani S.p.A., Novara, Italy   ·

Ghiani M. Dipartimento di Ingegneria Mineraria, Centro CNR, Università di Cagliari, Italy

Giavarini C. Department of Chemical Engineering, University of Rome, Rome, Italy

Giesekke E. W. Council for Mineral Technology, Mintek, Randburg, South Africa

Gil J. P. Instituto de Investigaciones Mineras, Universidad Nacional de San Juan, San Juan, Argentina

Gurvich S. M. Gintsvetmet, Moscow, U.S.S.R.

Gutierrez L. V. Instituto de Investigaciones Mineras, Universidad Nacional de San Juan, San Juan, Argentina

Haber Jerzy Institute of Catalysis and Surface Chemistry, Polish Academy of Sciences, Kraków, Poland

Harris G. H. Lately Dow Chemical Co., Midland, Michigan, U.S.A.

Harris P. J. Council for Mineral Technology, Mintek, Randburg, South Africa

Healey A. F. Warren Spring Laboratory, Stevenage, Hertfordshire, England

Hoghooghi B. Center for Research in Mining and Mineral Resources, Department of Materials Science and Engineering, University of Florida, Gainesville, Florida, U.S.A.

Kelsall G. H. Department of Mineral Resources Engineering, Imperial College, London, England

Klimpel R. R. Mineral Processing Section, The Pennsylvania State University, University Park, Pennsylvania, U.S.A., and Dow Chemical Co., Midland, Michigan, U.S.A.

Kong Dekun Guangzhou Institute of Non-Ferrous Metals, Guangdong Province, China

Kongolo M. Centre de Recherche sur la Valorisation des Minerais de l'E.N.S.G. et L.A. 235 du CNRS 'Minéralurgie', Vandoeuvre Cédex, France

Kotlyarevsky I. L. Institute of Chemical Kinetics and Combustion, Siberian Department of the Academy of Sciences of the U.S.S.R., Novosibirsk, U.S.S.R.

Kowal Andrzej Institute of Catalysis and Surface Chemistry, Polish Academy of Sciences, Kraków, Poland

Kowal Joanna Faculty of Chemistry, Jagiellonian University, Kraków, Poland

Krasnukhina A. V. Central Research Institute of the Tin Industry, Ministry of Non-Ferrous Metals, Novosibirsk, U.S.S.R.

Laapas Heikki Helsinki University of Technology, Department of Mining and Metallurgy, Espoo, Finland

Lahtinen Ulla-Riitta Helsinki University of Technology, Department of Mining and Metallurgy, Espoo, Finland

Laskowski J. S. Department of Mining and Mineral Process Engineering, The University of British Columbia, Vancouver, British Columbia, Canada

Lukkarinen Toimi Helsinki University of Technology, Department of Mining and Metallurgy, Espoo, Finland

Ma Jiwu Baiyin Research Institute of Mining and Metallurgy, China

Mancini A. Geomineraria Italiana s.r.l., Turin, Italy

Mancini R. Dipartimento di Georisorse e Territorio, Politecnico di Torino e Centro di Studio per i Problemi Minerari del C.N.R., Turin, Italy

Marabini A. M. Istituto per il Trattamento dei Minerali, CNR, Rome, Italy

Marinakis K. I. Department of Mineral Resources Engineering, Imperial College, London, England

Massacci P. Dipartimento di Ingegneraria Chimica, dei materiali, della materie prime e metalurgia, Università di Roma La Sapienza, Rome, Italy

Matar J. A. Instituto de Investigaciones Mineras, Universidad Nacional de San Juan, San Juan, Argentina

Mathieu G. I. Energy, Mines and Resources Canada, CANMET, Ottawa, Ontario, Canada

Melven D. Warren Spring Laboratory, Stevenage, Hertfordshire, England

Mercanti A. Department of Chemical Engineering, University of Rome, Rome, Italy

Miller J. D. Department of Metallurgy, University of Utah, Salt Lake City, Utah, U.S.A.

Mingione P. A. Cyanamid International, Chemicals Division, Mining Technical Sales Service, Stamford, Connecticut, U.S.A.

Moudgil B. M. Center for Research in Mining and Mineral Resources, Department of Materials Science and Engineering, University of Florida, Gainesville, Florida, U.S.A.

Nagaraj D. R. Formerly Columbia University in the City of New York, New York, U.S.A. (now American Cyanamid Company, Stamford, Connecticut, U.S.A.)

Niewiara Robert Institute of Catalysis and Surface Chemistry, Polish Academy of Sciences, Kraków, Poland

Nocentini M. Dipartimento di Chimica, Siena, Italy

Pålsson B. I. Division of Mineral Processing, Luleå University of Technology, Luleå, Sweden

Parsonage P. Warren Spring Laboratory, Stevenage, Hertfordshire, England

Passariello B. Istituto per il Trattmento dei Minerali, CNR, Rome, Italy

Pearse M. J. Allied Colloids PLC, Bradford, England

Peretti R. Dipartimento di Ingegneraria Mineraria e Mineralurgica e Centro Studi Geominerari e Mineralurgici del CNR, Università di Cagliari, Italy

Pomazov V. D. Central Research Institute of the Tin Industry, Ministry of Non-Ferrous Metals, Novosibirsk, U.S.S.R.

Pradip Department of Materials Science and Mineral Engineering, University of California, Berkeley, California, U.S.A.

Prédali J. J. Minemet Recherche, Trappes Cédex, France

Price R. Imperial Chemical Industries PLC, Organics Division, Blackley, Manchester, England

Quan P. M. Imperial Chemical Industries PLC, Organics Division, Blackley, Manchester, England

Ransdell J. C. Center for Research in Mining and Mineral Resources, Department of Materials Science and Engineering, University of Florida, Gainesville, Florida, U.S.A.

Rubio J. Department of Metallurgical Engineering, Universidade Federal do Rio Grande do Sul, Porto Alegre, Brazil

Rybinski W. von Henkel KGaA, Dusseldorf, Federal Republic of Germany

Sarquís P. E. Instituto de Investigaciones Mineras, Universidad Nacional de San Juan, San Juan, Argentina

Satta F. Dipartimento di Ingegneria Mineraria, Centro CNR, Università di Cagliari, Italy

Schulz P. A. University of Regensburg, Regensburg, Federal Republic of Germany

Schwuger M. J. Henkel KGaA, Dusseldorf, Federal Republic of Germany

Scordamaglia R. Istituto Guido Donegani S.p.A., Novara, Italy

Selivanova N. V. Vniitsvetmet, Kamenogorsk, U.S.S.R.

Seward G. W. Acorga, Ltd., Blackley, Manchester, England

Shcherbakov V. A. Gintsvetmet, Moscow, U.S.S.R.

Sirois L. L. Energy, Mines and Resources Canada, CANMET, Ottawa, Ontario, Canada

Solari J. A. Formerly Department of Metallurgical Engineering, Universidade Federal do Rio Grande do Sul, Porto Alegre, Brazil (now Department of Mining and Mineral Process Engineering, University of British Columbia, Vancouver, Canada)

Smith R. W. Department of Chemical and Metallurgical Engineering, Mackay School of Mines, University of Nevada Reno, Nevada, U.S.A.

Somasundaran P. Columbia University in the City of New York, New York, U.S.A.

Sun Kuoxiong Baiyin Research Institute of Mining and Metallurgy, China

Townson B. Imperial Chemical Industries PLC, Organics Division, Blackley, Manchester, England

Van Deventer J. S. J. Department of Chemical and Metallurgical Engineering, University of Stellenbosch, South Africa

Watson D. Warren Spring Laboratory, Stevenage, Hertfordshire, England

Wei Tien-Lin Department of Chemical and Metallurgical Engineering, Mackay School of Mines, University of Nevada Reno, Nevada, U.S.A.

Wright R. Warren Spring Laboratory, Stevenage, Hertfordshire, England

Yu Longling Baiyin Research Institute of Mining and Metallurgy, China

Zhou Weizhi Guangzhou Institute of Non-Ferrous Metals, Guangdong Province, China

Zucca A. Dipartimento di Ingegneraria Mineraria e Mineralurgica e Centro Studi Geominerari e Mineralurgici del CNR, Università di Cagliari, Italy

Zuleta M. Instituto de Investigaciones Mineras, Universidad Nacional de San Juan, San Juan, Argentina

Contents

Use of alkyl imino-bis-methylene phosphonic acids as collectors for oxide and salt-type minerals

D. N. Collins, R. Wright and D. Watson

Synopsis

Vacuum flotation experiments have indicated that the imino-bis-methylene phosphonic acids (IBMPA) have potential as collectors for the selective flotation of minerals.

Twenty-two minerals were tested over a wide pH range with IBMPA collectors with chain lengths varying from *n*-propyl (3 carbon) to dodecyl (12 carbon). The flotation response varied in both the chain length required to promote flotation and in the pH sensitivity of the position of the incipient flotation areas.

Both of these effects give rise to potential areas of selectivity: for example, with the alkaline-earth salt minerals the relative floatability was baryte > fluorite > calcite > apatite > dolomite > scheelite with selection of reagents in the C_4–C_8 chain length. A batch flotation test on a carbonatite ore has shown good selectivity between apatite and dolomite under the indicated conditions.

The pH sensitivity gave rise to potential selectivity in the oxide minerals studied: some minerals are more responsive at acid pH, some have two areas of flotation and one mineral responds specifically in the alkaline region. Some silicate minerals (e.g. garnet and tourmaline) show greater flotation areas than many of the oxide minerals, especially in the acid pH ranges, and, although in some cases (e.g. with wolframite and cassiterite) a flotation 'edge' is available in the neutral pH range, it is generally indicated that the use of specific silicate depressants will be necessary to achieve good oxide–silicate separation. The relative order of floatability of the oxides was hematite, wolframite, cassiterite, chromite, rutile, columbite–tantalite, monazite, pyrochlore and uraninite. Batch testwork on a cassiterite ore indicated a high degree of selectivity with respect to the mafic silicates when depressants were used. The 2-ethyl hexyl derivative compares favourably with styrene phosphonic acid (SPA) as a collector for this mineral. Good results have also been achieved in the flotation of wolframite with the *n*-octyl compound.

The paper is based on work done for Albright and Wilson, Ltd., on the evaluation of alkyl imino-bis-methylene phosphonic acids for potential use as collectors for the flotation of ore minerals.

The amino phosphonic acids are sequestering agents for a number of multivalent metal ions and some are in commercial use for scale inhibition and corrosion control. When, as part of the present programme of work, alkyl substituted imino phosphonic acids of the general structure shown in (I) were considered for possible use as flotation collectors, it was thought that the compounds would need to have an alkyl group of significant chain length. The

$$R{-}N\diagdown \begin{matrix} CH_2P{=}\!\!\!<^{OH}_{OH} \\ CH_2P{=}\!\!\!<^{OH}_{OH} \end{matrix} \qquad (I)$$

study was therefore concentrated on the alkyl chain length range C_3–C_{12} and sodium salts of the reagents were prepared because of their very high water solubilities.

Initial screening of the reagents was carried out by vacuum flotation test procedures on a variety of different mineral systems, principally of the oxide and salt mineral types, to identify the response of these minerals over the pH range and to establish the carbon chain length required. Some preliminary batch flotation studies have been included on cassiterite and phosphate samples.

Description of reagents and minerals examined

The list of reagents examined is shown in Table 1 and the minerals used, together with the source and notional formulae, are shown in Table 2.

Vacuum flotation testwork

Procedure

Tests were performed in standard glass tubes attached to a vacuum pump by a six-branch manifold. Reagent stock solutions were made up at 0.1% active strength and used the same day. pH was controlled by means of dilute sulphuric acid or sodium hydroxide solution, as required. Reagent quantities were measured into the glass tube by means of disposable pipettes, which were used for one reagent and then discarded. The total volume of liquid in each tube was 25 ml, the balance, after allowing for reagent addition, being distilled water.

The water was first placed in the tube and then a standard volume (0.20 ml) of mineral sample was added. The mineral particles were $-0.150 + 0.075$ mm in size and were prepared by grinding in a stainless-steel mill, sizing and storage under distilled water. The tube was then placed on an automatic shaker for 2 min to condition the mineral to the selected pH. The collector was then added and the tube was returned to the shaker for a 2-min conditioning. The tube was then attached to the manifold and the vacuum was applied. After the flotation had been observed, the tube was removed from the manifold and the pH of the solution was measured and recorded. The flotation behaviour of the mineral in the tube was recorded either as full float, three-quarter float or nil float.

Each of five float tests consisted of tests at one pH value but different reagent concentrations. The concentrations tested were 10, 20, 50, 100 and 200 ppm (active). Sets of tests were carried out at different pH values but over the same range of reagent concentrations. By plotting the

Table 1 Reagents tested (cassiterite and wolframite)

Briquest® reagent	Sodium salt
231–25S*	*iso*-propyl imino-bis-methylene phosphonic acid
2N31–25S	*n*-propyl imino-bis-methylene phosphonic acid
2N41–25S	*n*-butyl imino-bis-methylene phosphonic acid
2N61–25S	*n*-hexyl imino-bis-methylene phosphonic acid
2N71–25S	*n*-heptyl imino-bis-methylene phosphonic acid
281–25S	2-ethyl hexyl imino-bis-methylene phosphonic acid
2N81–25S	*n*-octyl imino-bis-methylene phosphonic acid
291–25S	*iso*-nonyl imino-bis-methylene phosphonic acid
2121–25S	dodecyl imino-bis-methylene phosphonic acid

Briquest® is a trade mark of Albright and Wilson, Ltd. 25S*, sodium salt (25% active).

flotation values for all these tests on a graph of pH versus reagent concentration it was possible to draw a flotation area for the mineral and reagent under test.

Although the magnitude of flotation was based on a personal visual assessment, the full flotation area represented flotation of large agglomerates of mineral to the surface of the liquid with some retention of these agglomerates at the surface. Three-quarter flotation represented flotation of agglomerates to the surface but with no retention at the surface. All other states were classified as non-flotation.

Two sets of tests were carried out. In the first the effect of carbon chain length was studied with the minerals cassiterite and wolframite only. Both minerals were tested with all nine collectors listed in Table 1. In the second set the comparative response of different minerals was investigated. To restrict the amount of testwork a reagent of intermediate flotation response (*n*-octyl) was tested with the 22 minerals of Table 2. Later, some more weakly floating

Table 2 Description and sources of mineral samples

Mineral	Origin	Notional formula
Apatite	India	$Ca_5F(PO_4)_3$
Barite	Pennines (U.K.)	$BaSO_4$
Calcite	Mendips (U.K.)	$CaCO_3$
Cassiterite	Malaya	SnO_2
Chlorite	California	$(Mg,Fe)_5Al(AlSi_3)O_{10}(OH)_9$
Chromite	Philippines	$FeCr_2O_4$
Columbite	Nigeria	$(Fe,Mn)Nb_2O_6$
Dolomite	Leicester (U.K.)	$CaMg(CO_3)_2$
Fluorite	Pennines (U.K.)	CaF_2
Garnet	Australia	$A''_3B''_2(SiO_4)_3$ A = Ca, Mg, Fe or Mn; B = Fe, Al, Cr or Ti
Garnierite	Oregon	$(Ni,Mg)SiO_3 . nH_2O$
Hematite	Labrador	Fe_2O_3
Monazite	Nigeria	$(Ce,La,Y,Th)PO_4$
Pyrochlore	Nigeria	$(Na,Ca)_2(Nb,Ta)_2O_6(O,OH,F)$
Quartz	Brazil	SiO_2
Rutile	Australia	TiO_2
Scheelite	Bolivia	$CaWO_4$
Smithsonite	Arizona	$ZnCO_3$
Tantalite	Manitoba	$(Fe,Mn)Ta_2O_6$
Tourmaline (schorlite)	Devon (U.K.)	$XY_3Al_6(BO_3)_3(Si_6O_{15})(OH)_4$ (X = Na,Ca Y = Mg,Fe^{2+},Al,Li)
Uraninite	Canada	UO_2
Wolframite	France	$(Fe,Mn)WO_4$

minerals were examined with two longer-chain collectors and strongly floating minerals with two lower-chain length collectors.

Results

General

The results obtained are shown in Figs. 1–7. The flotation response varied in both the chain length required to promote flotation and in the pH sensitivity of the position of the incipient flotation areas.

Thus, barite and fluorite are strong floaters, even with a C_4 chain length collector, and the onset of flotation would be expected to be associated with even shorter chain length collectors. The onset of calcite flotation occurs with the C_4 collector, that of apatite and dolomite flotation occurs with the C_6 collector and that for scheelite with the C_8 collector. The different sizes of the flotation areas for a given chain length compound therefore suggest the existence of an 'envelope' between different minerals wherein selective flotation can be achieved, that on the alkaline side probably being the most relevant. A selection can therefore be made of the appropriate member of the homologous series to enable the desired separation between two or more minerals to be achieved to maximize the selectivity potential.

In addition to the chain length effect, the minerals show distinct differences in response to pH changes when floated with these collectors. Some are more responsive at acid pH, some have two areas of flotation and one mineral responds specifically in the alkaline region. These different effects give rise to potential areas of selectivity for different types of minerals—the alkaline-earth salt types for discrimination by chain length and the oxide types for discrimination by pH. Before the response of these two groups is discussed the general effect of chain length is described.

Effect of chain length on cassiterite and wolframite flotation

The effect of collector chain length was studied with the minerals wolframite and cassiterite initially, the flotation areas obtained being shown in Figs. 1 and 2.

The range of flotation response (three-quarters) tends to show a similar trend for both minerals. No significant response was obtained for the *iso*-propyl, *n*-propyl or *n*-butyl derivatives, but from hexyl to dodecyl the flotation response starts at acid pH and the area becomes progressively larger, extending over a wider pH range until, for the longest chain length reagent, the area covers the whole of the pH range examined (2–11). The *iso*-nonyl and dodecyl derivatives additionally show full flotation areas over a wide pH range. There is a general tendency for wolframite to float over a slightly larger range of conditions than the cassiterite with a particular collector, although the overall response of both minerals to the reagents was markedly similar. The intermediate chain length collectors (2-ethyl hexyl, *n*-octyl and *iso*-nonyl) tend to show two areas of maximum effectiveness—one under very acid conditions and the other in the neutral pH range. This effect is highly pronounced for the *n*-octyl compound for cassiterite (Fig. 2), no flotation being observed between pH 3 and 4.5. No explanation can be given for this phenomenon, or if it is a function of the collector or the mineral, but a similar response has been observed before with cassiterite with *n*-octyl acid phosphate[1] and the presence of metal ions (Ca^{++}, Fe^{+++}) in solution has also been found[2] to have a similar effect on cassiterite flotation response, causing greatest depression in the intermediate pH range.

The 2-ethyl hexyl derivative has a flotation response

intermediate to the *n*-heptyl and *n*-octyl derivatives for the cassiterite, but an area intermediate to the *n*-hexyl and the *n*-heptyl for the wolframite. The overall effect of the branch chain is therefore to reduce the area in relation to total number of carbons in the chain, but to increase the area with respect to chain length. The degree of area change is obviously mineral-dependent and this could have some effect on reagent selectivity.

showed a similar type of response to calcite, but generally had a smaller flotation area and did not respond to flotation above pH 9. Dolomite produced only a moderate flotation area and flotation was restricted to the pH 5–8 range and for scheelite, which also floated at these pH values, the flotation area was restricted to very high levels of collector concentration. In terms of flotation potential the minerals respond in the order baryte ≡ fluorite > calcite > apatite

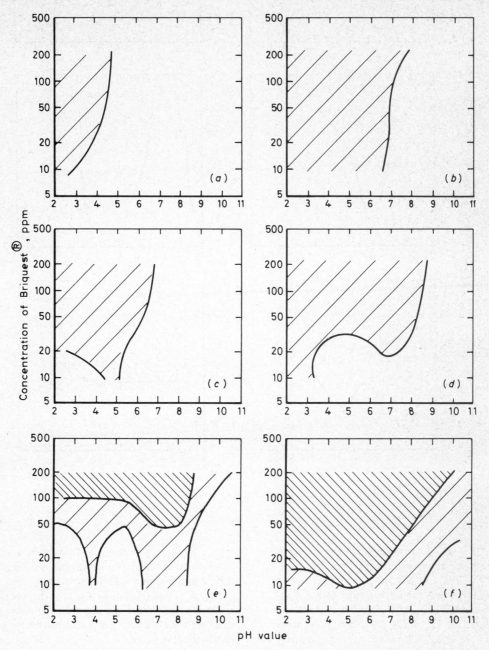

Fig. 1   Flotation curves for wolframite with collectors of varying chain length: (*a*), reagent 2N61–25S; (*b*), 2N71–25S; (*c*), 281–25S; (*d*), 2N81–25S; (*e*), 291–25S; (*f*), 2121–25S

Selectivity in alkaline-earth salt group
The flotation diagrams of the alkaline-earth salt minerals with the *n*-octyl derivative are shown in Fig. 3. The two most floatable minerals, baryte and fluorite, give a strong flotation response over the whole pH range investigated. Calcite floated over a wide range, but its response fell at both the acid and alkaline extremes, which indicates a potential separation pH (from baryte or fluorite), particularly in the very alkaline region (pH > 10). Apatite

> dolomite > scheelite with good potential for separation of baryte and fluorite from calcite, calcite from apatite and apatite from dolomite. Previous testwork with sodium oleate as collector on the baryte, fluorite, calcite and apatite showed no separation potential. The most unusual result, however, is the relatively poor flotation area achieved with the scheelite, which normally floats strongly with oleic acid[3] and has a flotation area similar to that of calcite with this collector. In practice the separation of scheelite from both

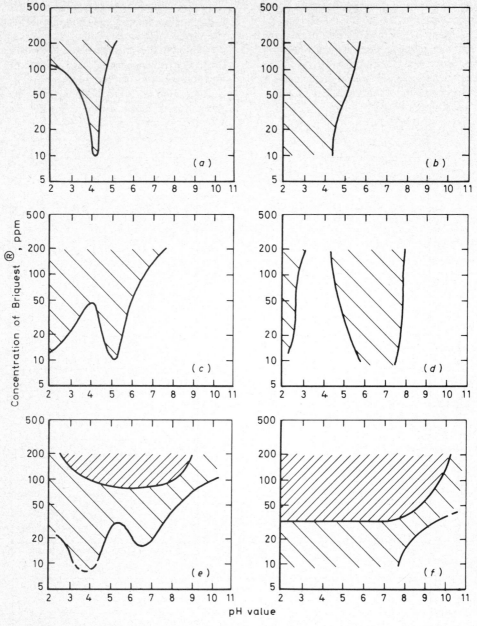

Fig. 2   Flotation curves for cassiterite with collectors of varying chain length (reagents for (a)–(f) as in Fig. 1)

calcite and fluorite is difficult and the potential for reverse flotation of these minerals from scheelite could be significant.

The use of shorter chain length collectors (n-hexyl and n-butyl) still resulted in large flotation areas for both the baryte and fluorite (see Fig. 4(a)–(d)), although the areas of full flotation were drastically reduced for the shortest chain length compound. A potential separation area for baryte is developing with the n-butyl compound at high pH (>9.5).

The flotation areas of both these minerals with respect to calcite have improved with the shorter chain length collectors (Fig. 4(a)–(f)) with potential flotation of baryte and/or fluorite at pH >9 (n-hexyl) and pH >8 (n-butyl).

The areas of apatite and dolomite flotation have been reduced with the n-hexyl derivative (Fig. 5(a) and (b)) and no flotation was observed for either mineral with the n-butyl compound. Selectivity between the minerals has not been improved with the shorter chain length collector, owing to a greater relative reduction in the apatite area. The use of the branched-chain 2-ethyl hexyl derivative (Fig. 5(c)

and (d)) has, surprisingly, led to an increase in both flotation areas and, more important, to a larger area for differential flotation (pH 8–10).

Fig. 5((e) and (f)) shows that the scheelite area has increased significantly by use of longer chain collectors, but even with the dodecyl compound the flotation is not strong in the alkaline range.

Selectivity in oxide group

In addition to the cassiterite and wolframite previously examined, other oxide minerals were also studied with the n-octyl derivative (Fig. 6). Hematite (Fig. 6(a)) floated very strongly below pH 7.5 and flotation extended up to pH 8. In comparison with the data obtained for cassiterite and wolframite it is clear that little separation of these minerals will be achieved in the absence of depressants. Chromite (Fig. 6(b)) also floated strongly at near neutral pH (5.5–7.0), with a wider area of flotation at high collector concentrations (pH 3.5–8.0). Columbite, tantalite and monazite (Fig. 6(c)–(e)) floated moderately well under acid pH conditions with maximum flotation around pH 5–6 for

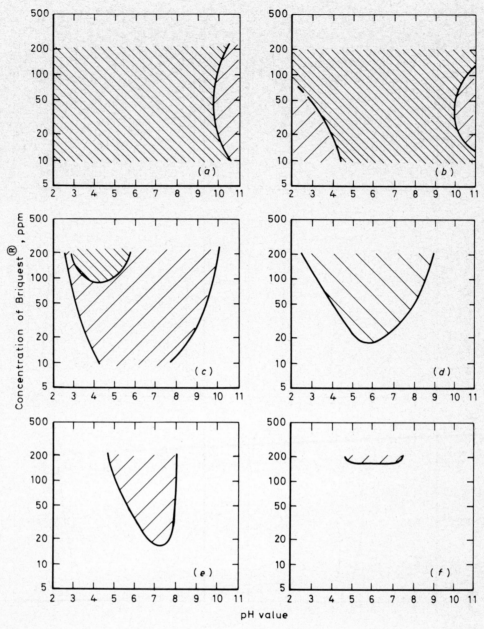

Fig. 3   Flotation curves for salt minerals with *n*-octyl derivative: (*a*), baryte; (*b*), fluorite; (*c*), calcite; (*d*), apatite; (*e*), dolomite; (*f*), scheelite (reagent 2N81–25S used throughout)

the latter two minerals. Columbite was quite strongly floating under very acid conditions. Rutile (Fig. 6(*f*)) floated only at very high collector concentrations and did not respond to longer chain length collectors. Coloration of the solution was, however, observed above this mineral on storage and oxidation of the surface was suspected. Acid (H$_2$SO$_4$) washing of the rutile at pH 3 followed by a water wash did result in a significant flotation area below pH 7 (Fig. 7(*d*)). This method of pretreatment restored the cassiterite flotation area, which also tended to deteriorate when the mineral was stored for long periods. It can be argued that acid pretreatment under these conditions restored the flotation properties to those which were achieved with fresh mineral surfaces and that freshly ground rutile would probably have a flotation area as shown in Fig. 7(*d*). Pyrochlore showed no tendency to float with the *n*-octyl derivative and very little flotation area was achieved with the *iso*-nonyl compound, but quite a strong flotation area was obtained in the pH 8–11 region with the dodecyl compound (Fig. 7(*e*) and (*f*)) and selectivity might be expected with respect to silicates in this pH range.

Uraninite showed no significant flotation areas with any of the collectors.

The silicate mineral flotation curves shown in Fig. 7(*a*)–(*c*)) have relevance to oxide mineral flotation since these minerals are often associated with many oxide ores. Silica itself showed no flotation area with the *n*-octyl derivative, but garnet (Fig. 7(*a*)) floated strongly below pH 7 and tourmaline (schorlite) floated strongly below pH 6 (Fig. 7(*b*)). Chlorite (Fig. 7(*c*)) floated less strongly, but flotation extended over the whole pH range and was at a maximum at around pH 5–6. On this evidence the selectivity of the collector for the oxides in relation to the silicates is not good. Garnet and tourmaline would float as strongly as most oxide minerals, the only significant flotation areas being in the pH 6–8 region for wolframite, hematite and cassiterite. Chlorite would show some tendency to float with all oxide minerals and, apart from the above three oxide minerals, would have an optimum range very similar to most of the oxides. Depression of chlorite may be possible at very acid pH (rutile and columbite float well under these conditions), but there are likely to be problems under very

5

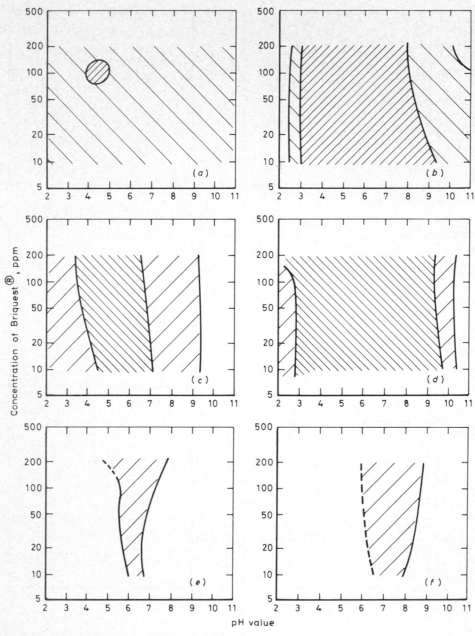

Fig. 4 Flotation curves for baryte ((*a*) and (*b*)), fluorite ((*c*) and (*d*)) and calcite ((*e*) and (*f*)) (reagents 2N41–25S and 2N61–25S used throughout)

acid pH conditions with the release of cations from the ore and the sequestering action of this collector type with cations such as Fe and Ca.

Differential flotation of oxides from silicates often relies on the use of specific depressants for silicate minerals (e.g. Na_2SiF_6 and Na_2SiO_3). These are currently used in the flotation of cassiterite,[4] wolframite[5] and tantalite[6] from mafic silicates with styrene phosphonic acid, sulphosuccinamate and other anionic collectors. Our own experience in wolframite, cassiterite and rutile flotation has also proved the need for depressants and, in particular, the use of Na_2SiF_6 has led to significant improvements in process selectivity. Most depressants do modify the flotation area of the oxide minerals and Na_2SiF_6, for example, has been found to reduce the optimum flotation pH of cassiterite with the collector *iso*-heptyl phosphonic acid to lower pH values.[2] The effectiveness of any collector for oxide mineral flotation is therefore dependent on the selective action of depressants with that collector, which may influence the optimum flotation pH. The fact that the current study has shown only hematite, wolframite and

cassiterite to be potentially separable from mafic silicates may, therefore, not discount the possibility of separating other oxide minerals, but the relative order of floatability of the oxides may be significant in their ultimate response.

Summary of vacuum flotation test data

A summary of the vacuum flotation data and potential application areas is shown in Table 3 (included are some inferential data on alternative collectors and comments on the necessity for using depressants).

Batch flotation testwork

Cassiterite flotation
To compare the performance of the alkyl imino-bis-methylene phosphonic acids with styrene phosphonic acid (SPA) as collectors for cassiterite tests were performed on a Cornish tin ore containing significant quantities of chlorite and tourmaline. The conditions selected were based on those previously used for the styrene phosphonic acid with

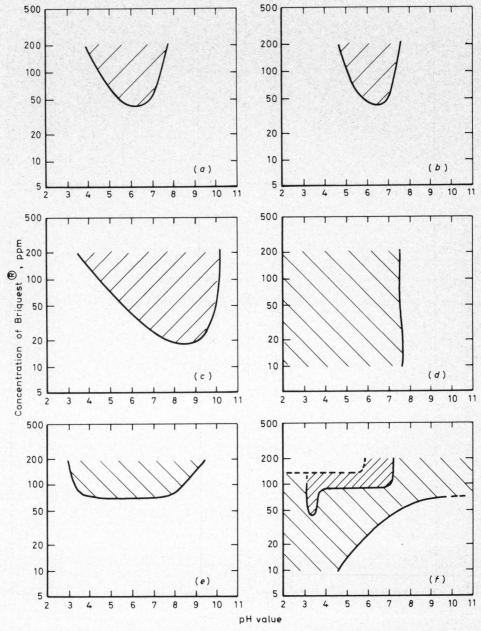

Fig. 5 Flotation curves for apatite ((a), reagent 2N61–25S, and (c), 281–25S), dolomite ((b), 2N61–25S, and (d) 281–25S), and scheelite ((e), 291–25S, and (f) 2121–25S) with variable chain length collectors

the depressants Na$_2$SiO$_3$ and Na$_2$SiF$_6$ and, in the light of the vacuum flotation data, they may not be optimum for the imino-bis compounds. The conditions for flotation are presented in Table 4, tin flotation being restricted to rougher flotation with staged collector additions. The pH of tin flotation was maintained just above pH 5 on the basis of the vacuum flotation curves.

From the results presented in Fig. 8 it is clear that the imino compounds are more effective in terms of recovery potential for a given active reagent addition and also in terms of maximum recovery achievable. The selectivity potential of SPA appears, however, better and, in this respect, the 2-ethyl hexyl derivative is more effective than the n-octyl derivative of the imino compounds. Examination of the data in Fig. 8(a) indicates that the 2-ethyl hexyl curve, if extended, is rapidly approaching the SPA curve. This implies that cleaning of the concentrate is likely to lead to significant grade improvement and that the ultimate difference in selectivity may be minimal. It can also be argued that if the stage additions of the imino compounds had been considerably reduced better rougher performance

data could also have been achieved. A further advantage of the use of the imino compounds is the short conditioning times that are required as a result of their higher solubility. The high concentrate grades obtained show the high selectivity achieved between cassiterite and the mafic silicates. On other cassiterite and wolframite samples the 2-ethyl hexyl and n-octyl compounds have shown better selectivity potential over the SPA collector.

Phosphate flotation
Testwork was carried out on a Greenland carbonatite phosphate ore containing approximately 14% fluorapatite, 70% dolomite, 5% ankerite and 3% amphibole. The minerals were crystalline and, consequently, mineral flotation areas should correspond closely to those obtained in the vacuum flotation work on the apatite and dolomite described earlier. The liberation size of the apatite was around 0.2 mm and flotation tests were carried out on ore samples ground to 80% passing 0.105 mm followed by two-stage desliming at 0.010 mm. Both n-octyl and 2-ethyl hexyl collectors were investigated. The conditions of the testwork

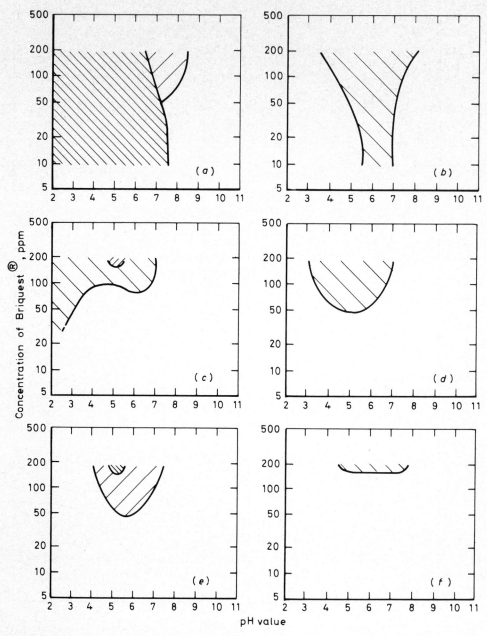

Fig. 6   Flotation of oxide minerals ((a), hematite; (b), chromite; (c), columbite; (d), tantalite; (e), monazite; (f), rutile) with n-octyl derivative (2N81–25S)

are shown in Table 5 and the results that were obtained are presented in Table 6.

Both collectors have achieved good selectivity between the apatite and the dolomite, the n-octyl derivative performing better under conditions of test with a rougher recovery of more than 92% and a final cleaner grade of 13.3% P. Rougher recovery with the 2-ethyl hexyl compound was significantly lower (80%) for a similar concentrate weight recovery and cleaning of the concentrate was also somewhat less effective. It is possible that more selective flotation could be achieved with this reagent at higher pH values, but the collector level required (already greater than the 2N81 reagent) may need to be increased to even higher levels.

The results, however, confirm the findings of the vacuum flotation tests, which defined the working pH range for selective flotation, although the degree of selectivity achieved does not necessarily match the area of 'window' developed. Overall, the results achieved on this ore are highly encouraging when it is borne in mind that no selective depressants have been used and the application of

these reagents to crystalline apatite ores, in particular, is strongly indicated.

Conclusions

The paper describes the evaluation of the alkyl imino-bis-methylene phosphonic acids as potential collectors for ore minerals. A screening process based on the use of the vacuum flotation technique has shown that reagents with a carbon chain length that varies from C_4 to C_{12} have collecting properties. In general, the degree of response of a given mineral has been shown to increase with increase in the chain length of collector used and the carbon chain length required for onset of flotation governs the relative floatability of the specific mineral. This is exemplified in the flotation of alkaline-earth salt minerals, the potential for the selective separation of baryte, fluorite, calcite, apatite, dolomite and scheelite having been demonstrated with the appropriate selection of collector from the homologous series. Batch flotation testwork on a carbonatite ore has shown that high selectivity can be achieved between apatite

Table 3 Summary of flotation data and potential application areas from Figs. 1–7 (with inferential data)

Mineral	Associated minerals	Indicated collectors (imino-bis-methylene phosphonic acid)	Indicated preferred pH range	Comments
Barite	Fluorite	n-butyl	>9.5	
	Calcite, dolomite	n-butyl to n-octyl	>7 to >10	
Fluorite	Calcite, dolomite, apatite	n-butyl to n-octyl	7–9.5 to >10	
	Scheelite	n-octyl (2 ethyl hexyl)	>8	
Calcite	Apatite, dolomite	n-octyl	9–10	
	Scheelite	n-octyl (2-ethyl hexyl)	>8	
Apatite	Dolomite	2-ethyl hexyl	8–10	
		n-octyl	8–9	
Wolframite	Quartz	n-octyl	5–8	
	Garnet	n-octyl	8–8.5	Alternative use of silicate depressants possibly at lower pH range
	Tourmaline	n-octyl	7–8.5	
	Chlorite	n-octyl	7–8.5	
Cassiterite	Quartz	n-octyl	5–8	
		2-ethyl hexyl	4.5–6.5	
	Tourmaline	n-octyl (2-ethyl hexyl)	6.5–8	Alternative use of silicate depressants possibly at lower pH range
	Chlorite	As above	7–8	
	Garnet	As above		
Chromite	Quartz	n-octyl ⎫ iso-nonyl and	5.5–7	
	Chlorite	As above ⎬ 2-ethyl hexyl	6–7	Alternative use of silicate depressants possibly at lower pH range
	Tourmaline	As above ⎭ alternatives	6–7	
	Garnet		–	
Columbite	Quartz	n-octyl (iso-nonyl)	5–7	
	Mafic silicates			Depressants required
Tantalite	Quartz	n-octyl (iso-nonyl)	4–7	
	Mafic silicates			Depressants required
Monazite	Quartz	n-octyl (iso-nonyl)	4.5–7	
	Mafic silicates			Depressants required
Rutile (acid washed)	Quartz	n-octyl (iso-nonyl)	4–6	
	Mafic silicates			Depressants required
Pyrochlore	Silicates	Dodecyl	8–11	Not yet validated with comparative results with silicate minerals
Uraninite				Not floated

and dolomite at a pH 8.5–9 with n-octyl and 2-ethyl hexyl derivatives—the area of selectivity indicated by the vacuum flotation studies.

Although a similar pattern of response was observed with oxide minerals, it was established that some silicates showed a higher potential for flotation than many oxides—particularly in the acid pH range. The selective flotation of such oxides as cassiterite and wolframite from silicates may depend on the greater tendency of these minerals to float at the neutral to slightly alkaline pH range rather than on exploitation of the effect of collector chain length. The use of specific silicate depressants is, however, likely to be necessary and will be essential for the practical separation of most oxide minerals.

Previous experience has shown that the depressants may modify the flotation areas and alter the optimum pH for selectivity. The flotation area is still likely to be constrained within the original pH range, however, and the relative floatability of the oxide minerals is likely to have a significant bearing on the degree of selectivity achieved. Batch testwork on a tin ore with standard depressants has shown that good selectivity can be achieved between the

Table 4   Tin flotation—Cornish tin ore

Sample	−0.5 +0.1 mm sand product from mill
Grind	To 88% passing 0.075 mm 64.7% passing 0.053 mm
Standard conditions	1 kg charge 2.2-1 flotation cell Softened water
(1) *Grind*	500 g/t Na_2SiO_3
(2) *Sulphide float*	200 g/t KAX (potassium amyl xanthate) Condition 2 min Natural pH Float with 10 g/t Dow 250 (frother)
(3) *Deslime*	Sulphide tail deslimed at 10 μm (equivalent quartz spheres) with two stages of cyclone desliming
(4) *Tin float*	400 g/t Na_2SiF_6; condition 5 min pH 5–5.2 (H_2SO_4)

Details of tin floats

Test no.	Flotation reagent	Reagent concentration, g/t	Conditioning time, min	pH of float	Flotation time, min	Product
2	Styrene	300*	20	5.0	5	Conc. 1
	phosphonic	200	5	5.0	7	Conc. 2
	acid	500	5	5.0	10	Conc. 3
4	Briquest	300	2	5.2	5	Conc. 1
	281–S	200	2	5.2	5	Conc. 2
		500	2	5.2	5	Conc. 3
5	Briquest	300*	2	5.2	5	Conc. 1
	2N81–S	200	2	5.2	5	Conc. 2
		500	2	5.2	5	Conc. 3

*A frother was required for the styrene phosphonic acid float: 50 g/t Dow 250 added with first addition of SPA in float 2 and 20 g/t with each subsequent addition of SPA. Float 4 required no frother; 15 g/t Dow 250 added with first addition of 2N81–S in float 5.

Table 5   Conditions for apatite flotation

Stage		Test 1	Test 2
Rougher flotation	Collector	2N81–25S 100 g/t	281–25S 125 g/t
	pH	8.5	8.8
	Kerosene	50 g/t	50 g/t
Scavenger flotation	Collector	25 g/t	25 g/t
Cleaner flotation	First stage	2-l cell (no reagents)	2-l cell (recycle rougher water)
	Second stage	1-l cell (no reagents)	2-l cell (recycle first cleaner water)

cassiterite and the mafic silicates. The 2-ethyl hexyl derivative was more effective than the *n*-octyl compound and compares favourably with SPA as a tin collector. No attempt was made to assess the optimum pH for the tin flotation. Other work on cassiterite and wolframite ores (not reported here) has been equally encouraging and for the wolframite flotation, with the *n*-octyl derivative, some selectivity was observed between wolframite and hematite.

Although correlation of vacuum flotation data with batch data should be treated with a certain amount of caution, owing to such effects as mineral crystallinity, mineral interactions, pulp cations and depressants, the technique offers a sound starting point for identification of potential selectivity between different minerals, operating pH range and determination of the most effective chain length of collector for use on specific minerals. The alkyl imino-bis-methylene phosphonic acids have been shown to have significant potential as collectors for a range of minerals of the salt and oxide type. The reagents have much higher solubility than the alkyl phosphonic acids and with a pK_1 value of <2 they are active over a wide pH range.

Acknowledgement

The authors would like to thank the Director, Warren Spring Laboratory, for permission to publish this paper and Albright and Wilson, Ltd., both for the release of the data from the testwork programme undertaken on that company's behalf and for the supply of the various reagents.

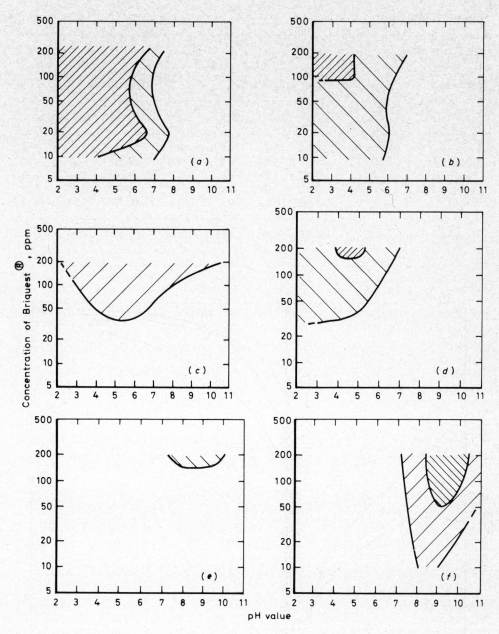

Fig. 7 Flotation of silicate and oxide minerals: (*a*), garnet; reagent 2N81–25S; (*b*), tourmaline; 2N81–25S; (*c*), chlorite; 2N81–25S; (*d*), rutile, acid washed; 2N81–25S; (*e*), pyrochlore; 291–25S; (*f*), pyrochlore; 2121–25S

Table 6   Results of apatite flotation

Test 1 (2N81–25S)

Product	Wt%	Assay, %			Distribution, %		
		P	**Mg**	**Ca**	**P**	**Mg**	**Ca**
Cleaner conc.	4.47	13.3	2.5	26.8	30.15	1.31	6.07
Cleaner tail 2	5.29	10.7	3.5	25.1	35.68	2.17	6.73
Cleaner tail 1	14.64	3.61	7.2	21.1	26.80	12.36	15.65
Scavenger conc.	11.92	0.90	8.9	19.1	5.44	12.45	11.54
Final tail	63.68	0.06	9.6	18.6	1.93	71.71	60.01
	100.00	(1.97)	(8.53)	(19.74)	100.00	100.00	100.00

Continued overleaf

Table 6   (continued)

Test 2 (281–25S)

Product	Wt%	Assay, %			Distribution, %		
		P	Mg	Ca	P	Mg	Ca
Cleaner conc.	7.45	10.1	4.1	24.7	42.01	3.54	7.98
Cleaner tail 2	8.63	5.92	6.2	28.6	28.52	6.21	10.70
Cleaner tail 1	9.01	1.83	8.6	23.7	9.20	8.99	9.26
Scavenger conc.	3.41	1.84	8.4	24.0	3.50	3.32	3.55
Final tail	71.50	0.42	9.4	22.1	16.77	77.94	68.51
	100.00	(1.79)	(8.62)	(23.06)	100.00	100.00	100.00

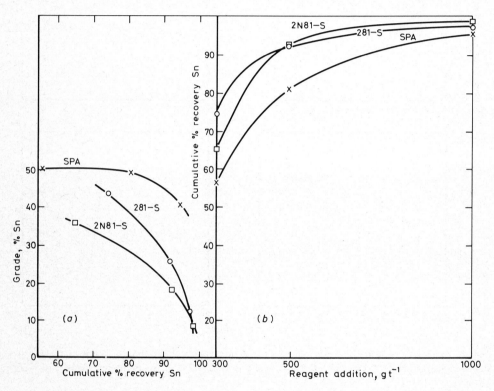

Fig. 8   Grade versus cumulative recovery (*a*) and cumulative recovery versus reagent addition (*b*)

References
1.   Collins D. N. Investigation of collector systems for the flotation of cassiterite. *Trans. Instn Min. Metall. (Sect. C: Mineral Process. Extr. Metall.)*, **76**, 1967, C77–93.
2.   Guzman A. B. Studies on the flotation of cassiterite. Thesis presented to the National Faculty of Engineering, Oruro, Bolivia, 1968.
3.   Manser R. M. and Rossi del Cerro E. E. Flotation of scheelite from calcite-containing ores, part 1: fundamental flotation characteristics. *Warren Spring Laboratory Rep.* LR 91, Oct. 1968, 12 p.
4.   Rabelink Th. B. M. The physical nature of tin flotation—the Billiton minerals story. Paper presented to National meeting of Minerals Engineering Society, Camborne School of Mines, Sept. 1982.
5.   Hu Weibai Wang Dianzuo and Jin Huaai. Flotation of wolframite slime—practice and technological innovation. In *Preprints—XIV international mineral processing congress, Toronto, 1982*, session IV, pap. 10, 14 p.
6.   Burt R. O. *et al.* The flotation of tantalum minerals. Reference 5, session IV, pap. 12, 19 p.

Effect of surfactants in fine grinding

Heikki Laapas, Ulla-Riitta Lahtinen and Toimi Lukkarinen

Synopsis

The effect of grinding aids was studied by use of laboratory-scale tumbling, vibratory and attrition mills. The test materials were quartz, calcite, talc and wollastonite. Successful grinding was found to depend on the dispersion state of a particular material, which could be controlled with grinding aids. The chosen additives were sodium oleate for quartz, triethanolamine for calcite, a salt of a polycarboxylate for talc and sodium hexametaphosphate for wollastonite. All of these worked well in both wet and dry grinding, with the exception of sodium hexametaphosphate (only in wet grinding).

Additives improved grinding in the tumbling mill generally below 10–15 µm, but they were in most cases harmful at coarser sizes.

Owing to the high shear rate in vibratory and attrition mills the influence of surfactants was more complicated and could be related in each case to grinding mechanism and to material characteristics.

Most of the samples ground without additives were found to be so aggregated that their use would be scarcely possible in practice. Moreover, it was found that grinding at a highly aggregated state produced micro-cracks, which increase the specific surface area of the product without creating any new particles.

A large amount of energy is consumed in various comminution processes and the energy demand is especially high in the production of very fine powders, such as pigments and fillers. As the production of such powders is increasing rapidly, even a small decrease in energy consumption can lead to substantial savings.

Grinding efficiency may be increased by the use of grinding aids, these chemicals being said to improve the grinding rate in several ways. For example, it is suggested that they decrease the surface energy of particles or enhance crack propagation (the so-called Rehbinder effect[1]). A frequent explanation is also the prevention of grinding media coating. These mechanisms are important, but there remain two factors that are expected to have a dominating influence on the grinding rate—the dispersion state of the powder and its fluidity. These phenomena are controlled to a great extent by the chemical environment of grinding.

In usual grinding operations in mineral processing the effect of surfactants has been found to be less important, except in the grinding of cement. In fine (almost colloidal) powders, however, the forces of particle–particle interaction are increased, thus retarding grinding mechanisms due to enhanced aggregation and decreased fluidity. In this size range it is to be expected that better dispersion may lead to a better grinding result.

Experimental

Quartz, calcite, talc and wollastonite were used as test materials. Quartz and calcite were both obtained as pebbles of about 10 cm in diameter. These pebbles were crushed in a laboratory jaw and cone crusher to give a suitable feed material for grinding tests. Wollastonite and talc were flotation concentrates from local processing plants and their fineness was suitable for further grinding.

For each of these materials a specific dispersant was chosen as a grinding aid. Quartz was dispersed with sodium oleate, which has been established to work well.[2] Owing to its ionic nature sodium oleate is capable of changing the zeta-potential of quartz in water, thereby preventing aggregation and agglomeration. In the dry state it also adsorbs on quartz and decreases the strong electrostatic attraction between quartz particles. For calcite, triethanolamine was used as a grinding aid: this reagent, widely used in cement grinding,[3] is said to work in ways similar to sodium oleate in quartz grinding. Talc was dispersed with a salt of a polycarboxylate, which is commonly used as a dispersing agent in Finnish talc plants. Its effect in a wet environment is either through ionic repulsion or through steric hindrance. In dry grinding it acts similarly to sodium oleate or to triethanolamine. Wollastonite was dispersed in wet grinding with sodium hexametaphosphate, which is a well-known dispersant. It changes the zeta-potential of most minerals drastically, thus creating a strong ionic repulsion. No suitable dispersant was found for dry grinding of wollastonite.

The test samples were ground, on a laboratory scale, by use of tumbling, vibratory and attrition batch mills. The tumbling mill (Mergan; Outokumpu Oy, Finland) size is 268 mm in diameter × 268 mm and it is suspended horizontally to form a freely swinging pendulum.[4] The angle of swing, measured by an angle transmitter, gives the torque created on the mill and is proportional to the net power input. The integration of the signal from the angle transmitter yields the net energy consumption. As grinding medium a mixture ($\frac{1}{3} : \frac{1}{3} : \frac{1}{3}$) of 20-, 30- and 40-mm steel balls was used for quartz and calcite, whereas 15-mm alumina balls were used for talc and wollastonite. Wet grinding was carried out at 60% solids (by weight).

The vibratory mill (OPPO; Podmore and Sons, Ltd., England) has two opposite mills (130 mm in diameter × 127 mm), which are mechanically vibrated by shafts connected to an eccentric unit.[2] The net energy input was registered with a kWh meter. The grinding medium for quartz and calcite was 12-mm steel balls. For talc and wollastonite 15-mm alumina balls were used. The pulp density in wet grinding was 60% solids.

A Vollrath sand-mill was used for attrition grinding. This mill, which is used in the paint industry, consists of a vertical cylindrical container (2-l capacity) with a mixer consisting of five discs fixed on a vertical shaft. The grinding action is created by rotating the mixer at a speed of 2850 rev/min. Energy consumption was measured by a kWh meter. ZrO beads (0.6–2 mm) were used as grinding medium and the pulp density was 55% solids by weight.

The products of the grinding tests were evaluated by measuring their size distribution. A suitable method for talc and wollastonite samples was X-ray sedimentometry (SediGraph). Quartz and calcite products, however, contained substantial amounts of metallic iron from the steel balls. This was detrimental to sedimentation analysis and a Coulter Counter was used. The specific surface area of the products was determined by gas adsorption measurement (Quantachrome continuous flow instrument). Some products were also subjected to viscosity measurement (Brabender rotating viscometer; cone and plate geometry).

Results and discussion

Figs. 1–7 show the effect of grinding energy on the median diameter as well as on the specific surface area of the test samples when different grinding procedures are used.

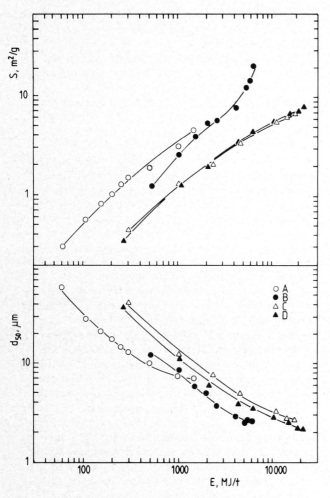

Fig. 1 Median diameter (d_{50}) and specific surface area (S) of quartz as a function of net energy consumption (E) in dry grinding: A, tumbling mill; B, tumbling mill, sodium oleate 0.3%; C, vibratory mill; D, vibratory mill, sodium oleate 0.3% (initial material: $d_{50} = 715\ \mu m$; $S = 0.09\ m^2/g$)

According to Figs. 1 and 2, wet and dry grinding of quartz in tumbling mill is decreased by the addition of sodium oleate when the median diameter is greater than 10 μm, but at finer sizes it is enhanced. The grinding aid obviously increases the fluidity of coarser quartz to such an extent that the breakage probability is decreased. At coarse particle sizes the interparticle forces are so small that no dispersant is needed to prevent agglomeration.

Dry vibratory grinding of quartz is enhanced (Fig. 1) at all particle sizes by the addition of sodium oleate. This behaviour, contrary to grinding in the tumbling mill, is attributed to different grinding mechanisms. The high power rate and the impacts between grinding medium and quartz particles in the vibratory mill promote strong

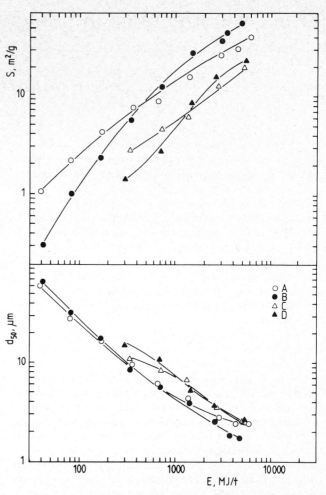

Fig. 2 Median diameter (d_{50}) and specific surface area (S) of quartz as a function of net energy consumption (E) in wet grinding: A, tumbling mill; B, tumbling mill, sodium oleate 0.1%; C, vibratory mill; D, vibratory mill, sodium oleate 0.1% (initial material: $d_{50} = 715\ \mu m$; $S = 0.09\ m^2/g$)

electrostatic charging, which increases agglomeration. This is prevented by the use of a surface-active agent. On the other hand, in wet vibratory grinding water is sufficient to prevent electrostatic attraction and the influence of surfactant is less important (Fig. 2).

The results of grinding calcite in the tumbling mill are analogous to those of quartz (Figs. 3 and 4). The median particle size of 10 μm seems to be the limit for the use of the grinding aid. Owing to strong aggregation dry grinding ceases beyond this limit without additive. Dry grinding of calcite in the vibratory mill is markedly enhanced by the addition of triethanolamine: this is again attributable to increased fluidity and to better dispersion, as indicated by the free-flowing nature of the product. Unlike quartz, the wet vibratory grinding of calcite was enhanced by the grinding aid. Calcite agglomerates easily in water and this is promoted by the violent grinding action in a vibratory mill. This phenomenon was reduced by the addition of triethanolamine. The specific surface area of the vibratory mill product was lower when the grinding aid was added (Fig. 4). When grinding calcite in an agglomerated state a substantial amount of energy is consumed to produce micro-cracks instead of new particles.

Fig. 4 shows that attrition grinding of calcite is enhanced by the addition of triethanolamine. The improvement and the increased fineness are caused by the rheology of the slurry (Table 1). The grinding action in an attrition mill is induced through mixing, which is controlled by the flow behaviour of the slurry.

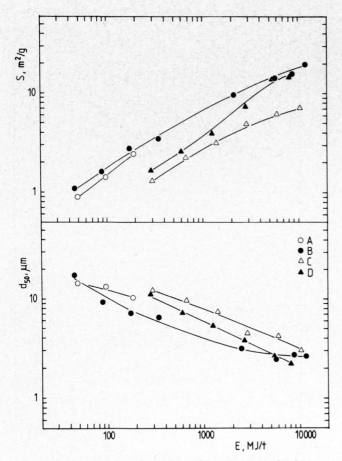

Fig. 3   Median diameter (d_{50}) and specific surface area (S) of calcite as a function of net energy consumption (E) in dry grinding: A, tumbling mill; B, tumbling mill, triethanolamine 0.3%; C, vibratory mill; D, vibratory mill, triethanolamine 0.3% (initial material: $d_{50} = 140$ μm; $S = 0.26$ m²/g)

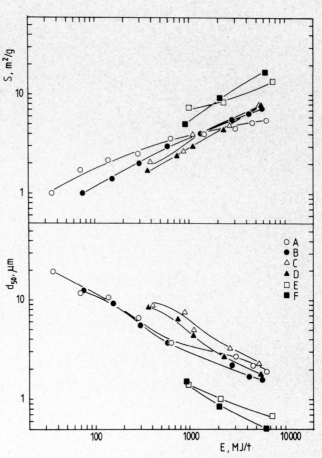

Fig. 4   Median diameter (d_{50}) and specific surface area (S) of calcite as a function of net energy consumption (E) in wet grinding: A, tumbling mill; B, tumbling mill, triethanolamine 0.3%; C, vibratory mill; D, vibratory mill, triethanolamine 0.3% (initial material: $d_{50} = 140$ μm; $S = 0.26$ m²/g); E, attrition mill; F, attrition mill, triethanolamine 0.3% (initial material: $d_{50} = 70$ μm; $S = 0.83$ cm²/g)

Figs. 5 and 6 show that the use of the additive (a salt of a polycarboxylate) improves the grinding rate of talc in a tumbling mill at all size ranges when ground dry, but only below 15 μm when ground wet. In a vibratory mill the grinding aid is harmful in dry grinding and has no influence on wet grinding. The grinding rate of talc in attrition milling was not affected by the grinding aid. In dry grinding the additive increased the flowability of talc. In a tumbling mill this is advantageous, but in a vibratory mill

the flaky and free-flowing talc powder avoids the grinding action, which is caused to some extent by the friction between particles. In wet vibratory milling the dispersant did not change the pulp viscosity (Table 1) and the grinding rate remained unaffected. In attrition milling the viscosity of the slurry was lower when the grinding aid was used (Table 1), but this did not influence the grinding rate (this can also be attributed to the particle shape and softness of talc, both of which decrease the interaction between particles and grinding media).

Dry grinding of wollastonite was found to be difficult. The tendency of the material to form aggregates was high, probably because of its needle-like structure. No efficient dispersant could be found for dry grinding. In wet grinding the most obvious improvement in grinding rate caused by the additive is again noticed in a tumbling mill. The grinding aid, sodium hexametaphosphate, was a very effective dispersant and it decreased considerably the slurry viscosity (Table 1). The grinding rate in vibratory and attrition milling, however, remained unaffected: this is related to the high power input. Although the products were equivalent in particle size, their rheological behaviour was totally different (Table 1). The very fine wollastonite slurries that were produced without the additive were so viscous that grinding and handling would be impossible in practice. The specific surface areas (Fig. 7) demonstrated again that less surface is produced in vibratory and attrition mills when additive is used. This is another example of increased micro-crack production in very viscous slurries.

Table 1   Effect of grinding aid on apparent viscosity of some ground products at shear rate of 166 s⁻¹

Sample	Mill type	Median size, μm	Additive*	Apparent viscosity, mPa s
Talc	Vibratory	2.7	A	2010
Talc	Vibratory	3.0	–	2010
Talc	Attrition	2.7	A	362
Talc	Attrition	2.3	–	697
Calcite	Attrition	0.5	B	2573
Calcite	Attrition	0.7	–	3618
Wollastonite	Vibratory	1.8	C	160
Wollastonite	Vibratory	2.0	–	infinite
Wollastonite	Attrition	2.6	C	255
Wollastonite	Attrition	2.2	–	infinite

*A, salt of a polycarboxylate, 0.1%; B, triethanolamine, 0.3%; C, sodium hexametaphosphate, 0.2%.

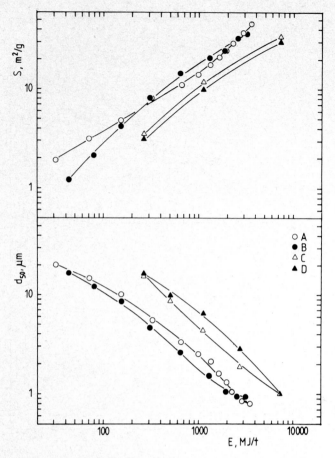

Fig. 5 Median diameter (d_{50}) and specific surface area (S) of talc as a function of net energy consumption (E) in dry grinding: A, tumbling mill; B, tumbling mill, salt of a polycarboxylate 0.3%; C, vibratory mill; D, vibratory mill, salt of a polycarboxylate 0.3% (initial material: d_{50} = 85 μm; S = 1.53 m²/g)

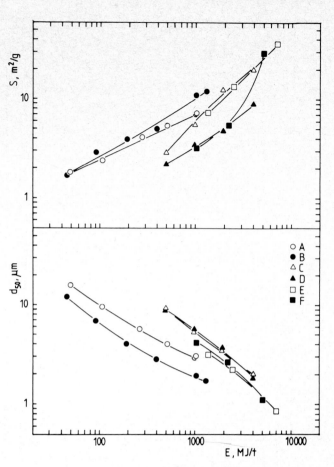

Fig. 7 Median diameter (d_{50}) and specific surface area (S) of wollastonite as a function of net energy consumption (E) in wet grinding: A, tumbling mill; B, tumbling mill, sodium hexametaphosphate 0.2%; C, vibratory mill; D, vibratory mill, sodium hexametaphosphate 0.2%; E, attrition mill; F, attrition mill, sodium hexametaphosphate 0.2% (initial material: d_{50} = 70 μm; S = 0.31 m²/g)

Summary

The grinding efficiency of quartz, calcite, talc and wollastonite has been shown to be influenced by the dispersion state of the material. Successful grinding, especially at finer sizes, demands proper shearing conditions within the charge. In this sense too high or too low fluidity generally means reduced grinding rate. The flow behaviour of a particular material is easily affected by changing its dispersion: this can be done by adding surface-active agents.

The additives that were used in this work improved grinding in a tumbling mill below 10–15 μm, but were in most cases harmful at coarser sizes. In a tumbling mill the shear rate is relatively low and an excessive fluidity of the coarse material decreases the grinding rate. In wet grinding this would be avoided by increasing the pulp density.

In vibratory and attrition mills the shear rate is very high and the influence of surfactant is more complicated. Dry vibratory grinding of quartz was unsatisfactory without an additive, owing to strong electrostatic charging, whereas water was a sufficient dispersant in wet grinding. The

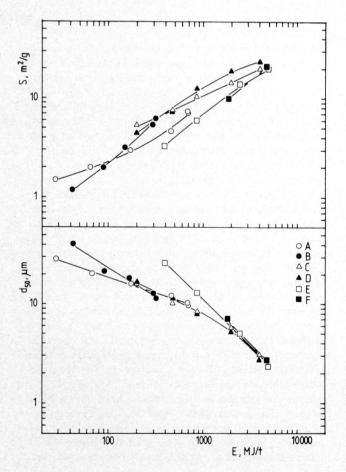

Fig. 6 Median diameter (d_{50}) and specific surface area (S) of talc as a function of net energy consumption (E) in wet grinding: A, tumbling mill; B, tumbling mill, salt of a polycarboxylate 0.1%; C, vibratory mill; D, vibratory mill, salt of a polycarboxylate 0.1%; E, attrition mill; F, attrition mill, salt of a polycarboxylate 0.1% (initial material: d_{50} = 85 μm, S = 1.53 m²/g)

additive used for calcite improved the dispersion state as well as the grinding rate both in vibratory and attrition mills.

The behaviour of talc in vibratory and attrition grinding was related to its flaky and soft nature. In dry vibratory grinding the additive decreased the grinding rate due to excessive fluidity, but in other cases grinding remained unaffected.

Wollastonite proved to be difficult to grind dry. It had a strong tendency to form aggregates—probably because of its needle-like structure. No dispersant was found to be capable of preventing aggregation in dry grinding. In wet grinding the additive decreased the viscosity of the wollastonite slurry, but the grinding rate in vibratory and attrition mills was not affected. This is attributed to a high shear rate and to the textural character of this slurry.

Additionally, it was found that grinding in a highly aggregated state produced micro-cracks, which increased the specific surface area of the product without creating any new particles.

Although all the samples could be ground without additive at least to some extent, their handling would be impossible in most cases in practice because of their low fluidity. By using grinding aids the flow behaviour of both dry powders and mineral slurries can be improved and, hence, the materials become more suitable for continuous processing.

References
1.   Klimpel R. R. and Austin L. G. Chemical additives for wet grinding of minerals. *Powder Technol.*, **31**, 1982, 239–53.
2.   Öner M. *et al*. The effects of sodium oleate upon ultra-fine grinding of quartz. *Madencilik,* **20,** 1981, 23–35. (Turkish text)
3.   Duda W. H. *Cement-data-book* (Wiesbaden: Bauverlag GmbH, 1976).
4.   Niitti T. Rapid evaluation of grindability by a simple batch test. In *Proceedings Ninth international mineral processing congress, Prague, 1970* (Prague: Ústav pro Výzkum Rud, 1970), vol. 1, 41–5.

Use of dialkyl and diaryl dithiophosphate promoters as mineral flotation agents

Phillip A. Mingione

Synopsis
The use of dialkyl and diaryl dithiophosphates as flotation collectors dates back to the discovery and use of xanthates: they have found diverse application in the flotation treatment of metallic and sulphide base and precious metals throughout the mining industry. Their outstanding features include high collecting activity and selectivity, particularly in regard to iron sulphide minerals in alkaline circuit. Although they have replaced chemically dissimilar collectors, the greatest usage of dithiophosphates lies in combination with another collector type to enhance the collecting properties of each.

The use of dithiophosphate (DTP) compounds and their free acids, dithiophosphoric acid (DTPA), as flotation collectors was discovered and patented in 1926 by Whitworth[1] only a year after Keller had discovered and patented xanthates for the same usage.[2] Whitworth's patent was subsequently assigned to the American Cyanamid Company, which has been the major supplier of dithiophosphates and their free acids to the world mining industry since 1930 under the trade names AEROFLOAT[R] and AERO[R] Promoters. Thus, their use as metallic and sulphide mineral flotation collectors has a history that is almost equal to that of the best known and most widely used collector type—the xanthates.

By reacting phosphorus pentasulphide (P_2S_5) most commonly with phenols or alcohols, dithiophosphoric acid is produced. If to be used in the free acid form, the product is usually a diaryl DTPA. Dithiophosphates are produced by neutralizing the DTPA (in this case usually a dialkyl DTPA) with an organic or inorganic base, of which the sodium salt form predominates, but potassium and ammonium salt forms are also commercially available. The structure of a dithiophosphate is shown in Fig. 1.

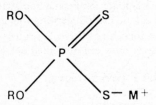

R = ARYL OR ALKYL GROUP

M = ALKALI METAL OR ALKYL AMMONIUM GROUP

Fig. 1 Dithiophosphate structure

The dialkyl dithiophosphates have little or no frothing characteristics until the alkyl chain length reaches about 5 carbons, whereupon the collector may sometimes display frothing properties. The particular salt form of the

dithiophosphate will also influence its frothing characteristics. The diaryl dithiophosphates will display light to moderate frothing characteristics owing to the phenols from which they are made.

Dithiophosphates belong to the broad range of thiol collectors that includes the xanthates, thiocarbamates and mercaptobenzothiazole. As such, they have similar applications, i.e. as collectors for metallic and sulphide base-metal ores and ores containing precious metals.

Industrial usage worldwide for more than fifty years has identified and established the following characteristics of dithiophosphate collectors: (1) they are particularly effective for improving the recovery of both precious metals and base metals; (2) they are more selective collectors than most other thiol collectors, particularly against pyrite in alkaline pulps: this may allow treatment with a lower pulp alkalinity; (3) their selectivity is particularly useful in the treatment of polymetallic ores; and (4) they can increase flotation rates.

Examples are given later that highlight these characteristics. The selectivity of dithiophosphates is explored further below.

It is widely held that dithiophosphates are weak collectors in comparison with xanthates or dialkyl thionocarbamates (formerly produced as Z-200 by the Dow Chemical Co.): Glembotskii and co-workers[3] and Poling[4] attributed this feature to the higher water solubility of heavy metal dithiophosphates in comparison with the corresponding heavy metal complexes of xanthates or thionocarbamates, which render the dithiophosphates more readily affected by depressants. It is true that in many cases dithiophosphates cannot completely replace a less selective collector type, but this should not be taken to mean that they are weak—rather that under the circumstances they could not equal that collector type, which may have been better suited to the ore. No single collector type can be expected to perform optimally on all the precious and base-metal mineral deposits of the world—if it did, the variety of collectors that is presently available would not exist. Dithiophosphates have replaced xanthates and thionocarbamates at a number of plants, which demonstrates their metallurgical and economic advantage. But the belief that dithiophosphates are weak collectors has probably prevented or hindered their serious consideration and comprehensive testing with many ores.

The most successful method of application and greatest usage of dithiophosphates is with another collector type to enhance the collecting properties of both. This synergism is a dithiophosphate characteristic acknowledged by Glembotskii and co-workers.[3]

The two collector types that are used most widely in conjunction with dithiophosphates are xanthates and sodium mercaptobenzothiazole (Na-MBT). Such usage frequently results in reduced total collector consumption and/or improved metallurgical results than would be possible with the use of either of the constituent collectors individually. The proportion of dithiophosphate in the collector combination can vary widely from the minor constituent to the major. Often, the dithiophosphate is used as the principal collector in a rougher flotation stage to maximize selectivity, followed by a scavenger flotation stage with use of xanthate to maximize recovery. In many cases the best metallurgical results can be obtained by separately dosing dithiophosphate and xanthate at the same addition point or points in the circuit. This tends to maintain a balance of selectivity and collection power in the circuit by minimizing the concentration of collector in the pulp at any one point.

When dithiophosphates are utilized with Na-MBT the most common practice is to dose both collectors together at the same addition point(s) and, if they are stage added, to use a constant proportion of each. It is, therefore, convenient to prepare a physical mixture of the two collectors. To this end the AERO 400 Series Promoters produced by American Cyanamid Co. are commercially available.

The DTP/Na-MBT combinations are useful for floating almost all sulphide minerals and precious metals. Sodium MBT is a strong collector that significantly modifies the properties of the mixed collector combination. In neutral to acid circuits the DTP/Na-MBT combinations are powerful general-purpose sulphide mineral collectors, being very useful in applications in which it is desired to remove all sulphide minerals from an ore or an existing non-sulphide mineral concentrate by use of a bulk flotation process (examples would include the removal of sulphide minerals from an iron (hematite/magnetite) concentrate, the recovery of auriferous pyrite, or of other iron sulphides that may have associated valuable metals). Activation of iron sulphide minerals with copper sulphate sometimes improves their recovery.

In alkaline circuits the DTP/Na-MBT combinations demonstrate considerably more selectivity than they do in neutral to acid circuits. The presence of Na-MBT helps to improve recoveries of tarnished or oxidized base metals, particularly those of copper and lead. For such usage the collector combination is frequently added to the grinding stage, these combinations generally benefiting from maximum conditioning time with the pulp. In the treatment of lead–copper–zinc ores with the standard sequential method of flotation the use of DTP/Na-MBT combinations would generally be as a supplemental collector in the lead–copper flotation stage and sometimes as the primary collector in the subsequent activated zinc flotation stage.

Dithiophosphates are available with a diverse range of hydrophobic groups, which gives the user flexibility in

optimizing his collector system. Table 1 lists some of the most common alkyl and aryl groups present in commercially available materials.

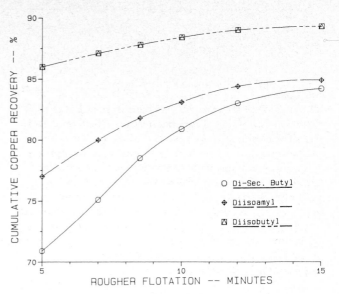

Fig. 2   Effect of varying alkyl group on dithiophosphate collecting properties

Because the dithiophosphate molecule has a double hydrophobic group arrangement (Fig. 1), a relatively modest change in the length or structure of this group will often show a signficant change in collecting properties (an example is presented in Fig. 2, which shows the differences in collecting properties of di-secondary butyl, di-isobutyl and di-isoamyl dithiophosphates on a South American copper sulphide ore). All three collectors were utilized at the same dosage with a pulp pH of 10.5. It can be seen from Fig. 2 that, in this particular case, the di-isobutyl DTP has a much higher copper flotation rate than does the di-secondary butyl DTP, the di-isoamyl DTP having performance characteristics between these two.

Since ores can be very specific in their flotation responses to different types of collectors, only comprehensive testing can determine which type will provide optimum metallurgical and economic performance. Similarly, with the variety of alkyl/aryl groups with which dithiophosphates are available, only testing can determine if any one in particular holds an advantage in use. Although there is considerable overlapping in areas of application, certain generalizations can be made regarding the use of individual dithiophosphate collectors (Table 1) for particular types of ores and processes: these are presented below.

AEROFLOAT promoters

Sodium AEROFLOAT promoter (Na-diethyl dithiophosphate) and AEROFLOAT 211 promoter (Na-di-isopropyl dithiophosphate)

These two promoters are primarily copper and zinc sulphide collectors. As a result of their short alkyl chains, they display outstanding selectivity against iron sulphides in alkaline circuit, wherein lies their greatest utility.

To date, their widest application has been found as primary collectors for activated sphalerite, where actively floating pyrite limits the usage of xanthates as secondary collectors. As sphalerite becomes more marmatitic (greater substitution of iron for zinc in the crystal lattice) their effectiveness diminishes somewhat owing to their selectivity against iron minerals. The diethyl DTP is affected more

Table 1   Alkyl and aryl groups of commonly available dithiophosphates

Hydrophobic group	Trade name example*
Diethyl	Sodium AEROFLOAT Promoter
Diethyl + di-secondary butyl	AEROFLOAT 208 Promoter
Di-isopropyl	AEROFLOAT 211 Promoter
Di-secondary butyl	AEROFLOAT 238 Promoter
Dimethylamyl	AEROFLOAT 249 Promoter
Di-isobutyl	AERO 3477 Promoter
Di-isoamyl	AERO 3501 Promoter
Dicresyl	AEROFLOAT 241 and 242 Promoters

*All examples except 241/242 are sodium salt forms in concentrated aqueous solution. 241/242 are ammonium salt forms and are water-soluble.

than the di-isopropyl DTP in this regard. Use of a greater amount of another collector type is recommended when the zinc mineral is highly marmatitic.

Neither of these two promoters is an efficient galena collector. They can therefore be utilized for the selective flotation of copper minerals in the treatment of ores that contain both copper and lead.

In copper flotation AEROFLOAT 211 promoter is being used in cleaning circuits where actively floating pyrite presents a selectivity problem in producing a final concentrate with acceptable overall metallurgy. Low dosages (2–5 g of 211 per ton of original plant feed) are used with cleaner circuit pH values >11 to maintain adequate total copper recovery while depressing pyrite to produce the desired concentrate grade.

AEROFLOAT 238 promoter (Na-di-secondary butyl dithiophosphate)

The 238 promoter is the most widely used dithiophosphate for the treatment of copper ores. Because it is a very effective collector for all of the common sulphide copper minerals, as well as metallic copper, it is also used in the flotation treatment of copper converter slags.

AEROFLOAT 238 promoter is also a good collector of silver sulphides (argentite and the ruby silver minerals) and gold and its alloy, electrum. Recoveries of these precious metals, as well as copper minerals, are particularly enhanced when 238 is used with xanthates. Copper minerals frequently have some of these precious metals associated, so the conjoint usage of 238 with xanthate is its most widespread method of application in the treatment of copper ores.

A more specific use of 238 is for the treatment of finely disseminated copper ores. These ores are typically highly pyritic, may also have minor amounts of other base-metal sulphides and require very fine grinding for adequate mineral liberation. Granulometries of $100\% < 30$ μm are not unusual in the alkaline circuit selective copper flotation stage, 238 being used as the sole collector. A non-selective bulk flotation with use of a xanthate collector and a coarser grind may precede the selective copper flotation stage. The selective copper flotation process is more viable with 238 owing to its excellent selectivity against pyrite and any other unwanted base-metal sulphides, as well as its fine particle collecting ability.

Used with Na-MBT (in the form of AERO 404 promoter), di-secondary butyl DTP has wide utility in the alkaline circuit treatment of precious metal ores, copper, lead and zinc sulphide ores and where minor constituents of these base-metal ores are tarnished or oxidized. It also has usage in the acid circuit flotation of pyrite and auriferous pyrite.

AEROFLOAT 208 promoter (Na-diethyl + Na-di-secondary butyl dithiophosphates)

AEROFLOAT 208 promoter combines the properties of sodium AEROFLOAT and AEROFLOAT 238 promoters and possesses unique properties of its own. It is an excellent collector for metallics of copper, gold and silver, as well as the commonly found copper sulphide minerals. Its greatest area of application is for the treatment of ores that contain these values as metallics or fixed sulphides and metallics, and also is in wide use for the flotation of copper converter slags. It is most commonly utilized with a xanthate secondary collector.

As with all the shorter alkyl group dithiophosphates, 208 is selective against pyrite and sphalerite. Although not normally considered a good galena promoter, 208 is used in

one silver–lead–zinc plant as the only collector in the silver–lead circuit.

AEROFLOAT 249 promoter (Na-dimethylamyl dithiophosphate)

This promoter is among the most powerful of the more commonly available dialkyl dithiophosphates. Its use has been limited to a copper flotation plant in which recovery of coarse middlings particles poses a problem, yet the selectivity of a dithiophosphate was still desired. AEROFLOAT 249 is also a collector for activated zinc sulphides.

Because of its alkyl group structure this promoter exhibits considerable frothing characteristics. Clearly, its use must be limited to applications in which its frothing properties would not be detrimental to plant circuit control.

AERO 3477 promoter (Na-di-isobutyl dithiophosphate)

AERO 3477 promoter is a strong, fast-acting promoter for precious metals and copper, silver and zinc sulphide ores. Its ability to collect coarse middlings particles makes it effective for use with coarse grinds, but provides better selectivity against pyrite in comparison with xanthates in copper and zinc flotation. Accelerated flotation rates are common with this particular dithiophosphate (Fig. 2).

In many plants 3477 has either replaced xanthates or oily collectors, or reduced total collector consumption, at the same time providing improved metal recoveries. A significant reduction in pulp alkalinity has been reported with its use. Plant usage has increased steadily and it is now one of the most widely used of the dialkyl dithiophosphates for the recovery of precious metals, all copper sulphide minerals and sphalerite. It is also in use for the flotation of nickel sulphides, and for antimony sulphides (stibnite) activated by lead nitrate.

Experience with this fast-acting promoter indicates that in most cases it should not be added to the grind—it is usually preferable to add it to a classifier overflow or conditioner, and it can be stage added in the rougher flotation circuit.

As with the combination of AEROFLOAT 238 promoter/Na-MBT, AERO 3477 promoter in combination with Na-MBT (in the form of AERO 407 promoter) has utility for the treatment of a wide range of precious and base-metal ores.

AERO 3501 promoter (Na-di-isoamyl dithiophosphate)

Usage and performance characteristics of AERO 3501 promoter are very similar to those of 3477. Because 3501 has a longer alkyl group, it tends to be a stronger collector than 3477. For the same reason it may display substantial frothing characteristics in some applications that may limit its dosage to enable controlled frothing conditions to be maintained. In such cases a combination of 3501 and a dithiophosphate with a shorter alkyl group (such as 3477), or 3501 and xanthate should alleviate the problem.

AERO 3501 promoter has also been found to be an excellent molybdenite collector. Like some of the aforementioned dialkyl dithiophosphates, 3501 used in combination with Na-MBT (in the form of AERO 412 promoter) is an excellent collector for a wide range of precious and base-metal ores.

AEROFLOAT 241 and 242 promoters (ammonium dicresyl dithiophosphates)

AEROFLOAT 241 and 242 are water-soluble diaryl

dithiophosphates. They are manufactured as the ammonium salts of their free acid collector counterparts. Of all the common dithiophosphate collectors, these two are the most specific for galena and silver minerals. Their usage has been predominantly for the flotation of galena, or galena associated with silver and/or copper minerals, when some or all of these are found with sphalerite and pyrite.

They are very selective against sphalerite and pyrite, and are most commonly used with lead circuit pH values between 7.5 and 8.7. Because of their selectivity, the use of 241 or 242 may also enable a reduction in sphalerite depressant consumption during the lead flotation stage. Some of these characteristics are demonstrated emphatically in *Example 6* (see later).

Bulk lead–(silver)–copper concentrates produced with 241 or 242 are readily amenable to separation. These bulk concentrates usually have a Pb:Cu ratio greater than 2:1. The dichromate and SO_2/starch processes to depress galena (and silver), while floating a copper concentrate, are the most successful plant methods of separation.

AEROFLOAT 242 promoter is essentially the same as 241, but it contains 6% thiocarbanilide as a supplementary collector for galena, silver and copper minerals. It is therefore a stronger collector than 241, but is still selective against sphalerite and pyrite. The usage of 242 exceeds that of 241 by a substantial margin.

Being in the ammonium salt form, 241 and 242 show considerably reduced frothing characteristics in comparison with their dithiophosphoric acid counterparts. This is attributable partly to the nature of the ammonium salt and partly to neutralization of free cresylic acid present in the original dithiophosphoric acid collector.

Examples of applications

Example 1
The synergistic collecting effect of combining AERO 3477 promoter with sodium isopropyl xanthate (SIPX) on an ore that contains platinum group metals (PGM) is shown in Fig. 3 (the PGM consist of platinum, rhodium, palladium, osmium, iridium and ruthenium, plus gold).

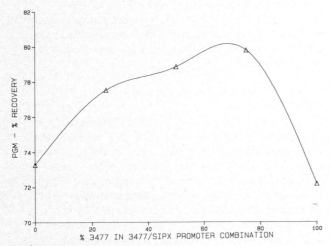

Fig. 3   Effect of AERO 3477 promoter/sodium isopropyl xanthate combination on PGM recovery

A constant collector combination dosage of 100 g/t was maintained, the proportions of 3477 and SIPX varying from 0% 3477/100% SIPX to 100% 3477/0% SIPX (pulp pH 8.5). Fig. 3 shows that optimum PGM recovery is obtained with an approximately 70% 3477/30% SIPX collector combination, which is superior to either 100% SIPX or 100% 3477 as collector.

Example 2
The details of a plant trial of AEROFLOAT 238 promoter combined with a Na-MBT (50%) collector for auriferous pyrite recovery are given in Table 2. This plant normally floats in acid circuit (pH 4.5) with 65 g/t Na-MBT collector with typical recoveries of 35% of the gold and 70% of the sulphur.

Table 2   Auriferous pyrite flotation

Flotation feed	0.38 g/t Au, 1.0% S
Flotation conditions	pH 4.5 (H$_2$SO$_4$)
	55 g/t CuSO$_4$
Standard reagents	65 g/t Na-MBT (50%)
	20 g/t frother
Test reagents	43 g/t Na-MBT (50%)
	9 g/t AF238
	17 g/t frother
Typical plant recoveries	Au, 35%; S, 70%

Plant test results

	Test reagents		Standard reagents	
	Grade	% Recovery	Grade	% Recovery
Au	6.84 g/t	45.97	6.17 g/t	35.73
S	33.23%	79.87	29.88%	73.84

In the test 22 g/t of the Na-MBT collector was replaced by 9 g/t of 238: significant increases in gold and sulphur recoveries and modest increases in concentrate grades were obtained by use of the Na-MBT/238 collector combination. A slight decrease in frother consumption was also noted. Metallurgical gains and overall reductions in reagent consumption were realized by the use of the tested collector combination.

Example 3
Laboratory testing was conducted on the zinc circuit flotation feed of a copper–zinc plant that normally used sodium normal propyl xanthate (SNPX) as the zinc collector. Tests were made that involved replacement of all of the SNPX with AEROFLOAT 211 promoter and partial replacement of SNPX with 211 or sodium AEROFLOAT promoter.

Table 3   Zinc flotation

SNPX, g/t	AF 211, g/t	NaAF, g/t	Conc. wt%	Zn, %	Fe, %	Distribution, % Zn	Fe
40	—	—	8.4	16.8	13.7	90.6	8.2
—	40	—	5.3	20.7	11.5	72.5	4.4
20	20	—	5.6	25.5	12.4	95.6	5.2
20	—	20	7.1	20.3	12.3	95.1	6.5

Zn circuit feed, 1.5% Zn and 14% Fe; flotation pH 9.3; 400 g/t CuSO$_4$ as Zn activator.

From the data in Table 3 it can be seen that 211 could not directly replace all of the SNPX. The replacement of half of the SNPX with either 211 or sodium AEROFLOAT promoter, however, produced significant increases in zinc recoveries, as well as improved concentrate grades owing to better pyrite rejection. The 211/SNPX combination was the more effective of the two that were tested and provided better metallurgical results than those from either the use of SNPX or 211 alone.

Example 4
A plant trial of AERO 3501 promoter was carried out at a copper flotation plant, the standard thionocarbamate collector being replaced by 3501. The rougher circuit pH was 11 and the cleaner circuit pH was 12. Granulometry of the rougher feed was 4–5% +210 μm, with an average feed of 1.3% Cu.

The standard reagents utilized were 17 g/t thionocarbamate collector and 40 g/t MIBC frother. The three-week metallurgical average gave a final concentrate of 25.9% Cu with 92.1% recovery. For comparison, the three-week average with 14 g/t 3501 and 35 g/t MIBC frother gave a final concentrate of 26.3% Cu with 92.9% recovery. Thus, total replacement of the thionocarbamate collector by 3501 demonstrated the ability of the latter to provide at least metallurgical equivalence, as well as reduced collector and frother consumptions.

Example 5
A copper flotation plant that formerly used a xanthogen formate collector is now using AERO 3477 promoter. The 3477 has given 1–2% increased copper recovery and accelerated flotation rates with about a 20% reduction in the former collector dosage. Most significant is that the use of 3477 has allowed the rougher circuit pH to be dropped from pH 10.5 to 9.2 and the cleaner circuit has changed from pH 12 to 11.5. Lime savings have been in the order of 2–3 kg/t. In addition to the improved metallurgy, substantial economic benefits accrued from reduced reagent costs.

Example 6
A flotation investigation was undertaken to simplify and improve the lead circuit operation of a plant that treats a lead–zinc ore. The plant has a complex lead roughing–scavenging–cleaning circuit owing to the large amount of zinc that reports to the lead concentrate. This results in circulating loads of 200% in the lead circuit.

A standard laboratory test was developed that simulated actual plant practice regarding reagent additions and the typical metallurgical results obtained. The lead rougher flotation data for this test are presented in Table 4.

The standard test utilized a 2:3 NaCN/ZnO mixture and zinc sulphate as sphalerite depressants, Na-isobutyl xanthate, AERO 404 promoter and AEROFLOAT 242 promoter as the galena collectors and MIBC as the frother. Although rougher plus scavenger lead recovery was 96.4%, zinc recovery into the lead concentrate was 52.2%. Two stages of cleaning with a total of 100 g/t cyanide mixture

Table 4   Selective lead flotation with lead–zinc ore

Plant—standard laboratory test

	pH	2:3 NaCN/ZnO	Reagents, g/t 404	ZnSO$_4$	SIBX	MIBC	242
Grind		20	5				
Pb rougher	8.1			40	20	48	
Pb scavenger	8.0	20					5

	Wt%	Assays, % Pb	Zn	Distribution, % Pb	Zn
Combined Pb concentrate	12.60	26.0	29.92	96.4	52.2
Pb scavenger tailings	87.40	0.14	3.95	3.6	47.8
Calculated feed	100.00	3.39	7.22	100.0	100.0

AEROFLOAT 242 promoter test

	pH	2:3 NaCN/ZnO	Reagents, g/t 404	ZnSO$_4$	242	MIBC
Grind		30	2.5			
Pb rougher	8.1			40	12.5	12

	Wt%	Assays, % Pb	Zn	Distribution, % Pb	Zn
Pb rougher concentrate	7.00	43.8	12.40	92.9	11.8
Pb rougher tailings	93.00	0.25	6.98	7.1	88.2
Calculated feed	100.00	3.30	6.93	100.0	100.0

produced a final lead concentrate of about 55% Pb and
14% Zn, containing 82% of the lead values and 10% of the
zinc values.

In contrast to the above, a reagent schedule with
AEROFLOAT 242 promoter as the principal galena
collector was developed (see Table 4).

The amounts of cyanide mixture, 404 and MIBC were
reduced, SIBX was eliminated and 242 was increased to
12.5 g/t (the 404 is used to increase the recovery of oxidized
lead minerals, which constitute about 10% of the total lead
in the ore). The data show that a single-stage rougher
concentrate assaying 43.8% Pb and 12.4% Zn could be
obtained with 92.9% of the lead values and only 11.8% of
the zinc values. Cleaning of the rougher concentrate with no
further cyanide mixture additions produced a final lead
concentrate of about 55% Pb and 12% Zn. It contained
88% of the lead values and 10% of the zinc values.

Microscopic examination of the lead concentrates clearly
indicated the immediately preceding test results as the best
that are practical with this ore. Lead concentrate grades
lower than about 12% Zn were not likely since the
sphalerite present was either rimmed with covellite or had
micro-inclusions of covellite, chalcopyrite and/or galena.
Use of AEROFLOAT 242 promoter therefore
demonstrated good galena collecting power with maximum
practical selectivity against sphalerite evident in the lead
rougher flotation stage. This would minimize the circulating
load in the lead cleaner circuit as well as reduce and
simplify reagent additions and circuit control.

Conclusions

Dithiophosphate collectors have very diverse applicability
for the flotation treatment of sulphide and metallic base-
and precious-metal ores. Often regarded in the past as being
weak collectors, the increasing usage of dithiophosphates
worldwide is ample evidence of their efficacy as flotation
collectors. Although they can replace other types of
collectors—indeed, this has happened—the greatest usage of
dithiophosphates lies in combination with other collector
types to enhance the collecting properties that each
possesses.

References
1. Whitworth F. T. Australian Patent 2404, 1926.
2. Keller C. H. U.S. Patent 1 544 216, 1925.
3. Glembotskii V. A. Klassen V. I. and Plaksin I. N. *Flotation*
(New York: Primary Sources, 1963), 124–8.
4. Poling G. W. Reactions between thiol reagents and sulfide
minerals. In *Flotation: A.M. Gaudin memorial volume* Fuerstenau
M. C. ed. (New York: AIME, 1976), vol. 1, 334–63.

Concentration of fine wolframite particles at the iso-octane–water interface

G. H. Kelsall and K. I. Marinakis

Synopsis
The isotherms for the adsorption of sodium oleate and dodecylamine at the wolframite–water interface have been determined at various concentrations and pH values, both reagents having been used as wolframite flotation collectors. The form of the adsorption isotherms indicated that amine adsorption on wolframite was mainly electrostatic in nature. Sodium oleate reacted chemically with the lattice cations on the wolframite surface, which resulted in the formation of iron and/or manganese oleate. The concentration of the lattice ions in solution after equilibration of a wolframite sample at various pH values was measured both in the presence and absence of sodium oleate. The difference in the two sets of values supported the hypothesis of a chemical reaction between oleate and lattice cations.

Maximum concentration of the −13.6 μm wolframite particles at the oil–water interface occurred in the pH range 6–10 and 2–6 with oleic acid–sodium oleate and dodecylamine as collectors, respectively. These results can be rationalized in terms of the adsorption isotherms, solution equilibria and surface charge on the wolframite.

Wolframite ($(Fe,Mn)WO_4$) and scheelite ($CaWO_4$) are the most economically important minerals of tungsten. Both are concentrated from their ores by gravity methods because of their high density and generally coarse liberation size. The efficiency of gravity methods declines sharply with decreasing particle size and they are ineffective at sizes below 20–30 μm: this feature, together with the increasing need to process low-grade disseminated tungsten ores, necessitates the development of new processes that are capable of treating material at fine particle sizes.

In recent years flotation has been used as a complement to or even as a substitute for gravity separation techniques. Flotation is, however, also inefficient in the treatment of very fine particles (<10 μm), and to improve the flotation product grade a prior desliming step is used, which results in tungsten losses in the slime product. Two-liquid flotation is one technique that is capable of treating material at particles sizes below 10 μm and some encouraging results have been obtained in the treatment of cassiterite slimes[1] and clays[2] on the laboratory and pilot-plant scales, respectively. Two-liquid flotation has, however, never been applied to the treatment of tungsten mineral fines. As with conventional flotation, it exploits differences in the inherent or imposed surface chemical properties of the minerals to be separated: a knowledge of the surface chemical properties of wolframite is therefore a prerequisite for the development of such a process used for concentration of its fines.

Wolframite is an iron–manganese tungstate, the iron and manganese content of which can vary between that of pure ferberite (0–3.6% Mn, 18.4–14.7% Fe) to pure hübnerite (14.5–18.1% Mn, 3.7–0% Fe). Therefore, the surface chemical properties of wolframite will depend on the exact composition of the mineral sample—a fact that that has been neglected by most authors on the subject.

The solubility of the mineral has been little studied, and the few data in the literature[3,4,5] are probably unreliable. Wolframite has been reported to be positively charged in acid and negatively charged in alkali. The quoted iep values vary from pH 2–2.6 for hübnerite[6,7,8] to pH 5.5–6.5 for ferberite[5,9] (iep of wolframite at about pH 4[10,11]).

Flotation of wolframite is carried out in alkaline or acidic solutions with sodium oleate–oleic acid as collector. Its adsorption on wolframite has been studied extensively, but no consensus about the mechanism yet exists, though postulates include (a) coulombic attraction[12] of negatively charged oleic acid micelles on to the positively charged wolframite surface at pH<4 and (b) chemisorption[10-15] that results in the formation of iron and/or manganese oleate(s) on the wolframite surface, followed by physical adsorption of neutral oleic acid molecules[10,12,13] on the chemisorbed layer.

Maximum flotation recovery of wolframite with an oleic acid–sodium oleate collector has been found at pH values that vary from around 9[14,15] to 4,[13] the latter pH also being the iep of the wolframite sample used. Houot[11] concluded that the optimum pH was around 8, at which adsorption mechanism (b) occurred, but the recovery–pH relationship showed a second maximum at pH <4, at which mechanism (a) would be operative. The recovery in the latter pH range was lower than that at pH 8, possibly reflecting the less hydrophobic surface produced by adsorption of oleate micelles.

Cationic collectors have also been used in the flotation of wolframite,[5,16,17] though this was achieved only at pH values above the iep, with a maximum recovery at pH 8–9. This coincided with the pH values at which maximum adsorption was measured, which was thought to be electrostatic in nature, so explaining the poor selectivity.

In the present investigation the adsorption of an anionic collector (sodium oleate) and a cationic collector (dodecylamine) at the wolframite–water interface was studied to define the adsorption mechanism(s) involved by determination of the extent of adsorption as a function of surfactant concentration and pH. The solubility of wolframite was also determined as a function of pH and surfactant concentration. Finally, small-scale two-liquid flotation tests were carried out with fine wolframite particles and sodium oleate or dodecylamine as collectors to establish the optimum pH value(s) for wolframite recovery.

Experimental

Materials
Hand-picked pure wolframite crystals from Panasqueira mine, Portugal, were crushed with a hammer and ground in an agate vibratory mill for 40 min. Semi-quantitative X-ray fluorescence spectroscopic analysis showed that the sample was essentially pure wolframite with traces of sulphur and lead (<0.5%). Quantitative analysis of random wolframite particles was carried out with an electron-probe X-ray microanalyser (Camebax), which gave the wolframite composition as 74.49% WO_3, 15.49% Fe and 2.61% Mn. The specific surface area of the particles used in adsorption and two-liquid flotation tests was determined by the BET method to be 1.38 m^2 g^{-1}. Particle size analysis by a Malvern 3600D particle size analyser with laser light diffraction

showed that all the particles in the sample were of a size below 13.6 μm.

Surfactant-free triple-distilled water and analytical grade reagents were used throughout the work. 10^{-3} kmol m^{-3} stock oleic acid and dodecylamine solutions were made up weekly by dissolving a known amount of the compound in the predetermined amount of sodium hydroxide or hydrochloric acid, respectively, under intense stirring and heating to 333K. High-purity iso-octane, previously passed through a column of activated alumina to remove trace surfactants, was used in the two-liquid flotation tests.

Procedure

In the solubility studies batches of 0.5 g of wolframite particles were equilibrated in 100-cm^3 Erlenmeyer flasks for a predetermined time. In all tests 50 cm^3 of 0.1 kmol m^{-3} NaClO$_4\cdot$H$_2$O solution was used as an indifferent electrolyte, and the pH was adjusted with perchloric acid or sodium hydroxide prior to addition of the wolframite sample. To study the dissolution rate 1 g of wolframite particles was stirred in 500 cm^3 of 0.1 kmol m^{-3} NaClO$_4\cdot$H$_2$O solution (with or without oleate addition) at the required pH, samples being taken for tungsten, iron and manganese analysis. Small pH changes occurred during the tests, so final pH values are quoted in the results. All solubility experiments were carried out with high-purity ($>$ 99.999%) argon passing through the solutions to prevent oxidation of ferrous and manganous species.

In the adsorption experiments 0.5 g of wolframite particles was shaken with 50 cm^3 of the reagent solution for 30 min, unless otherwise stated. After agitation, one-half of the solution was used for pH measurement; after removal of the solids by centrifugation the remainder was used for determination of the equilibrium oleate or dodecylamine concentration. The amount of surfactant adsorbed was determined as the difference between the initial and equilibrium surfactant concentrations.

In the two-liquid flotation experiments a tall 250-cm^3 glass beaker was used, equipped with three stainless-steel baffles and a stirrer, driven by a variable-speed motor. 1 g of wolframite particles was conditioned in the collector solution for 10 min, during which time the pH was kept constant by perchloric acid or sodium hydroxide additions, as necessary. After conditioning, the pH was measured, 25 cm^3 of iso-octane was added and the mixture was stirred for 5 min. The resulting emulsion was transferred to a separating funnel for phase disengagement, the solids from each phase being weighed after having been dried. Mixing and conditioning were carried out at 1000 rev/min.

Tungsten, iron and manganese concentrations in solution were determined on a Perkin Elmer 5500 inductively coupled plasma emission spectrometer connected to a Perkin Elmer 3600 data station. Oleate and dodecylamine concentrations were determined by the methods of Gregory[18] and Pearce and Streatfield,[19] respectively.

Results and discussion

Sodium oleate–oleic acid–wolframite system

Effect of oleic acid on solubility of wolframite
Fig. 1 shows the tungstate, iron and manganese ion concentrations in 0.1 kmol m^{-3} NaClO$_4$ as a function of pH after 30 days' contact with excess wolframite. The dissolution process was very slow, the 'equilibration' time being dependent on the pH; shorter times were required in acidic solutions (pH$<$6.0) than in neutral or alkaline solutions. The iron and manganese concentrations in the pH range 6–12 and the tungstate concentrations in the pH range 6–10 could not be determined as

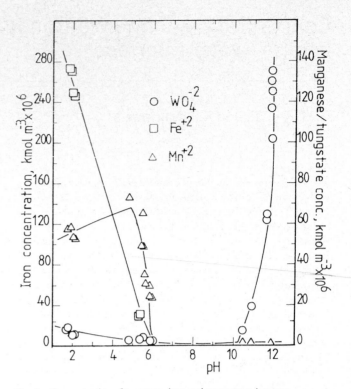

Fig. 1 Concentration of tungstate, iron and manganese ions as a function of pH in 0.1 kmol m^{-3} NaClO$_4$ solution saturated with respect to wolframite (conditioning time, 30 days)

they were below the detection limit of the analytical technique (i.e. $<$100 ppb). It is evident from Fig. 1, however, that wolframite exhibits minimum solubility at pH values between 6 and 10, and that its solubility increases above and below those pH values.

In addition to Fe^{2+}, Mn^{2+} and WO$_4^{2-}$, the hydroxy complexes of these metals will be present at concentrations that are dependent on the pH (see Appendix). Precipitation of the corresponding metal hydroxide will also occur—either in the bulk solution or on the surface of the wolframite—once the solubility product is exceeded. This implies that the concentration of iron, manganese and tungsten in solution is controlled by the solubility product of the compound with the lowest solubility at a given pH value. This would result in the

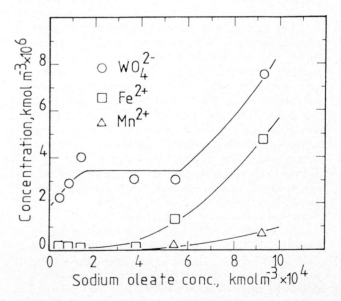

Fig. 2 Effect of oleate concentration on concentration of iron, manganese and tungsten in saturated wolframite suspensions at pH 10.5 $\pm$ 0.3 (conditioning time, 4 days)

non-stoichiometric dissolution of wolframite—a hypothesis supported by the results shown in Fig. 1. The minimum concentration of iron, manganese and tungsten, and hence the minimum solubility of wolframite, was obtained at pH values between 6 and 10. The concentration of iron (Fe^{2+}) and manganese (Mn^{2+}) increased below pH 6, and that of tungsten (WO_4^{2-}) increased above pH 10.5. These results are in good agreement with the theoretical predictions (shown in graphical form in Figs. 1 and 2 of the Appendix).

The effect of oleate on wolframite solubility is shown in Fig. 2 for pH 10.5 ± 0.3—chosen because wolframite is usually floated from an alkaline pulp, the oleate solubility is higher in alkaline solutions and the concentration of iron–manganese is lower, which prevents bulk precipitation of the oleate in the form of iron–manganese oleates. Iron and manganese concentrations at this pH were hardly detectable at oleate concentrations below 4 x 10^{-4} kmol m^{-3}, but they increased significantly above that value. Initially, the tungsten concentration increased with oleate additions up to 2 x 10^{-4} kmol m^{-3}, remained constant to 6 x 10^{-4} kmol oleate m^{-3} and increased further above that figure.

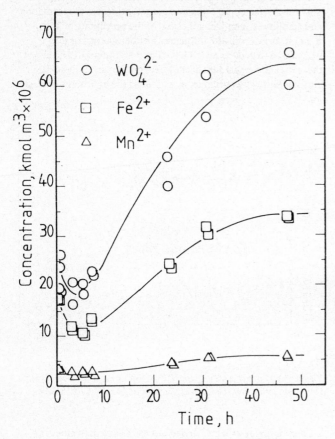

Fig. 3 Concentration–time data for dissolution of wolframite in presence of 4.7 x 10^{-4} kmol m^{-3} sodium oleate at pH 11.9 ± 0.1

The concentration–time data for wolframite dissolution are shown in Fig. 3 for a sodium oleate concentration of 4.7 x 10^{-4} kmol m^{-3} and pH 11.9. The concentration of iron, manganese and tungsten decreased initially owing to the precipitation of ferrous or manganous oleate, reaching minimum values after 5 h of 11.8 x 10^{-6}, 2.2 x 10^{-6} and 20.5 x 10^{-6} kmol m^{-3}, respectively. After longer times the concentrations of all three species increased gradually.

Values quoted in the literature for the solubility product of iron and manganese oleates vary widely.[21] Recent data[22] gave the solubility products of both iron and manganese oleates as 3.98 x 10^{-16} kmol^3 m^{-9}. If this value is correct, iron and manganese oleate will be formed in 2 x 10^{-5} kmol oleate m^{-3} solution

whenever the metal ion concentrations are above 1 x 10^{-6} kmol m^{-3}.

Such precipitation would decrease the iron and manganese concentrations and increase the lattice anion (WO_4^{2-}) concentrations, the reaction being limited by depletion of oleate in solution. That this was not observed suggests that either equilibrium conditions were not attained in the experiments, the results of which are shown in Figs. 2 and 3, or that at least part of the oleate did not precipitate as metal oleate in bulk solution but on the wolframite surface.

If WO_4^{2-} ions are lost preferentially from the wolframite lattice at high pH, OH$^-$ ions from solution must replace them for electroneutrality to be maintained. This would produce iron and/or manganese hydroxide surface phases. Conversely, when Fe^{2+} and Mn^{2+} ions are dissolved at low pH, protons from solution would be incorporated in the lattice, producing a tungstic acid (H_2WO_4) surface phase (see Appendix). Such a scheme is congruous with the observed pH changes that accompany wolframite dissolution across the pH range studied.

Amount of oleate abstracted by wolframite

The amount of oleate abstracted from an aqueous solution by wolframite was measured at pH 10.5 ± 0.3 as a function of the oleate concentration (Fig. 4). Complete abstraction of oleate occurred at initial oleate concentrations below that necessary to form a close-packed vertically orientated monolayer, assuming a cross-sectional area of 20.5 x 10^{-20} m^2 for the oleate group.[23] At higher oleate concentrations the amount abstracted increased steadily and attained a maximum value at an 'equilibrium' oleate concentration of 4.0 x 10^{-4} kmol m^{-3}, decreasing slightly thereafter owing to wolframite dissolution (Figs. 2 and 3).

Abstraction of oleate by wolframite was found to be a rapid

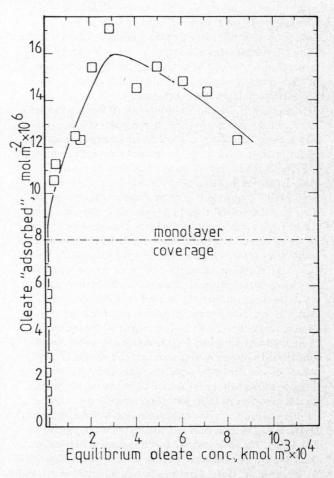

Fig. 4 Amount of oleate abstracted by wolframite as a function of equilibrium oleate concentration at pH 10.5 ± 0.3 (conditioning time, 30 min)

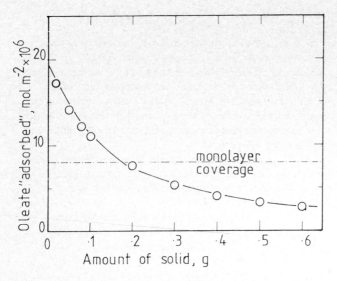

Fig. 5 Amount of oleate abstracted by wolframite at various solid/liquid ratios at initial oleate concentration of 4.7×10^{-5} kmol m^{-3} and pH 9.2–7.8 (conditioning time, 30 min).

process and an apparent equilibrium was reached in less than 1 min. In all subsequent experiments, however, an equilibration time of 30 min was used. Tests conducted at different solid to liquid ratios (Fig. 5) showed that the abstraction was dependent on the amount of solids present, which suggests that the process was irreversible.

In a sodium oleate solution oleate anions predominate at alkaline pH values ($>$8.0), at which the wolframite surface is negatively charged.[11] Therefore, electrostatic attraction was probably not responsible for the adsorption of oleate on wolframite—at least at these pH values. Furthermore, coulombic adsorption is restricted to less than a monolayer, unless it is followed by other types of adsorption, such as hydrophobic association and/or hydrogen bonding. The first two mechanisms of adsorption are, however, reversible, which was not so in the present system. In addition, the formation of hydrogen bonds between the lattice ions on the wolframite surface and the oleate ions in solution is not favourable, which makes this mechanism very unlikely. Moreover, adsorption could not be chemical in nature because it was a rapid process and exceeded a monolayer.

Recently, it was proposed that the mechanism of adsorption of oleate by calcite, fluorite and barite[24] and myristic acid by calcite and scheelite[25] was by precipitation of the corresponding metal soaps on the mineral surfaces. It is reasonable to assume that a similar mechanism is operative in the wolframite–oleate system, i.e. the oleate ions in solution react with the lattice cations on the wolframite surface to form an iron–manganese oleate. At low oleate concentrations (below those necessary for the completion of a monolayer) complete abstraction of oleate from solution would take place, followed by an increase in the tungsten concentration and a decrease in the iron and manganese concentrations (Fig. 2). With increasing oleate concentrations the precipitated metal soaps on the wolframite surface would inhibit the dissolution of wolframite and the reaction of the oleate ions with the lattice cations would be controlled by diffusion through the metal oleate film, producing an apparent equilibrium state. At high oleate concentrations the loosely adherent layers of iron and manganese oleates on the wolframite surface would become detached, leading to the resumption of dissolution. The latter is shown by the increase in the tungsten concentration in solution observed at oleate concentrations above 6×10^{-4} kmol m^{-3} (Figs. 2 and 3). The concentrations of iron and manganese also appeared to increase because of the inability of the analytical technique to discriminate between dissolved species and colloidal precipitates.

Metal oleate colloids have high negative electrophoretic mobilities at alkaline pH values,[26] oleate ions acting as potential-determining ions. At high oleate concentrations ($>6 \times 10^{-4}$ kmol m^{-3}) it was observed that the final solutions were cloudy, even after prolonged centrifuging. The same phenomenon, i.e. the formation of a stable colloidal suspension, has been reported by several authors,[24,26,27] being ascribed to the stabilization of the metal oleate covered mineral particles by adsorption of the excess oleate ions in the double layer. In the wolframite system the presence of metal oleate colloids is more likely, giving rise to the increase in the apparent iron and manganese concentrations in solution and the decrease in oleate abstraction (Fig. 4) at high concentrations. With the analytical techniques used only total iron, manganese, tungsten and oleate concentrations in solution and/or in suspension could be determined.

Two-liquid flotation of wolframite with oleic acid
From the results presented in Figs. 4, 5 and 6 it was concluded that oleate precipitates on the surface of wolframite. Therefore, its effectiveness as a collector will be dependent on the strength of adhesion of the precipitate on the mineral and not on the amount abstracted. Any parameter that influences the formation and stability (strength of adhesion) of the precipitate on the mineral surface will also influence the flotation response of wolframite with oleic acid. The pH of the solution will be one of these parameters because of the effect on the rate of dissolution and solubility of wolframite, as well as on the hydrolysis of oleate ions.

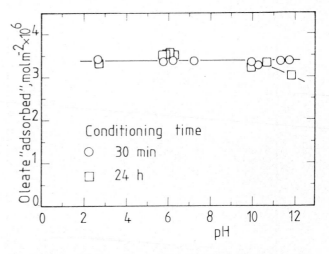

Fig. 6 Amount of oleate abstracted by wolframite as a function of pH at two conditioning times (initial oleate concentration, 4.7×10^{-5} kmol m^{-3})

Abstraction tests were carried out at various pH values at a constant oleate concentration of 4.7×10^{-5} kmol m^{-3} (Fig. 6). At all pH values studied almost total abstraction of oleate occurred, the same results being obtained with equilibration times of 30 min and 24 h. These results are in agreement with the mechanism of oleate abstraction proposed above, and especially at pH values above 8, at which the oleate ions predominate in solution. At pH $<$ 8 oleic acid precipitates, which may account for most of its abstraction. This is also reflected in the results of two-liquid flotation tests shown in Fig. 7. The maximum concentration of the wolframite particles at the iso-octane–water interface occurred at pH values $>$6, decreasing sharply at lower values. At the higher oleate concentrations used the oil droplets were overloaded with coagulated hydrophobic wolframite particles, so some sank to the bottom of the separating funnel. This may account for the slight decrease in recovery observed at pH $>$6; whereas the decrease at pH values $<$ 6.0 was due mainly to the extraction of the neutral oleic acid molecules into the

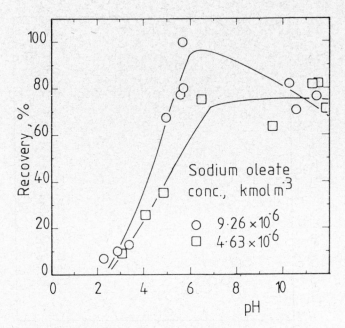

Fig. 7   Effect of pH on concentration of wolframite at iso-octane–water interface with oleic acid–sodium oleate as collector

organic phase, rather than to their adsorption on to the wolframite particles, rendering them hydrophilic/oleophobic.

Dodecylamine–wolframite system

Effect of dodecylamine on solubility of wolframite
Fig. 8 shows the effect of dodecylamine on the concentration of iron, manganese and tungsten in a wolframite-saturated solution at pH 1.9 ± 0.1. The manganese concentration ($5.5 \pm 0.2 \times 10^{-5}$ kmol m^{-3}) was essentially that obtained in the absence

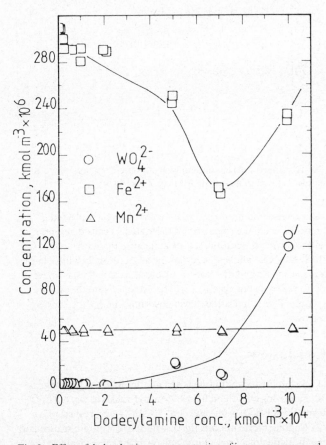

Fig. 8   Effect of dodecylamine on concentration of iron, manganese and tungsten in wolframite-saturated solution at pH 1.9 ± 0.1 (conditioning time, 4 days)

of amine, independent of the concentration of the latter. The tungsten concentration was also constant at 5.0×10^{-6} kmol m^{-3} for small dodecylamine additions ($< 7.0 \times 10^{-4}$ kmol m^{-3}), but increased abruptly at higher dodecylamine concentrations, possibly owing to the formation of complexes of the type $[(RNH_3^+)_n WO_4]^{(n-2)+}$. The concentration of iron decreased at low amine concentrations, however, attaining a minimum value of 1.71×10^{-4} kmol m^{-3} at an amine concentration of 7×10^{-4} kmol m^{-3}, and then increased at higher amine concentrations.

Adsorption of dodecylamine on wolframite
The uptake of dodecylamine by wolframite at pH values 2.0 and 6.0 ± 0.2 is presented in Figs. 9 and 10. Irreversibility tests conducted by the dilution at constant pH method showed that some of the amine could be desorbed from the wolframite surface. The adsorption process was rapid, however, and equilibrium was established in less than 30 min. The adsorption isotherm curve shown in Fig. 9 is characterized by three well-defined regions: (1) at low amine concentrations the adsorption displayed a marked dependence on the dodecylamine concentration; (2) the adsorption remained constant; and (3) the adsorption increased with increasing concentration.

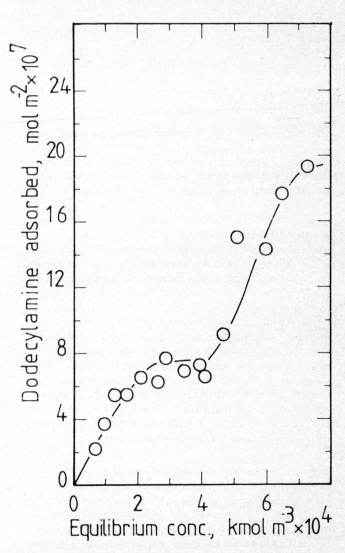

Fig. 9   Adsorption isotherm of dodecylamine on wolframite at pH 2.0 (conditioning time, 30 min)

The adsorption isotherm at pH 6.0 (Fig. 10) displayed only the first two regions of the isotherm obtained at pH 2.0, but the amount of amine adsorbed was greater than that at the lower pH value. At pH 2.0 the amount of dodecylamine adsorbed was far less than that needed for the formation of a close-packed

29

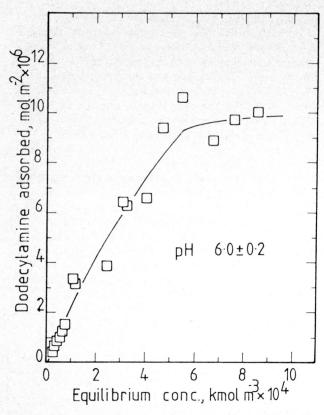

Fig. 10   Adsorption isotherm of dodecylamine on wolframite at pH 6.0 (conditioning time, 30 min)

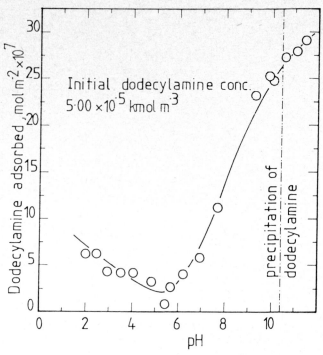

Fig. 11   Adsorption of dodecylamine on wolframite as a function of pH (conditioning time, 30 min)

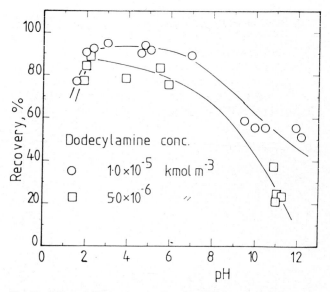

Fig. 12   Effect of pH on concentration of wolframite at iso-octane–water interface with dodecylamine as collector

vertically orientated monolayer, assuming a surface area of the dodecylammonium head group of 20×10^{-20} m^{-2}, whereas at pH 6.0 adsorption produced a complete monolayer. This indicates that the adsorption took place on distinct sites on the surface and that lateral interactions between the adsorbed species were negligible.

The adsorption of amines on wolframite has been attributed[5,17] to coulombic attraction between the negatively charged wolframite surface and the cationic amine species. The iep value of the wolframite sample used was at pH 4.0,[11] so the surface of the mineral was positively charged below this value. Therefore, electrostatic adsorption of the dodecylammonium cations on wolframite at pH 2 is unfavourable. The adsorption of amines on other salt-type minerals, e.g. calcite, has been ascribed[28,29] to the formation of an amino–carbonate complex on the calcite surface, and a similar mechanism might be applicable in the present system. Thermodynamic data on the formation of such complexes are, however, non-existent, but it is known that tungsten can be extracted into an organic phase with amines as extractants.[30] In addition to the mechanism proposed above, coulombic adsorption also can take place at pH 6, which explains the higher adsorption of amine at this pH value.

Two-liquid flotation of wolframite with dodecylamine
The adsorption of dodecylamine on wolframite at various pH values is presented in Fig. 11 for an amine concentration of 5.0×10^{-5} kmol m^{-3}. The adsorption was almost constant at pH values below 6, but it increased sharply above this value. Electrostatic attraction and adsorption of the neutral dodecylamine molecules at pH values above 6 were responsible for the increasing adsorption at alkaline pH values. At even higher pH values, i.e. above 10.4, dodecylamine began to precipitate, which may account for the apparently high adsorption values obtained.

The recovery of fine wolframite particles at the iso-octane–water interface (Fig. 12) was found to depend on the pH of the solution. Maximum recovery was obtained in the pH range 2–6, although the adsorption of amine at the same pH

values was a minimum. This discrepancy can be explained, however, when the chemistry of the system is considered prior to and following the addition to the aqueous pulp of iso-octane. In the former case all the dodecylamine added initially will be in the aqueous phase and therefore available for adsorption, whereas in the latter, and above pH 6, it will be extracted into the organic phase.[31] This will result in lower adsorption and, hence, lower recovery.

Conclusions

(1) Solubility of wolframite is at a minimum in the pH range 6–10, increasing above and below these pH values as a result of the formation of WO_4^{2-} ions and ($Fe^{2+} + Mn^{2+}$) ions, respectively.
(2) Sodium oleate inhibits the dissolution of wolframite owing to the formation of a layer of iron and/or manganese oleate on the surface. The effect of dodecylamine is more complex and its exact mode of action is not well understood.

(3) The mechanism of adsorption of oleic acid on wolframite is the precipitation of iron and manganese oleates on the surface, whereas that of dodecylamine is the formation of a tungstate–amine complex on the surface and/or electrostatic attraction at pH values above the iep of wolframite.
(4) The maximum concentration of the –13.6 μm wolframite particles at the oil–water interface occurred in the pH ranges 6–10 and 2–6.

Acknowledgement

The authors are grateful to the Science and Engineering Research Council (SERC) for the provision of a grant to support the work and for a research assistantship for K.I.M. Thanks are also due to the Mineral Industries Research Organisation (MIRO) for additional support.

References
1. Marinakis K. I. and Shergold H. L. Treatment of tin-bearing slimes with the two-liquid flotation process. Internal report, Imperial College, London, 1982.
2. Shergold H. L. and Lofthouse C. H. The purification of kaolins by the two-liquid separation process. In *Proceedings of the 12th international mineral processing congress, 1977* (São Paulo, Brazil: D.N.P.M., M.M.E., 1982), vol. 2, 28–56.
3. Povarennykh A. S. The cause for the different behaviour of molybdenum and tungsten in endogenic processes. *Geol. Zh. Akad. Nauk Ukr. R. S. R.*, **21**, no. 5 1961, 39–47. (Russian text); *Chem. Abstr.*, **56**, 1962, 1180b.
4. Urusov V. S. Ivanova G. F. and Khodakovskii I. L. Energetic and thermodynamic properties of molybdates and tungstates and some features of their geochemistry. *Geokhimiya*, no. 10 1967, 1050–63. (Russian text); *Geochem. Int.*, **4**, no. 5 1967, 950–63.
5. Viswanathan K. V. and Majumdar K. K. Adsorption of long chain electrolytes at the solid–liquid interface, part III: Wolframite–water system. BARC-603, Bhabha Atomic Research Centre, Bombay, 1972.
6. Cibulka J. and Dobiás B. Electrokinetic explanation of the adsorption of sodium lauryl sulphate and cetyltrimethylammonium bromide on the phase boundary — wolframite–solutions. *Rudy*, **13**, no. 4 1965, 7–11. (Czech text); *Chem. Abstr.*, **63**, 1965, 7941e.
7. Jin Hua-Ai and Li B-D. Activation mechanism of metal cation in wolframite flotation. *Yu Se Chin Shu*, **32**, no. 3 1980, 48–55. (Chinese text); *Chem Abstr.*, **95**, 1981, 136272j.
8. Li B-D. and Jin Hua-Ai. Study on the flotation of wolframite slimes. *Ye Se Chin Shu*, **32**, no. 1 1980, 48–55. (Chinese text); *Chem. Abstr.*, **95**, 1981, 173146s.
9. Huh Y. H. *et al.* A basic study on the flotation of wolframite. *Taehan Kwangsan Hakhoe Chi*, **17**, no. 3 1980, 176–80. (Korean text); *Chem. Abstr.*, **94**, 1981, 107063r.
10. Abeidu A. M. Comparative studies on flotation of tungstate minerals. *J. Mines Metals Fuels*, **22**, no 4 1974, 107–9.
11. Houot R. Contribution à l'étude de la flottation de la wolframite. *Sciences Terre, Mem.* no. 7, 1965, 96 p.
12. Shevlyakov M. I. and Kuz'kin S. F. Mechanism of sodium oleate action on the surface of basobismutite, wolframite and muscovite. *Izv. vyssh. ucheb. Zaved., Tsvet. Metall.*, **12**, no. 2 1969, 14–18. (Russian text); *Chem. Abstr.*, **71**, 1969, 53941e.
13. Abeidu A. M. Flotation studies on wolframite. *Trans. Instn Min. Metall. (Sect. C: Mineral Process. Extr. Metall.)*, **84**, 1975, C5–10.
14. Mukai S. and Kano G. Effects of collector and hydrogen ion concentration on flotation of nonsulfide minerals. *Nippon Kogyo Kaishi*, **77**, 1961, 1071–7. (Japanese text); *Chem. Abstr.*, **57**, 1962, 473c.
15. Mukai S. *et al.* Effect of collector ion concentration and hydrogen ion concentration on the floatability of non-sulphide minerals. *Mem. Fac. Engng Kyoto Univ.*, **24**, no. 2 1962, 270–90. (English text)
16. Itoh S. and Okada T. Electrokinetic properties and floatability of wolframite. *Tohoku Kogyo Gijutsu Shikensho Hokoku*, **11**, 1980, 29–33. (Japanese text); *Chem. Abstr.*, **93**, 1980, 135670j.
17. Schubert H. Flotierbarkeit und Strukturbeziehungen bei kationaktiver Flotation. *Freiberger Forschungsh.* A77, 1957, 74 p.
18. Gregory G. R. E. C. The determination of residual anionic surface-active reagents in mineral flotation liquors. *Analyst*, **91**, 1966, 251–7.
19. Pearce A. S. and Streatfield E. L. German Patent 1 190 229, 1965; *Chem. Abstr.*, **63**, 1965, 2748f.
20. Naumov G. B. Ryzhenko B. N. and Khodakovsky I. L. *Handbook of thermodynamic data* (Moscow: Atomizdat, 1971). (Russian text); Translated by the U.S. Geological Survey NTIS PB-226 722, 1974.
21. Du Rietz C. Fatty acids in flotation. In *Progress in mineral dressing: transactions of the international mineral processing congress, Stockholm, 1957* (Stockholm: Almqvist & Wiksell, 1958), 417–33.
22. Du Rietz C. Chemisorption of collectors in flotation. In *Proceedings 11th international mineral processing congress, Cagliari, 1975* (Cagliari: Istituto di Arte Mineraria, 1975), 375–403.
23. Lovell V. M. Goold L. A. and Finkelstein N. P. Infrared studies of the adsorption of oleate species on calcium fluoride. *Int. J. Mineral Process.*, **1**, 1974, 183–92.
24. Marinakis K. I. The action of sodium silicate on the flotation of salt-type minerals with oleic acid. Ph.D. thesis, University of London, 1980.
25. Atademir M. R. Kitchener J. A. and Shergold H. L. The surface chemistry and flotation of scheelite, II: Flotation collectors. *Int. J. Mineral Process.*, **8**, 1981, 9–16.
26. Matijević E. Leja J. and Nemeth R. Precipitation phenomena of heavy metal soaps in aqueous solutions, I: Calcium oleate. *J. Colloid Interface Sci.*, **22**, 1966, 419–29.
27. Paterson J. G. and Salman T. Adsorption of sodium oleate on cupric and ferric hydroxides. *Trans. Instn Min. Metall. (Sect. C: Mineral Process. Extr. Metall)*, **79**, 1970, C91–102.
28. Solnyshkin V. I. and Cheng Yu. L. Mechanism of reaction of cationic reagents and flotation regulators with apatite, scheelite and calcite. *Obogashch. Rud. Uglei Akad. Nauk SSSR Inst. Gorn. Dela*, 1963, 147–58. (Russian text); *Chem. Abstr.*, **61**, 1964, 331 g.
29. Kuz'kin S. F. and Cheng Y. L. The separation of apatite from calcite by flotation with cationic collectors. *Izv. vyssh. ucheb. Zaved., Tsvet. Metall.*, **6**, no. 1 1963, 42–7. (Russian text); *Chem. Abstr.*, **59**, 1963, 2426a.
30. Coleman C. F. Amine as extractants. *Nucl. Sci. Engng*, **17**, 1963, 274–86.
31. Shergold H. L. and Mellgren O. Concentration of minerals at the oil/water interface. *Trans. Am. Inst. Min. Engrs*, **247**, 1970, 149–59.
32. Baes C. F. Jr. and Messmer R. E. *The hydrolysis of cations* (London: Wiley, 1976), 512 p.

Appendix

*Solubility of manganous tungstate**

$$MnWO_{4(s)} \rightleftharpoons Mn^{2+} + WO_4^{2-} \qquad Ksp_1 = 1.41 \times 10^{-9}$$

$$Mn^{2+} + H_2O \rightleftharpoons MnOH^+ + H^+ \qquad K_{11} = 3.46 \times 10^{-11}$$

$$Mn^{2+} + 2H_2O \rightleftharpoons Mn(OH)_{2(aq)} + 2H^+ \qquad K_{12} = 6.31 \times 10^{-23}$$

$$Mn(OH)_{2(s)} \rightleftharpoons Mn(OH)_{2(aq)} \qquad K = 1.41 \times 10^{-8}$$

$$Mn^{2+} + 3H_2O \rightleftharpoons Mn(OH)_3^- + 3H^+ \qquad K_{13} = 1.58 \times 10^{-35}$$

$$Mn^{2+} + 4H_2O \rightleftharpoons Mn(OH)_4^{2-} + 4H^+ \qquad K_{14} = 5.01 \times 10^{-49}$$

$$2Mn^{2+} + H_2O \rightleftharpoons Mn_2OH^{3+} + H^+ \qquad K_{21} = 1.35 \times 10^{-10}$$

$$2Mn^{2+} + 3H_2O \rightleftharpoons Mn_2(OH)_3^+ + 3H^+ \qquad K_{23} = 3.39 \times 10^{-26}$$

$$H_2WO_{4(aq)} \rightleftharpoons H^+ + HWO_4^- \qquad K_1 = 2.51 \times 10^{-5}$$

$$HWO_4^- \rightleftharpoons H^+ + WO_4^{2-} \qquad K_2 = 3.16 \times 10^{-4}$$

$$H_2WO_{4(s)} \rightleftharpoons H_2WO_{4(aq)} \qquad K = 1.99 \times 10^{-8}$$

Mass balance

$[Mn^{2+}] + [MnOH^+] + [Mn(OH)_{2(aq)}] + [Mn(OH)_{2(s)}] + [Mn(OH)_3^-] + [Mn(OH)_4^{2-}] + 2[Mn_2OH^{3+}] + 2[Mn_2(OH)_3^+] = [H_2WO_{4(aq)}] + [H_2WO_{4(s)}] + [HWO_4^-] + [WO_4^{2-}]$

$[Mn(OH)_{2(s)}] = 0 \qquad pH < 9.8$

$[H_2WO_{4(s)}] = 0 \qquad pH > 5.7$

For $5.7 < pH < 9.8$

* Data from Naumov G. B. Ryzhenko B. N. and Khodakovsky I. L. *Handbook of thermodynamic data* (Moscow: Atomizdat, 1971) (U.S.G.S. trans. NTIS PB-226 722, 1974) and Baes C. F. Jr. and Messmer R. E. *The hydrolysis of cations* (London: Wiley, 1976), 512 p.

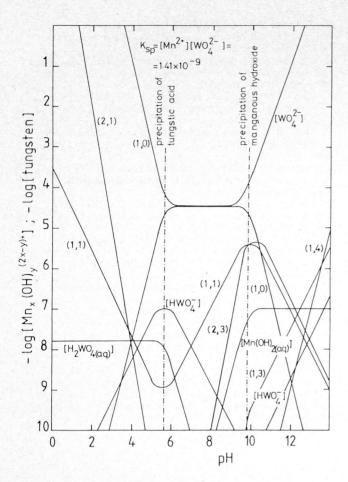

Fig. 1 Concentrations of soluble species in saturated solutions of $MnWO_4$ as a function of pH

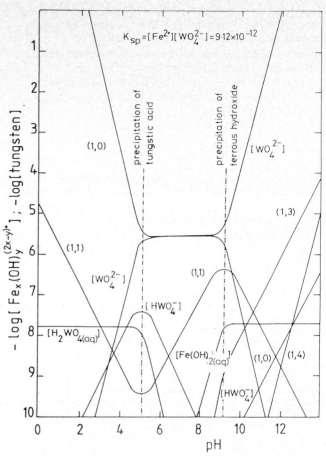

Fig. 2 Concentrations of soluble species in saturated solutions of $FeWO_4$ as a function of pH

$$[Mn^{2+}]^2 = \frac{1 + \dfrac{[H^+]}{K_2} + \dfrac{[H^+]^2}{K_1 K_2}}{1 + \dfrac{K_{11}}{[H^+]} + \dfrac{K_{12}}{[H^+]^2} + \dfrac{K_{13}}{[H^+]^3} + \dfrac{K_{14}}{[H^+]^4}} K_{sp_1}$$

$$[Mn_2OH^+] = [Mn_2(OH)_3^+] = 0$$

Solubility of ferrous tungstate*

$FeWO_{4(s)} \rightleftharpoons Fe^{2+} + WO_4^{2-}$	$K_{sp_2} = 9.12 \times 10^{-12}$
$Fe^{2+} + H_2O \rightleftharpoons FeOH^+ + H^+$	$K_{11} = 3.16 \times 10^{-10}$
$Fe^{2+} + 2H_2O \rightleftharpoons Fe(OH)_{2(aq)} + 2H^+$	$K_{12} + 2.51 \times 10^{-20}$
$Fe(OH)_{2(s)} \rightleftharpoons Fe(OH)_{2(aq)}$	$K = 1.99 \times 10^{-8}$
$Fe^{2+} + 3H_2O \rightleftharpoons Fe(OH)_3^- + 3H^+$	$K_{13} = 1.00 \times 10^{-31}$
$Fe^{2+} + 4H_2O \rightleftharpoons Fe(OH)_4^- + 4H^+$	$K_{14} = 1.00 \times 10^{-46}$
$H_2WO_{4(aq)} \rightleftharpoons HWO_4^- + H^+$	$K_1 = 2.51 \times 10^{-5}$
$HWO_4^- \rightleftharpoons WO_4^{2-} + H^+$	$K_2 = 3.16 \times 10^{-4}$
$H_2WO_{4(s)} \rightleftharpoons H_2WO_{4(aq)}$	$K' = 1.99 \times 10^{-8}$

Mass balance

$[Fe^{2+}] + [FeOH^+] + [Fe(OH)_{2(aq)}] + [Fe(OH)_{2(s)}] +$
$[Fe(OH)_3^-] + [Fe(OH)_4^-] = [WO_4^{2-}] + [HWO_4^-] + [H_2WO_{4(aq)}] +$
$[H_2WO_{4(s)}]$

$[Fe(OH)_{2(s)}] = 0 \qquad pH < 9.3$

$[H_2WO_{4(s)}] = 0 \qquad pH > 5.2$

* See Naumov and co-workers and Baes and Messmer, *op. cit.*

For $5.2 < pH < 9.3$

$$[Fe^{2+}]^2 = \frac{1 + \dfrac{[H^+]}{K_2} + \dfrac{[H^+]^2}{K_1 K_2}}{1 + \dfrac{K_{11}}{[H^+]} + \dfrac{K_{12}}{[H^+]^2} + \dfrac{K_{13}}{[H^+]^3} + \dfrac{K_{14}}{[H^+]^4}} Ksp_2$$

$$[Fe(OH)_{2(s)}] = [H_2WO_{4(s)}] = 0$$

Depressant function in flotation of calcite, apatite and dolomite

P. Parsonage, D. Melven, A. F. Healey and D. Watson

Synopsis

The effects of sodium silicate, gum arabic and sodium tripolyphosphate on the zeta-potentials and Hallimond tube flotation of calcite, apatite and dolomite by sodium oleate have been studied. All three reagents can act as both slime dispersants and depressants. On monomineralic products at pH 9.5 gum arabic and sodium silicate both act as depressants for calcite, have a lower depressant effect on dolomite and little effect on apatite flotation. Attempts to use these reagents as selective depressants in mineral mixtures, however, led to strong depression of all three minerals.

The effects of the ions released by dissolution of the carbonates on the behaviour of the depressants have therefore been investigated. It has been shown that for gum arabic to act as a depressant a certain level of calcium ion is required, and it is postulated that it becomes involved in a bridging mechanism between the polymeric molecule and the mineral surface. The level of free calcium ion required to produce depression of apatite by gum arabic is less than that present in a solution at equilibrium with calcite at pH 9.5. Magnesium ion does not have the same effect on the depression of apatite, although its influence on the zeta-potential of the mineral is similar to that of calcium. Depression of apatite by sodium silicate also occurs if more than a critical level of calcium is present in solution. Altering the chemical conditions to reduce the free calcium level leads to enhanced flotation of the minerals in the presence of gum arabic and sodium silicate.

Sodium tripolyphosphate causes depression of the three minerals. The mechanisms whereby the three reagents act as depressants and dispersants are discussed in terms of the nature of their adsorption at the solid–liquid interface. Evidence shows that with gum arabic and sodium silicate hydrophilic adsorbed layers are formed on calcite, whereas the mode of action of polyphosphate is to adsorb strongly at surface cation sites and to confer a high negative charge to the mineral surface.

The work reported here is a development from an earlier enquiry into the effects of slime coating in flotation in which it was shown that the formation of slime coatings depended on the zeta-potentials of the mineral particles and the slime particles and that this could either aid or hinder selective flotation.[1] Prevention of slime coating may be achieved by the use of dispersants to increase the zeta-potentials of the components, but such reagents may also act as flotation depressants.

To obtain more information on reagents that affect mineral zeta-potential, and on the effects of their presence on subsequent flotation with sodium oleate, the behaviour of three known slime dispersants—sodium silicate, gum arabic and sodium tripolyphosphate—with respect to the flotation of calcite, dolomite and apatite have been investigated.

The nature of the mineral surfaces in the presence of these

reagents has been studied by determining the relationship between their zeta-potentials and their susceptibility to coagulation by an indifferent electrolyte. The effects of ions released from the carbonates on the flotation of apatite have been studied to explain the poor selectivity obtained when mixtures of the minerals are floated. The results are discussed in terms of the mechanism of the depressant effect and the effect of dissolved ions.

Experimental methods

Minerals

The following pure minerals were used in the testwork (R.F.D. Parkinson and Co. Ltd., England): calcite (Mendips, England), dolomite (Leicestershire, England) and fluor-apatite (India). Samples were prepared for the flotation tests by grinding 1-kg lots of –1.7 mm crushed sample at 50% solids concentration with double-distilled deionized water in a stainless-steel mill. The ground samples were sized to –150 +75 μm by wet-screening and stored in airtight glass jars away from sunlight under frequently changed double-distilled water. This size fraction material was used for all of the flotation tests described here.

Reagents

Sodium oleate was prepared as a 10^{-3} M stock solution by the saponification of purified oleic acid (Hopkin and Williams) with slight excess of the stoichiometric amount of sodium hydroxide. Fresh reagent was prepared every three or four days.

Gum arabic (Sigma Chemicals, London) is a branched polymer of galactose, rhamnose, arabinose and glucuronic acid as the calcium magnesium and potassium salts with a molecular weight of approximately 250000. It was prepared freshly each day at a concentration of 0.084%.

Sodium silicate (BDH waterglass solution) had a reagent composition of 132 g/l Na and 204 g/l Si. The stock solution for the testwork was freshly prepared each day at a concentration of 0.94% and the pH was adjusted to 9.5 unless otherwise stated.

Sodium tripolyphosphate, STPP, $Na_5P_3O_{10}$ (Albright and Wilson) was used in a stock solution at a concentration of 0.368% (10^{-2} M).

Microelectrophoretic measurements

A Rank Bros. particle microelectrophoresis apparatus mark II with rotating prism attachment was used in the flat cell configuration. Pure samples of the minerals were ground in distilled water by use of a McCrone micronizing mill to produce particles of <10 μm. Electrophoretic mobilities were converted to zeta-potential by the Smoluchowski equation.

Particles were conditioned at 0.7 g/l concentration at the test pH for 3 min, followed by a 10-min conditioning in the presence of reagent. For tests that involved the addition of calcium or magnesium ions these were added to the clear stock solution at the required pH before the introduction of the slime particles.

Flotation tests

A modified Hallimond tube with a 60-μm capillary was used. The tube capacity was approximately 150 ml. One measure of pure mineral or mixture (approximately 1 g) was conditioned at the experimental pH at an ionic strength of 2.10^{-3} M (NaClO$_4$) for 3 min, depressant was added and conditioning was continued for a further 5 min (if no depressant was to be added, this stage was left out). Thereafter, collector was added and conditioning was continued for a further 10 min. The sample was stirred throughout the conditioning period and the experimental pH was maintained by use of perchloric acid or sodium hydroxide, if necessary. After the conditioning period the mineral and conditioning solution were transferred to the Hallimond tube and 20 cm^3 of air was passed. The concentrate and tailings were recovered and weighed. Where mixtures were floated, the products were analysed by heavy liquid separation at densities of 2.8 and 3.0 g cm^{-3}.

Abstraction of tripolyphosphate by calcite
The determination of tripolyphosphate abstraction by calcite was carried out by grinding a 1-g sample of the mineral in the micronizing mill and conditioning for 10 min at pH 9.5, 2.10^{-3} M NaClO$_4$, with varying concentrates of STPP in a total volume of 100 ml. The suspensions were centrifuged, filtered and analysed for phosphorus.

Coagulation tests
Suspensions of minerals prepared as for the electrophoretic measurements were conditioned at 0.7 g l^{-1} solids at pH 9.5, 2.10^{-3} M NaClO$_4$, with 0.1 g/l of each of the reagents for a period of 10 min. After conditioning, 3-ml samples of the suspension were each mixed with 1 ml of various concentrations of NaCl in 1-cm spectrophotometer cells and allowed to settle for 1h. Thereafter, the transmittance of the supernatants was measured at 500 nm by use of a Pye Unicam SP 6-400 spectrophotometer. The electrophoretic mobility of the particles in each suspension was measured and the critical concentration of indifferent electrolyte required to cause coagulation was calculated by the method of Shaw.[2]

Size analysis
Particle size distributions in the ground suspensions were measured by laser diffraction with a Malvern 3300 particle size analyser with model-independent software.

Results

The flotation response of apatite, calcite and dolomite at pH 9.5 is shown in Fig. 1. The effects of increasing concentrations of sodium silicate, gum arabic and sodium tripolyphosphate with a collector concentration of 1.43 mol dm^{-3} oleate are shown in Figs. 2, 3 and 4. The variation in zeta-potentials of the minerals with the reagents present is shown in Figs. 5, 6 and 7. The size distributions of the suspensions used for the electrophoretic and coagulation experiments are shown in Fig. 8.

All three reagents are effective depressants for calcite. Dolomite shows evidence of some depression, but in no instance is the flotation suppressed completely. Apatite retains its floatability in the presence of gum arabic and sodium silicate, but is depressed by polyphosphate.

Sodium silicate
For sodium silicate it was noted that if the stock silicate solution was equilibrated at different pH values or in more concentrated solution, its effectiveness as a depressant was altered. High concentration of the stock solution or high equilibration pH (12.7) favoured depression of dolomite and a slight reduction in the flotation of apatite. A more acidic equilibration pH of the stock solution (pH 6) also favoured relatively more depression of the dolomite, but did not affect the apatite, which remained strongly floatable.

Measurements of the change in zeta-potential of the three minerals in the presence of sodium silicate at pH 9.5 (Fig. 5) indicate that silicate is adsorbed by all of the minerals, but whereas calcite is almost completely depressed (Fig. 2), dolomite is depressed to a lesser extent and apatite is unaffected. The influence of the reagent on the flotation is not solely a function of its adsorption at the mineral surface in the absence of collector.

Examination of calcite particles depressed by sodium silicate at pH 9.5 by use of scanning electron microscopy did not reveal any evidence of the presence of colloidal silica at the calcite surface.

Gum arabic
The effects of gum arabic on the flotation and electrokinetic properties of the three minerals at pH 9.5 are shown in Figs. 3 and 6. As for sodium silicate, gum arabic causes an increase in negative zeta-potential of all three minerals and is an effective slime dispersant, but although adsorption is taking place, only calcite is strongly depressed. The flotation of apatite is hardly affected and dolomite shows intermediate behaviour.

With concentrations greater than 0.01 g l^{-1} gum arabic the zeta-potentials of the three minerals level off and are very similar, being about −40 mV. This suggests that the individual differences between the minerals are becoming less important and that the charge properties of the surfaces are beginning to be controlled by the presence of the gum arabic.

Sodium tripolyphosphate (STPP)
The influence of STPP on the flotation and zeta-potentials of the minerals is shown in Figs. 4 and 7. This reagent is effective in conferring a high negative zeta-potential on the three minerals and should therefore be a good dispersant. The lowering of the zeta-potentials to less negative values for STPP concentrations greater than 1 g l^{-1} is probably a function of the increased ionic strength of the solution, the values recorded being close to the maximum observable for particles with high surface potential.[3]

Fig. 4 shows that at levels below about 0.4 g l^{-1} STPP acts as a depressant for the three minerals, but that for higher concentrations its effectiveness in depressing the carbonates is reduced, so at high reagent levels (>5 g l^{-1}) calcite and dolomite float well, whereas apatite remains depressed.

To determine whether the action of the polyphosphate was solely by sequestering calcium ions in solution or by adsorbing at the calcite surface the amount of STPP abstracted from solution by a fine suspension of calcite was determined (Fig. 9). These results are evidence that the polyphosphate ions are absorbed by the calcite surface.

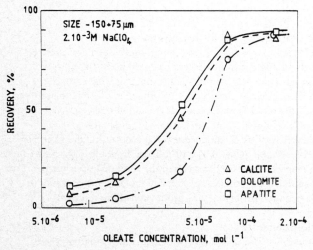

Fig. 1   Recovery of calcite, dolomite and apatite with oleate

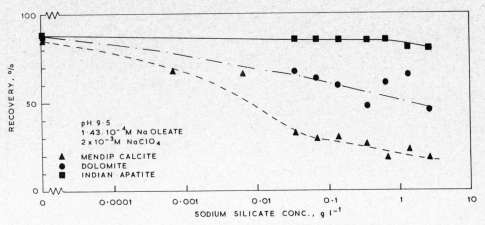

Fig. 2 Effect of sodium silicate on flotation of –150 +75 μm calcite, dolomite and apatite

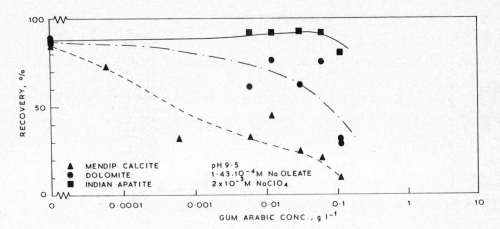

Fig. 3 Effect of gum arabic on flotation of –150 +75 μm calcite, dolomite and apatite

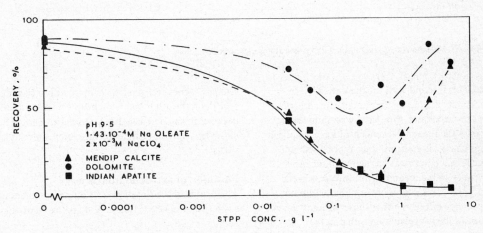

Fig. 4 Effect of sodium tripolyphosphate on flotation of –150 +75 μm calcite, dolomite and apatite

Stability of suspensions of calcite, dolomite and apatite to coagulation by sodium chloride in presence of reagents

The stability of suspensions of the three minerals in the presence of 0.1 g l^{-1} of gum arabic, sodium silicate and STPP with increasing concentrations of NaCl is shown in Fig. 10. The stability was monitored by measuring the transmittance of the supernatant after a 1-h settling. Higher values of transmittance indicate that aggregation of particles and hence higher settling rates are occurring. Increasing electrolyte concentration will decrease the repulsion between particles by compressing the electrical double layers and at a critical concentration should lead to destabilization of the suspension. For particle surfaces that owe their stability solely to charge effects the critical coagulation

concentration of electrolyte can be calculated from the measured zeta-potentials.[2] Particles that are sterically stabilized by adsorbed hydrophilic layers will be less sensitive to electrolyte concentration.

The critical coagulation concentrations of sodium chloride on the assumption of charge effects only, calculated from the zeta-potential data of Figs. 5, 6 and 7, are marked in Fig. 10. For minerals dispersed by STPP the onset of instability, as indicated by a sudden rise in the transmittance readings, corresponds well with the predicted critical coagulation concentration. This indicates that the mechanism of dispersion by STPP is primarily by the development of high surface potentials.

For sodium silicate the critical sodium chloride coagulation

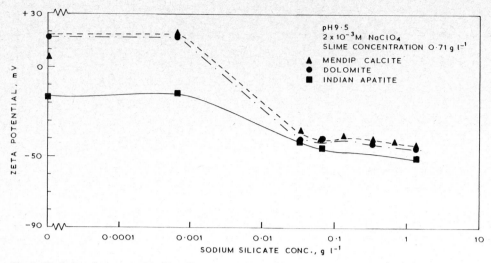

Fig. 5   Variation of zeta-potential with sodium silicate concentration

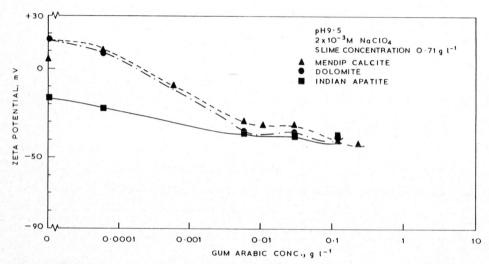

Fig. 6   Variation of zeta-potential with gum arabic concentration

concentration does not correspond with the theoretical concentration but is about six times higher for apatite and about ten times higher for the carbonates. Similarly, with gum arabic present, about ten times the theoretical concentration is required before any significant change in transmittance is obtained, and even then the change is much less marked than with the other two reagents. The results with gum arabic and silicate present are therefore evidence that the surfaces of the minerals are not stabilized simply by charge effects but that steric stabilization is also occurring. The most likely explanation is that in the presence of these two reagents adsorbed hydrophilic polymeric layers are present, extending from the surface of the mineral into the solution. The presence of such layers explains the depressive

effect that these reagents have in flotation. In the presence of STPP, on the other hand, such a mechanism does not exist and depression can be viewed as a competitive effect between the oleate and polyphosphate for the cation sites of the mineral surface.

Flotation of artificial mixtures
The results of the flotation tests on monomineralic samples suggest that selective flotation of apatite from calcite may be

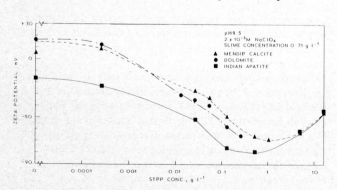

Fig. 7   Variation of zeta-potential with STPP concentration

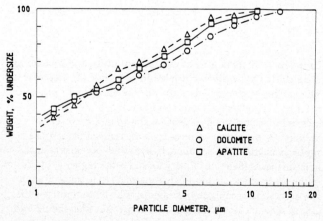

Fig. 8   Size analysis of suspensions used for electrophoretic and coagulation tests

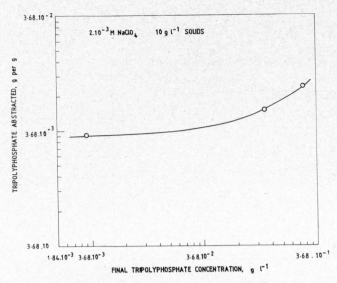

Fig. 9 Abstraction of tripolyphosphate by calcite at pH 9.5

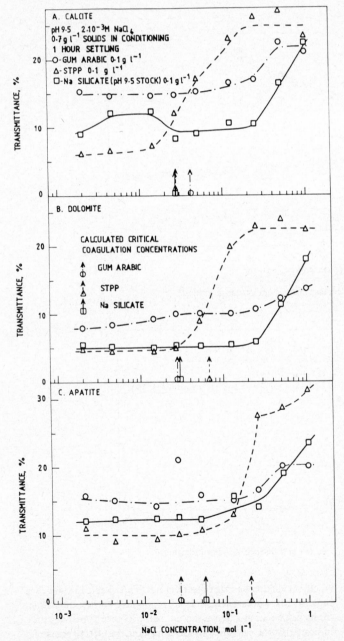

Fig. 10 Coagulation tests: effect of NaCl concentration on supernatant transmittance of calcite, dolomite and apatite suspensions in presence of sodium silicate, gum arabic and sodium tripolyphosphate

achieved by use of gum arabic or sodium silicate as calcite depressants. This conclusion was reached by Mishra,[4] who suggested the use of sodium metasilicate at pH 10 as a depressant for calcite in the separation of apatite and calcite with sodium oleate as collector. As is shown in Fig. 11, however, flotation of a mixture of the minerals predicted to give selective flotation of apatite results in the depression of all three minerals with no significant selectivity. This depression of apatite must be connected with the presence of dissolved species from the

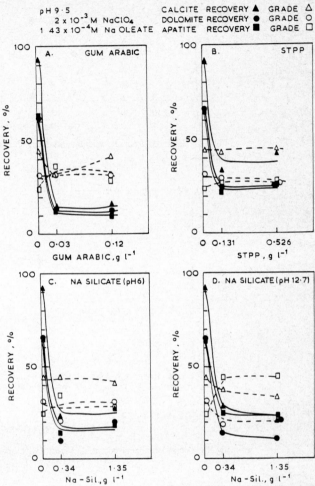

Fig. 11 Flotation of artificial mixture of apatite–calcite–dolomite in presence of various depressants

carbonate minerals in solution. Consequently, tests were performed in which the ions that may be released by dissolution of the carbonates were added to the solution in which apatite was being floated. The effects of calcium, magnesium and carbonate ions on the flotation of apatite in the presence and absence of gum arabic depressant are shown in Fig. 12. Increased calcium levels in the absence of depressant result in some lowering of recovery, probably as a result of the precipitation of the collector with the calcium ions to form insoluble calcium oleate. In the presence of both calcium ions and gum arabic, however, a very marked depression of apatite occurs, recovery being reduced to nearly zero at calcium levels greater than 10^{-4} M.

Unlike calcium, magnesium ions do not appear to have this effect on rendering apatite depressable by gum arabic. The slight lowering of recovery that occurs at concentrations greater than 10^{-3} M Mg is explainable as pseudo-depression caused by precipitation of magnesium oleate. At lower concentrations the apatite remains floatable in the presence of both magnesium ions and gum arabic.

Carbonate ions, either with or without gum arabic present,

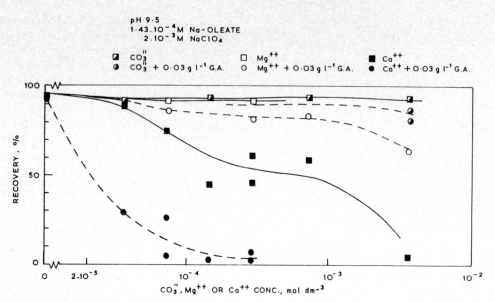

Fig. 12   Effect of carbonate, calcium and magnesium ions on depression of apatite in presence and absence of gum arabic

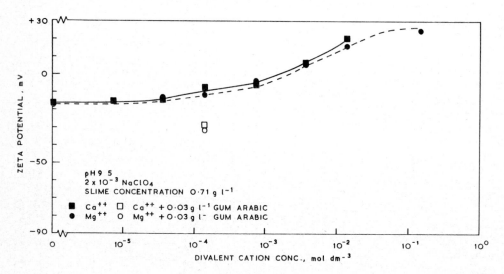

Fig. 13   Variation of zeta-potential of apatite with calcium and magnesium ion concentration

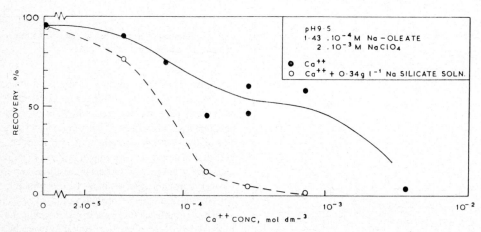

Fig. 14   Effect of calcium ions in depression of apatite in presence and absence of sodium silicate

have no significant depressant effect on apatite flotation. The variation of zeta-potential with changes in Mg and Ca concentration is shown in Fig. 13. Both ions have a similar effect and cause a charge reversal at about 2.10^{-3} M. The similiar effects of the two ions indicate that the influence of gum arabic is not determined by electrostatic effects. Also, the change in zeta-potential on the addition of gum arabic is similar (about –20 mV)

whether calcium ions are present or not (Figs. 6 and 13), which suggests that a great increase in adsorption is not the explanation for its behaviour as a depressant in their presence. These results indicate that the calcium ions are enhancing the effectiveness of the gum arabic as a depressant without increasing its adsorption at the mineral surface.

Sodium silicate equilibrated at pH 6 and then adjusted to

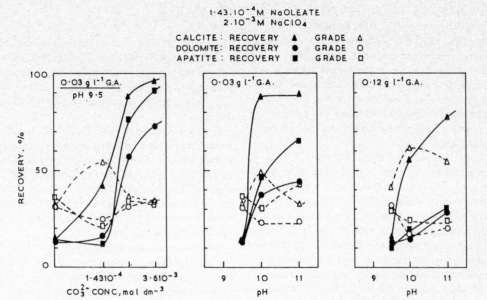

1·43.10^{-4} M NaOLEATE
2.10^{-3} M NaClO$_4$

CALCITE : RECOVERY ▲ GRADE △
DOLOMITE: RECOVERY ● GRADE O
APATITE : RECOVERY ■ GRADE □

Fig. 15 Flotation of artificial mixture of apatite–calcite–dolomite in presence of gum arabic at various pH and CO_3^{2-} concentrations

pH 9.5 shows a similar effect on apatite flotation when calcium ions are present (Fig. 14), which explains the poor selectivity obtained with this reagent on mixtures of the three minerals.

Just as the depression of the minerals with gum arabic can be achieved by increasing the calcium ion content, so their floatability can be restored by conditioning with reagents that somewhat reduce the level of calcium in solution. Fig. 15 shows the effect of conditioning in sodium carbonate solution at pH 9.5 and of increasing the pH to 11 with sodium hydroxide (no carbonate added). In both cases dissolution of calcite, and hence calcium, level in solution is reduced. The results show that increased flotation of all minerals is achieved, calcite showing the greatest response, although in no case were pure products obtained.

Discussion

The effects of sodium silicate on depression of flotation are known to be sensitive to the extent of polymerization, which, in turn, is dependent on the pH, silica/soda ratio and concentration.[5,6] The rate of polymerization is highest in the pH range 8–10, in which both singly ionized silicate anion, $SiO(OH)_3^{1-}$, and undissociated silicic acid, $Si(OH)_4$, are major species. At pH values above about pH 11 $SiO_2(OH)_2^{2-}$ is the major phase, little undissociated silicic acid is present and the amount of polymerized sodium silicate is very low.[7]

Chemical interaction between silicate species and calcium and magnesium can take place. Reaction between the cations and the $SiO(OH_3)^{1-}$ ion is weak, the stability constants given by Santschi and Schindler[8] for the formation of $MSiO(OH)_3^+$ being $10^{0.39}$ for Ca and $10^{0.64}$ for Mg. A stronger interaction exists between the cations and the $SiO_2(OH)_2^{2-}$ ion, the stability constants for the formation of $MSiO_2(OH)_2$ being $10^{3.09}$ (Ca) and $10^{4.17}$ (Mg).

The greater depression of the apatite and dolomite observed with silicate equilibrated at pH 12.7 suggests that the presence of the divalent silicate ion is necessary for their depression—because of competitive adsorption with the oleate at the cation sites. Solubility products for the oleates have been reported by Du Rietz[9] as $10^{-10.8}$ for $MgOl_2$ and $10^{-12.4}$ for $CaOl_2$.

When equilibrated at pH 9.5, as in most of the tests reported here, the level of $SiO_2(OH)^{2-}$ will be low and the silicate will mainly be in the singly charged or uncharged state and will tend to polymerize mainly as uncharged polysilicic acid molecules. The chemical interaction of any ionized groups on the polymeric

molecule will be much weaker than that for the divalent silicate species. Weak hydrogen bonding between the hydrogen atoms on the polysilicic acid and the oxygen in the anions on the mineral surface may also occur. Although, individually, the interactions will be weak, provided that the free energy of adsorption is negative, significant adsorption will still take place if the number of units in each polymeric molecule is large enough to give a sufficiently negative net free energy of adsorption for the whole molecule. This type of adsorption is analogous to that shown by high molecular weight polymeric reagents, such as polyacrylamide and polyethylene oxide, which can adsorb by the formation of multiple weak bonds. The concentration of NaCl required to cause the coagulation of suspensions of the minerals in the presence of sodium silicate at pH 9.5 is several times greater than would be required if the suspensions were stable simply because they possess a high zeta-potential. This is evidence for the presence of hydrophilic polymeric species adsorbed at the surface causing steric stabilization and also depression of flotation. In the presence of oleate either desorption of the silicate may occur owing to the high chemical interaction between the cations and the oleate ion, or adsorption may take place, the silicate hydrogen bonding to the anions.

The presence of about 10^{-4} M Ca^{2+} in solution is required to cause the depression of apatite by sodium silicate at this pH. It has been proposed by Somasundaran[10] that calcium is not truly potential–determining for apatite in alkaline pH, but that it specifically adsorbs in its hydrated state in the Stern layer. The adsorbed calcium ions will therefore be in a different energetic state than those in the crystal lattice and this may lead to a greater effective anchoring of the polymeric silicate over the apatite surface when such concentrations are present, and hence lead to greater depression. Such calcium concentrations will be present in equilibrated solutions in contact with calcite at this pH[11] and would explain the depression of flotation of apatite by silicate in the presence of calcite.

The second reagent studied—gum arabic—is also a polymeric species in aqueous solution. It is a polysaccharide and contains strongly hydrated polar groups such as –OH, –COOH and –CHO. Possible adsorption mechanisms are (1) hydrogen bonding of the alcoholic –OH groups to oxygens in the anionic CO_3^{2-} and PO_4^{3-} groups on the mineral surface, (2) chemical interaction by complexing of the surface calcium ions with such groups as the carboxylate on the glucuronic acid component or

(3) electrostatic adsorption of the negatively charged components of the gum arabic on to the positively charged carbonate surfaces. It is probable that all three mechanisms are involved in determining the overall free energy of adsorption on a given surface and that the contribution of each mechanism will vary, depending on the mineral. For example, the hydrogen-bonding component should be greater for phosphates than for carbonates,[12] whereas the electrostatic component will aid adsorption on the positively charged carbonates and hinder it on the negatively charged apatite.

Coagulation tests on the three minerals indicate that stabilizing layers of gum arabic are present at the three mineral surfaces—similar to the case when sodium silicate is present. Likewise, the reagent does not cause depression of the apatite in the absence of about 10^{-4} M Ca^{2+} in solution. It may be postulated therefore that in the presence of calcium adsorption of hydrated calcium ions takes place on the surface of the apatite, causing the observed reduction in zeta-potential and providing more sites to anchor the polymeric molecule to the surface, and hence reduce desorption in the presence of oleate. For starch, which is similar chemically to gum arabic, it has been observed[13] that in the oleate flotation of barite at pH 8 good flotation occurred in the presence of 40 ppm starch unless more than 10–20 ppm (2.5–5 10^{-4} M) $CaCl_2$ were present and that, in the absence of starch, flotation was actually activated by calcium.

These synergistic effects were not observed in the case of magnesium ions and gum arabic, even though the effect of Mg on the zeta-potential of the apatite was similar to that of calcium. This suggests that reduction of the electrostatic repulsion is not the main mechanism in enhancing the depressant effect but that it may be due to a weaker chemical interaction between the magnesium ion and the functional groups on the gum arabic molecule. Stability constants for the complexing of the alkaline earths with molecules such as glucuronic acid have not been located in the literature, but related molecules, such as D-gluconic acid, the hydrolysis product of galactose, have higher stability constants with calcium ($K = 10^{1.21}$) than with magnesium ($K = 10^{0.7}$)[14], although in neither case is the interaction very strong.

It is therefore probable that, as was postulated for sodium silicate, gum arabic adsorbs by multiple weak bonds to adsorbed calcium ions to give a hydrophilic coating and that the desorption in the presence of oleate is related to the extent of surface adsorption of calcium from solution. For adsorbed magnesium ions the interaction will be less strong, leading to a less firmly held hydrophilic layer.

The depressant action of STPP is different in kind from that shown by the two other reagents. Like gum arabic and sodium silicate, it confers a high negative zeta-potential on the minerals, but the coagulation tests show that, as would be expected, no stabilizing hydrophilic layers are present with this reagent. Recent work[15] suggested that hexametaphosphate and pyrophosphate were not adsorbed by calcite and that their depressant action was by complexing calcium ions in solution, causing more to dissolve and so lower the number of calcium sites on the mineral surface. The present results, however, show that tripolyphosphate is adsorbed by calcite. Chemical interaction between tripolyphosphate and the alkaline earths is strong, the stability constants for 1:1 complexes being $10^{8.1}$ for Ca-TPP and $10^{8.6}$ for Mg-TPP.[14] This means that the polyphosphate ions will compete strongly with the oleate ions for the cation sites at the mineral surface, which results in depression of apatite as well as of carbonates.

The increase in flotation shown by calcite and dolomite at very high STPP concentrations (greater than 1 g l^{-1}) has not been accounted for in this study. Further work is necessary to explain this phenomenon.

Conclusions

The modes of action of the three reagents studied are different.

Sodium tripolyphosphate disperses by adsorbing at the cation sites on the mineral surfaces and increasing the negative zeta-potential. In the presence of oleate it will compete strongly for sites and reduce the adsorption of collector, thereby causing depression.

Gum arabic and polymeric sodium silicate adsorb by multiple weak bonds to form hydrated layers at the mineral surface. Dispersion is produced both by the increase in negative zeta-potential that results and by the stabilizing effect of the hydrated layers. The hydrophilic nature of the layers causes depression of flotation. The depressant effect in the presence of oleate is sensitive to the level of free calcium ion in solution. Magnesium ions do not show the same effect.

The results as a whole demonstrate some of the interactions that may take place in mixed mineral pulps and their effects on the subsequent flotation behaviour. These effects may not be evident when the minerals are tested separately.

Acknowledgement

This work was funded by the EC Raw Materials Programme and the Materials and Chemicals Requirements Board of the Department of Trade and Industry.

References
1. Parsonage P. Watson D. and Hickey T. J. Surface texture, slime coatings and flotation of some industrial minerals. In *Preprints – XIV international mineral processing congress, Toronto, 1982*, session V, pap. 5, 22 p.
2. Shaw D. J. *Introduction to colloid and surface chemistry, 2nd edn* (London: Butterworths, 1974).
3. Lyklema J. and Overbeek J. Th. G. On the interpretation of electrokinetic potentials. *J. Colloid Sci.*, **16**, 1961, 501–12.
4. Mishra S. K. Electrokinetic properties and flotation behaviour of apatite and calcite in the pesence of sodium oleate and sodium metasilicate. *Int. J. Mineral Process.*, **9**, 1982, 59–73.
5. Joy A. S. and Robinson A. J. Flotation. In *Recent progress in surface science* Danielli J. F. Pankhurst R. G. A. and Riddiford A. C. eds (London: Academic Press, 1964), vol. 2, 169–260.
6. Fuerstenau M. C. Gutierrez G. and Elgillani D. A. The influence of sodium silicate in non-metallic flotation systems. *Trans. Am. Inst. Min. Engrs*, **241**, 1968, 319–23.
7. Gimblett F. G. R. *Inorganic polymer chemistry* (London: Butterworths, 1963), 462 p.
8. Santschi P. H. and Schindler P. W. Complex formation in the ternary systems Ca II–H_4SiO_4–H_2O and Mg II–H_4SiO_4–H_2O. *J. chem. Soc., Dalton 2*, 1974, 181–4.
9. Du Rietz C. Fatty acids in flotation. In *Progress in mineral dressing: transactions of the international mineral processing congress, Stockholm, 1957* (Stockholm: Almqvist & Wiksell, 1958), 417–33.
10. Somasundaran P. Zeta potential of apatite in aqueous solution and its change during equilibration. *J. Colloid Interface Sci.*, **27**, 1968, 659–66.
11. Somasundaran P. and Agar G. E. The zero point of charge of calcite. *J. Colloid Interface Sci.*, **24**, 1967, 433–40.
12. Somasundaran P. Adsorption of starch and oleate and interactions between them on calcite in aqueous solutions. *J. Colloid Interface Sci.*, **31**, 1969, 557–65.
13. Hanna H. S. and Gruner H. Über den Einfluß von Elektrolyten auf die Fluß- und Schwerspatflotation mit Ölsäuren. *Freiberger Forschungsh.* A510, 1972, 61–70.
14. Martell A. E. and Smith R. M. *Critical stability constants; volume 3 – other organic ligands* (New York: Plenum Press, 1977), 495 p.
15. Li Changgen and Lü Yongxin. Selective flotation of scheelite from calcium minerals with sodium oleate as a collector and phosphates as modifiers, II. The mechanism of the interaction between phosphate modifiers and minerals. *Int. J. Mineral Process.*, **10,** 1983, 219–35.

Anionic activator function in cationic flotation of hematite

Tien-Lin Wei and Ross W. Smith

Synopsis
In the cationic flotation of hematite with multivalent anionic substances as activators it is demonstrated that the charged protonated species are especially active. In most systems studied to date activation is strongest when such species are present in maximum concentration— much in the way that hydroxy species are active in the anionic flotation of quartz. Thus, for each anionic modifier there is a pH region of maximum effectiveness that depends on the substance's pK_a values. Further, these protonated species function as activators, even at pH values more basic than the mineral's point of zero charge.

In the anionic flotation of hematite with these same modifiers as depressants the depressing action is generally greatest when the modifier is primarily present in a protonated form.

Because of the general non-selective nature of flotation collectors it is seldom possible to obtain satisfactory recovery of the to be floated constituent of a flotation pulp without the use of modifying agents. Indeed, commercial froth flotation, as currently practised, would be impossible without such modifiers.

The number of classes of modifiers, as well as of individual chemicals, is very large. Adjustment of pH is, of course, the ubiquitous modifier. Inorganic modifiers (as either activators or depressants) are commonly used: these can be either anionic or cationic. Organic modifiers can be ionic (such as lignin sulphonates or glycolic acid) or non-ionic, such as many of the starches. The function of an ionic modifier can be to adsorb on to and coat a mineral surface, thereby making it amenable to collector adsorption. Alternatively, the modifying ion can compete with a collector of the same polarity for adsorption sites on a mineral and thereby prevent collector adsorption. The modifier can physically smear a surface, either causing enhanced or reduced adsorption of a collector, depending on the system in question. A modifier can physically mask the hydrophobic nature of a collector-coated surface. The modifier can change the nature of a collector; it can even destroy the collector if the modifier is an oxidizing agent. Other modes of action may also be possible.

Almost all classes of modifiers have been studied in the past and various mechanisms for the manner in which they work have been proposed. Considering ionic substances, Fuerstenau and co-workers[1-4] studied in detail the manner in which multivalent cations function as modifiers in oxide and silicate mineral flotation. According to these authors, it is hydroxy complexes of the cations that are surface-active and, thus, they function as activators in anionic flotation (and depressants in cationic flotation). In particular, they found in anionic flotation that the recovery is greatest over the pH range in which the first hydroxy complex of the activating multivalent cation is present in maximum concentration.

Baldauf[5] studied the mechanisms whereby certain hydrophilic organic substances function in flotation systems, particularly in fluorite and barite flotation. Not only did Baldauf discuss the importance of the ionic and non-ionic group of such modifiers but he also considered the effects of the modifier as a chelating agent. The mode of action of hydrophilic organic ions has also been studied by Last and Cook[6] and Sutherland and Wark.[7] Cooke, Iwasaki and their colleagues[8-11] studied in great detail the depressing action of starches and related substances. Of particular interest is their conclusion regarding the covering, or smearing, of a hydrophobic surface with starch molecules: the mode of action of the starches is therefore not through competition with collector ions and, in fact, starches often enhance collector adsorption while functioning as depressants. Kulkarni and Somasundaran[12] noted the modifying effect of total ionic strength in a flotation system. Of particular interest here is the inter-relationship between ionic strength and temperature.

Although the function of anionic modifiers has often been studied, certain details of their mode of action are not clearly understood. Obviously, various mechanisms can be responsible for the manner in which they work. For example, if the anion is an oxidizing entity, such as dichromate ion, obviously in some cases it functions as a depressant by destroying a collector or by modifying a surface via its oxidation. Interaction among activators and depressants in a variety of systems has been discussed by Sutherland and Wark[7] and by Hanna and Somasundaran.[13]

It has been deduced, or implied, that a hydrolysis product of an anion is the surface-active modifying species (the protonated anion). For example, Sutherland and Wark[7] presented evidence that HS^- rather than H_2S or S^{2-} is the depressing species in anionic sulphide mineral flotation. It is possible that the $HSiF_6^-$ ion is the activating species in cationic feldspar and beryl flotation at acid pH values in the presence of a fluoride or fluorosilicate.[14-18] Under some conditions $HCrO_4^-$ may be a depressing species in the anionic flotation of chromite.[19] It appears that HSO_4^- can depress anionic flotation of beryl.[20] Considering hydrous oxides and divalent acid anions, Davis and Leckie[21] showed experimental data and calculations that indicated that protonated anionic forms, such as $HCrO_4^-$, $HSeO_4^-$ and HSO_4^-, plus complexes formed with these species, are likely to be the surface-active adsorbing species. Huang and Wu[22,23] presented data that show strong adsorption of $HCrO_4^-$ on to calcinated coke and activated carbon.

In the present investigation the role of protonated anionic modifier species in the cationic flotation of hematite was studied by Hallimond tube flotation.

Materials and methods

The hematite sample used was black specular hematite from Republic, Michigan. Table 1 shows the quantity of contaminants present as estimated by emission spectrographic analysis.

Hematite samples for the flotation experiments were prepared by initial crushing and screening to the desired size (–65 +150 mesh) in a mortar and pestle, followed by leaching in a hot 0.1 M HCl solution for 15 min. After leaching, the mineral was rinsed with double-distilled water until the pH of the pulp was that of the double-distilled water only. The mineral was then wet-screened with double-distilled water. It was then oven-dried and, finally, ro-tapped for 30 min to ensure the desired size of the mineral (–65+150 mesh).

Table 1 Spectrographic analysis of hematite

Metal	%
Al	1.0
Fe	Major
Mg	0.05
Mn	0.01
Si	0.60
Ti	0.03

The collector used for the cationic flotation investigations was reagent grade dodecylamine hydrochloride purchased from Eastman Kodak Co. Also, for one series of tests the anionic collector sodium dodecylsulphate was used (this substance was of reagent grade).

Reagent grade sodium hydroxide and hydrochloric acid were used for pH adjustment. Double-distilled water was used to prepare all the solutions.

The anionic modifiers used were L-ascorbic acid, citric acid, selenious acid (puratronic 99.999%), succinic acid, sulphuric acid and chromic acid. All the reagent grade modifiers used were purchased from Alfa Ventron Division of Thiokol Corporation.

These modifiers were selected because they possess a great variety of pK_a values, including those with relatively narrow and relatively wide pH ranges of significant protonated anion concentration. Table 2 lists the pK_a values of the modifiers.

The listed pK_a values for L-ascorbic, succinic and citric acids are average values for 25°C from Serjeant and Dempsey[24] and from Kortum and co-workers.[25] The pK_a values for the other acids are average values for 25°C from Hogfeldt.[26] In Fig. 1 are shown log concentration diagrams for the six divalent modifiers for a total concentration each of 1×10^{-4} M. Fig. 2 is a similar diagram for citric acid. These diagrams clearly indicate the general pH regions of dominance of the various aqueous species of the acids.

The micro-flotation was carried out in a Hallimond tube of a type that has been described elsewhere.[27,28] Purified nitrogen

Table 2 pK_a values of anionic modifiers studied at 25°C

Acid	Formula	pK_{a1}	pK_{a2}	pK_{a3}
Sulphuric	H_2SO_4	Very low	1.95	—
Chromic	H_2CrO_4	0.16	6.30	—
Selenious	H_2SeO_3	2.61	7.79	—
Telluric	H_2TeO_4	7.69	11.03	—
L-ascorbic	(structure)	4.16	11.53	—
Succinic	CH_2–COOH / CH_2COOH	4.21	5.67	—
Citric	HO–C–COOH	2.93	4.48	5.97

* The two groups that ionize

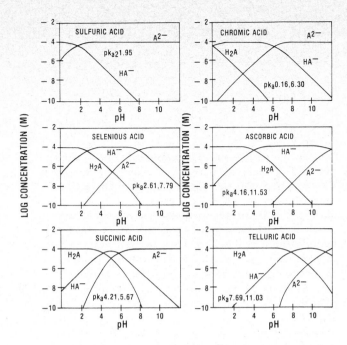

Fig. 1   Log concentration diagrams for 1×10^{-4} M solutions of sulphuric, chromic, selenious, ascorbic, succinic and telluric acids

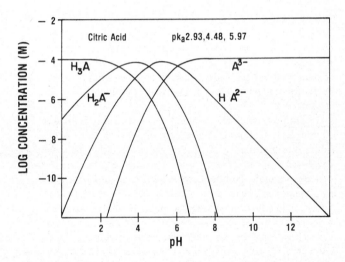

Fig. 2   Log concentration diagram for 1×10^{-4} M solutions of citric acid

was the flotation gas used. Exactly 100 ml of gas was passed through the tube at a flow rate of 100 ml/min.

A –65 +150 mesh size fraction of hematite was used as the flotation feed (sample weight, 1.0 g). In preparation for flotation this sample was placed in a beaker containing the collector–modifier solution and the pH was adjusted. The suspension was then agitated in a shaking water-bath for 15 min at a temperature of 26°C. After conditioning, the suspension was placed in the Hallimond tube and flotation was carried out. Final pH recorded was the flotation pH reported.

Experimental results and discussion

Initially, the flotation behaviour of the hematite tested was measured as a function of pH, dodecylammonium chloride (1×10^{-4} M) and sodium dodecylsulphate (1×10^{-3} M) both being used as collectors. Fig. 3 shows the data obtained (base line data are given for hematite flotation in the absence of modifiers). From Fig. 3 it can also be deduced that the point of zero charge (pzc) of the hematite studied was between pH 6 and 7—the pH region usually reported for pzc values of naturally occurring hematite.

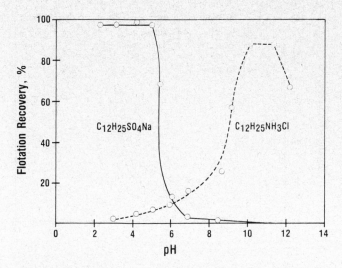

Fig. 3 Flotation recovery of hematite as a function of pH with 1×10^{-4} M dodecylammonium chloride and 1×10^{-3} M sodium dodecylsulphate as collectors

Fig. 4 illustrates the effect of sulphate additions on dodecylamine hydrochloride flotation of hematite. Concentrations of sulphate studied were 1×10^{-4}, 1×10^{-3} and 0.1 M. It is to be noted that sulphate functions as an activator only at pH values more acid than pH 4. Such activation is consistent with the protonated species being the most active modifier species (consider the sulphuric acid's log concentration diagram for sulphate in Fig. 1). In fact, when the substance is present in the concentration 0.1 M it becomes a depressant. This is, in part, due to an ionic strength effect decreasing flotation[12] and, perhaps, also to oxidation of the collector by the sulphate.

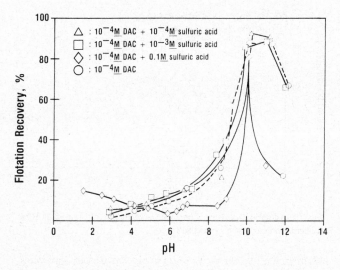

Fig. 4 Flotation recovery of hematite as a function of pH with DAC as collector and sulphuric acid as modifier

Fig. 5 shows data similar to those of Fig. 2 for the system containing chromate as the multivalent modifier. Concentrations of chromate studied were 1×10^{-4}, 1×10^{-3} and 0.1 M. Since the pK_a values for this substance are approximately 0.16 and 6.3, if the protonated species is particularly active, one might expect maximum activation at about pH 6.3. In fact, activation appears greater near pH 8. The chromate ion is not stable, however, with respect to chromic ion at acid pH values. Thus, the chromate ion is probably reduced to chromic ion at pH values equal to and more acidic than about pH 6. Under such conditions no activation should take place and, in a cationic flotation system, depression is possible. Indeed, there is such depression of the

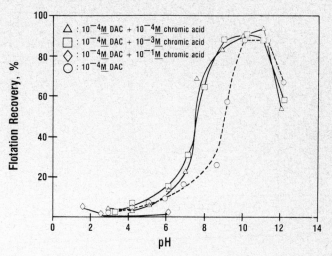

Fig. 5 Flotation recovery of hematite as a function of pH with DAC as collector and chromic acid as modifier

chromate concentrate at 0.1 M. Such depression is probably also due, in part, to the previously noted ionic strength effect. It is also possible that at pH 8 a complex formed between the doubly charged and the protonated species is responsible for activation.

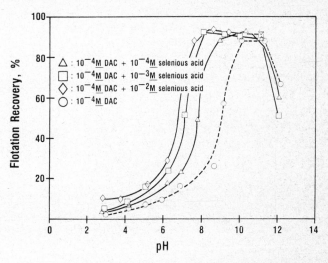

Fig. 6 Flotation recovery of hematite as a function of pH with DAC as collector and selenious acid as modifier

As in Figs. 4 and 5, Fig. 6 shows the flotation behaviour of hematite as a function of pH and concentration of selenious acid. The pK_a values for this acid are 2.61 and 7.79. Selenious acid concentrations studied were 1×10^{-4} and 1×10^{-3} M, and 1×10^{-2} M. If the protonated species is the most active activation species, it would be expected that maximum activation would be in the vicinity of pH 7.8—as it is. Also, because of the wide spacing between pK_a values (note the log concentration diagram for selenious acid in Fig. 1) one would expect activation to extend over a wide pH range both above and below pH 7.8. Such is also the case.

Fig. 7 shows the effect of the use of telluric acid as the modifier. Tellurate concentrations used were 1×10^{-4} and 1×10^{-3} M. The pK_a values for this substance are located approximately at pH 7.69 and 11.03 (see log concentration diagram for telluric acid in Fig. 1). The wide spacings of these values indicated that there should be good activation in cationic flotation over a wide pH range, primarily above pH 7.69, with little below this pH value. In fact, there is a rather precipitous drop in activation as pH is lowered below the region pH 7 and pH 7.5. It should be noted that tellurous acid is also stable at

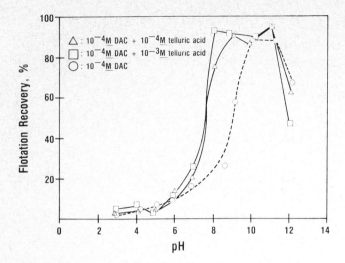

Fig. 7 Flotation recovery of hematite as a function of pH with DAC as collector and telluric acid as modifier

relatively low pH values[26] (pK_{a1} 4.89, pK_{a2} 9.03) and could also contribute to the activation. The contribution must be small, however, in view of the little or no activation indicated below pH 6.

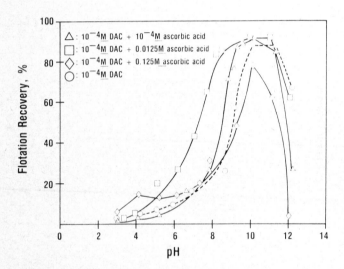

Fig. 8 Flotation recovery of hematite as a function of pH with DAC as collector and L-ascorbic acid as modifier

Fig. 8 graphically illustrates the effect of the presence of L-ascorbic acid as modifier. Ascorbate concentrations of 1 x 10^{-4}, 0.0125 and 0.125 M were studied. The pK_a values for this substance lie at pH 4.16 and pH 11.53 (note log concentration diagram for ascorbic acid in Fig. 1). Based on pK_a values alone, and assuming the protonated species to be the most surface-active species, good activation should exist between these two pH values. Such is roughly the case for the two lower concentrations of ascorbate. Also, the additional OH groups on the ascorbate ion may contribute to bonding of the substance on to hematite. Apparently, ionic strength effects (for the 0.125 M system) result in net depression at pH values more basic than about pH 8.5.

In Fig. 9 the effect of succinate on the cationic flotation of hematite is demonstrated. Concentrations of the modifier were 1 x 10^{-4}, 1 x 10^{-3} and 1 x 10^{-2} M. The pK_a values for succinic acid are 4.21 and 5.67 (see log concentrations diagram for succinic acid in Fig. 1). Because of the narrow pH distance between the two pK_a values, and assuming the protonated species to be the most active, one should expect that activation would not be great with use of this substance and mainly between pH 4 and 6. Some

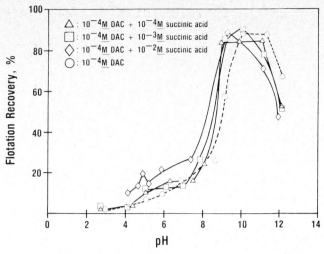

Fig. 9 Flotation recovery of hematite as a function of pH with DAC as collector and succinic acid as modifier

activation does occur in this pH region. In addition, a little activation exists almost up to pH 10, above which the substance appears to function as a modest depressant.

Fig. 10 illustrates the effect of the triprotic citric acid on the flotation of hematite. The pK_a values for citric acid are 2.93, 4.48 and 5.97 (also note log concentrations diagram in Fig. 2). Acid concentrations studied were 1 x 10^{-4}, 1 x 10^{-3} and 1 x 10^{-2} M. Being a triprotic substance, it should be expected that citrate would be a strong activator, at least over the pH range pH 2.9–6. It is, indeed, a strong activator over this pH range and, in

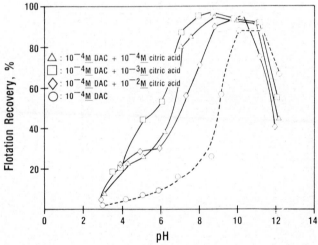

Fig. 10 Flotation recovery of hematite as a function of pH with DAC as collector and citric acid as modifier

addition, it is a strong activator up to pH 9 or greater. Two items may account for this latter fact: (1) the OH group on the structure, which could be available for hydrogen bonding to the hematite surface, and (2) citrate is a strong chelating agent for iron.[5]

Summary

The results obtained roughly confirm the hypothesis that protonated forms of multivalent anionic activators are particularly active. For sulphate, selenite, tellurate and L-ascorbate the hypothesis fits the data quite well. Data for the succinate system roughly fit the hypothesis. For the citrate system the data fit the hypothesis well at lower pH values, but activation is greater than expected at higher pH values. This phenomenon is probably related mainly to the strong chelating affinity of the citrate ion for iron sites on hematite. Data for the chromate system do not fit the hypothesis. This is probably due to the conversion of Cr^{6+} to Cr^{3+} at pH values more acidic than approximately pH 6.

References

1. Fuerstenau M. C. Role of metal ion hydrolysis in oxide and silicate flotation sytems. In *Advances in interfacial phenomena of particulate/solution/gas systems; application to flotation research* Somasundaran P. and Grieves R. B. eds (New York: American Institute of Chemical Engineers, 1975), 16–23. (*AIChE Symp. Series* no. 150, vol. 71)
2. Palmer B. R. Gutierrez G. B. and Fuerstenau M. C. Mechanisms involved in the flotation of oxides and silicates with anionic collectors, part 1. *Trans. Am. Inst. Min. Engrs*, **258**, 1975, 257–60.
3. Palmer B. R. Fuerstenau M. C. and Aplan F. F. Mechanisms involved in the flotation of oxides and silicates with anionic collectors, part 2. *Trans. Am. Inst. Min. Engrs*, **258**, 1975, 261–3.
4. Fuerstenau M. C. and Palmer B. R. Anionic flotation of oxides and silicates. In *Flotation: A. M Gaudin memorial volume* Fuerstenau M. C. ed. (New York: AIME, 1976), 148–96.
5. Baldauf H. Ein Beitrag zum Wirkungsmechanismus hydrophilierender organischer Stoffe bei der Flotation. *Freiberger Forschungsh.* A619, 1980, 84 p.
6. Last G. A. and Cook M. A. Collector–depressant equilibria in flotation, II. Depressant action of tannic acid and quebracho. *J. phys. Chem.*, **56**, 1952, 643–8.
7. Sutherland K. L. and Wark I. W. *Principles of flotation* (Melbourne: Australasian Institute of Mining and Metallurgy, 1955), 489 p.
8. Chang C. S. Cooke S. R. B. and Huch R. O. Starches and starch products as depressants in amine flotation of iron ore. *Trans. Am. Inst. Min. Engrs*, **196**, 1953, 1282–6.
9. Iwasaki I. Carlson W. J. Jr. and Parmerter S. M. The use of starches and starch derivatives as depressants and flocculants in iron ore beneficiation. *Trans. Am. Inst. Min. Engrs*, **244**, 1969, 88–98.
10. Balajee S. R. and Iwasaki I. Adsorption mechanism of starches in flotation and flocculation of iron ores. *Trans. Am. Inst. Min. Engrs*, **244**, 1969, 401–6.
11. Balajee S. R. and Iwasaki I. Interaction of British gum and dodecylammonium chloride at quartz and hematite surfaces. *Trans. Am. Inst. Min. Engrs*, **244**, 1969, 407–11.
12. Kulkarni R. D. and Somasundaran P. Effects of reagentizing temperature and ionic strength and their interactions in hematite flotation. *Trans. Am. Inst. Min. Engrs*, **262**, 1977, 120–5.
13. Hanna H. S. and Somasundaran P. Flotation of salt-type minerals. Reference 4, 197–272.
14. Smith R. W. Activation of beryl and feldspars by fluorides in cationic collector systems. *Trans. Am. Inst. Min. Engrs*, **232**, 1965, 160–8.
15. Smith R. W. and Smolik T. J. Infrared X-ray diffraction study of the activation of beryl and feldspars by fluorides in cationic collector systems. *Trans. Am. Inst. Min. Engrs*, **232**, 1965, 196–204.
16. Sulin D. B. and Smith R. W. Hallimond tube investigation of fluoride activation of beryl and feldspars in cationic collector systems. *Trans. Instn Min. Metall. (Sect. C: Mineral Process. Extr. Metall.)*, **75**, 1966, C333–6.
17. Warren L. J. and Kitchener J. A. Role of fluoride in the flotation of feldspar: adsorption on quartz, corundum and potassium feldspar. *Trans. Instn. Min. Metall. (Sect. C: Mineral Process. Extr. Metall.)*, **81**, 1972, C137–47.
18. Smith R. W. and Akhtar S. Cationic flotation of oxides and silicates. Reference 4, 87–116.
19. Smith R. W. and Allard S. G. Effects of pretreatment and aging on chromite flotation. *Int. J. Mineral Process.*, **11**, 1983, 163-74.
20. Lai R. W. M. and Smith R. W. Flotation of beryl, spodumene and quartz with anionic collectors in the absence of multivalent metal activators. *Trans. Am. Inst. Min. Engrs*, **235**, 1966, 392–5.
21. Davis J. A. and Leckie J. O. Surface ionization and complexation at the oxide/water interface, 3. Adsorption of anions. *J. Colloid Interface Sci.*, **74**, 1980, 32–43.
22. Huang C. P. and Wu M. H. Chromium removal by carbon adsorption. *J. Wat. Pollut. Control Fed.*, **47**, 1975, 2437–46.
23. Huang C. P. and Wu M. H. The removal of chromium (VI) from dilute aqueous solution by activated carbon. *Water Res.*, **11**, 1977, 673–9.
24. Serjeant E. P. and Dempsey B. *Ionization constants of organic acids in aqueous solution* (Oxford, etc.: Pergamon, 1979). (*IUPAC Chem. Data Series* no. 23)
25. Kortum G. F. A. Vogel W. and Andrussow K. *Dissociation constants of organic acids in aqueous solution* (London: Butterworth, 1961), 368 p.
26. Hogfeldt E. *Stability constants of metal–ion complexes, part A – inorganic ligands* (Oxford, etc.: Pergamon, 1982). (*IUPAC Chem. Data Series* no. 21)
27. Fuerstenau D. W. Metzger P. H. and Seele G. O. How to use the modified Hallimond tube for better flotation testing. *Engng Min. J.*, **158**, March 1957, 93–5.
28. Smith R. W. and Lai R. W. M. On the relationship between contact angle and flotation behavior. *Trans. Am. Inst. Min. Engrs*, **235**, 1966, 413–8.

Decomposition of xanthates in flotation solutions

Horst Dautzenberg, Andrzej Kowal, Joanna Kowal and Wolfgand Dietzel

Synopsis
A description is given of the kinetics of sodium ethyl xanthate decomposition that takes into account not only the primary reaction ($ROCSSNa + H_2O \rightarrow ROH + CS_2 + NaOH$) but also the hydrolysis of CS_2 as well as the formation of by-products—mono-, di-, trithiocarbonates and pseudo-xanthate.

The dependences of concentration on time were obtained for eleven components of the reaction mixture by solving a set of differential equations following the proposed kinetic scheme.

Sodium ethyl xanthate, used as a collector in the flotation of sulphide ores, is known to be unstable in aqueous solution. It was established[1,2,3] that the decomposition of xanthates of low molecular weight alcohols proceeds by the splitting of molecular carbon disulphide with the formation of an equivalent amount of alcohol and hydroxide:

$$ROCSSNa + H_2O \rightarrow ROH + CS_2 + NaOH$$

To describe the kinetics of xanthate decomposition in aqueous media one should consider the process of hydrolysis of CS_2 formed in the primary reaction. This process is followed, however, by subsequent and parallel reactions that involve the formation and decomposition of thiocarbonates and alkyl monothiocarbonate (pseudo-xanthate).[4,5,6]

The processes that occur in xanthate solution are presented schematically in Fig. 1.

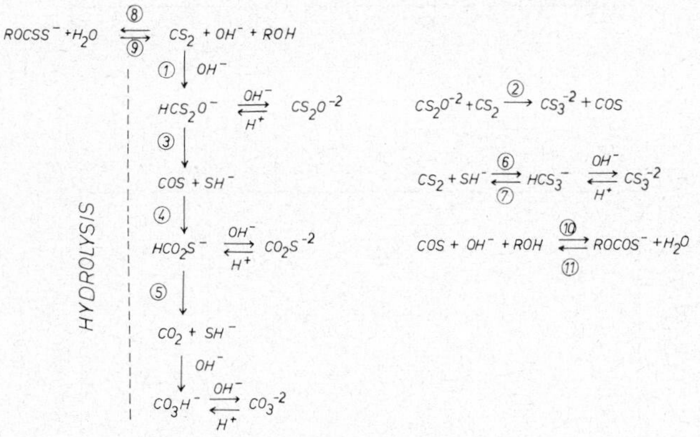

Fig. 1 Main processes occurring in xanthate solution

The main products formed in xanthate solution are carbon disulphide, hydroxide, alcohol; mono-, di- and trithiocarbonate; carbonate; hydrosulphide; and carbonyl sulphide and alkyl monothiocarbonate.

The mechanism and kinetics of xanthate decomposition, as well as the hydrolysis of carbon disulphide and the formation of by-products, have been studied previously.[1-14] From these studies one can obtain the simplified kinetic scheme described by equations 1–11 (RD, rate-determining).

$$CS_2 + OH^- \xrightarrow{RD} CS_2OH^- \xrightarrow[Fast]{OH^-} CS_2O^{-2} + H_2O \tag{1}$$

$$CS_2O^{-2} + CS_2 \longrightarrow CS_3^{-2} + COS \tag{2}$$

$$CS_2O^{-2} + H_2O \rightleftharpoons CS_2OH^- + OH^-$$
$$\qquad \xrightarrow{RD} COS + SH^- \tag{3}$$

$$COS + OH^- \xrightarrow{RD} COSOH^- \xrightarrow[Fast]{OH^-} CO_2S^{-2} + H_2O \tag{4}$$

$$CO_2S^{-2} + H_2O \rightleftharpoons CO_2SH^- + OH^-$$
$$\qquad \xrightarrow{RD} CO_2 + SH^-$$
$$\qquad \xrightarrow{OH^-} CO_3H^{-2} \tag{5}$$

$$SH^- + CS_2 \xrightarrow{RD} CS_3H^- \xrightarrow[Fast]{OH^-} CS_3^{-2} + H_2O \tag{6}$$

$$CS_3^{-2} + H_2O \rightleftharpoons CS_3H^- + OH^-$$
$$\qquad \xrightarrow{RD} CS_2 + SH^- \tag{7}$$

$$ROH + OH^- \rightleftharpoons RO^- + H_2O$$
$$\qquad \downarrow CS_2$$
$$\qquad \xrightarrow{RD} ROCSS^- \tag{8}$$

$$ROCSS^- + H_2O \longrightarrow ROH + CS_2 + OH^- \tag{9}$$

$$ROH + OH^- \rightleftharpoons RO^- + H_2O$$
$$\qquad \downarrow COS$$
$$\qquad \xrightarrow{RD} ROCOS^- \tag{10}$$

$$ROCOS^- + H_2O \rightleftharpoons ROH + COS + OH^- \tag{11}$$

Based on our results[2,3,11-14] and other literature data[4-9] for the kinetics of these reactions the following functions for the rate constants were derived:[15]

$$k_1 = 0.0275 \exp [36.24 \, (1 - 293.2/T)] \qquad \text{min}^{-1} \, \text{dm}^3 \, \text{mol}^{-1} \tag{12}$$

$$k_2 = 17.9 \exp [27.02 \, (1 - 293.2/T)] \qquad \text{min}^{-1} \, \text{dm}^3 \, \text{mol}^{-1} \tag{13}$$

$$k_3 = \frac{0.0073}{[\text{OH}^-]} \exp [43.29 \, (1 - 293.2/T)] \qquad \text{min}^{-1} \, \text{dm}^3 \, \text{mol}^{-1} \tag{14}$$

$$k_4 = 200 \exp [22.67 \, (1 - 293.2/T)] \qquad \text{min}^{-1} \, \text{dm}^3 \, \text{mol}^{-1} \tag{15}$$

$$k_5 = \frac{6.48}{[\text{OH}^-]} \exp [39.68 \, (1 - 293.2/T)] \qquad \text{min}^{-1} \, \text{dm}^3 \, \text{mol}^{-1} \tag{16}$$

$$k_6 = 2.56 \exp [36.41 \, (1 - 293.2/T)] \qquad \text{min}^{-1} \, \text{dm}^3 \, \text{mol}^{-1} \tag{17}$$

$$k_7 = \frac{4.7 \times 10^{-7}}{[\text{OH}^-]} \exp [44.66 \, (1 - 293.2/T)] \quad \text{min}^{-1} \, \text{dm}^3 \, \text{mol}^{-1}$$
$$\text{(approximate)} \tag{18}$$

$$k_8 = 0.078 \exp [28.86 \, (1 - 293.2/T)] \qquad \text{min}^{-1} \, \text{dm}^6 \, \text{mol}^{-2} \tag{19}$$

$$k_9 = 9.8 \times 10^{-6} \exp [31.43 \, (1 - 293.2/T)] \quad \text{min}^{-1} \tag{20}$$

$$k_{10} = 148 \exp [13.74 \, (1 - 293.2/T)] \qquad \text{min}^{-1} \, \text{dm}^6 \, \text{mol}^{-2}$$
$$\text{(approximate)} \tag{21}$$

$$k_{11} = 5.2 \times 10^{-4} \exp [34.35 \, (1 - 293.2/T)] \quad \text{min}^{-1} \tag{22}$$

The dependences of the reaction rate constants on the ionic strength are not available, but available data suffice to enable the course of xanthate decomposition in dilute and moderately concentrated solution (up to about 1 mol/dm³) to be calculated.

Table 1

y_1	CS$_2$		Carbon disulphide
y_2	Na$_2$CS$_2$O	(CS$_2$O^{-2})	Dithiocarbonate
y_3	Na$_2$CS$_3$	(CS$_3^{-2}$)	Trithiocarbonate
y_4	COS		Carbonyl sulphide
y_5	Na$_2$CO$_2$S	(CO$_2$S^{-2})	Monothiocarbonate
y_6	NaSH	(SH$^-$)	Hydrosulphide
y_7	NaOH	(OH$^-$)	Hydroxide
y_8	ROCSSNa	(X$^-$)	Xanthate
y_9	ROCOSNa	(PX$^-$)	Pseudo-xanthate (alkyl monothiocarbonate)
y_{10}	ROH	(Et)	Ethanol
y_{11}	Na$_2$CO$_3$	(CO$_3^{-2}$)	Carbonate

By use of the symbols shown in Table 1 a set of differential equations in accordance with the kinetic scheme can be obtained.

$$\dot{y}_1 = -k_1 y_1 y_7 - k_2 y_1 y_2 - k_6 y_1 y_6 + k_7 y_3 - k_8 y_1 y_7 y_{10} + k_9 y_8 \tag{23}$$

$$\dot{y}_2 = k_1 y_1 y_7 - k_2 y_1 y_2 - k_3 y_2 \tag{24}$$

$$\dot{y}_3 = k_2 y_1 y_2 + k_6 y_1 y_6 - k_7 y_3, \tag{25}$$

$$\dot{y}_4 = k_2 y_1 y_2 + k_3 y_2 - k_4 y_4 y_7 - k_{10} y_4 y_7 y_{10} + k_{11} y_9 \tag{26}$$

$$\dot{y}_5 = k_4 y_4 y_7 - k_5 y_5 \tag{27}$$

$$\dot{y}_6 = k_3 y_2 + k_5 y_5 - k_6 y_1 y_6 + k_7 y_3 \tag{28}$$

$$\dot{y}_7 = -2k_1 y_1 y_7 + k_3 y_2 - 2k_4 y_4 y_7 - k_5 y_5 + k_5 y_5 / \\ (1 + 10^3 y_7) - k_6 y_1 y_6 + k_7 y_3 - k_8 y_1 y_7 y_{10} \\ + k_9 y_8 - k_{10} y_4 y_7 y_{10} + k_{11} y_9 \tag{29}$$

$$\dot{y}_8 = k_8 y_1 y_7 y_{10} - k_9 y_8 \tag{30}$$

$$\dot{y}_9 = k_{10} y_4 y_7 y_{10} - k_{11} y_9 \tag{31}$$

$$\dot{y}_{10} = -\dot{y}_8 - \dot{y}_9 \tag{32}$$

$$\dot{y}_{11} = k_5 y_5 \tag{33}$$

($\dot{y}_1 - \dot{y}_{11}$ denote the rates of processes described by equations 1–11; the fifth term in the equation for $\dot{y}_7$ considers the equilibrium CO$_3^{-2}$ + H$^+$ ⇌ CO$_3$H$^-$)

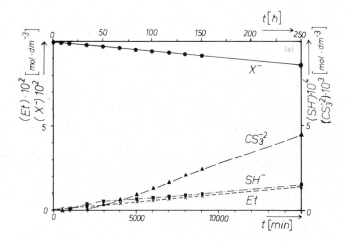

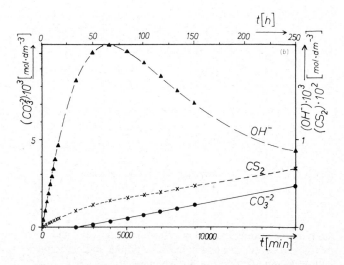

Fig 2   Dependences of concentration of xanthate (X$^-$), CS$_3^{-2}$, SH$^-$ ions and ethanol (Et) on time, calculated for purified xanthate solution (initial concentration, mol/dm³: $c_X^0 = 10^{-1}$; $c_{OH}^0 = 10^{-7}$; others $c^0 = 0$; stored at 20°C) (a) and of CS$_2$ and OH$^-$, CO$_3^{-2}$ ions on time, calculated for purified xanthate solution (b) (initial concentration and temperature as for (a))

48

Progress in numerical integration methods[16] allowed us to carry out digital calculations to obtain the concentration–time dependences for reagents taken into account.

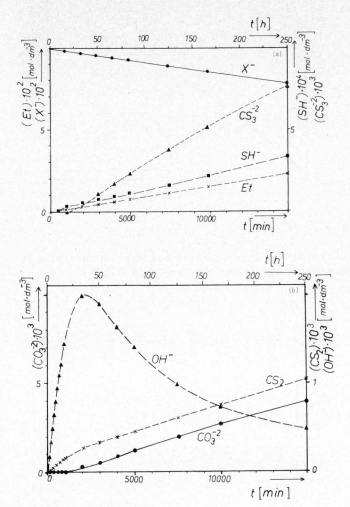

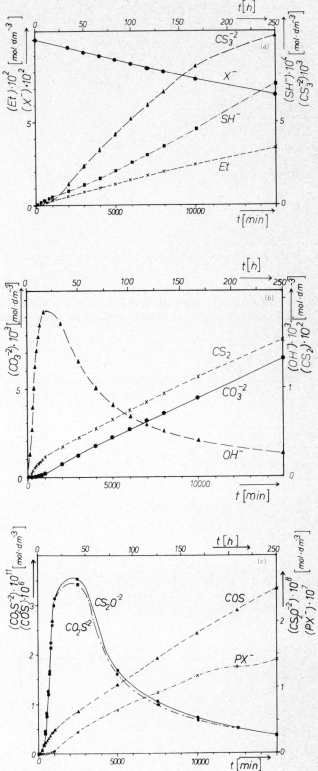

Fig. 3 Dependences of concentration of xanthate (X^-), CS_3^{-2} SH^- ions and ethanol (Et) on time, calculated for purified xanthate solution (a) and of concentration of CS_2 and OH^-, CO_3^{-2} ions on time, calculated for purified xanthate solution (b) (initial concentrations as for Fig. 2; 25°C)

The calculations were carried out on the assumption of the following conditions.

(1) *Initial concentrations* [mol/dm³]

$c_{X^-}^0 = 0.1$; $c_{OH^-}^0 = 10^{-7}$; others $c^0 = 0$ (temperature, 20, 25, 30 and 35°C)

(2) *Initial concentrations* [mol/dm³], according to Polish Standard (industrial solution)

$c_{X^-}^0 = 7.8 \times 10^{-2}$; $c_{OH^-}^0 = 5.65 \times 10^{-3}$; $c_{CS_2}^0 = 1.58 \times 10^{-4}$; $c_{CS_3}^0 = 2.34 \times 10^{-3}$; $c_{HS}^0 = 2.89 \times 10^{-3}$; others $c^0 = 0$ (temperature, 25°C)

The results for purified xanthate solution (1) and industrial solution (2) are presented in Figs. 2–6 (the time-dependences of concentration of CS_2O^{-2}, COS, CO_2S^{-2} and PX^- are shown only for a temperature of 30°C as they are very low and these products are not important as flotation-effecting impurities).

The main products of xanthate decomposition that influence the process of flotation of sulphide minerals are hydrosulphide (HS^-) and trithiocarbonate (CS_3^{-2}) ions: these are termed the active impurities.

It is known from flotation practice that there is a critical value of the ratio of active impurity concentration to

Fig. 4 Dependences of concentration of xanthate (X^-), CS_3^{-2} SH^- ions and ethanol (Et) on time, calculated for purified xanthate solution (a), of CS_2 and OH^-, CO_3^{-2} ions on time, calculated for purified xanthate solution (b) and of COS and CS_2O^{-2}, CO_2S^{-2}, pseudo-xanthate (PX^-) ions on time, calculated for purified xanthate solution (c) (initial concentrations as for Fig. 2(a); 30°C)

xanthate concentration. The flotation process does not occur if this value is exceeded.

Analysis of the kinetic data showed the dependence of concentration of active impurities and xanthate ions on the time of solution storage (Fig. 7). It was concluded, for example, that the concentration of active impurities is only

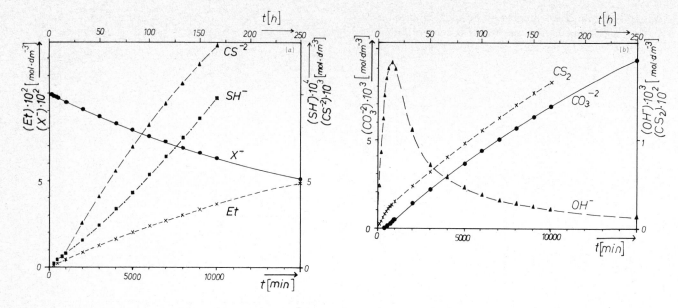

Fig. 5   Dependences of concentration of xanthate (X^-), CS_3^{-2} SH^- ions and ethanol (Et) on time, calculated for purified xanthate solution (a) and of CS_2 and OH^-, CO_3^{-2} ions on time, calculated for purified xanthate solution (b) (initial concentrations as for Fig. 2(a); 35°C)

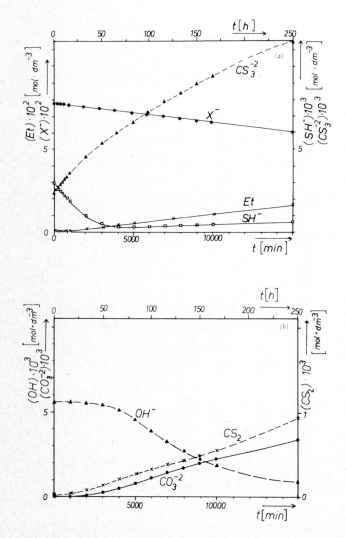

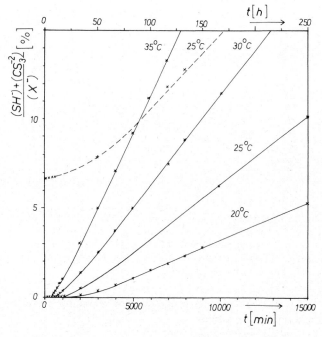

Fig. 7   Dependence of ratio of concentration of active impurities ((SH^-) + (CS_3^{-2})) to xanthate (X^-) concentrations versus reaction time (unbroken curves, purified xanthate solution, stored at temperatures shown; broken curve, industrial solution stored at 25°C)

an order of magnitude lower than that of xanthate ions after 90 h of storage of industrial solution. These results should not be neglected in optimizing a modern flotation process.

Experimental verification of the theoretical calculations for xanthate and the main decomposition products was carried out readily by use of an ion-selective electrode sensitive to xanthate ions.[17,18,19]

Fig. 6   Dependences of concentration of xanthate (X^-), CS_3^{-2}, SH^- ions and ethanol (Et) on time, calculated for industrial solution (initial concentration, mol/dm³: $c_{X^-}^0 = 7.8 \times 10^{-2}$; $c_{OH^-}^0 = 5.65 \times 10^{-3}$; $c_{CS_2}^0 = 1.58 \times 10^{-4}$; $c_{CS_3^{-2}}^0 = 2.34 \times 10^{-3}$; $c_{HS^-}^0 = 2.89 \times 10^{-3}$; others $c^0 = 0$; stored at temperature 25°C) (a) and of CS_2 and OH^-, CO_3^{-2} ions on time, calculated for industrial solution (b) (initial concentration and temperature as for (a))

References
1.   Leja J. *Surface chemistry of froth flotation* (New York: Plenum Press, 1982), 228–43.
2.   Bär H. J. Dautzenberg H. and Philipp B. Zur Kinetik des Äthylxanthogenatzerfalles in wässriger alkalischer Lösung. *Z. phys. Chem.*, **237**, 1968, 145–56.

3.   Philipp B. Dautzenberg H. and Schmiga W. Zur Kinetik der Xanthogenatbildung und -zersetzung bei einigen niedermolekularen Alkoholen und einfachen Zuckern. *Faserforsch. Text Tech.*, **20**, 1969, 111–8; 179–84.

4.   Philipp B. Zur Kinetik der Umsetzung von Schwefelkohlenstoff mit Natronlauge. *Faserforsch. Text Tech.*, **6**, 1955, 433–52; 509–20.

5.   Wroński M. Kinetyka reakcji między wodorotlenkiem sodowym i dwusiarczkiem węgla. *Roczn. Chem.*, **32**, 1958, 848–61.

6.   Hovenkamp S. G. Reaktionen im System Schwefelkohlenstoff—Natronlauge. Dissertation, Delft, 1965.

7.   Wroński M. Zur Kinetik der Xanthogenatreaktion von einfachen Alkoholen. *Z. phys. Chem.*, **211**, 1959, 113–7.

8.   Philipp V. and Fichte Ch. Kinetische Untersuchungen zur Zersetzung von Xanthogenaten. *Faserforsch. Text Techn.*, **11**, 1960, 118–24; 172–9.

9.   Hovenkamp S. G. Sodium dithiocarbonate as a by-product in xanthating reactions: a contribution to the chemistry of viscose. *J. Polymer Sci.*, pt C, no. 2, 1963, 341–55.

10.   Garbacik J. Najbar J. and Pomianowski A. Kinetics of reaction of xanthate with hydrogen peroxide. *Roczn. Chem.*, **46**, 1972, 85–97.

11.   Philipp B. and Dautzenberg H. Kinetische Untersuchungen zur Bildung und Zersetzung von Monothiocarbonat in wässriger Lösung. *Z. phys. Chem.*, **229**, 1965, 210–24.

12.   Dautzenberg H. and Philipp B. Zur Kinetik der Additionsreaktionen zwischen CS_2 und verschiedenen Anionen unter besonderer Berücksichtigung ihrer Abhängigkeit von der Hydroxylionenkonzentration. *Faserforsch. Text Tech.*, **20**, 1969, 213–8.

13.   Dautzenberg H. and Philipp B. Untersuchungen zu Kinetik und Mechanismus der Zersetzung von Xanthogenaten in wässrig-alkalischer Lösung. *Z. phys. Chem.*, **234**, 1970, 364–79.

14.   Philipp B. and Dautzenberg H. Zur Bildungsgeschwindigkeit von Na-Äthylmonothiocarbonat im Vergleich zu Na-Äthylxanthogenat. *Z. phys. Chem.*, **231**, 1966, 270–3.

15.   Dautzenberg H. Mathematic modelling in xanthate chemistry. Ph.D. thesis, in preparation.

16.   Kaps R. and Rentrop P. Generalized Runge–Kutta methods of order four with stepsize control for Stiff ordinary differential equations. *Num. Math.*, **33**, 1979, 55–68.

17.   Kowal A. Polish Patent 98 361, 1980.

18.   Kowal A. Hungarian Patent 179 286, 1981.

19.   Kowal A. and Niewiara R. Determination of xanthate and its impurities in flotation solutions. Paper presented to 4th biennial international symposium on electroanalysis, Cardiff, April 1983.

Determination of concentration of xanthate and products of its decomposition in solutions for flotation of sulphide ores

Andrzej Kowal, Jerzy Haber and Robert Niewiara

Synopsis
The process of decomposition of sodium ethyl xanthate was investigated. The concentrations of the main components of the reaction mixture, i.e. xanthate, OH⁻ ions and CS_2, as well as the concentration of active impurities depressing the process of chalcocite flotation, were determined as functions of time of solution storage. The experimental results were compared with previous theoretical calculations based on the proposed kinetic scheme. Model flotation experiments showed that chalcocite ore recovery depends on the time of xanthate solution storage.

To discover the optimum conditions for the flotation process it is necessary to know the composition of the collector solution that is introduced into the flotation equipment. Sodium ethyl xanthate is commonly used in the flotation of copper sulphide ores. The xanthate solution at a concentration of several per cent is added to the flotation equipment.

Theoretical calculations, based on the proposed kinetic scheme of xanthate decomposition, including the hydrolysis of CS_2 as well as the formation of by-products (mono-, di- and trithiocarbonates and pseudo-xanthate), are presented elsewhere.[1] The dependences of concentration of reaction mixture components on time, for purified and industrial xanthate solutions, showed that the main xanthate decomposition products are CS_3^{-2}, HS^-, OH^- and CS_2.

The depressing effect of sulphides and trithiocarbonates on the process of flotation of sulphide minerals is well known[2] and, hence, we developed the method of simultaneous measurement of xanthate concentration (c_{x^-}) and the concentration of active impurities of depressing properties (c_z).[3] This method is based on the ion-selective electrode (AX) sensitive to xanthate ions[4,5] and the 'Xanthate Analyser' apparatus, which permit the ready determination of the ratio (c_z)/(c_{x^-}).

The aim of this paper was to verify the theoretical calculations and to correlate the experimentally found (c_z)/(c_{x^-}) with chalcocite ore recovery in a model flotation process.

Experimental

Reagents and solutions analysed
Fluka AG sodium ethyl xanthate was purified by recrystallization and used to prepare what is termed a purified xanthate solution. An industrial xanthate solution was prepared from sodium ethyl xanthate (Xanthate Production Plant-Cuprum, Rudna, Poland), which was stored at a temperature of below 10°C for six months.

The constant ionic strength (0.2 mol dm⁻³) of the analysed solutions was maintained by the addition of KNO_3.

Solution container
To avoid the evaporation of volatile reagents the solution was stored in a glass cylinder closed by a mobile piston (Fig. 1). The solution was injected from the container to a measuring cell.

Potentiometric titration assembly
The assembly for potentiometric titration (Fig. 2) consists of the automatic burette (OP 930/1, Radelkis, Hungary), the measuring cell, containing an analysed solution, and the

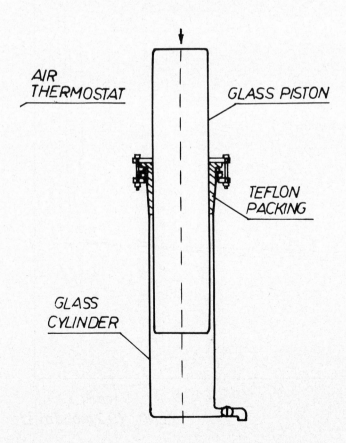

Fig. 1   Solution container

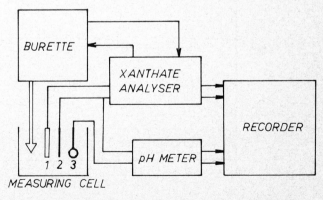

Fig. 2   Schematic representation of assembly for potentiometric titrations: 1, silver xanthate electrode (AX); 2, reference electrode (SCE); 3, glass electrode

three electrodes (sensitive to xanthate ions (AX), glass and reference). The solution was stirred by a magnetic stirrer. The xanthate analyser controls the action of the automatic burette and measures the potential of the AX electrode versus the SCE electrode as a function of volume of AgNO₃ solution added to the xanthate solution in the measuring cell. The xanthate analyser can analyse the titration curves and estimate the first and the second end point.

pH values were measured by a pH meter (N 517 Mera, Poland).

By use of the assembly described above one can determine the concentration of X^-, OH^- and the sum of concentrations of ions (Z), which form silver salts characterized by solubility products lower than that of silver xanthate.

Determination of CS_2 concentration

The concentration of CS_2 was determined by the method of Philipp and co-workers by use of a special measuring cell[6] and dc polarograph (GWP 673, German Academy of Sciences, Berlin, GDR).

Model flotation experiments

The flotation experiments were carried out with a laboratory flotation machine (Academy of Mining and Metallurgy, Kraków, Poland).

A standard procedure was applied to enable the relative amounts of copper recovered in consecutive experiments carried out with xanthate solution stored for various time periods at different temperatures (20, 25 and 30°C) to be compared.

The initial amount and composition of ore sample, the volume of water and concentrated xanthate solution stored for a given time, the temperature of the flotation process and the flotation time were kept constant throughout the experiments.

Results and discussion

Typical titration curves obtained for purified xanthate solution stored at 30°C for 2, 48, 97 and 144 h are presented in Fig. 3. The first curve shows only one potential jump in the range −350 to +50 mV versus SCE associated with the titration of xanthate ions. Solutions stored for longer periods are characterized by two or more potential jumps. Ions titrated ahead of xanthate ions are called 'active impurities' (Z).

The values of X^-, Z, CS_2 and OH^- concentration were determined experimentally at three constant temperatures of solution storage (20, 25 and 30°C) for purified xanthate solutions and at 25°C for the industrial xanthate solution.

The experimental results were compared with the theoretical calculations described earlier[1] and are shown in Figs. 4, 5 and 6.

The general tendency of concentration changes during the xanthate solution storage is as predicted by the theoretical calculations. Xanthate, however, decomposes more quickly than the calculations suggest. The lower concentrations of CS_2 indicate that the process of CS_2 hydrolysis is more efficient, which is connected with the faster reactions of active impurity formation in real systems in comparison with theoretical calculations.

A similar trend can be observed for industrial xanthate solution, apart from CS_2, for which experimental

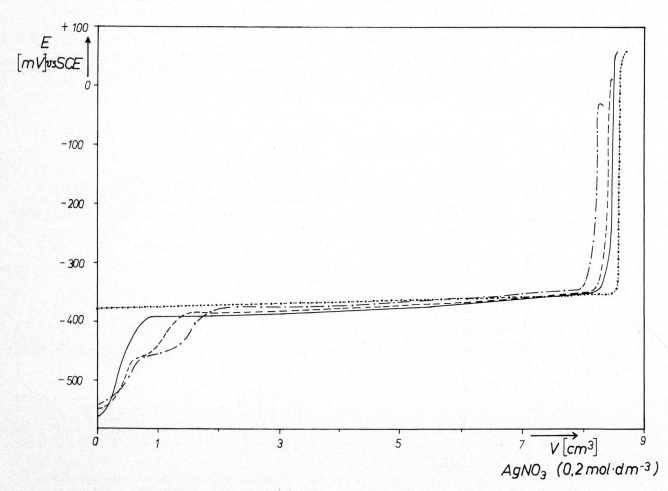

Fig. 3 Potentiometric titration curves recorded for purified xanthate solution stored at 30°C for various times (------ 2 h; ——— 48 h; --- 97 h; ·—·— 144 h)

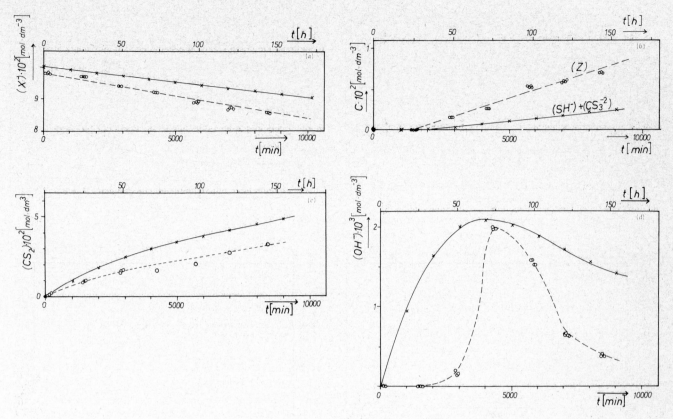

Fig. 4   Dependence of (*a*) xanthate concentration (X⁻) on time for purified xanthate solution (--- experimental, ⎯ calculated theoretically), (*b*) active impurity concentration on time for purified xanthate solution (--- (Z), experimental, ⎯ (SH⁻) + (CS₃⁻²) calculated theoretically), (*c*) CS₂ concentration on time for purified xanthate solution (--- experimental, ⎯ calculated theoretically) and (*d*) OH⁻ concentration on time for purified xanthate solution (--- experimental, ⎯ calculated theoretically) (all solutions stored at 20°C)

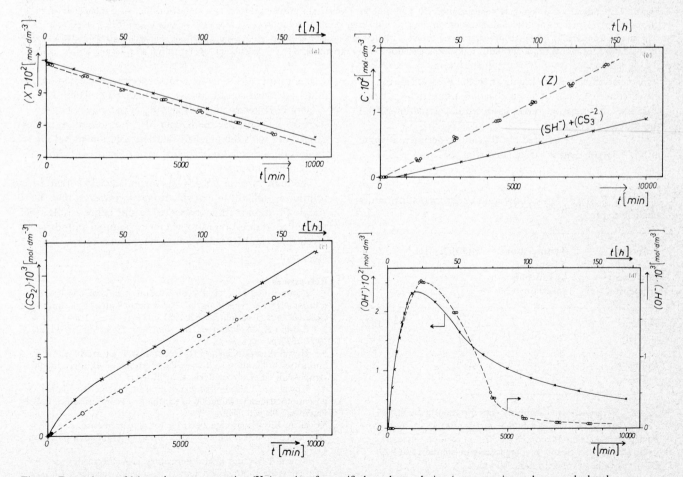

Fig. 5   Dependence of (*a*) xanthate concentration (X⁻) on time for purified xanthate solution (--- experimental, ⎯ calculated theoretically), (*b*) active impurity concentration on time for purified xanthate solution (--- (Z), experimental, ⎯ (SH⁻) + (CS₃⁻²), calculated theoretically), (*c*) CS₂ concentration on time for purified xanthate solution (--- experimental, ⎯ calculated theoretically) and (*d*) OH⁻ concentration on time for purified xanthate solution (--- experimental, ⎯ calculated theoretically) (all solutions stored at 30°C)

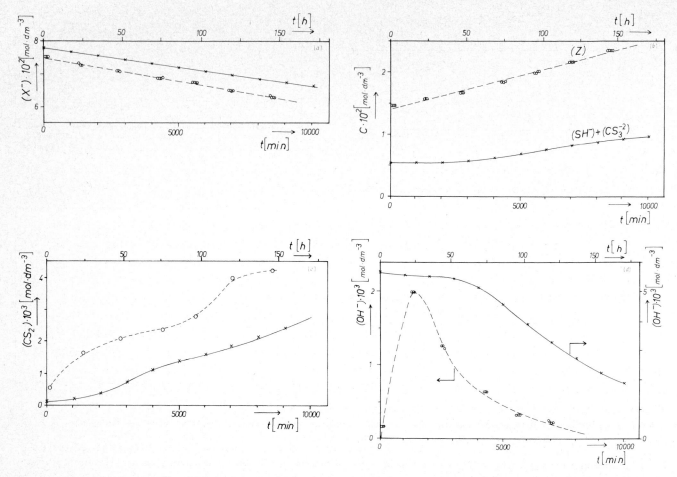

Fig. 6 Dependence of (a) xanthate concentration (X^-) on time for industrial xanthate solution (– – – experimental, —— calculated theoretically), (b) active impurity concentration on time for industrial xanthate solution (– – – (Z), experimental, —— (SH^-) + (CS_3^{-2}), calculated theoretically), (c) CS_2 concentration on time for industrial xanthate solution (– – – experimental, —— calculated theoretically) and (d) OH^- concentration on time for industrial xanthate solution (– – – experimental, —— calculated theoretically) (all solutions stored at 25°C)

concentration values are higher than the theoretical (the initial concentrations of CS_2 and active impurities are larger than the concentration values assumed in calculations[1] for the industrial solution).

It should also be pointed out that the experimental value of (Z) is larger than the calculated sum (SH^-) + (CS_3^{-2}) because mono- and dithiocarbonate ions can be titrated with

Table 1 Results of model flotation experiments for natural chalcocite ore

Solution to flotation apparatus	Temperature of storage of xanthate solution, °C	$[(Z)/(X^-)]_{t_{\frac{1}{2}}}$, %	$t_{\frac{1}{2}}$, h
Purified xanthate	20	10.7	167
	25	11.8	114
	30	11.4	80
Industrial xanthate	25	29.5	92

(Z)/(X⁻) is ratio of active impurity concentration to xanthate concentration, $t_{\frac{1}{2}}$ is time of solution storage after which mass of floated chalcocite ore is reduced by 50% in relation to maximum value obtained for freshly prepared xanthate solution and $[(Z)/(X^-)]_{t_{\frac{1}{2}}}$ is value of concentration ratio for $t_{\frac{1}{2}}$.

SH^- and CS_3^{-2} ahead of xanthate ions (the simple electrochemical method of their separate determination is not, however, fully developed to date).

The results of model flotation experiments carried out under standard conditions are summarized in Table 1.

Copper recovery is less than 50% if the value of $[(Z)/(X^-)]_{t_{\frac{1}{2}}}$ is greater than about 11% for a flotation process carried out with the purified xanthate solution stored for various periods of time. The value of $t_{\frac{1}{2}}$ decreases with temperature increase.

The high value of $[(Z)/(X^-)]_{t_{\frac{1}{2}}}$ for industrial xanthate solution is difficult to explain. It is felt, however, that the simple titration method presented in this paper enables the fundamental question as to whether a solution stored for a given time can be used in a flotation process to be answered.

References
1.   Dautzenberg H. *et al.* Decomposition of xanthates in flotation solutions. In *Reagents in the mineral industry* Jones M. J. and Oblatt R. eds (London: IMM, 1984), 47–51.
2.   Gaudin A. M. *Flotation, 2nd edn* (New York: McGraw-Hill, 1957), 573 p.
3.   Kowal A. and Niewiara R. Determination of xanthate and its impurities in flotation solutions. Paper presented to international symposium on electroanalysis, Cardiff, April 1983.
4.   Kowal A. Method of preparation of indicator electrode for potentiometric determination of xanthate ion concentration. Polish Patent no. 98 361, 1980.
Kowal A. Silver xanthate electrode for potentiometric determination of xanthate ion concentration. Hungarian Patent no. 179 286, 1981.
5.   Kowal A. Krauss E. and Pomianowski A. Electrodes for measuring the xanthate ion activity in aqueous solutions. *Chemia analyt.*, **26**, 1981, 441–7.
6.   Philipp B. Dautzenberg H. and Lang H. Kinetische Untersuchungen zur Zersetzung von Thiocarbaminaten. *Faserforsch. TextTech.*, **19**, 1968, 325–32.

New processes to float feldspathic and ferrous minerals from quartz

G. I. Mathieu and L. L. Sirois

Synopsis

Marine and beach sands are abundant in nature, but they are rarely exploited, probably because of a complex mineralogy and a rather low commercial value. Such sands are generally composed of quartz and feldspars, with minor amounts of pyroxene, amphibole and iron-, magnesium- and titanium-bearing minerals. Some goethite–limonite coating is occasionally observed on the silica and feldspar grains. To recover the commodities economically at marketable grade the processes must be simple, cheap, reliable and environmentally acceptable.

The Canadian Centre for Mineral and Energy Technology (CANMET) has undertaken studies with the private sector to beneficiate the Gulf of St. Lawrence sands for the production of silica sands that meet foundry and glassmaking specifications and feldspar products of glass grade and ceramic quality.

Extensive laboratory testwork preceded the development of a treatment flowsheet that was demonstrated at the pilot-plant scale. The raw sand used contained 88% quartz and 10% feldspar as its main values, with 1% iron-bearing minerals. The procedure included novel flotation approaches for the separation of the feldspar and iron-bearing minerals from the quartz, such as the use of an experimental iron collector operating at natural pH and the co-flotation of feldspar and iron-bearing minerals with a new combination of anionic–cationic promotors. The two main flotation products—quartz and feldspar concentrates—are subsequently upgraded to various market specifications by acid leaching and/or magnetic separation.

Other features of the processing technology comprised the non-utilization of fluorine compounds in the flotation circuits along with a low consumption of the new reagents for greater safety and economy, and the minimal surface cleaning by sulphuric acid leach with multiple re-utilization of the liquor to yield significant savings in acid and equipment.

Several approaches to the treatment of a marine sand from the Gulf of St. Lawrence were tested initially on the laboratory scale: these included scrubbing, multiple flotation, magnetic separation and acid leaching. A progressive processing flowsheet was adopted that combined two circuits—one for the recovery of quartz sand at minimal cost by the flotation of the feldspar and iron minerals by use of a new combination of anionic–cationic collectors, the other for upgrading the silica and feldspar products to market requirements. The latter were achieved, essentially, by further flotation, acid leaching and/or magnetic separation. A summary of the degree of processing with corresponding analyses of seven products is shown in Table 1.

Product (1) is satisfactory for iron foundry sand and for glass fibre production; product (2) is suitable for the production of coloured glass containers and for steel foundry sand; product (3) is applicable to the production of colourless and clear flat glass;

products (4) and (5) are suitable for use as fluxes in furnaces, in roofing, tiles and other building materials; product (6) satisfies the specifications of glassmaking feldspar; and product (7) meets the chemical requirements for ceramic use.

In summary, the foundry grade sand was attained by primary flotation, whereas glassmaking quartz and feldspar required additional flotation, acid leach and/or magnetic separation. Only the flotation aspects are discussed in great detail here, but the other processes are also outlined for completeness.

Background

Important sand deposits located in shallow undersea water northeast and southwest of the Magdalen Islands, Canada, were identified recently and claimed by Magdalen Silica, Inc. Proven reserves are said to be 100 000 000 t and additional sand is transported every year from the north by glaciers and ocean currents. A 2-t sample of the raw marine sand was submitted for investigation to CANMET Mineral Sciences Laboratories. The material contained 88% quartz and 10% feldspar, the remaining 2% being composed mainly of sea shells, ferromagnesian minerals, metal oxides and clay–limonite coating on the quartz and feldspar grains.

The purpose of the study was to produce, by economical means, steel foundry and glassmaking sands, as well as feldspar concentrates that meet both glass and ceramic specifications. A cursory examination of the Magdalen sample indicated that the first objective could be met by removing the alkali silicates from the raw sand, whereas the other goals would require the additional removal of harmful metal oxides and iron coating from the valuable grains.

The approach that was used in developing a flowsheet to concentrate the quartz and feldspar values consisted of minimizing the number and the cost of the unit operations to render the whole process as economically attractive as possible. For instance, conventional methods[1,2] that use double flotation techniques (one for feldspar and one for iron minerals), both preceded by alkali scrubbing, were discarded in favour of a novel technique that employs two promotors for the simultaneous removal of both feldspar and iron minerals. These reagents did not necessitate the addition of a silica depressant (normally hydrofluoric acid) during conditioning and flotation, and permitted recycling of process water for economy.

Marine sand study

Chemical and mineralogical analysis of raw sand

A. E. Gregory, a specialist in sand processing, wrote: 'Before any attempt can be made to design a processing plant for sand a detailed study should be made, based on mineralogical and chemical analyses ... If the distribution of impurities in the sand is known it is possible to predict which method of treatment is likely to yield the best results. ... Every sand must be considered on its own.'[3]

A representative head sample was cut from several bags of the 2-t shipment received from Magdalen Silica Sand, Inc. A portion was pulverized in an agate mortar and chemically analysed (Table 2).

Table 1 Analyses (%) of processed quartz and feldspar sand

| Analysis | Washed raw sand | Processed silica sand | | Feldspar products | | |
| | | Primary flotation + | H₂SO₄ leach | Primary and secondary flotation + | H₂SO₄ leach magnetic separation + | Grinding magnetic separation |
	(1)	(2)	(3)	(4)-(5)	(6)	(7)
SiO₂	95.1	99.3	99.6	72.9-66.3	67.3	67.1
Al₂O₃	2.2	0.26	0.18	14.3-18.0	18.3	18.4
K₂O+Na₂O	1.4	0.14	0.09	10.3-13.3	13.9	14.0
Fe₂O₃	0.2	0.10	0.03	0.6- 0.5	0.11	0.08-0.05

Table 2 Chemical analysis of Magdalen head sample

Analysis	Symbol	%
Silica		
Total	SiO₂	95.0
Quartz	SiO₂	~88.0
Silicates (all as oxides)		
Aluminium	Al₂O₃	2.17
Potassium	K₂O	1.13
Sodium	Na₂O	0.30
Calcium	CaO	0.10
Metal oxides		
Iron (as ferric oxide)	Fe₂O₃	0.23
Titanium (as dioxide)	TiO₂	0.06
Magnesium (as oxide)	MgO	0.15
Chromium (as chromic oxide)	Cr₂O₃	9 ppm
Loss on ignition	LOI	0.40

In this work the determinations of low alumina, iron, magnesium and titanium oxides were all made by optical emission spectrometry. The higher alumina, iron, magnesium and titanium, as well as all the K₂O, CaO and total SiO₂, were determined by X-ray analysis. Finally, sodium oxide and quartz were chemically analysed. Wet chemistry was also used periodically to verify the instrumental determinations, which proved to be reliable.

The total feldspar content was calculated according to the formula:

$$\text{Total feldspar, \%} = \left(\frac{K_2O}{16.92} + \frac{Na_2O}{11.82} + \frac{CaO}{20.16} \right) 100$$

or, more simply by multiplying the % Al₂O₃ by 4.8.

A 500-g sample was riffled from the head sample and screened and the fractions were weighed and analysed for alumina and iron oxide (Table 3). The calculated feldspar contents in the sized fractions are also reported.

Table 3 Screen test of Magdalen head sample with size distribution of Al₂O₃ and Fe₂O₃

| Size, μm | Wt% | Analysis, % | | | Distribution, % | |
		Al₂O₃	Feldspar	Fe₂O₃	Feldspar	Fe₂O₃
+590	0.2*	—	—	—	—	—
-590+297	33.0	1.67	8.0	0.18	24.9	25.4
-297+210	47.5	2.32	11.1	0.20	50.0	41.2
-210+149	18.3	2.84	13.6	0.33	23.4	25.9
-149	1.0	3.72	17.8	1.72	1.7	7.5
Total	100.0	2.21	10.6	0.23	100.0	100.0

* Mostly sea shell.

A number of dark particles, believed to be chromium or titanium minerals, were observed in the fine fraction, i.e.

-149 μm. Its titanium and chromium oxides were then determined by chemical analysis. The high concentration of these undesirable impurities in the fines was confirmed (0.6% TiO₂ and 55 ppm Cr₂O₃). Iron oxides are also highly concentrated in this fraction.

For the mineralogical studies a 500-g sample was submitted to a dense liquid separation (2.7 sp.gr.); both the sink and float products were then treated by high-intensity magnetic separation. It was observed that most of the heavies and a significant portion of the lights were magnetic. The weight distribution between the sink fraction and the magnetic and non-magnetic light fractions is given in Table 4 with their main mineralogical components. Microphotographs of the sand are shown in Fig. 1.

Table 4 Mineralogical composition of Magdalen sand[4,5]

Product	Wt %	Mineral	Estimated content, %
Light fractions:		Quartz (SiO₂)	80
		K-feldspar (KAlSi₃O₈)	6
Non-magnetic	91.8	Na-feldspar (NaAlSi₃O₈)	2
		Quartz-feldspar (intergrowth)	2-4
		Ca-feldspar (CaAl₂Si₂O₈)	0.2
		Clay-limonite coating	0.2
		Ilmenite, chlorite, rutile (as fine inclusions in quartz and silicates)	0.1
Slightly magnetic (Sala conc.)	6.4	Entrained quartz	2.0
		Quartz and feldspars (with iron minerals inclusions)	2.0
		Altered feldspars	2.0
		Iron-bearing silicates	0.4
Moderately magnetic (Frantz conc.)	1.6	Fe-rich clay mineral	0.1
		Fe, Mg, K, Al, Si biotite	0.1
		Fe, Mg, Al, Si pyroxene	0.1
		Intergrowths of iron minerals with quartz and feldspar	1.3
Heavies: Highly magnetic (except rutile)	0.2	Ilmenite	0.15
		Chlorite	0.05
		Rutile	0.05
		Silicate-iron oxide middlings	0.05
		Chromite (spinel)	Tr

This mineralogy indicated the necessity of three main unit operations to beneficiate the sand fully—flotation to separate the feldspar and iron minerals from the quartz, acid leach to dissolve the iron oxide coating on the valuable minerals surfaces and magnetic separation to remove the acid-insoluble iron species from the glass and ceramic grade products. Each of these processes was first to be tested and analysed separately, subsequently being integrated in an overall flowsheet to produce quartz and feldspar concentrates that satisfy the requirements specified in Table 5.

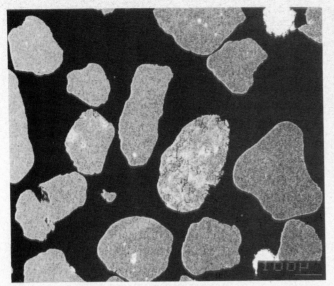 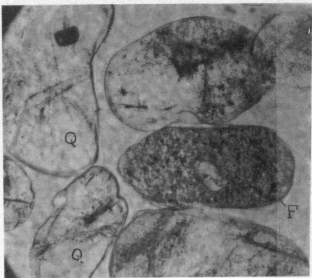

Fig. 1   Photomicrographs of Magdalen quartz–feldspar sand: (*a*) (*left*), dark grey grains quartz, light grey feldspar and white particles ilmenite, rutile and spinel; (*b*) (*right*), turpid quartz and alkali-feldspar grains with opaque inclusions of Fe–Ti-bearing minerals (transmitted light, 1-mm view)

Table 5   Specifications of commercial quartz and feldspar products[6,7,8]

Composition and physical characteristics	Quartz sand		Feldspar concentrate	
	Foundry	Glass	Glass	Ceramic
	(1) (2)	(3) (4)		
Total SiO_2, %	95 - 99	97 - 99	65 - 68	65 - 68
	(1) (2)	(3) (4)		
Quartz, %	90 - 96	96 - 98	NS	8.0 (max)
Al_2O_3, %	0.5	0.3	18.5 ± 0.6	18.0 (min)
$K_2O + Na_2O$, %	0.3	0.2	12.5 ± 1.0	13.0 (min)
		(3) (4)		
Fe_2O_3, %	NS	0.3 - 0.03	0.1 (max)	0.08 (max)
		(3) (4)		
LOI, %	0.2	0.5 - 0.2	0.5	0.4
Size	600 x 74 μm and AFS no. 45 to 55		420 x 74 μm	98% - 74 μm
Shape	Spherical and semi-angular		NS	NS

(1) Non-ferrous and (2) steel foundry sand; (3) coloured and (4) clear glass sand.
NS, no specifications; AFS no., American Foundry Grain Fineness Number.

Feldspar–iron separation from quartz by flotation

Prior to every flotation test the +590 μm and –149 μm fractions were discarded, this material being high in impurities and accounting for only 1.2% of the sand by weight. This operation also removed the salt water.

New technique versus conventional approach

An initial series of tests was aimed at comparing the novel cationic–anionic flotation approach with conventional two-stage flotation for the removal of feldspar and iron minerals from quartz. In both cases no scrubbing was used before the flotation as the marine sand had been submitted to natural attrition. The two procedures are described in Appendix 1 and exemplified by a series of tests (Fig. 2 illustrates the results obtained).

The non-HF single flotation method proved to be as effective as the classical approach, and less hazardous chemicals are used. The lower consumption of collector is also important. In searching the literature it was found that the simultaneous use of cationic and anionic collectors has been reported by Ranney[9] in

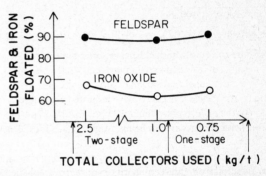

Fig. 2   Single versus double-stage flotation of feldspar and iron minerals

various applications. In such cases the floatability is explained by either two successive adsorptions or the formation of a hydrophobic complex.

Effect of pH, conditioning time, collector concentration and process water recycling

A parametric study of feldspar–iron flotation was made by varying pH (2.0–2.4), conditioning time (3–10 min) and collector dosage (0.45–0.85 kg/t), as these factors were identified as highly significant in Malghan's non-HF feldspar flotation studies.[10] For economic and environmental reasons our investigation also comprised an assessment of process water recirculation. This variable was studied by a series of locked-cycle tests in which the used water was recycled according to the pattern illustrated in Fig. 3. The reagents, conditions and results of this series of flotation tests are reported in detail in Appendix 2 and represented graphically in Figs. 4 and 5.

The parametric study showed the following trends.
(1) The grade of the silica concentrates is relatively constant at 97.6 to 98.4% quartz, the highest purity being obtained for the higher pH values and more abundant collector dosage; on the other hand, under similar conditions the quality of the feldspar floated is impaired by these factors.
(2) The recovery of quartz is favoured by a low pH, as well as by minimal addition of collectors; conversely, increased pH and reagent concentration improve the feldspar (and iron) recoveries, but at the cost of the grade because of too much quartz co-flotation, particularly at pH >2.2.
(3) The 8-min conditioning at pH 2.2 gave the best flotation separation, as is shown by the following calculated selectivity

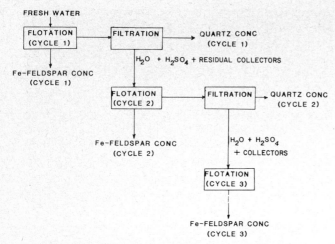

Fig. 3   Illustration of locked-cycle tests with process water recycling

indices and total weighed recoveries of the valuable minerals (quartz and feldspar):

Conditioning at pH 2.2:   3 min   5 min   8 min   10 min

$$SI = \sqrt{\frac{Qc.Fc}{(100-Qc)(100-Fc)}} \quad = \quad 9.8 \quad 13.1 \quad 14.0 \quad 11.8$$

$$TWR = 0.88\,Qc + 0.10\,Fc \quad = \quad 87.8 \quad 92.7 \quad 93.7 \quad 91.0$$

Qc and Fc are the quartz and feldspar reporting in their respective concentrates expressed in per cent; $(100 - Qc)$ and $(100 - Fc)$ are the misplaced valuable constituents.

(4) Finally, the locked-cycle tests have indicated a possible reduction of the collectors by about 40% (i.e. from 0.75 to 0.45 kg/t), comparable concentrates being produced (see Figs. 4 and 5).

In summary, the optimum conditioning time and pH for the feldspar flotation from quartz in marine sand were established at 8 min and 2.2, respectively: these are slightly different from

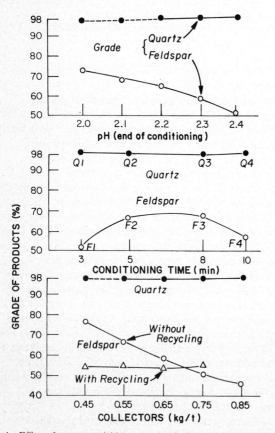

Fig. 4   Effect of process variables on grade of primary flotation products

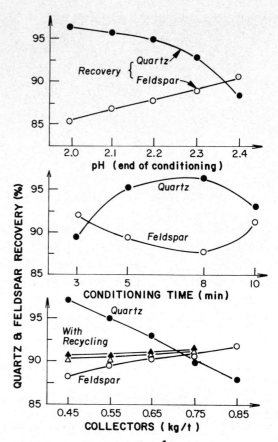

Fig. 5   Effect of flotation variables on quartz and feldspar recovery

those of 5 min and 2.4 previously established by Malghan[10] and Neal[11] for pegmatite-type ores.

Upgrading of feldspar concentrate
To be of high commercial value the feldspar product must contain at least 17.5% Al_2O_3, i.e. 86% total feldspar. Mineralogical examination of the rougher feldspar–iron flotation concentrates showed a high proportion of free quartz. Cleaner flotation was therefore selected to upgrade the feldspar concentrate. After the first cleaning stage no further upgrading was achieved because the grain surfaces were too highly coated with chemicals. Their complete refreshing was therefore necessary. With this objective, grinding, scrubbing and acid leaching were investigated successively. For the pre-treatment by acid leach a subsequent alkali attrition was required to restore feldspar floatability. After each pre-treatment differential flotation was tested at three levels of collectors—at low concentration to obtain the best feldspar grade, at higher dosage to maximize the recovery and, finally, at the intermediate level in an attempt to optimize both grade and recovery. A summary of

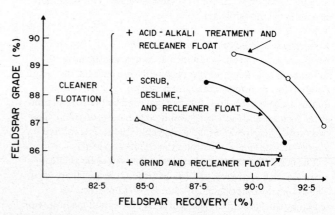

Fig. 6   Feldspar final upgrading grade–recovery curves

the conditions and results of the feldspar upgrading tests is given in Appendix 3 and grade–recovery curves are compared in Fig. 6.

All the methods gave satisfactory feldspar grade. The first approach, however, is of less interest because of high reagent consumptions and low feldspar recoveries. Only the two other avenues were pursued with magnetic separation and/or acid leach to produce glass and ceramic feldspars

Impurities removal from quartz and feldspar

The silica concentrates at 98.1–98.4% quartz, with an AFS number of 49 and an angularity coefficient of 1.16, were readily acceptable for steel foundry moulding. On the other hand, the iron levels at 0.10 to 0.12% Fe_2O_3 were too high for clear glass manufacturing. Microscopic examination of a representative sample showed that most of the remaining iron occurs as a mixture of an iron-rich clay and oxide mineral, probably limonite, either coated or intergrown with the quartz grains. This marked acid leaching as the best way to further reduce the iron content to meet the colourless glass specifications. Sulphuric and hydrochloric acids were tested: in both cases the rate of iron dissolution depended on acid concentration, contact time, leach temperature and nature of acid. Concentrated hydrochloric acid (75% volume) at 95°C lowered the iron oxide to 0.017% after 2 h and 0.012% after 6 h, whereas it took 5 h to attain 0.035% Fe_2O_3 with 35% sulphuric acid at 70°C (Fig. 7).

The feldspar, being more heavily coated by limonite and contaminated by metallic oxides and ferromagnesian minerals, i.e. 0.6% Fe_2O_3, was more difficult to purify. Neither magnetic separation nor acid leach alone was capable of reducing the iron oxide to a satisfactory level, but a combination of the two processes was successful. This was demonstrated by a sequence of tests that involved acid leach with and without magnetic separation, the results of which are illustrated in Fig. 7. Briefly, a 6-h, 70°C H_2SO_4 leach complemented by high-intensity magnetic separation (H-I, Stearns) reduced not only the Fe_2O_3 but also the Ti and Mg oxides to acceptable levels for flint-glass feldspar (0.10% Fe_2O_3, 0.05% TiO_2 and MgO); when treating the same leach residue by high-gradient separation (HGMS, Sala) after grinding to –74 and 45 μm, respectively, ceramic (0.07% Fe_2O_3) and porcelain (0.05% Fe_2O_3) grades were achieved. The most significant results are recorded in Appendix 4 with the pertinent procedures.[12]

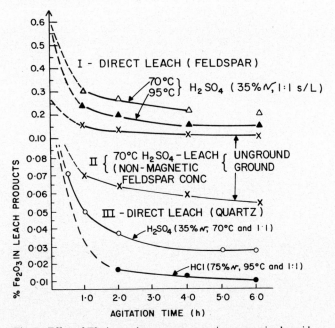

Fig. 7 Effect of $T°$, time and pre-treatment on iron extraction by acid leach

After the laboratory testwork had been analysed an overall flowsheet that incorporated the best features was designed and a pilot plant was assembled accordingly. The pilot-plant study had the specific goal of demonstrating the processes on a larger scale. A flow chart of the equipment assembly and a summary of the operating conditions and results are shown in Appendices 5 and 6. (The results obtained were comparable with those on the laboratory scale.)

Conclusions

The main objective of this work was to develop technically feasible, economic and safe (from a health and environmental point of view) processes for beneficiating raw marine sand to produce foundry sand, glassmaking quartz and glass and ceramic feldspars. A representative sand from the Gulf of St. Lawrence was utilized for the experimentation.

It has been demonstrated that N-tallow-1,3-propane diamine dioleate plus a high molecular weight petroleum sulphonate were selective flotation collectors for feldspar and iron minerals, without the help of hazardous hydrofluoric acid as quartz depressant. By carefully controlling the pH and the dosage of these reagents a sand suitable for steel foundry use was readily produced by increasing the quartz content and reducing the undesirable alkalis.

	Raw sand	Foundry sand
Quartz, %	89.00	98.5
Al_2O_3, %	2.16	0.26
K_2O, %	1.13	0.09
Na_2O, %	0.30	0.05
CaO, %	0.16	0.1

The glass sand was produced similarly, except that a sulphuric acid leach stage was performed on the silica flotation product to remove the iron oxide coating on the grains (the iron content was thereby reduced from 0.1 to 0.03% Fe_2O_3 for clear glass applications). In addition to rejecting feldspar and iron from glass sand, the processing method also eliminated most of the other metallic oxide impurities (see below).

	Raw sand	Glass sand
SiO_2, %	95.0	99.6
Feldspar, %	10.1	0.8
Fe_2O_3, %	0.23	0.026
MgO, %	0.15	0.05
TiO_2, %	0.05	0.02
Mn, ppm	25	4
Cr_2O_3, ppm	9	2
Chlorite, ppm	110	30

The feldspar, being more heavily coated by limonite and contaminated by quartz, oxides and ferromagnesian minerals, was more difficult to upgrade. The entrained free quartz was first removed by additional selective flotation without and with surface preparation, after which a combination of acid leach and magnetic separation (plus pebble-grinding for ceramic grade) reduced the impurities to the requirements of the glass and ceramic industries. The Magdalen feldspars then compared favourably with the best high-potash feldspars produced worldwide (Table 6).

The sand was processed with minimal equipment and low total reagent consumption, e.g. 0.63 kg/t of collectors, 0.6 kg/t of caustic and 2.5 kg/t of sulphuric acid for flotation, and less than 40 kg/t of H_2SO_4 for quartz and feldspar leaching, with recycling of the used acid 10 times. Only three screens, two conditioners, one scrubber and flotation capacity limited to 4 min of retention time were required for the feldspar–quartz separation. Leaching was made on less than 56% of the original material, magnetic separation on about 10% and grinding on only 5%. This pattern

Table 6   Comparative composition of high-potash feldspars

Component	King Mountain K-40	Magdalen Glass-grade	Oy Lolya FFF-grade	Magdalen Ceramic	K/S Norfloat Potash	Magdalen Porcelain
Al_2O_3	18.3	18.3	18.5	18.3	18.7	18.2
K_2O	10.1	11.4	8.1	11.3	11.1	11.3
Na_2O	3.8	2.7	5.0	2.7	3.4	2.7
CaO	0.4	0.4	0.6	0.4	0.5	0.3
SiO_2	67.1	66.9	67.5	66.3	65.4	66.9
Fe_2O_3	0.07	0.11	0.10	0.08	0.06	0.05
LOI	0.3	0.3	NA	0.3	0.3	0.3

of progressive processing is economically attractive as it permits the matching of the plus value of the products with their additional costs. The metallurgy did not suffer because of these economies, overall quartz and feldspar recoveries of 92.9% and 71.9%, respectively, being achieved, despite a complex mineralogy.

Acknowledgement

The authors wish to acknowledge the assistance in this investigation of M. Raicevic and A. Boire for the laboratory tests and T. F. Berry, J. Rouleau, E. Brady and R. Bredin for the pilot-plant work. They also thank W. Petruk and P. R. Mainwaring for the mineralogical examinations, R. E. Horton for the optical emission spectrometry, J. L. Dalton and J. Leung for the X-ray fluorescence analyses and J. Hole and his staff for the chemical analyses. They are also extremely grateful to B. H. Lucas and E. I. Szabo, who were in charge of the hydrometallurgy and foundry testwork, respectively. The drawings were prepared by J. D. MacLeod.

Finally, the authors are indebted to W. MacDaniel and P. Neil, North Carolina Minerals Research Laboratory, for their technical collaboration with regard to the new flotation technique. The officials of Magdalen Silica, Inc., kindly furnished the marine sand sample for this study and expressed a great interest during the project. They are grateful to J. Arnold, President, Magdalen Silica Sand, Inc., for allowing them to present the results of this work.

References

1.   Redeker I. H. Flotation of feldspar, spodumene, quartz and mica from pegmatites in North Carolina, USA. In *Proceedings thirteenth annual meeting of Canadian mineral processors, Ottawa, 1981* Veillette G. comp., 1981, 136–53.
2.   Feldspar and nepheline syenite—rivals in a flux. *Ind. Minerals* no. 100, Jan. 1976, 15–26.
3.   Gregory A. G. The extraction and processing of sands for glass manufacture. *Cement Lime Gravel*, **39**, April 1964, 125–34.
4.   Petruk W. Private communication; Mineralogy of mill products from Marmine sands. *CANMET Division Rep.* MRP/MSL 81-95 (TR), 1981.
5.   Mainwaring P. R. Mineralogy of Magdalen sand. *CANMET Mineralogy Rep.* M-3307, 1982.
6.   Sanders C. A. *Foundry sand practice, 6th edition* (Skokie, Illinois: American Cyanamid Co., 1973), 477.
7.   Chemical Analysis Committee. Specifications for and recommended procedures for the testing and analysis of glassmaking sands 1978. *Glass Technol.*, **19**, no. 5, Oct. 1978, 93–101.
8.   Watson I. Feldspathic fluxes—the rivalry reviewed. *Ind. Minerals* no. 163, April 1981, 21–45.
9.   Ranney M. W. ed. *Flotation agents and processes* (Park Ridge, N. J.: Noyes Data Corporation, 1980), 372 p.
10.   Malghan S. E. Effect of process variables in feldspar flotation using non-hydrofluoric acid system. *NCSU Minerals Res. Lab. Publ.* no. 79-10-P, 1979.
11.   Neal J. P. Confirmatory tests on feldspar flotation without F^- ion. *NCSU Minerals Res. Lab. Publ.* no. 81-11-9, 1981.
12.   Lucas B. H. and Prud'homme P. Private communication, 1982.

Appendix 1

Feldspar–iron flotation: single-stage versus two stages

Reagents and conditions

Operation	Time, min	Density, % solids	Reagents kg/t			pH
			HF	H$_2$SO$_4$	Collectors*	
Test 1						
Fe conditioning	5	65	—	1.2	1.2 (PS)	2.1
Fe flotation	4	25	—	—	—	2.4
Feldspar conditioning	5	60	1.0	0.2	1.3 (TAA)	2.2
Feldspar flotation	4	24	—	—	—	2.5
Test 2						
Fe conditioning	5	65	—	—	0.5 (CX)	6.9
Fe flotation	3	25	—	—	—	6.8
Feldspar conditioning	5	65	—	1.1	0.5 (PDD)	2.0
Feldspar flotation	3	24	—	—	—	2.5
Test 3						(PS) + (PDD)
Fe-feldspar conditioning	5	65	—	1.3	0.3 + 0.45	2.9
Fe-feldspar flotation	3	25	—	—	—	2.4

* PS, petroleum sulphonate; TAA, tallow amine acetate; PDD, propane diamine dioleate; CX-62 is an experimental iron mineral collector manufactured by Hercules, Inc.

Results obtained

Test products		Wt %	Analysis, %			Distribution, %		
			Feldspar	Fe$_2$O$_3$	Quartz	Feldspar	Fe$_2$O$_3$	Quartz
	Fe conc	1.6	10.4	4.90	79.7	1.7	34.0	1.4
	Feldspar conc	16.0	55.2	0.49	42.7	89.1	34.0	7.7
1	Quartz conc	82.4	1.1	0.089	98.2	9.2	32.0	90.9
	Feed (calc)	100.0	9.9	0.23	89.0	100.0	100.0	100.0
	Fe conc	1.0	13.1	5.55	78.1	1.3	27.3	0.9
	Feldspar conc	16.4	55.1	0.43	43.0	88.2	34.6	7.9
2	Quartz conc	82.6	1.3	0.094	98.1	10.5	38.1	91.2
	Feed (calc)	100.0	10.2	0.20	88.9	100.0	100.0	100.0
	Fe-feldspar conc	17.4	54.0	0.81	43.8	90.1	64.2	8.6
3	Quartz	82.6	1.2	0.096	98.1	9.9	35.8	91.4
	Feed (calc)	100.00	10.1	0.22	100.0	100.0	100.0	100.0

Appendix 2

Effect of variables on feldspar–iron flotation separation from quartz

Constants	Variables		Results				
			Quartz concentrate		Feldspar–iron concentrate		
			SiO$_2$ (quartz), %	Recovery, %	Feldspar content, %	Feldspar recovery, %	Fe$_2$O$_3$ floated, %
I Collectors PS, 0.25 kg/t PDD, 0.50 kg/t Conditioning time, 5 min	pH	2.0	97.6	96.5	73.0	85.4	53.4
		2.1	97.8	95.5	68.1	86.9	56.9
		2.2	97.9	94.6	64.7	87.6	54.0
		2.3	98.0	92.7	58.3	88.6	59.0
		2.4	98.1	88.7	50.2	90.8	65.7
II PS, 0.15 kg/t PDD, 0.40 kg/t pH 2.2	Conditioning time, min	3	98.3	89.1	50.6	92.0	60.0
		5†	98.1	95.3	66.9	89.6	—
		8†	98.0	96.5	68.9	87.6	—
		10	98.4	93.1	57.3	91.2	54.0
III Conditioning time, 5 min	Collector dosage, kg/t*	0.45	97.9	97.3	76.4	86.7	55.2
		0.55	98.1	94.9	67.1	89.5	57.2
		0.65	98.2	93.0	59.3	90.0	62.4
		0.75	98.2	90.1	52.5	90.6	64.1
		0.85	98.3	87.7	46.6	91.7	68.6
pH, 2.2	With recycling	0.75	98.1	91.5	55.9	90.1	59.6
		0.65	98.2	90.7	53.9	90.6	63.2
		0.55	98.0	91.0	54.9	90.6	60.3
		0.45	98.2	90.5	53.4	91.0	60.8
		0.45	98.0	90.9	54.5	89.6	59.9

* In test series III PDD/PS collector ratio maintained at 3:1.

† Average of laboratory and pilot-plant test results.

Appendix 3

Feldspar upgrading techniques and results

	Procedure	Reagents consumed (original feed) kg/t			Analysis of feldspar concentrates, %						Feldspar recovered, %
					Feldspar components				Total feldspar	Fe$_2$O$_3$	
		NaOH	H$_2$SO$_4$	Collector†	Al$_2$O$_3$	K$_2$O	Na$_2$O	CaO			
Cleaner flotation	+ Grinding and recleaner float	—	0.81	0.52	18.1	10.7	2.5	0.55	87.1	0.72	85.0
		—	0.81	0.62	17.6	10.5	2.5	0.56	85.9	0.74	91.3
		—	0.85	0.56	17.9	10.6	2.5	0.47	86.1	0.71	88.8
	+ Scrubbing, desliming and recleaner float	0.6	0.65	0.23	18.1	10.8	2.6	0.53	88.4	0.56	88.0
		0.6	0.67	0.25	17.3	10.5	2.5	0.61	86.8	0.60	91.6
		0.6	0.67	0.24	18.0	10.8	2.5	0.59	87.9	0.58	89.9
	+ Acid leach, alkali scrub and recleaner float	0.6	13* + 0.6	0.16	18.6	11.3	2.7	0.34	89.9	0.18	88.7
		0.6	13* + 0.6	0.18	17.7	11.0	2.6	0.33	87.2	0.20	93.3
		0.6	13* + 0.6	0.17	18.4	11.1	2.7	0.40	89.0	0.19	91.7

* Estimated H$_2$SO$_4$ consumed for leaching assuming 6% moisture lost in filter cakes and reusing acid solution five times.

† Anionic/cationic collector ratio 10:1.

Appendix 4

Conditions and results of magnetic separation and acid leach

Feed	Unground feldspar (–600 μm) (0.6% Fe_2O_3)		Ground feldspar (–74 μm) (0.7% Fe_2O_3)	

Direct magnetic separation

Products	Stearns: 0.5 T, 1-mm gap		Sala: 0.9 T, 20 mm/s	
Non mags	0.28% Fe_2O_3		0.13% Fe_2O_3	
Magnetics	7.0% Fe_2O_3 (feldspar lost, 4.6%)		4.6% Fe_2O_3 (feldspar lost, 9.7%)	

Direct acid leach (% Fe_2O_3 in residues)

Time, h	H_2SO_4 (35% vol, 70°C, 1:1)	HCl (75% vol, 70°C, 1:1)	H_2SO_4 (35% vol, 70°C, 1:1)	HCl (75% vol, 70°C, 1:1)
1	0.30	0.18	0.27	0.22
2	0.27	0.16	0.24	0.18
4	0.22	0.16	0.21	0.16
6	0.21	0.16	0.19	0.15

Acid leach of non-magnetic fractions (% Fe_2O_3 in residues)

Time, h	H_2SO_4 (35% vol, 70°C, 1:1)	HCl (75% vol, 70°C, 1:1)	H_2SO_4 (35% vol, 70°C, 1:1)	HCl (75% vol, 70°C, 1:1)
1	0.16	0.12	0.070	0.057
2	0.14	0.11	0.066	0.051*
4	0.13	0.10	0.061	0.051*
6	0.12	0.10	0.056	0.046*

Magnetic separation of leach residues
(H_2SO_4: 35% vol, 70°C, 5 h and 1:1 s/l; Stearns: 0.5 T, 1-mm gap; grind –74 μm and Sala at 0.9 T and 20 mm/s)

Analysis, %	Feed	Scrub and float concentrate			Acid–alkali treatment and float concentrate		
		Leach residue	H-I Stearns, non-mags	HGMS Sala, non-mags	Leach residue	H-I Stearns, non-mags	HGMS Sala, non-mags
Fe_2O_3	0.60	0.20	0.12	0.080	0.19	0.12	0.078
TiO_2	0.11	0.076	0.05	0.025	0.074	0.04	0.028
MgO	0.25	0.10	0.06	0.04	0.06	0.04	0.04
Feldspar lost, %		1.5		7.2	—	1.3	7.4

1:1 = solid/liquid ratio.
* Porcelain grade.

Appendix 5

Pilot-plant layout for sand benefication

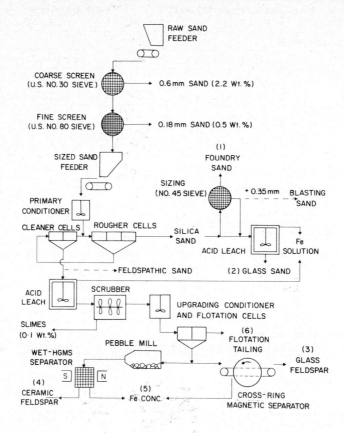

Appendix 6

Pilot-plant production of foundry sand, glassmaking quartz and feldspar of glass and ceramic grades

Flotation, leaching, grinding and magnetic separation conditions
(feed rate, 70 kg/h, dry basis)

Operation	Time, min	Dilution % solids	Reagents, kg/t				
			H_2SO_4	PS	PDD	pH_i	pH_f
(1) Feldspar flotation							
Rougher conditioning	8	60	1.0	0.10	0.45	1.8	2.2
Rougher flotation	2	28_i–24_f	0.7	—	—	2.2	2.3
Cleaner flotation	1	15_i–6_f	0.4	0.01	0.03	2.3	2.4
Akali scrubbing		75	(0.6 NaOH)			13.6	13.4
Upgrading conditioning	5	60	0.25	—	0.08	2.1	2.3
Upgrading flotation	1	25_i–8_f	0.10	—	—	2.3	2.6

(2) Acid leach (quartz and feldspar) 35% H_2SO_4, 70°C, 6 h and 1:1 s/l

(3) H-I Stearns (dry) magnetic separation, 0.5 T, 1-mm gap

(4) Pebble-grinding, 4 x 40 min to 100% –74 μm

(5) Sala HGMS (wet) magnetic separation, 1.3 T, 24 mm/s

Weight and analysis of products

Products		Wt %	Silica		Total feldspar	Analysis, % Feldspar components			Oxides				
			Quartz	SiO_2		Al_2O_3	K_2O	Na_2O	CaO	Fe_2O_3	MgO	TiO_2	LOI
Quartz	Foundry	41.8	98.5	99.3	1.2	0.26	0.09	0.05	0.1	0.10	0.1	0.03	0.2
	Glass	41.8	99.0	99.6	0.8	0.18	0.06	0.03	0.01	0.026	0.05	0.02	0.1
Feldspar	Glass	4.3	8.2	67.3	91.1	18.3	11.2	2.7	0.41	0.11	0.04	0.04	0.4
	Ceramic	4.3	7.6	67.1	91.8	18.4	11.3	2.7	0.43	0.07	0.04	0.03	0.3
Flotation middling		3.8	82.6	92.6	16.7	4.1	1.7	0.7	0.15	0.14	0.09	0.09	0.7
Fe conc (magnetics)		1.2	16.7	64.6	79.4	17.8	9.5	2.4	0.66	3.2	1.3	1.0	1.9
Wastes (+0.6 mm, –0.18 mm and slimes)		2.8	81.2	69.3	23.6	5.1	2.0	0.8	1.10	1.5	1.7	0.7	2.1
Feed (calc)		100.0	88.8	95.1	10.9	2.27	1.26	0.34	0.13	0.15	0.13	0.06	0.3
Feed (assay)		—	89.0	95.0	10.1	2.16	1.13	0.30	0.16	0.23	0.15	0.05	0.4

Material balance, %

Products	Wt%	Quartz	Feldspar	Al_2O_3	K_2O	Na_2O	CaO	Fe_2O_3	MgO	TiO_2	LOI
Quartz (foundry and glass)	83.6	92.9	7.6	8.1	5.0	9.7	36.4	36.0	47.2	35.5	47.6
Feldspar (glass and ceramic)	8.6	0.8	71.9	69.4	76.5	67.9	28.5	5.3	2.6	5.1	11.4
Flotation middling	3.8	3.5	5.8	6.8	5.1	7.6	4.5	3.6	2.6	5.8	10.1
Fe conc (magnetics)	1.2	0.2	8.7	9.4	9.0	8.4	6.2	26.3	11.8	20.4	8.6
Wastes (+0.6 mm, –0.18 mm and slimes)	2.8	2.6	6.0	6.3	4.4	6.4	24.4	28.8	35.8	33.2	22.3

Effect of alkyl substituents on performance of thionocarbamates as copper sulphide and pyrite collectors

P. K. Ackerman, G. H. Harris, R. R. Klimpel and F. F. Aplan

Synopsis

The floatability of chalcopyrite, chalcocite, bornite, covellite and pyrite has been evaluated by use of a series of thionocarbamates containing variations in the *N*-alkyl and *O*-alkyl substituent groupings. Both recovery and rate criteria were used to evaluate the effectiveness of these collectors. As a crude approximation, the collector strength may be represented by the total number of carbon atoms in both the *N*- and *O*-alkyl groups, but the introduction of iso groupings in the *N*-alkyl position and unsaturation in both groupings leads to decreased collector effectiveness. Both the separate and the overall influence of the *N*- and *O*-alkyl substituents on steric accessibility, electron density and hydrophobicity of the adsorbed collector must be considered when their influence on collector performance is evaluated.

The order of the decreasing mineral floatability with thionocarbamate collectors is chalcocite $\geq$ chalcopyrite $>$ bornite $>$ covellite $\geq$ pyrite. Approximately the same order has previously been found with other thiol collectors, except that bornite and covellite are generally floated more easily with the thionocarbamates. All of the copper sulphides are floated easily with the thionocarbamates, many of them in both acidic and alkaline solutions. Use of the *O*-ethyl grouping leads to greater floatability of pyrite than does the *O*-isopropyl grouping.

This paper is a part of a continuing study into the effectiveness of various collectors for the common copper sulphide minerals and pyrite with both flotation recovery and rate as criteria of merit. Previous work by Aplan and his associates on coal systems[1,2,3] and by Klimpel and his colleagues on copper and taconite systems[4,5,6] has shown that changes in the reagent system can and often do cause significant differences in the time–recovery profiles associated with flotation.

In our previous studies of thiol collectors for copper sulphides and pyrite we found that the rate of flotation can be a powerful tool in assessing differences in collector performance that might otherwise not be apparent from the recovery criteria alone.[7,8,9] It was demonstrated that a simple first-order rate equation may be used to characterize the floatability of the bulk of the floatable material during micro-flotation. With the copper minerals chalcopyrite, chalcocite, bornite and covellite, and pyrite, the flotation effectiveness of common sulphhydryl collectors (xanthates, dixanthogen, dithiophosphate, xanthogen formate and a thionocarbamate (Z-200), and colloidal electrolyte-type collectors (carboxylic acids, sulphate, amine and glyoxalidine) have been studied[7,8,9] Further, our studies have shown that the optimal hydrocarbon chain length for a xanthate collector to obtain maximum flotation recovery and rate for a given mineral represents a balance between solubility of the xanthate, solubility of the mineral, rate of formation of dixanthogen, semiconductor type, abstraction of xanthate by metal ions and preferred hydrophobic species, among other factors.[9]

Thionocarbamate collectors probably function by forming a chelation complex with the mineral cation. The first reference to the use of chelating agents for flotation collectors was by Gutzeit,[10] who noted that compounds that form ring structures with metal ions might also be used as flotation reagents. Others[11-17] have since recognized that reagents used in analytical chemistry to precipitate or chelate metal ions in solution might also work as flotation collectors. One of these reagent classes, the dialkyl dithiocarbamates, $[R_2NC(S)SNa]$, has been used extensively in analytical chemistry for precipitation of metals as highly insoluble complexes,[18] possibly by forming stable four-membered rings.[19] Their potential for use as sulphide collectors is well known owing to their similarity in structure and chemical properties to the alkyl xanthates, but their use has probably been restricted because of their relatively higher production costs.[20]

A related series of compounds, the dialkyl thionocarbamates, $[RNHC(S)OR]$, has been used since the 1950s as a flotation collector—specifically for copper sulphides[21]—under the trade names Dow Z-200 [*N*-ethyl-*O*-isopropyl] and Minerec 1331 [*N*-methyl-*O*-butyl].[22] The effectiveness of these reagents as selective collectors for sulphides is evidenced by their effectiveness as a copper sulphide collector and their relative effectiveness for the rejection of pyrite. The dialkyl thionocarbamates have been shown by Glembotskii[16] to selectively extract certain metal ions, i.e. Co(I,II), Ag, Hg(II) and Au(III), but not Fe, Zn, Co or Ni, and to float chalcopyrite preferentially to pyrite.

Background

It has been observed previously[9,13,23,24] that, for xanthate and similar collectors, variation of the length of the alkyl chain substituent altered the flotation behaviour and contact angle of the various minerals tested. Gaudin and Sorenson[23] demonstrated that for the flotation of chalcocite the best recovery occurred with *n*-heptyl xanthate (C_7), the following alkyl xanthate groups floating the mineral in decreasing order: *n*-nonyl (C_9), iso-amyl (C_5), *n*-propyl (C_3), ethyl (C_2) and methyl (C_1).

Wark and Cox[24] showed the dependence of the contact angle on the nature of the alkyl group of the collector with xanthates and several other sulphhydryl collectors on sulphides. The contact angles of the C_4, C_5 and C_8 iso-alkyl xanthates were found to be consistently higher than their corresponding *n*-alkyl xanthates. This would appear to indicate that iso-alkyl groups adsorb differently than the *n*-alkyl groups. Wark and his associates[13,24] also noted that when the collector contains two different R groups, i.e. methyl phenyl and ethyl phenyl dithiocarbamates, the smaller group apparently determines the angle of contact. This would appear to indicate that the two R groups act differently in the system.

Ackerman and co-workers[9] noted in the micro-flotation of certain copper sulphides and pyrite that with increasing *n*-alkyl chain length of the xanthates a minimum in the concentration necessary to achieve 50% recovery existed between amyl (C_5) and octyl (C_8) xanthate. With iso-alkyl xanthates it was observed that the advantage of using an iso-alkyl group over the corresponding *n*-alkyl group disappeared beyond about C_3 or C_4. It is interesting to note that the flotation results with the iso-alkyl groups are not in accord with the contact angle data cited above in which the iso-amyl grouping would appear to be superior to its *n*-alkyl form: this is quite possibly related to the problem of solubilizing the reagents in the flotation cell owing to their differing solubilities.

Harris[25] compiled a listing of the solubilities of *n*-alkyl and iso-alkyl xanthates and noted that the iso-alkyl xanthates up to iso-butyl (C_4) are less water-soluble than are the comparable *n*-alkyl xanthates. It would be expected that as the solubilities of these reagents decrease, up to some certain point, their ability to confer hydrophobicity to the mineral, and hence collector strength, would increase. Considering that the thionocarbamates have two alkyl substituents, it would seem reasonable that varying the chain length and branching of either substituent would have an even more pronounced effect than in the xanthate system.

Bogdanov *et al.*[26] found by use of infrared spectroscopy that dialkyl thionocarbamates chemisorbed on to chalcopyrite and pyrite to form four- or five-membered chelates of the type shown in Fig. 1. They also identified *O*-butyl-*N*-ethyl thionocarbamate present in molecular form on pyrite at pH 6.3 and 10.2.

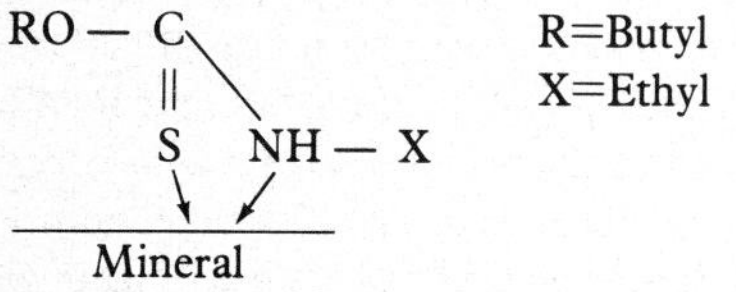

Fig. 1   Chemisorption of dialkyl thionocarbamate on mineral surface

Glembotskii[16] and, more recently, Nagaraj[17] discussed the preference of thionocarbamates for copper ions over iron ions following Pearson's principle of hard and soft acids and bases, i.e. hard acids bind strongly to hard bases and soft acids bind strongly to soft bases.[27] According to Glembotskii,[16] minerals can also be divided into hard and soft acids based on their adsorptive capacity, the copper in chalcopyrite being a soft acid and the iron in pyrite a hard acid.

The heteroatoms (O, S and N) in the thionocarbamates, however, belong to different groups in terms of donor capacity, O and N being the hardest and S the softest base.[27] Glembotskii[16] determined the atom with the greatest reactive capacity to be the S, followed by O and N. He also showed that the sulphur atom has a much greater steric accessibility (for coordination by a metal). The sequence for steric accessibility of the heteroatoms is in the same sequence as that of reactive capacity (S>O>N). Therefore, according to Pearson's principle, the dialkyl thionocarbamates should react with the ions of metals that would preferentially form a strong coordinate bond with sulphur, i.e. the soft acids.[16] Glembotskii[16] has shown that the dialkyl thionocarbamates actively float chalcopyrite (containing copper, a soft acid) in the presence of pyrite (containing iron, a hard acid). Since changing the electron density on the reactive centre of the reagent should alter the strength and selectivity of its collector effect on minerals,[16] any alkyl or aryl substituent change should affect the performance of the collector.

Bogdanov *et al.*,[26] Glembotskii[16] and Bogdanov *et al.*[28] have already noted the effect of replacing the *N*-alkyl substituent of thionocarbamates with aryl substituents on the flotation recovery and collector adsorption of, principally, chalcopyrite and pyrite. They found that by increasing the electron density on the reagent centre (by replacing the *N*-alkyl group with a phenyl or benzyl group) the strength of the collector increased, but the selectivity against pyrite decreased.[16]

It is the purpose of this study to evaluate the effect of various *N*-alkyl and *O*-alkyl substituents on the collector effectiveness of dialkyl thionocarbamates for the copper sulphide minerals—chalcopyrite, chalcocite, bornite and covellite. An evaluation of the effect of these alkyl substituents on the selectivity of the reagent between the copper sulphides and the gangue sulphide mineral, pyrite, is also made.

Experimental materials and methods

Minerals
The minerals that were used in this study—chalcopyrite ($CuFeS_2$), chalcocite (Cu_2S), bornite (Cu_5FeS_4), covellite (CuS) and pyrite (FeS_2)—were obtained from Ward's Natural Science Establishment, Rochester, New York. They were analysed chemically and spectroscopically to determine the approximate composition and the impurities present. All the minerals, except for the bornite, were 95% or greater in purity; the bornite sample contained about 5% quartz and ~15% of what is believed to be digenite.[7]

Reagents
The dialkyl thionocarbamates that were used were approximately of 95% or higher purity and are listed in Table 1. The reagents were supplied by the Walnut Creek facility of the Dow Chemical Corporation from a prior commercial study, and they were synthesized by or made under the direction of one of the present authors (G.H.H.).

Experimental apparatus and procedure
Flotation testing was done with the micro-flotation cell made from a 150-cm^3 porous frit funnel and previously described by Fuerstenau.[29] Pre-purified commercial tank nitrogen was passed through a gas train to ensure the elimination of any oily contaminants that might be present. pH was monitored continually with an Orion model 801A pH meter. Froths were removed continuously with a glass microscopic slide and collected in increments of 20, 40 and 120 s.

Micro-flotation tests were performed on the various minerals

Table 1   Reagents used in this study

Reagent name	Formula	Abbreviation
N-methyl-*O*-ethyl thionocarbamate	$CH_3NHC(S)OCH_2CH_3$	*N*-Me-*O*-Et
N-ethyl-*O*-ethyl thionocarbamate	$CH_3CH_2NHC(S)OCH_2CH_3$	*N*-Et-*O*-Et
N-isopropyl-*O*-ethyl thionocarbamate	$(CH_3)_2CHNHC(S)OCH_2CH_3$	*N*-IP-*O*-Et
N-butyl-*O*-ethyl thionocarbamate	$CH_3(CH_2)_3NHC(S)OCH_2CH_3$	*N*-Bu-*O*-Et
N-isobutene-*O*-ethyl thionocarbamate	$CH_2C(CH_3)CH_2NHC(S)OCH_2CH_3$	*N*-IBe-*O*-Et
N-dihydro-*O*-isopropyl thionocarbamate	$H_2NC(S)OCH(CH_3)_2$	*N*-H_2-*O*-IP
N-methyl-*O*-isopropyl thionocarbamate	$CH_3NHC(S)OCH(CH_3)_2$	*N*-Me-*O*-IP
N-isopropyl-*O*-isopropyl thionocarbamate	$(CH_3)_2CHNHC(S)OCH(CH_3)_2$	*N*-IP-*O*-IP
N-propene-*O*-isopropyl thionocarbamate	$CH_2CHCH_2NHC(S)OCH(CH_3)_2$	*N*-Pe-*O*-IP
N-propyne-*O*-isopropyl thionocarbamate	$CHCCH_2NHC(S)OCH(CH_3)_2$	*N*-Py-*O*-IP
N-methyl-*O*-isobutyl thionocarbamate	$CH_3NHC(S)OCH_2CH(CH_3)_2$	*N*-Me-*O*-IBu

with the different collectors at a constant concentration of 1×10^{-5} M/1, prior testing having shown this concentration to be favourable for differentiation between various thiol collectors.[7,30] For each collector and mineral the flotation tests were run at three set pH values (5.0, 8.5 and 10.5). The latter two values represent most of the current industrial preference, whereas the former pH would be desirable to minimize lime usage in a flotation plant. More details on this procedure may be found elsewhere.[7,30] Based on previous results and innumerable test replications, the recoveries obtained were found to be accurate within about 2%.

Rate measurement and calculation

Generally speaking, flotation rate has not been measured, *per se*, in most laboratory collector studies—instead, only flotation recovery at a fixed time is recorded. This gives only one point on the time–recovery profile, other than the origin, and only the grossest indication of flotation rate. Previous investigators have apparently assumed that differences in collectors of comparable type do not influence the time rate recovery of mass from the cell in any major way. It has been shown, however, for micro-flotation laboratory testing,[7,8,9] and in coal,[1,2,3] in copper and in taconite ore systems,[4,5,6] that changes in reagents can, and often do, show significant changes in the flotation time–recovery profiles.

The use of both the flotation recovery and rate criteria allows a better evaluation to be made of proposed collector mechanisms since, for example, a high rate and high recovery would indicate that reactions are occurring rapidly in comparison with a low rate and a high recovery.

Since the flotation recovery has been shown to be linear over the first 40 s in the system under study[7] a first-order equation of the following form was used to characterize the initial flotation rate. The equation used is

$$\text{First-order flotation rate constant, min}^{-1} = \frac{2.303 \left[\begin{array}{l} \log \text{wt\% rem.} \\ \text{in cell at } T_1 \end{array} - \begin{array}{l} \log \text{wt\% rem.} \\ \text{in cell at } T_2 \end{array} \right]}{T_1 - T_2} \quad (1)$$

where time is given in minutes.

For convenience the rate constant, K, was determined by equation 1 and the ultimate recovery, R_∞, taken as that recovery obtained after a relatively long flotation time for this system (2 min). In spite of the limitations of this procedure, the rates so calculated agree reasonably well with those calculated by the more sophisticated formula of Klimpel.[4]

The overall efficacy of a given reagent at the fixed concentration of 1×10^{-5} M/1 for each of the five minerals at pH 5.0, 8.5 and 10.5 may be quickly assessed from Table 2. These data are extracted from the more comprehensive data of Figs. 1–11 of the Appendix. To facilitate the data presentation the following arbitrary criteria were developed, based on preliminary testing, to rank the collector effectiveness:

Ranking	Recovery % R_∞	Symbol	Flotation rate constant, min^{-1} K	Symbol
Poor	0.0– 50.0	☐	0.0–0.5	○
Intermediate	50.0– 90.0	◨	0.5–2.0	◑
Good	90.0–100.0	■	2.0+	●

The flotation rate (Table 2) is often a more sensitive method of discriminating between collectors than is the recovery criterion alone. The rate criterion is especially helpful in discerning a superior collector when two collectors may show the same high recovery of a mineral. For example, the flotation of chalcopyrite at pH 5 with *N*-butyl-*O*-ethyl (Fig. 3 of Appendix) and *N*-isopropyl-*O*-ethyl (Fig. 4 of Appendix) shows

that although both collectors give high recoveries, the former is better on the basis of the rate criterion. The faster-floating reagent would require a smaller number of flotation cells, and in some cases less reagent would be required to achieve an equivalent recovery.

To ensure that all possible interactions among the reagents, minerals and pH values were accounted for an analysis of variance was performed.[31] This statistical analysis supported the observations made in the text regarding the various possible interactions, i.e. that there is a significant difference between various reagents and between the copper sulphides and pyrite in flotation recovery.

Results and discussion

The thionocarbamates have two different alkyl substituents—one attached to the nitrogen and the other to the oxygen in the molecule. It would seem logical that each alkyl group should have a different effect on the ability of the reagent to act as a collector. Differences in the ease of adsorption, for steric reasons, would be expected to result in differences in conferring hydrophobicity to a mineral. These same differences should also result in differences in selectivity between minerals owing to the different positions occupied by each alkyl group in the molecule relative to the reactive grouping. To study the effect of different alkyl chain lengths and branching on the different heteroatoms in the molecule the *O*-alkyl substituents were held constant and the *N*-alkyl groups were varied, and then the *N*-alkyl group was held constant and the *O*-alkyl group was varied.

Table 2 was developed to assist in the assessment, at a glance, of both the recovery and the rate results for 11 reagents, five minerals and three pH values. The format is similar to that employed in previous papers,[7,8,9] so comparisons with other reagents used on the same minerals and at the same pH values are also facilitated. The basic information for this paper is presented in the diagrams given in the Appendix. Because of the problems that are involved in presenting the large amount of data this method of presentation was adopted to allow the reader to evaluate both the general data trends and the specific results.

Effect of varying *N*-alkyl substituent chain length

Figs. 1–3 of the Appendix demonstrate that as the *N*-alkyl substitute is changed from methyl (C_1) to ethyl (C_2) to butyl (C_4) while the *O*-alkyl grouping is held constant, the flotation recoveries and rates increase continually. (In comparing these diagrams it is suggested that the reader concentrate on the effect of reagent change on one mineral and at one pH at a time. The effect of increasing chain length on the flotation of pyrite is especially pronounced.)

The effect of changing the *N*-alkyl grouping is more conveniently seen by re-plotting the recovery and rate data for the *O*-alkyl thionocarbamates (Figs. 1–5 of Appendix) as a function of the total alkyl chain length (both *N*- and *O*-alkyl groups) (see Fig. 2). A regular increase in both flotation recovery and rate is observed as the length of the *N*-alkyl chain is increased at either pH 5 or 10.5, except for the *N*-isopropyl and *N*-isobutene groups. Flotation rates generally follow recoveries (i.e. high recoveries give high rates, low recoveries low rates), but as the recoveries approach 100%, differences between collectors for the various minerals are best distinguished by the rate criteria. The effect on increasing the *N*-alkyl chain length is as expected in that increasing the alkyl chain length should increase the collector strength—as a result of (1) the increased electron-donating effect of a longer alkyl chain[32] on the reactive grouping, which should strengthen the collector–mineral bond, and (2) the greater insolubility of the reagent, which, on adsorption, should result in a more hydrophobic coating on the mineral.

Table 2 Simplified recovery and rate data for flotation of copper sulphides and pyrite with dialkyl thionocarbamates

Reagents: Dialkyl Thionocarbamates	Chalcopyrite ($CuFeS_2$) pH 5.0		pH 8.5		pH 10.5		Chalcocite (Cu_2S) pH 5.0		pH 8.5		pH 10.5		Bornite (Cu_5FeS_4) pH 5.0		pH 8.5		pH 10.5	
N-Methyl-O-Ethyl	■	◒	⬓	◒	□	○	⬓	◒	⬓	◒	□	○	■	◒	■	◒	⬓	◒
N-Ethyl-O-Ethyl	■	◒	⬓	◒	⬓	◒	■	●	⬓	◒	⬓	◒	⬓	◒	⬓	◒	⬓	◒
N-Isopropyl-O-Ethyl	■	◒	⬓	◒	⬓	○	■	●	⬓	◒	⬓	◒	⬓	◒	⬓	◒	⬓	◒
N-Butyl-O-Ethyl	■	●	■	●	■	●	■	●	■	●	■	●	■	●	■	●	■	●
N-Isobutene-O-Ethyl	■	●	■	◒	⬓	◒	■	●	■	●	■	●	■	●	■	●	⬓	●
N-Dihydro-O-Isopropyl	⬓	○	□	○	□	○	⬓	◒	□	○	□	○	□	○	□	○	□	○
N-Methyl-O-Isopropyl	■	●	■	◒	⬓	◒	⬓	◒	⬓	◒	⬓	◒	■	●	⬓	◒	⬓	◒
N-Isopropyl-O-Isopropyl	■	●	■	◒	⬓	◒	■	●	■	●	■	●	■	●	■	●	■	●
N-Propene-O-Isopropyl	■	●	⬓	◒	⬓	◒	■	●	⬓	◒	⬓	◒	⬓	◒	⬓	◒	⬓	◒
N-Propyne-O-Isopropyl	⬓	◒	□	○	□	○	⬓	◒	□	○	□	○	⬓	◒	□	○	□	○
N-Methyl-O-Isobutyl	■	●	■	◒	■	●	■	●	⬓	◒	⬓	◒	■	●	⬓	◒	⬓	◒

Reagents: Dialkyl Thionocarbamates	Covellite (CuS) pH 5.0		pH 8.5		pH 10.5		Pyrite (FeS_2) pH 5.0		pH 8.5		pH 10.5	
N-Methyl-O-Ethyl	⬓	◒	⬓	○	□	○	□	○	□	○	□	○
N-Ethyl-O-Ethyl	⬓	◒	⬓	◒	⬓	◒	⬓	○	⬓	○	□	○
N-Isopropyl-O-Ethyl	⬓	◒	⬓	○	□	○	□	○	□	○	□	○
N-Butyl-O-Ethyl	■	●	■	●	■	◒	⬓	◒	⬓	◒	⬓	○
N-Isobutene-O-Ethyl	■	●	■	●	■	●	⬓	◒	⬓	◒	⬓	○
N-Dihydro-O-Isopropyl	⬓	◒	⬓	◒	□	○	□	○	□	○	□	○
N-Methyl-O-Isopropyl	⬓	◒	⬓	◒	⬓	◒	□	○	□	○	□	○
N-Isopropyl-O-Isopropyl	⬓	◒	■	●	■	●	□	○	□	○	□	○
N-Propene-O-Isopropyl	■	◒	■	◒	■	◒	□	○	□	○	□	○
N-Propyne-O-Isopropyl	□	○	□	○	□	○	□	○	□	○	□	○
N-Methyl-O-Isobutyl	■	●	■	●	■	●	⬓	◒	⬓	◒	⬓	○

Ranking	Recovery % R_∞	Symbol	Flotation Rate (min^{-1}) K	Symbol
poor	0.0- 50.0	□	0.0-0.5	○
intermediate	50.0- 90.9	⬓	0.5-2.0	◒
good	90.0-100.0	■	2.0+	●

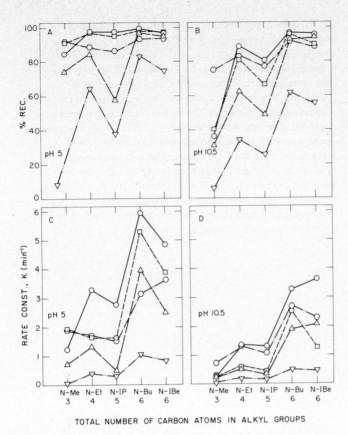

Fig. 2 Flotation of copper sulphides and pyrite with *N*-substituted-*O*-ethyl thionocarbamates:

A, *C*, recovery and rate data at pH 5.0; *B*, *D*, recovery and rate data at pH 10.5 (□ chalcopyrite; ○ chalcocite; ◯ bornite; △ covellite; ▽ pyrite)

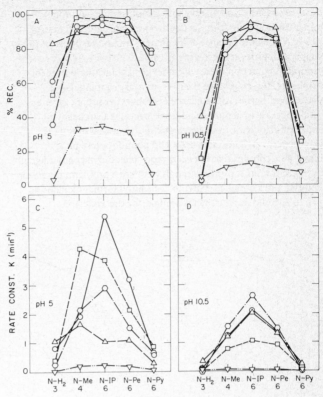

Fig. 3 Flotation of copper sulphides and pyrite with *N*-substituted-*O*-isopropyl thionocarbamates:

A, *C*, recovery and rate data at pH 5.0; *B*, *D*, recovery and rate data at pH 10.5 (□ chalcopyrite; ○ chalcocite; ◯ bornite; △ covellite; ▽ pyrite)

It might be expected that if an isopropyl (C₃) group were to be substituted in the *N*-alkyl position, the flotation rate and recovery would fall between that of the *N*-ethyl (C₂) and *N*-butyl (C₄) group. Comparison of the data in Fig. 2 or Figs. 2–4 of the Appendix for a given mineral at a given pH shows, however, that instead of the values for the *N*-isopropyl (C₃) group lying intermediate to those of the *N*-ethyl and *N*-butyl groups they are actually less than those for the *N*-ethyl group. A similar, though less severe, fall in floatability occurs when the *N*-isobutene grouping is substituted for the *N*-butyl form.

It is believed that the structure of the *N*-isopropyl group and, to a lesser extent, the *N*-isobutene group (Fig. 11 of Appendix) limits the accessibility of the nitrogen to participate in attachment to the copper (or iron) atoms on the mineral surface (see Fig. 1). In the thionocarbamate molecule the sulphur is, however, still the most accessible and most reactive atom, but for chelate ring formation the nitrogen must also be accessible. For the *N*-isopropyl and *N*-isobutene groups the methyl groups in these iso-alkyl groupings are closer to the nitrogen atom than the corresponding methyl group in the straight-chain form, forming a bulky group that limits the accessibility of the nitrogen to participate in the formation of the desired chelate ring.

The same sort of pattern may be seen for a series of *N*-alkyl substituents with *O*-isopropyl thionocarbamates: this is shown in Fig. 3, extracted from the primary data of Figs. 6–10 of the Appendix. Based on the total number of carbon atoms in the two alkyl groupings (except the triple-bonded propyne) the recovery values at pH 5 for the *O*-isopropyl form (Fig. 3) are roughly equivalent to those of the *O*-ethyl form (Fig. 2), except for pyrite, the floatability of which is decreased when the *O*-isopropyl grouping is used instead of the *O*-ethyl grouping. The flotation rates, however, show the very pronounced effect that the *N*-alkyl groups and unsaturation have on flotation. At pH 10.5 the *O*-isopropyl grouping appears to confer greater

selectivity (as indicated by a lower recovery of pyrite) than does the *O*-isopropyl grouping for comparable total alkyl carbon content. As before, use of *N*-iso-alkyl or unsaturated *N*-alkyl groupings floats pyrite less well than does the *O*-ethyl grouping of a comparable carbon content.

The superior floatability conferred on the minerals as a result of the greater number of carbon atoms in either the *N*- or *O*-alkyl groupings, or their total, is believed to be due to the decrease in solubility of the reagent with increasing carbon atom content. This provides a greater driving force to remove the reagent from water through adsorption on to the mineral and therefore increases the hydrophobicity of the collector coating.

The reagent Z-200 (approximately *N*-ethyl-*O*-isopropyl thionocarbamate) was also tested as a collector. Unfortunately, the reagent forms available to us contained impurities and so the data are not incorporated here with the pure thionocarbamate homologues. The reagent performed as might be expected by interpolation from Fig. 3,[7] except that the recoveries and rates for the copper sulphide minerals are slightly lower than would be expected. Surprisingly, however, selectivity against pyrite for the Z-200 is better than with other comparable thionocarbamates—possibly because Z-200 is not a pure thionocarbamate but a compositional mixture of isopropyl xanthate and ethyl amine.[21] The problems encountered in flotation testing with impure reagents, and this reagent in particular, will be detailed elsewhere.[33]

Effect of varying *O*-alkyl substituent chain length

Fig. 4 (based on Figs. 1, 7 and 11 of Appendix) shows that for the *N*-methyl form an increase in the number of carbon atoms in the *O*-alkyl grouping results in improved floatability. It is believed that short iso groupings are probably slightly better than their straight-chain analogues of comparable carbon content owing to their greater insolubility. Based on either recovery or rate data there is better discrimination between the copper sulphide minerals and pyrite with the *O*-ethyl grouping at pH 5 than at pH 10.5—mainly because of the better flotation response of the copper sulphides at the lower pH value. The two *O*-iso groupings confer on these collectors good collecting power for sulphides and, at least for the *O*-isopropyl grouping, good rejection of pyrite. Although the *O*-isobutyl grouping gives a small increase in copper sulphide recovery, it also causes a substantial increase in pyrite floatability over that of the *O*-isopropyl form. Thus, this latter compound represents a reasonable compromise between good collecting power and good pyrite rejection. If pyrite rejection were not a problem, the faster flotation rates obtained with the *O*-isobutyl form, especially at pH 10.5, could be a distinct advantage for this collector.

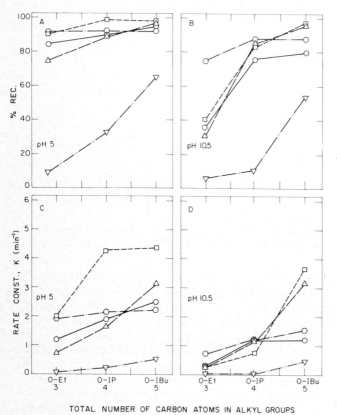

Fig. 4 Flotation of copper sulphides and pyrite with *N*-methyl-*O*-substituted thionocarbamates:
A, *C*, recovery and rate data at pH 5.0; *B*, *D*, recovery and rate data at pH 10.5 (□chalcopyrite; ○chalcocite; ◑bornite; △covellite; ▽ pyrite)

Comparison of Figs. 2 and 3 at either pH 5 or 10.5 demonstrates that the use of isopropyl grouping in the *N*-alkyl position decreases floatability in comparison with that of the straight-chain homologue in the *N*-alkyl position, but that the use of an isopropyl grouping in the *O*-alkyl position probably does not. Any decrease in floatability as a result of the use of an iso grouping in the *N*-alkyl position can be compensated by increasing the alkyl carbon content (i.e. substituting an *O*-isopropyl grouping for an *O*-ethyl grouping) (Figs. 4 and 8 of Appendix), or by increasing the collector concentration slightly. The substitution of an *O*-isopropyl grouping would also result in a decrease of pyrite floatability (Figs. 6–8 of Appendix) over that generally obtained with the O-ethyl forms (Figs. 2–5 of Appendix).

Unsaturation in *N*-alkyl substituent
From the data shown in Fig. 3 and Figs. 8–10 of the Appendix it will be noted that there is a decrease in the flotation recovery

when double or triple bonds are introduced into the *N*-alkyl substituent of thionocarbamates containing six carbon atoms. The decrease in recovery is slight (~10% for most of the copper minerals) when a double bond is introduced (*N*-propene), but substantial when the triple-bonded form (*N*-propyne) is considered. The rate reductions with these unsaturated forms are much more significant than the recovery decreases, particularly at pH 5.0. The increase in the unsaturation of the *N*-alkyl group causes a decrease in flotation rate and recovery for several reasons. For each degree of unsaturation in a carbon–carbon bond the bond length is shortened, which would make the molecule more soluble (cf. *N*-methyl with *N*-ethyl) and, hence, less hydrophobic. More importantly, the greater the degree of unsaturation the greater the number of electrons present to make the molecule more hydrophilic.

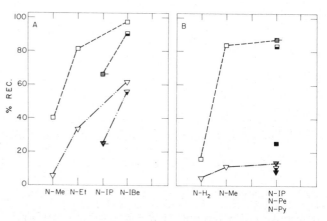

Fig. 5 Flotation recovery of chalcopyrite and pyrite with normal, iso and unsaturated *N*-alkyl groupings: *A*, *N*-substituted-*O*-ethyl groupings at pH 10.5; *B*, *N*-substituted-*O*-isopropyl groupings at pH 10.5 (□chalcopyrite; ▽ pyrite; □ ▽ normal alkyl; ■-▼ iso-alkyl; ▣ ▽ unsaturated, alkene; ■ ▼ unsaturated, alkyne)

Fig. 5 demonstrates the differences in collecting power for either chalcopyrite or pyrite between normal and iso-saturated and unsaturated *N*-alkyl groups. The differences among the *N*-isopropyl, *N*-propene and *N*-propyne groups with the *O*-isopropyl collector form should be noted. The decrease in recovery with the presence of the double bond is slight, but when the triple bond is present there is but little flotation.

Effect of pH
Reference to Figs. 1–11 of the Appendix shows that, in general, both recovery and rate decrease as the pH is raised for all the minerals at the collector concentration studied. The decrease is generally more pronounced for the rate than for the recovery criterion. The two evaluation criteria do not always follow in tandem as the pH is increased. At pH 5 little differentiation between the various copper sulphides can be seen with most of the reagents, but as the pH is increased to 10.5 differences between minerals and reagents become more pronounced.

Mineral differentiation
The data in Figs. 1–11 of the Appendix show that pyrite is almost always floated less well than any of the copper sulphide minerals. The four copper minerals float in a similar manner, though, on average, chalcocite and chalcopyrite are floated better than are bornite or covellite. The approximate order of mineral collection is chalcocite > chalcopyrite > bornite > covellite ≥ pyrite. This general sequence of mineral floatability is similar to that noted with other sulphydryl collectors (xanthate, dixanthogen, xanthogen formate or dithiophosphate): chalcocite ≥ chalcopyrite > covellite > bornite >> pyrite.[7] It is found,

however, that the flotation of covellite and, especially, bornite is generally much better with the thionocarbamates than with the other sulphydryl collectors. Covellite is seen to float significantly better than the other copper minerals only when the N-dihydro-O-isopropyl form is used (Fig. 6 of Appendix). The general order of floatability of the various minerals with a given collector does not generally change with pH and only in the case of covellite flotation with N-isopropyl-O-isopropyl thionocarbamate (Fig. 8 of Appendix) does the floatability go up from pH 5.0 to 10.5, though a few cases of a minimum in floatability at pH 8.5 are noted (see, for example, rate data for chalcopyrite in Fig. 11 of Appendix). If the goal is to float pyrite, it is reasonably well floated by the O-ethyl compounds—especially those of higher carbon content.

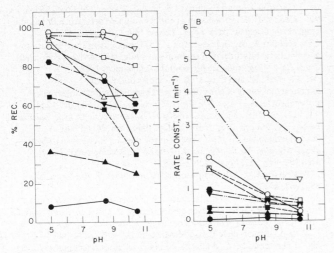

Fig. 6   Flotation recovery of chalcopyrite and pyrite with N-substituted O-ethyl thionocarbamates: open symbols chalcopyrite; filled symbols pyrite (○ N-methyl; □ N-ethyl; △ N-isopropyl; ○ N-butyl; ▽ N-isobutene)

Although most of the compounds tested float the copper sulphide minerals much better than they do pyrite, the O-isopropyl forms are generally seen to discriminate better between the copper sulphides, as a group, and pyrite than do the O-ethyl forms. This is more clearly seen in Figs. 6 and 7, where only the chalcopyrite and pyrite data are shown for the various thionocarbamates. Pyrite is much more poorly floated with the O-isopropyl than with the O-ethyl form. The di-isopropyl thionocarbamate (Fig. 7 and Fig. 8 of Appendix) is one of the

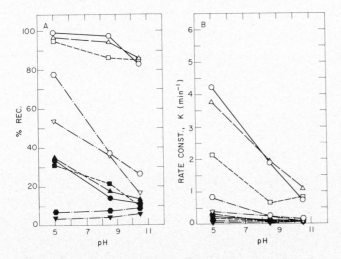

Fig. 7   Flotation recovery of chalcopyrite and pyrite with N-substituted O-isopropyl thionocarbamates: open symbols chalcopyrite; filled symbols pyrite (○ N-methyl; □ N-propene; △ N-isopropyl; ○ propyne; ▽ N-dihydro)

very best reagents for the discrimination of chalcopyrite and the other copper sulphides from pyrite based on both recovery and rate criteria. In addition, the N-methyl-O-isopropyl and N-methyl-O-ethyl compounds reject pyrite reasonably well (Figs. 6 and 7 and Figs. 1 and 7 of Appendix), though the latter does not float the copper minerals so well at pH 10.5. Although the recovery of the copper sulphides is approximately the same when thionocarbamates with the same total number of carbon atoms in both alkyl groupings are used (excepting when N-isopropyl-O-ethyl and N-propyne-O-ethyl are used), pyrite rejection is typically poorer when the longer N-alkyl substituents are used. In Fig. 6 it should be noted how high the recovery of pyrite is when N-butyl-O-ethyl is used in comparison with the use of N-isopropyl-O-isopropyl (Fig. 7). Comparison of the N-ethyl-O-ethyl with N-methyl-O-isopropyl forms shows this same pattern. The ability of the O-isopropyl forms to collect chalcopyrite and other copper sulphides in substantial preference to pyrite probably explains the popularity of the Z-200 (N-ethyl-O-isopropyl) collector. The loss of flotation rate in an alkaline medium, as opposed to an acidic medium, is compensated by a substantial decrease in the pyrite flotation rate.

When considering the choice of N-alkyl groups to achieve copper sulphide–pyrite selectivity one must consider not only the steric effects but the chain length of the group, owing to the electron-donating effect of alkyl groups. The longer the chain, the greater is the effect of the N-alkyl group on the reactive centre, decreasing the selectivity of the reagent against pyrite and increasing the reagent strength. No one effect totally determines how a given reagent will respond with a particular mineral as competing effects may occur in the same molecule, so care should be taken in the choice of substituents used in a reagent for the flotation of specific minerals.

Conclusions

(1) Both flotation recovery and rate are important criteria in the evaluation of collector–mineral systems.
(2) The adsorption and flotation performance of the thionocarbamates is influenced by the alkyl substituent groups, which control the hydrophobicity and steric accessibility of the reactive NCS grouping.
(3) As a crude approximation the collector strength of this class of collectors for copper sulphides and pyrite may be represented by the total number of carbon groups in both the O-alkyl and N-alkyl groupings. The introduction of iso groupings in the N-alkyl position and unsaturation in both groupings leads to decreased collector effectiveness.
(4) The O-alkyl group should have a slightly greater effect on hydrophobicity, whereas the N-alkyl group should control the accessibility of the reactive group to the mineral surface and the electron density of the reagent.
(5) With increasing unsaturation of the N-alkyl substituents the adsorbed reagent becomes less hydrophobic (more hydrophilic) as a result of shortening of bond lengths in the hydrocarbon chain and the increased presence of electrons associated with the unsaturation.
(6) The increasing length of the straight chain (hydrogen to butyl) of the N-alkyl substituent increases hydrophobicity, but causes little or no steric hindrance of the reactive grouping.
(7) The deleterious effect of an iso-alkyl group in the N-alkyl grouping on the accessibility to the mineral surface of the reactive NCS grouping is decreased by increasing alkyl chain length and, simultaneously, the surface hydrophobicity conferred by the adsorbed collector is increased.
(8) Owing to the steric hindrance of the reactive NCS grouping by the N-iso-alkyl groups when a straight-chain O-alkyl substituent is used, a straight-chain N-alkyl substituent is preferred. The disadvantage of an N-iso-alkyl substituent may

be obviated by the use of an O-iso-alkyl substituent.

(9) The insertion of an iso-alkyl group into the O-alkyl substituent confers, on adsorption on to the mineral, a greater hydrophobicity than does a straight-chain grouping of equal number as a result of the lesser solubility of an iso-alkyl grouping.

(10) In addition to the separate influence of N- and O-alkyl substituents on hydrophobicity, steric accessibility and electron density, the overall effect of both groupings must be considered, each, in its own way, exerting an influence on these factors.

(11) For an effective collector a balance must be sought in the alkyl groupings (either O- or N-) providing sufficient water solubility for ease of addition to the flotation system and adequate insolubility on adsorption to confer strong hydrophobicity. This situation can be achieved by altering the alkyl chain length and/or branching of the reagent.

(12) Greater differences in floatability between the various minerals and reagents are noted in alkaline than in acidic solutions. In acidic solutions the effect of the various N- and O-alkyl substituents is much less pronounced, many of the thionocarbamates being very effective collectors for the four copper minerals.

(13) In general, the copper minerals are floated much better than is pyrite at all three pH values, chalcocite being the fastest floating copper mineral, followed, in decreasing order, by chalcopyrite, bornite and covellite. Several of the reagents, most especially the O-isopropyl forms, show excellent selectivity between copper sulphide minerals and pyrite.

(14) If it is desired to float pyrite, the O-ethyl thionocarbamates would be attractive collectors, especially in acidic solutions.

Acknowledgement

This project is a part of a cooperative arrangement between Dow Chemical Company, Newmont Mining Corporation and The Pennsylvania State University. The authors wish to acknowledge the financial support received from The National Science Foundation to perform this work.

References

1. Aplan F. F. Coal flotation. In *Flotation: A. M. Gaudin memorial volume* Fuerstenau M. C. ed. (New York: AIME, 1976), 1235-64.
2. Rastogi R. C. and Aplan F. F. Coal flotation as a rate process. Paper submitted to *Trans. Am. Inst. Min. Engrs,* 1984.
3. Aplan F. F. Use of the flotation process for desulfurization of coal. In *Coal desulfurization* Wheelock T. D. ed. (Washington, D.C.: American Chemical Society, 1977), 70-82. (*ACS Symp. Series* 64)
4. Klimpel R. R. Selection of chemical reagents for flotation. In *Mineral processing plant design, 2nd edn* Mular A. L. and Bhappu R. B. eds (New York: AIME, 1980), 907-34.
5. Klimpel R. R. The engineering characterization of flotation reagent behaviour. In *Mill operators conference, North West Queensland Branch, 1982* (Parkville, Victoria: Australasian Institute of Mining and Metallurgy, 1982), 297-311.(*Symp. Series* 30)
6. Klimpel R. R. Froth flotation: the kinetic approach. Paper presented to *Mintek 50, Johannesburg, March 1984.* Paper A614.
7. Ackerman P. K. *et al.* Evaluations of flotation collectors for copper sulfides and pyrite: part I — common sulfhydral collectors. Paper submitted to *Int. J. Mineral Process.,* 1984.
8. Ackerman P. K. *et al.* Evaluations of flotation collectors for copper sulfides and pyrite: part II — non-sulfhydral collectors. Paper submitted to *Int. J. Mineral Process.,* 1984.
9. Ackerman P. K. *et al.* Evaluations of flotation collectors for copper sulfides and pyrite: part III — effect of xanthate chain length and branching. Paper submitted to *Int. J. Mineral Process.,* 1984.
10. Gutzeit G. Chelate-forming organic compounds as flotation reagents. *Trans. Am. Inst. Min. Engrs,* **169,** 1946, 272-86.
11. Ludt R. W. and deWitt C. C. The flotation of copper silicate from silica. *Trans. Am. Inst. Min. Engrs,* **184,** 1949, 49-51.
12. Last A. W. and Marquardson K. F. U.S. Patent 2 875 896, 1953.
13. Sutherland K. L. and Wark I. W. *Principles of flotation* (Melbourne: Australasian Institute of Mining and Metallurgy, 1955), 489 p.

14. Aplan F. F. and Fuerstenau D. W. Principles of nonmetallic mineral flotation. In *Froth flotation, 50th anniversary volume* Fuerstenau D. W. ed. (New York: AIME, 1962), 170-214.
15. Usoni L. Rinelli G. and Marabini A. M. Chelating agents and fuel oil: a new way to flotation. Paper presented at 1971 AIME annual meeting, New York, 1971. Paper no. 71-B-10.
16. Glembotskii A. V. Theoretical principles of forecasting and modifying collector properties. *Tsvet. Metally, Mosk.,* **51,** no. 5 1978, 86-9. (Russian text); *Tsvet. Metally, N. Y.,* **19,** no. 5 1978, 68-72.
17. Nagaraj D. R. Chelating agents in mineral processing. Paper presented at 1982 AIME annual meeting, Dallas, 1982.
18. Poling G. W. Reactions between thiol reagents and sulphide minerals. Reference 1, 334-63.
19. Zolotov Y. A. *Extraction of chelate compounds* (Moscow: Nauka, 1968), 313 p. (Russian text); Schmorak J. translator (Ann Arbor: Ann Arbor-Humphrey Science Publishers, 1970).
20. Leja J. *Surface chemistry of froth flotation* (New York, London: Plenum Press, 1982), 758 p.
21. Harris G. H. and Fischback B. C. U.S. Patent 2 691 635, 1954.
22. Crozier R. D. Processing of copper sulphide ores: froth flotation reagents — a review. *Min. Mag., Lond.,* **138,** April 1978, 332-9.
23. Gaudin A. M. and Sorenson P. M. Flotability of pure minerals and synthetic mixtures of pure minerals under standardized conditions. *Tech. Pap. Utah Engng Experimental Station* no. 4, 1928.
24. Wark I. W. and Cox A. B. Principles of flotation: I — an experimental study of the effect of xanthates on contact angles at mineral surfaces. *Trans. Am. Inst. Min. Engrs,* **112,** 1934, 189-244.
25. Harris G. H. Xanthates. In *Kirk–Othmer encyclopedia of chemical technology, 3rd edn* (New York: Wiley, 1984), vol. 24, 645-61.
26. Bogdanov O. S. *et al.* Trends in the search for effective collectors. *Tsvet. Metally, Mosk.,* **49,** no. 4 1976, 72-9. (Russian text); *Tsvet. Metally, N. Y.,* **17,** no. 4 1976, 79-85.
27. Pearson R. G. Hard and soft acids and bases. *J. Am. chem. Soc.,* **85,** 1963, 3533-9.
28. Bogdanov O. S. *et al.* Reagents chemisorption on minerals as a process of formation of surface compounds with a coordination bond. In *Proceedings of the 12th international mineral processing congress, 1977* (São Paulo, Brazil: D.N.P.M., M.M.E., 1982), vol. 2, 280-303.
29. Fuerstenau M. C. An improved micro-flotation technique. *Engng Min. J.,* **165,** Nov. 1964, 108-9.
30. Ackerman P. K. Evaluation of flotation collectors for copper sulfides and pyrite using rate and recovery criteria. M.S. thesis, The Pennsylvania State University, 1983.
31. Daubert N. C and Verity W. Analysis of variance, a statistical package program. The Pennsylvania State University Computation Centre, 1972.
32. Ingold C. K. *Structure and mechanism in organic chemistry* (Ithaca, N.Y.; London: Cornell University Press, 1969), 1275 p.
33. Ackerman P. K. Harris G. H. Klimpel R. R and Aplan F. F. The importance of reagent purity in the evaluation of flotation collectors. Paper in preparation.

Appendix

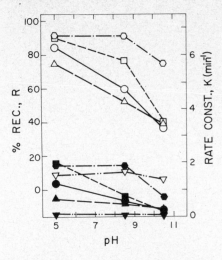

Fig. 1   Recovery and rate data for *N*-methyl-*O*-ethyl thionocarbamate (for Figs. 1-11 of Appendix open symbols = recovery and closed symbols = rate constant; □ chalcopyrite; ○ chalcocite; ◯ bornite; △ covellite; ▽ pyrite)

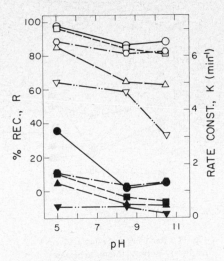

Fig. 2   Recovery and rate data for *N*-ethyl-*O*-ethyl thionocarbamate

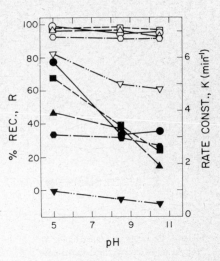

Fig. 3   Recovery and rate data for *N*-butyl-*O*-ethyl thionocarbamate

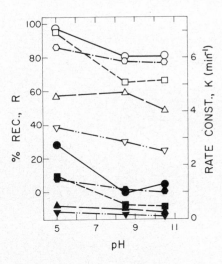

Fig. 4   Recovery and rate data for *N*-isopropyl-*O*-ethyl thionocarbamate

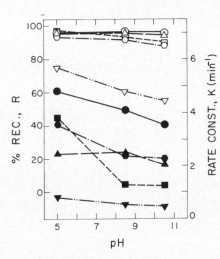

Fig. 5   Recovery and rate data for *N*-isobutene-*O*-ethyl thionocarbamate

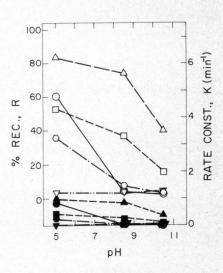

Fig. 6   Recovery and rate data for *N*-dihydro-*O*-isopropyl thionocarbamate

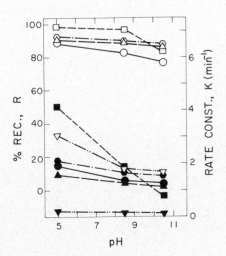

Fig. 7   Recovery and rate data for *N*-methyl-*O*-isopropyl thionocarbamate

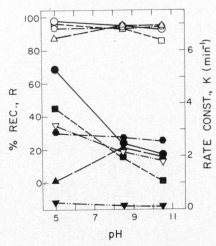

Fig. 8   Recovery and rate data for *N*-isopropyl-*O*-isopropyl thionocarbamate

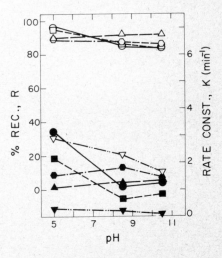

Fig. 9   Recovery and rate data for *N*-propene-*O*-isopropyl thionocarbamates

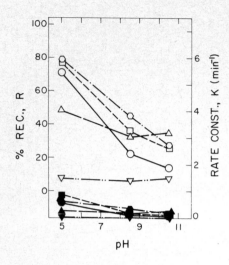

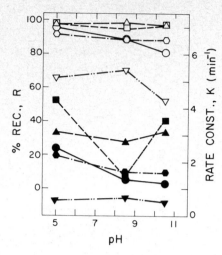

Fig. 10   Recovery and rate data for *N*-propyne-*O*-isopropyl thionocarbamate

Fig. 11   Recovery and rate data for *N*-methyl-*O*-isobutyl thionocarbamates

Spectroscopic study of potassium amylxanthate adsorption on finely ground galena: relations with flotation

M. Kongolo, J. M. Cases, A. Burneau and J. J. Prédali

Synopsis

Study of the poor recovery of galena achieved in the treatment of finely divided complex sulphides involved research into the surface properties of finely ground galena (<15 μm) and the collection of galena by potassium amylxanthate (KAX). Surface properties were studied before and after conditioning at pH 4, 8 and 11 and before and after Hallimond tube flotation. The Raman microprobe, infrared spectrometry and Fourier transform infrared spectrometry were used and the aqueous solutions were investigated—particularly by use of ultraviolet spectrometry.

The results show (1) the development of the composition of the surface phases with pH—lead sulphate and carbonate at acid pH and basic lead carbonate mainly at alkaline pH; (2) the presence of lead xanthate in multilayers and, in certain cases, of dixanthogen at collector concentrations in excess of 5×10^{-3} mole l^{-1}; and (3) the presence of a –PbAX surface complex at concentrations close to 10^{-3} mole l^{-1}.

The flotation of fines at alkaline pH appears to be activated by the presence of basic lead carbonate on the surface.

Galena recovery in the treatment of some finely disseminated complex sulphide ores is often difficult.[1] It would appear[2] that the poor recoveries are due to (1) the fact that the intimate mineralogical associations call for prolonged and costly grinding to enable liberation to be achieved—often only at sizes < 15 μm; (2) the coverage of the coarse pyrite grains by galena fines; and (3) the poor floatability of the fines. Flotation of galena fines in the Hallimond tube with potassium amylxanthate (KAX) becomes increasingly easier the higher the pH and with a collector concentration of at least 10^{-3} mole l^{-1}. For instance, for 5-μm particles obtained by wet grinding the pH of the collector solution must be not less than 10.7 for 100% recovery to be attained. Collector concentration, moreover, has to be at least five times greater than that needed to float particles in the range –104 + 74 μm.

In 1962 Greenler[3] used infrared spectra to study the collection of galena by ethylxanthate ions. He recognized various oxidation products on the surface of a fine precipitate of lead sulphide formed in such a way that the surface volume ratio was as large as possible. Depending on time, temperature and exposure to air, nitrogen, oxygen and carbon dioxide, the spectra were interpreted as characteristic of $PbCO_3$, $PbSO_4$, $PbSO_3$ and other compounds of unknown composition containing lead, sulphur and oxygen. After treatment with an 0.03 mole l^{-1} solution of potassium ethylxanthate (KEX) and filtration of the precipitate a compound was observed on the surface of the lead sulphide with the same spectrum as that of crystallized lead ethylxanthate $Pb(EX)_2$.[3] The quantity of xanthate remaining on the PbS surface after repeated washing with acetone was interpreted as a monolayer of xanthate ions bonded to the lead atoms by ion exchange. At the same time, Leja and co-workers,[4] by use of a technique that permitted examination of the infrared spectrum of a lead sulphide film deposited under vacuum, showed that the chemisorption of an oxygen monolayer was easily accomplished on the surface of the film to trap the electrons of the conduction band. Exposure to an additional quantity of oxygen caused the formation of PbS_2O_3 under the experimental conditions described. Immersion of this film in an aqueous solution of KEX at a concentration of 3×10^{-4} mole l^{-1} in the presence of oxygen was accompanied by the formation on the surface of $Pb(EX)_2$ multilayers that were characterized, in particular, by absorption towards 1210 cm^{-1}. The application of vacuum desorbed most of the three-dimensional compound and led to absorption at 1195 cm^{-1} attributed to a 1–1 complex between an atom of surface lead and a xanthate group of the first layer adsorbed, i.e.–PbEX. In the absence of oxygen the xanthate anions showed no affinity for the surface. Ethyldixanthogen, $(EX)_2$, however, was adsorbed under these conditions. The authors concluded that in the presence of oxygen the ethylxanthate anion oxidizes to ethyldixanthogen—a neutral species capable of being chemisorbed on the negatively charged surface of PbS on dissociation.

The electrochemical behaviour of a galena electrode studied by cyclic voltametry and electrolysed at controlled potential in a buffered medium reveals the presence, on the surface, of elemental sulphur and Pb^{2+} species, $Pb(OH)_2$ and $Pb(OH)Cl$, depending on the pH and the nature of the electrolyte.[5] In the presence of ethylxanthate and at pH 9–10 oxidation of the collector leads to the formation of ethyldixanthogen: the mechanism of the reaction is complicated by the adsorption of xanthate and dixanthogen.[6] In a basic oxidizing medium the dixanthogen is unstable and results in the formation of xanthate, monothiocarbonate and perxanthate ions.[7] The respective quantities of these ions depend largely on pH, the monothiocarbonate ion being unstable at close to neutral pH. The rate of decomposition of the dixanthogen at pH 9.1 is affected by the presence of nucleophilic ions, such as $S_2O_3^{2-}$, SO_3^{2-} and CN^-.[7] The xanthate ion, moreover, is unstable: at alkaline pH in the presence of dissolved oxygen, oxidation leads to the formation of monothiocarbonate[8] and at acid pH hydrolysis results in the formation of alcohol and carbon disulphide.[8,9,10]

From study of previous research it is clear that examination of the surfaces before and after adsorption of ethylxanthate has been limited to model media, microcrystalline precipitates, films deposited under vacuum and massive electrodes utilized in a buffered medium. To try to ascertain the mechanism that governs the collection of galena fines with KAX, and especially activation at alkaline pH, research has been undertaken to characterize the collector solutions and the surface states before and after flotation, classical and Fourier transform infrared and ultraviolet adsorption spectrometry and the Raman microprobe being employed.

Experimental

Materials

The galena that was used came from a mine in Kansas, U.S.A., and was supplied by Minemet Recherche. It contained the following impurities (ppm): 18 B, 12 Mn, 970 Sb, 351 Cu, 980 Ag, 318 Ba and 10 Bi, as well as traces of Al, Si, Mg and Fe. The material was dry-ground in an Abich mortar and the fractions

−210 +104 µm and −104 + 74 µm were obtained by sieving. The −15 and −5 µm fractions were obtained by grinding the −210 +104 µm fraction in an agate mortar. The particle size was checked by a Coultronics Sedigraph 5000 D. The particle-size fractions thus obtained were held in plastic bags without special precautions to prevent oxidation.

The flotation collector used was technical grade potassium *n*-amylxanthate (KAX) (Hoechst, Germany). The standards used for the spectroscopic studies were all Prolabo products of RP Normapur analytical grade, except for the diamylxanthogen, which was provided by the Mineral Processing Department of the BRGM, France, and the lead *n*-amylxanthate obtained by reaction in aqueous solution of stoichiometric quantities of potassium *n*-amylxanthate and lead acetate or nitrate, and Uvasol-quality hexane (Merck). The aqueous solutions were made by use of demineralized water of pH 5.7 and conductivity close to 1 µS. The gas used for flotation in Hallimond tube was compressed air (Air Liquide).

Apparatus and procedure

Flotation
The flotation tests were run in a Hallimond tube[11] with the use of 2 g of galena and 50 ml of collector solution during conditioning and 250 ml during flotation; conditioning time was 10 min and flotation time 1 min at a gas flow rate of 10 l h^{-1}. After flotation the products were dried both by draining under vacuum and by drying in the desiccator (also under vacuum).

Characterization of oxidation products by washing
To establish the nature and concentration of galena oxidation products that go into solution on contact with water various quantities of galena (−104 + 74 µm and −5 µm) were placed in 30 ml of demineralized water at pH 5.7 at 30°C and agitated by rotary stirring for 20 min, 24 h or 48 h. The lead present in the solution after separation of the solids by centrifugation (solution I) was then determined by atomic absorption.

Ultraviolet spectra
The ultraviolet spectra were recorded by a Beckman UV 5240 spectrometer, a slit width that varied from 0.02 to 0.05 nm and an absorbance sensitivity of 0.5, 1 or 2 full-scale units being used, starting from a solution in a 1-cm quartz cell. Because of parasitic light the spectrum is not very reliable at wavelengths shorter than 205 nm.

Infrared spectra
Most of the infrared spectra were obtained with a Perkin–Elmer 580 B spectrometer equipped with a data station. The slit width was about 4 cm^{-1}. The solid products in powder form were studied by transmission both in nujol mulls between CsI windows and in KBr pellets. The solid was ground in an agate mortar just before the spectra were obtained to decrease diffusion of infrared rays on the solid particles. The pellets were made by intimate mixing and grinding together of 2–3 mg of product and about 300 mg of KBr, followed by pressing at about 10 t cm^{-2}. The absorption between 950 and 1200 cm^{-1} of the Merck Suprapure potassium bromide used, although not very intense, prevented large absorbance scale expansion (this product may also be involved in ion-exchange reactions). For this reason nujol suspensions were often preferred. In this case the solid was included in the nujol before grinding, which was thus done in the absence of air. For comparison, the spectrum of a −5 µm galena sample was also obtained without grinding; here the surface species yield a spectrum at the same frequencies as the ground samples, but the quality is not as good.

The KBr or nujol spectrum was subtracted by normalizing absorbance by means of the weight of the pellet or of a nujol

absorption. Correction of the base line to decrease the contribution of the scattering was done, when necessary, by use of the Flat program of the Perkin–Elmer computer.

The spectra of some samples of galena were also obtained from their diffuse reflectance collected by the Harricks or Barnes accessories and analysed by Bruker IFS 110 or Nicolet 60 SX Fourier transform spectrometers. In this case the galena was used without additional grinding by mixing with KBr or KCl. The spectra then correspond to the ratio of reflectance of this sample to that of pure KBr or KCl.

Raman spectra
The spectra were recorded by means of a Raman effect Jobin Yvon Mole microprobe. Excitation was ensured by the 514.5-nm line of an argon laser and the slit width was about 4 cm^{-1}. The power used at the laser outlet is indicated in the key to the illustrations of the spectra. Frequency accuracy was around 5 cm^{-1}. Sensitivity is given and arranged in the diagrams in counts per second recorded by the photon counter: the smaller the number recorded, the greater is the sensitivity. The spectra were obtained by backscattering: the microscope serves both to focus the laser on an area measuring a few square microns and to collect the scattered light. For the galena samples the spectrum corresponds to a part of the surface of a single grain. The semiconductor properties of the galena cause absorption of the beam. To prevent the sample from becoming too hot it must be cooled or the incident power must be limited, which means a diminution in detection sensitivity. In some experiments the sample was cooled by placing it on a metal plate inside which circulated liquid nitrogen. This device was also used to obtain Raman spectra of solid lead *n*-amylxanthate (see Table 1). If the sample is at the ordinary temperature, it decomposes rapidly under the laser beam.

Results and discussion

Oxidation state of galena: influence of pH on conditioning

Surface study by vibration spectrometry
Galena has a fundamental transition above 200 cm^{-1}: the infrared and Raman spectra, obtained from finely divided galena, therefore characterize the ionic species that appear on the surface of the grains as a result of oxidation.

Figs. 1 and 2 illustrate the diffuse reflectance spectra of unconditioned −5 and −15 µm galena grains obtained with infrared Fourier transform spectrometers. They very clearly

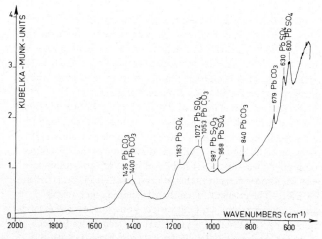

Fig. 1 Diffuse reflectance infrared Fourier transform spectrum of −5 µm galena before conditioning (Bruker IFS 110 spectrometer with Harricks accessory) (KBr reference; resolution, 2 cm^{-1}; 200 scans; measurement time, 200 s)

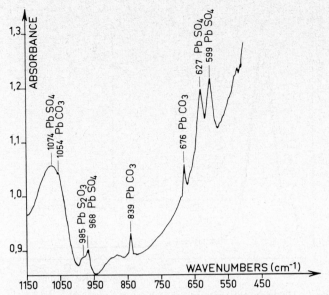

Fig. 2 Diffuse reflectance infrared Fourier transform spectrum of −15 μm galena before conditioning (Nicolet 60 SX spectrometer with Barnes accessory) (KBr reference; resolution, 2 cm^{-1}; 800 scans; measurement time, 635 s)

include the absorptions characteristic of lead sulphate at about 597, 631, 967, 1055 and 1171 cm^{-1} and of lead carbonate at about 678, 839, 1053, 1401 and 1432 cm^{-1}.[12] A shoulder at about 982 cm^{-1} could also be due to the presence of a small quantity of lead thiosulphate. This technique is thus particularly suitable for the study of the surface state of galena, giving results that are in complete agreement with those obtained much more laboriously by the classical infrared spectrometry procedure with the use of nujol mulls or KBr pellets (Fig. 3). The scattering of the infrared rays, the intensity of which varies with the wave number, makes it difficult to subtract the base line and, consequently, to identify broad bands of low intensity. On the other hand, the absorption peaks are little affected by the diverse weightings made to achieve this subtraction: for instance, the 3a spectrum, obtained by starting from a nujol mull with the same galena as in Fig. 1, has absorptions at about 597 and 631 cm^{-1}, 680 and 839 cm^{-1}, which characterize the presence of PbSO$_4$ and PbCO$_3$.

Fig. 3 also illustrates how conditioning influences the surface state of the galena. The quantity of lead carbonate relative to that of lead sulphate increases greatly with alkaline conditioning (pH 11, curve c) compared with that at pH 4 (curve b), as is shown by the four absorption peaks noted above. It is also evident that for the lead carbonate the relative intensity of the signal at 839 cm^{-1}

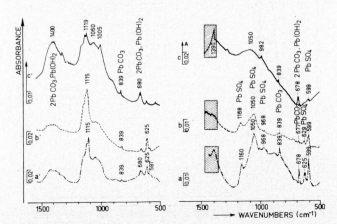

Fig. 3 Infrared absorption spectra of −5 μm galena: (a, a') before conditioning; (b, b') conditioned at pH 4.0; (c, c') conditioned at pH 11.0; (a, b, c) and (a', b', c') spectra, respectively, from nujol mulls and KBr pellets, after subtracting nujol and KBr absorption

decreases with increase in pH as a result of the formation of basic lead carbonate, 2PbCO$_3$.Pb(OH)$_2$.[12]

Nujol absorption makes the galena spectrum uncertain towards 1400 cm^{-1}. The spectra of galena in KBr pellets are therefore presented in parallel in Fig. 3 (curves a', b' and c'). These confirm the preceding observation, the broad band that characterizes PbCO$_3$ at about 1400 cm^{-1} being much more intense after conditioning in an alkaline medium (curve c') than in an acid medium (curve b'). On curve c' the intensities for 839 and 680 cm^{-1} also testify to the presence of basic lead carbonate. It should also be observed that the main absorption of the spectrum of KBr-pelleted galena is towards 1106 cm^{-1}, which is no longer characteristic of lead sulphate but, rather, of potassium sulphate owing to an exchange of ions with the matrix on the surface of the galena grains.

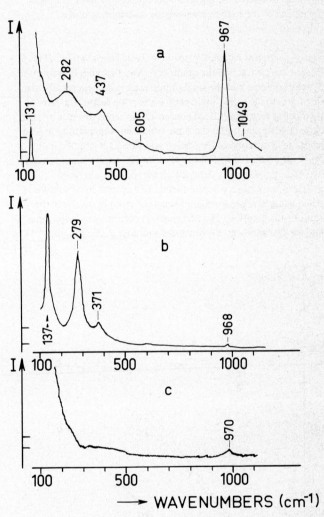

Fig. 4 Raman microprobe spectra from galena microcrystals (a) dry-ground, −104 +74 μm galena conditioned at pH 8.0 (T, −175°C; laser 0.4 W; 16 384 counts s^{-1} full scale*); (b) dry-ground, −104 +74 μm galena before conditioning (T, 20°C; laser 0.3 W; 4096 counts s^{-1} full scale*); and (c) freshly split galena (T, 20°C; 1024 counts s^{-1} full scale*)

Fig. 4(c) shows the Raman microprobe spectrum of a flake of freshly split monocrystalline galena: there is no band above 120 cm^{-1}, notwithstanding the considerable sensitivity that was used to record it. This spectral region will therefore be characteristic of surface changes. By way of example, the spectrum of galena conditioned at pH 8 has lines towards 135, 290, 437, 605, 967 and 1049 cm^{-1} (Fig. 4(a)). Comparison of curves a and b shows that these signals do not all correspond to the same chemical species, spectrum b having lines only towards

* Ordinate unit one-tenth of full scale.

135, 280 and 370 cm^{-1} despite the fact that the sensitivity used for this spectrum was four times greater than that for a. The bands are therefore grouped in two sub-assemblies. 437, 605, 967 and 1049 cm^{-1} characterize the SO$_4^{2-}$ anion, the most intense line at 967 cm^{-1} corresponding to the symmetrical stretching vibration: it would appear to be probable that the band towards 1050 cm^{-1} can also be attributed to a vibration of the SO$_4^{2-}$ ion. This spectral region also corresponds to the symmetrical vibration of the CO$_3^{2-}$ ion, however, the detection of which could therefore be hindered. 135, 280 and 370 cm^{-1} are due to another chemical species, not yet identified, the concentration of which is not correlated with that of the SO$_4^{2-}$ ion. It is neither elemental sulphur nor one of the oxygenated anions SO$_3^{2-}$, S$_2$O$_3^{2-}$ or CO$_3^{2-}$.

Since each Raman spectrum was obtained through a microscope starting from an area of about 1 μm^2 it was also possible to observe the marked heterogeneity of the surface of the galena owing to the very irregular distribution of the sulphate.

Study of solutions obtained by washing the galena: solution I (Fig. 5)
For the coarse fraction the quantity of lead that goes into solution depends on time and the solid/liquid ratio used, whereas for the fine fraction the solid/liquid ratio is the main factor, the rate then being very rapid. Lead concentration tends towards a value close to 400 ppm, under the same conditions the quantity of lead from the dissolution of the PbSO$_4$ and PbS$_2$O$_3$ being 29 ppm (1.4 x 10^{-4} mole l^{-1}) and 130 ppm (6.3 x 10^{-4} mole l^{-1}), respectively. The fact that solubility depends on the solid/liquid ratio indicates the presence on the surface of a species more soluble than galena: this can perhaps be characterized by studying the equilibrium solution. The ultraviolet spectrum of solution I has intense absorption at 207 nm and a shoulder at 255 nm, the

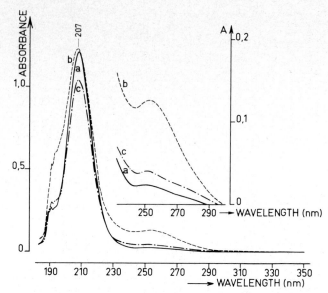

Fig. 6   Ultraviolet absorption spectra of wash waters from galena (*a*) –104 +74 μm (mixing time 60 min; lead concentration 21.6 ppm); (*b*) –5 μm (mixing time 10 min; lead concentration 40.9 ppm before dilution by 2); (*c*) –15 μm (mixing time 10 min; lead concentration 21.9 ppm; cell thickness 1 cm)

intensity depending on the sample of galena used but always being weak in comparison with its predecessor (Fig. 6). The 207-nm band is linked to the presence of Pb^{2+} and appeared with all the lead salts used (PbSO$_4$, Pb(CH$_3$CO$_2$)$_2$ and Pb(NO$_3$)$_2$). Only the thiosulphate ion has a relatively broad absorption towards 214 nm, the lead thiosulphate spectrum having a sub-peak at 255 nm (Fig. 7(*f*) and (*d*)). The shoulder at 255 nm in the solution I spectrum is therefore indicative of a variable quantity of thiosulphate, depending on the sample of galena used. Although the infrared spectrum indicates that the thiosulphate is a minority oxidation product in the samples examined, the relatively high solubility of this lead salt favours its dissolution. It is also observed that the shoulder at 255 nm is stronger in the equilibrium solution of the –15 μm material than on that finer than 5 μm. This fact tends to show that the surface concentration of thiosulphate is more important for the –15 μm material—which is also borne out by the diffuse reflectance spectra in Figs. 1 and 2.

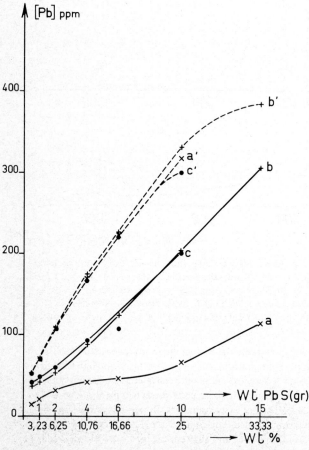

Fig. 5   Dissolved lead concentration versus galena weight introduced into 30 ml demineralized water (*T*, 20°C) (particle size: (*a, b, c*) = –104 +74 μm, (*a′, b′, c′*) = –5 μm; mixing time: (*a, a′*) 20 min; (*b, b′*) 24 h; (*c, c′*) 48 h)

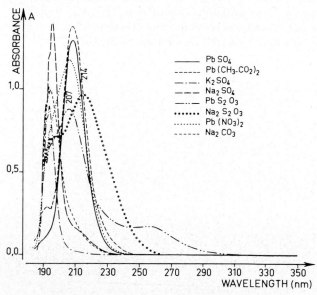

Fig. 7   Ultraviolet absorption spectra of reference aqueous solutions: (*a*) PbSO$_4$; (*b*) Pb(CH$_3$CO$_2$)$_2$; (*c*) Pb(NO$_3$)$_2$; (*d*) PbS$_2$O$_3$; (*e*) K$_2$SO$_4$; (*f*) Na$_2$S$_2$O$_3$; (*g*) Na$_2$CO$_3$ (cell thickness 1 cm)

Spectroscopic characterization of reagents used

Characteristic vibration frequencies

Table 1 summarizes the absorption and Raman diffusion wave numbers of potassium n-amylxanthate, n-amyldixanthogen and lead n-amylxanthate. This permits differentiation of the three compounds, especially with the aid of the values marked with an asterisk.

Table 1   Characteristic wave numbers (cm^{-1}) for potassium n-amylxanthate (KAX), n-amyldixanthogen $(AX)_2$, and lead n-amylxanthate $(Pb(AX)_2)$.

KAX		$(AX)_2$		$Pb(AX)_2$	
IR	R	IR	R	IR	R
	265		241		253
	363	320	303		346
	382		384	380	388*
	404				413
	448		436		
	495	480	483	485	495
509	514	504	504*		
		531			
	585	566			580
		650	(651)		645
	667*			662?	668*
		691	698		
743	751	732	739	725	
778	784	778	784		
	853	865	863		
	873	882			
	942	922		940	953
958	959	948	950		
976	983				
986	994			1005	
		1022		1021*	1017
	1049	1042	1054*		1044
1072*	1068			1063	1068
1090	1086				1077
		1121		1125	
1123	1137	1143	1131	1140	1139
	1171				1153
1210	1217	1210		1203	
		1230		1220*	
1250	1255	1260*	1271		
	1311		1309	1320	
	1356				
1380	1387	1380		1377	
1460	1446	1462	1447	1458	
1470			1464	1471	
		2290			
	2738	2510	2751		
2858	2863	2860	2865	2868	2863
2864	2887	2870	2878		2877
			2892		2901
2923	2915	2930	2906	2932	2939
2953	2935	2958	2946	2960	2955
	2963				2971

Purity of KAX

Curve b in Fig. 8 is the infrared absorption spectrum of the technical grade KAX that was used, curve a being that of the same reagent after purification. The technical product has additional absorptions at 530, 547, 670, 700, 835, 865, 885, 1006, 1026, 1220 and 1260 cm^{-1}. The group of wave numbers 1026, 1220 and 1260 cm^{-1} permits identification of the amyldixanthogen, the spectrum of which is given by curve c. Of the remaining wave numbers, several are close to those which characterize the $S_2O_3^{2-}$ ion (530, 547, 670 and 1006 cm^{-1}), and the 700 and 885 cm^{-1} pair could indicate traces of carbonate.[13] In line with the collector used it is therefore advisable to assume (1)

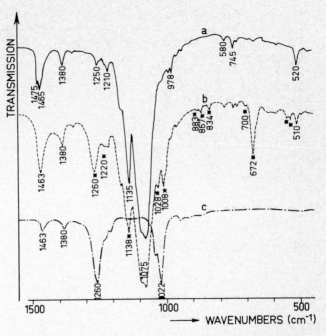

Fig. 8   Infrared absorption spectrum of (a) purified and (b) technical grade potassium n-amylxanthate in KBr pellets, and (c) of purified n-amyldixanthogen pure liquid film (asterisked peaks in spectrum (b) due to impurities)

partial oxidation to dixanthogen, which can be correlated with carbonation in accordance with the reaction[14]

$$2KAX + 1/2\,O_2 + CO_2 \rightarrow (AX)_2 + K_2CO_3$$

and (2) the presence of other impurities, such as a thiosulphate, which is not related, however, to the absorptions at 835 and 865 cm^{-1}. Impurities characterized by absorptions at about 540, 672, 835 and 1006 cm^{-1} also exist in the potassium amylxanthate (American Cyanamid AERO 350) used by Wilfong and Maust.[12]

The existence of a thiosulphate in the collector used would also explain the ultraviolet spectrum of an aqueous wash solution of lead xanthate obtained by precipitation starting from lead nitrate and technical grade KAX. The form of the spectrum closely resembles that of curve d in Fig. 7 (peak at 207 nm and shoulder characteristic of lead thiosulphate at 255 nm).

Study of galena collection by potassium n-amylxanthate

State of galena surface after collection

The infrared spectra of galena collected by flotation in solutions of variable concentrations of technical grade KAX were obtained both by transmission with a normal spectrometer (Figs. 9 and 10) and by diffuse reflectance by use of a Fourier transform spectrometer (Figs. 11, 12 and 13).

Fig. 9 shows that on the surface of galena freshly collected with a 0.1 mole l^{-1} solution of KAX (pH 10.8) (curve b) there is dixanthogen or perxanthate (absorptions at 1260 and 1023 cm^{-1}), lead xanthate, $Pb(AX)_2$, in multilayers (1220, 1125, 1023 and 1005 cm^{-1}), $PbCO_3$ (838 and 678 cm^{-1}) and traces of $PbSO_4$. The spectrum of crystallized lead xanthate is also shown for comparison (curve a). The dixanthogen could come from the technical grade xanthate used to prepare the solution. The proportion of this product decreases with time (curve c). Curve d illustrates the spectrum of galena collected some months earlier: the absorptions at 1745, 1715, 1260, 1135 and 1025 cm^{-1} characterize both dixanthogen and perxanthate,[15] whereas the 1190 and 1030 cm^{-1} bands correspond to a product that resembles lead xanthate but with a ν–COC frequency reduced from 1220 to 1190 cm^{-1}. According to Poling and Leja,[16] this

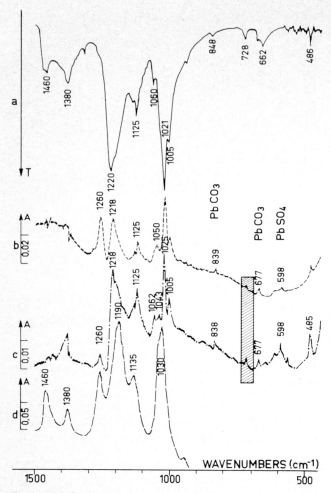

Fig. 9 (a) Infrared absorption spectrum of lead *n*-amylxanthate in KBr pellet; (*b, c*) absorption spectra of –5 μm galena collected with potassium *n*-amylxanthate (0.1 mole l⁻¹ solution, pH 10.8) in nujol mull after subtracting nujol absorption (time after flotation (*b*) 30 min, (*c*) 6 days); (*d*) absorption spectrum of KBr pellets with –15 μm galena collected two months earlier under same conditions as in (*b* and *c*) and kept in air

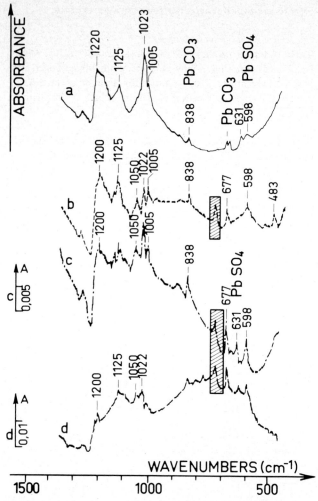

Fig. 10 Infrared absorption spectra of nujol mulls with –5 μm galena collected by flotation in potassium *n*-amylxanthate solutions (nujol absorption subtracted)

Spectrum	Concentration, mole l⁻¹	pH	Time after flotation
(*a*)	0.01	10.0	30 min
(*b*)	0.01	10.0	20 days
(*c*)	0.005	9.3	30 min
(*d*)	0.003	8.8	30 min

frequency shift permits differentiation of Pb(AX)₂ and –PbAX, which may correspond to a xanthate monolayer on the surface. The absorptions at 1745 and 1715 cm⁻¹ attributed by Jones and Woodcock[15] to perxanthate are characteristic more of a C=O than a C=S double bond.

In addition to PbSO₄ and PbCO₃, galena floated with a 10⁻² mole l⁻¹ KAX solution also has lead xanthate, Pb(AX)₂ (Fig. 10(*a*)), which trends towards –PbAX, with an absorption towards 1200 cm⁻¹ after 20 days (Fig. 10(*b*)). Immediately after flotation the proportion of dixanthogen is much smaller than that from an initial 10⁻¹ mole l⁻¹ KAX solution. Curves *c* and *d* permit evaluation of the detection limit with this first technique: collector solutions at KAX concentrations of 5 x 10⁻³ and 3 x 10⁻³ mole l⁻¹ permit flotation of a galena that still has the –PbAX spectrum. The adsorptions due to PbCO₃ and PbSO₄ become relatively more important than in the previous case, however, hindering detection of –PbAX starting from more dilute solutions.

With the second technique the diffuse reflectance spectrum of galena was obtained immediately after collection, followed by simple draining but involving no further grinding. Fig. 11 provides a comparison of the absorption spectra of –15 μm galena (*a*) before and (*b*) after collection with 10⁻² mole l⁻¹ KAX solution. Curves *c* in Figs. 11 and 12 were obtained by subtracting from spectrum (*b*) spectrum (*a*), weighted to eliminate the PbCO₃ band at 840 cm⁻¹ and, as far as possible, the overall contributions from the PbCO₃ and PbSO₄ remaining on the galena, to obtain the spectrum of the new surface species that

permitted flotation. Although elimination of all the signals characteristic of PbCO₃ and PbSO₄ may not have been achieved with the same normalization coefficient (negative bands at 600,

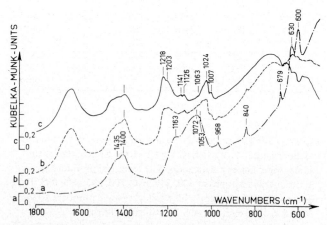

Fig. 11 Diffuse reflectance infrared Fourier transform spectra of –15 μm galena (*a*) before conditioning, (*b*) collected with potassium *n*-amylxanthate 0.01 mole l⁻¹, (*c*) weighted difference of spectrum *b* – spectrum *a* (KBr reference; resolution, 4 cm⁻¹; 1000 scans; measurement times, 1000 s; Bruker IFS 110 spectrometer with Harricks accessory)

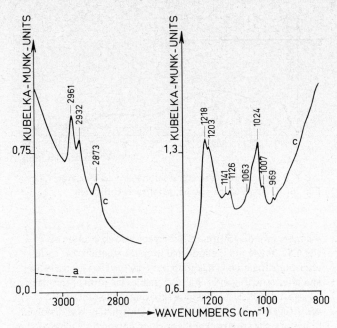

Fig. 12 Diffuse reflectance infrared Fourier transform spectra of $-15\,\mu$m galena collected with potassium n-amylxanthate (0.01 mole l^{-1}): (a) and (c) same spectra as in Fig. 11 with extended ordinate

630 and 679 cm^{-1} and positive bands at 1400 and 1435 cm^{-1} in curve c), the weighted difference spectrum confirms the formation of three-dimensional lead amylxanthate on the galena surface. This fact was also revealed by transmission spectroscopy, but the proposed technique is quicker and simpler. In Fig. 12 the weighted difference spectrum shows both the absorption of the skeleton and those of the CH stretching of Pb(AX)$_2$.

The same analytical method was applied to a galena floated with a 10^{-3} mole l^{-1} collector solution (Fig. 13). The difference spectrum here indicates very clearly the presence of the two

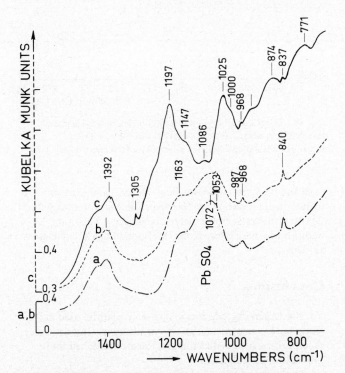

Fig. 13 Diffuse reflectance infrared Fourier transform spectra of $-15\,\mu$m galena: (a) before conditioning; (b) collected with potassium n-amylxanthate (10^{-3} mole l^{-1}); (c) weighted difference of spectrum b - spectrum a (KBr reference; resolution, 4 cm^{-1}; 1000 scans; measurement time; 1000 s; Bruker IFS 110 spectrometer with Harricks accessory)

absorptions characteristic of –PbAX at 1197 and 1025 cm^{-1}. It thus appears that this analytical technique permits detection of species on the surface of galena collected under experimental conditions close to those used for the flotation of galena fines.

During the course of numerous tests no molecule with the amyl group was detected by means of Raman microprobe spectra on the surface of galena collected by flotation. This is probably due to decomposition of the lead amylxanthate to lead sulphate under the laser, as has been observed with the pure product.

Composition of aqueous solutions after collection

Conditioning of galena with a KAX solution not only results in adsorption of collector on the surface but also gives rise to important parasitic reactions in solution. Examination of the ultraviolet spectrum of the solution reveals evidence of collector consumption. This phenomenon depends on time and on the particle size of the galena (Figs. 14 and 15).

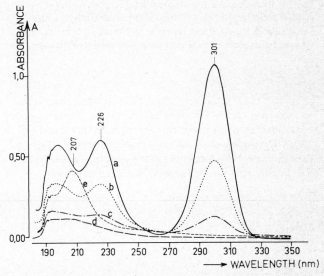

Fig. 14 Evolution with time of ultraviolet absorption spectra of aqueous potassium n-amylxanthate (10^{-4} mole l^{-1}) solution (30 ml) after mixing with –104 +74 μm galena (1 g): (b) 2 min; (c) 5 min; (d) 10 min; (e) 3 h; (a) before mixing (cell thickness, 1 cm)

Under the test conditions that were used consumption of collector is complete (disappearance of characteristic absorptions at 301 and 226 nm) after 10 min for a –104 +74 μm sample, a band then appearing at 207 nm owing to the dissolution of excess oxidation products. The same effect is obtained in less than 2 min with a –15 μm sample.

To ascertain the reasons for collector consumption other than by adsorption a study was made of the reaction in solution in the absence of galena. In this two-stage test the galena was first washed in water to give solution I; in the second stage increasing quantities of the solution were added to a solution of KAX. The ultraviolet spectrum of the mixture was recorded before and after centrifugation (Fig. 16(A) and (B), respectively). The absorption band of the xanthate ion at 301 nm decreases until it disappears between curves d and e, but a new absorption appears towards 240 nm, reaches a peak between curves d and e (Fig. 16(A)) and then decreases with mixtures f to i, where a third band at 207 nm, corresponding to the excess of solution I, becomes predominant.

These observations indicate a 1:2 stoichiometric reaction between the Pb^{2+} and AX$^-$ ions, the mixtures (d to e) containing twice as many of the latter as of the former. The reaction product is thus Pb(AX)$_2$. This interpretation is confirmed by a number of observations associated with the fact that PB(AX)$_2$ is insoluble

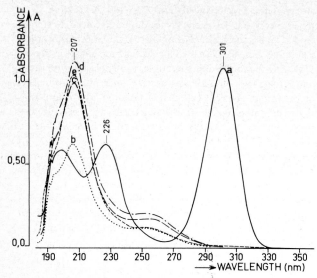

Fig. 15 Evolution with time of ultraviolet absorption spectra of aqueous potassium 10^{-4} mole l^{-1} solution (30 ml) after mixing with $-15\,\mu$m galena (1 g): (b) 2 min; (c) 5 min; (d) 10 min; (a) before mixing; (e) absorption spectrum of $-15\,\mu$m galena wash water (cell thickness, 1 cm)

$(K_s = 10^{-24})$.[2] (1) Before centrifugation the mixture contains a suspension of crystals that cause light scattering. The absorbance corresponding to this scattering was suppressed to obtain Fig. 16(A). The particle-size distribution curve determined by a Coulter model N4 sub-micron particle analyser reveals crystal size distribution between 100 and 250 nm and an average

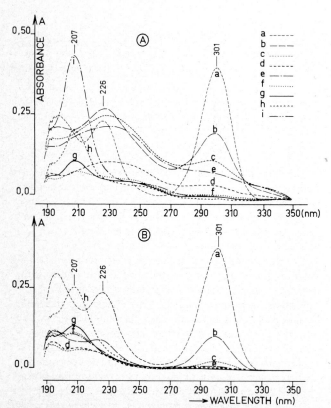

Fig. 16 Ultraviolet absorption spectra of galena wash water and potassium n-amylanthate (KAX): (A) before centrifugation (arbitrary absorbance subtracted from spectra displaying scattering); (B) after centrifugation. Concentrations before reaction (μmole l^{-1}): KAX, 29.5 (calculated from ultraviolet spectrum with extinction coefficient given by Pomianowski and Leja[14]); Pb^{2+}: (a) 0: (b) 9.2; (c) 11.5; (d) 13.8; (e) 16.1; (f) 18.4; (g) 23; (h) 32.2; (i) 46; pH of mixture (a) 6.40; (b) 6.33; (c) 6.41; (d) 6.47; (e) 6.07; (f) 5.99; (g) 5.95; (h) 5.86; (i) 5.82 (cell thickness, 1 cm)

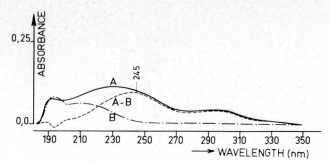

Fig. 17 Difference of ultraviolet absorption spectra of mixture (d) in Fig. 16 (A) before centrifugation; (B) after centrifugation

diameter around 150 nm. (2) Characteristic absorption of Pb(AX)$_2$ at 245 nm is eliminated from the solution spectrum after centrifugation. The difference between the spectra before and after centrifugation (Fig. 17) enables the form of this band to be ascertained. (3) The residue adhering to the tube after centrifugation and elimination of the supernatant was dissolved in hexane: the spectrum of the solution obtained then has all the absorptions characteristic of Pb(AX)$_2$ in hexane solution (Fig. 18).

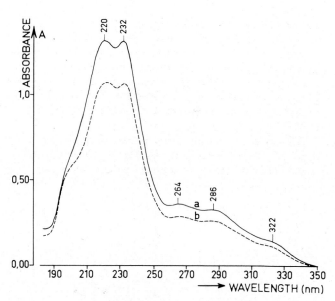

Fig. 18 Ultraviolet absorption spectra of (a) lead n-amylxanthate dissolved in n-hexane; (b) lead n-amylxanthate obtained after centrifugation and dissolution in n-hexane (cell thickness, 1 cm)

Before these tests were run there was some ambiguity in identifying the reaction product responsible for the absorption at 245 nm, which resembled that of dixanthogen. The study outlined here has indicated that this is solid Pb(AX)$_2$ in microsuspension.

Conclusions

(1) The technical grade potassium n-amylxanthate used in this study and in some mineral processing plants contains a number of impurities, such as dixanthogen, traces of carbonate and probably of thiosulphate.
(2) Under the grinding and storage conditions adopted for the galena used in the study the Raman and infrared spectra reveal marked surface heterogeneity and permit the certain identification of lead sulphate and carbonate on the surface before or after conditioning in an acid medium; the diffuse

reflectance spectra also reveal a very much smaller quantity of lead thiosulphate.

(3) Conditioning at pH 11 promotes the formation of a basic lead carbonate surface phase.

(4) The galena floated in a solution of potassium amylxanthate at a concentration greater than 5×10^{-3} mole 1^{-1} has multilayers of lead xanthate and, in some cases, dixanthogen on the surface. When exposed to air, these surface products tend to sublimate in time.

(5) At lower concentrations the infrared absorption of lead xanthate evolves in a way that permits characterization of the –PbAX monolayer at $1197 \, \mathrm{cm}^{-1}$. For the first time use of diffuse reflectance spectra has permitted the detection of this monolayer on galena fines collected by a 10^{-3} mole 1^{-1} potassium amylxanthate solution immediately after flotation and without additional treatment to obtain the infrared spectrum.

(6) Flotation of galena fines in the Hallimond tube is possible: (1) after the formation of the two-dimensional compound –PbAX (at collector concentrations around 10^{-3} mole 1^{-1}) and (2) with three-dimensional condensation of $Pb(AX)_2$. Other tests (not detailed in this paper)[1] show that the higher the pH, the easier is the flotation of galena fines. The formation of basic lead carbonate on the surface of galena fines appears to favour flotation.

(7) Under Hallimond tube conditions, and as a result of the solubility of the oxidation products, part of the collector is rapidly consumed in solution as $Pb(AX)_2$, which settles out readily in the presence of an excess of Pb^{2+} ions.

Acknowledgement

The authors would like to thank the Centre de Recherche sur la Géologie de l'Uranium (Nancy) for performing the Raman microprobe spectra; the Bruker and Nicolet companies for assistance with equipment; the EEC ('Raw Materials' Programme—Contract MSM 047 E); and the C.N.R.S. France (A.T.P. 'Economie des Matières Premières Minérales') for financial assistance.

References

1. Cases J. M. Finely disseminated complex sulphide ores. In *Complex sulphide ores* Jones M. J. ed. (London: IMM, 1980), 234–47.
2. Kongolo M. and Cases J. M. Valorisation des minerais sulfurés complexes finement divisés par flottation différentielle: amélioration de la récupération du plomb et de la qualité des concentrés. Compte-rendu de fin d'étude financée par la Commission des Communautés Européennes. Contract no. 02079 MPPF DG XII, 1982, 190 p.
3. Greenler R. G. An infrared investigation of xanthate adsorption by lead sulfide. *J. phys. Chem.*, **66**, 1962, 879–83.
4. Leja J. Little L. H. and Poling G. W. Xanthates adsorption studies using infrared spectroscopy. *Trans. Instn Min. Metall.*, **72**, 1962–63, 407–23.
5. Lamache M. Bauer D. and Pegouret J. Comportement électrochimique de la galène (PbS) dans les conditions de pH proches de celles de la flottation. *Electrochim. Acta*, **26**, 1981, 1845–50.
6. Huynh Thi O. Lamache M. and Bauer D. Comportement électrochimique de l'éthyl xanthate sur différents types d'électrodes: platine, or, galène, mercure. *Electrochim. Acta*, **26**, 1981, 33–44.
7. Jones M. H. and Woodcock J. T. Decomposition of alkyl dixanthogens in aqueous solutions. *Int. J. Mineral Process.*, **10**, 1983, 1–24.
8. Finkelstein N. P. Kinetic and thermodynamic aspects of the interaction between potassium ethyl xanthate and oxygen in aqueous solution. *Trans. Instn Min. Metall. (Sect. C: Mineral Process. Extr. Metall.)*, **76**, 1967, C51–9.
9. Granville A. Finkelstein N. P. and Allison S. A. Review of reactions in the flotation system galena–xanthate–oxygen. *Trans. Instn Min. Metall. (Sect. C: Mineral Process. Extr. Metall.)*, **81**, 1972, C1–30.
10. Klassen V. I. and Mokrousov V. A. *An introduction to the theory of flotation* (London: Butterworths, 1963), 235–46.
11. Cases J. M. Les phénomènes physicochimiques à l'interface: application au procédé de la flottation. Thèse d'Etat ès-Sciences Physiques, Nancy, 1967, 120 p. *Sciences Terre – Mémoire* no. 13, 1968, 120 p.
12. Wilfong R. L. and Maust E. E. Jr. Infrared spectra of compounds of importance in lead sulfide flotation. *Rep. Invest. U.S. Bur. Mines* 7963, 1974, 65 p.
13. Kazuo Nakamoto. *Infrared and Raman spectra of inorganic and coordination compounds, 3rd edn* (New York: Wiley-Interscience, 1977), 448 p.
14. Pomianowski A. and Leja J. Spectrophotometric study of xanthate and dixanthogen solutions. *Can. J. Chem.*, **41**, 1963, 2219–30.
15. Jones M. H. and Woodcock J. T. Perxanthates — a new factor in the theory and practice of flotation. *Int. J. Mineral Process.*, **5**, 1978, 285–96.
16. Poling G. W. and Leja J. Infrared study of xanthate adsorption on vacuum deposited films of lead sulfide and metallic copper under conditions of controlled oxidation. *J. phys Chem.*, **67**, 1963, 2121–6.

Flotation of sphalerite from pyrite by use of copper sulphate and sodium cyanide

M. Ghiani, F. Satta, M. Barbaro and B. Passariello

Synopsis

The results of systematic micro-flotation experiments conducted with the objective of establishing whether favourable conditions exist for the separation of sphalerite from pyrite by modulation of the action of xanthate with a combination of copper sulphate and sodium cyanide are reported. The findings of the study indicate that, by careful adjustment of the flotation pH and with the appropriate choice of dosage and molar ratio between copper sulphate and sodium cyanide, separation is possible.

In addition, an interpretation is given of the mechanism that governs the floatability of both minerals with varying pH and sodium cyanide/copper sulphate ratio.

Normal industrial practice for the flotation of zinc sulphide minerals involves the use of short-chain thio collectors after activation with copper sulphate.[1] When zinc sulphide is associated with pyrite or pyrrhotite in the crude ore selectivity is usually ensured by the high alkalinity (pH 10.7–12) of the pulp, preferably obtained with lime.[2,3]

Commercial experience has shown, however, that sphalerite–pyrite separation can also be achieved by use of the modulating action of copper sulphate in combination with soluble cyanide in a weakly alkaline pulp (pH 7.5–8). In the 'Sartori' plant of Monteponi mine, Sardinia, for instance, this technique has superseded the former, yielding considerable benefits in terms of reagents and even metal recovery in the beneficiation of a complex zinc ore with a high degree of pyrite contamination.[4]

Exactly how the sphalerite is recovered by this method in the froth without difficulty and in preference to pyrite is somewhat obscure.[5,6] Micro-flotation experiments[5,6] showed that, in the presence of copper sulphate, sphalerite flotation in neutral or weakly alkaline pulps is depressed significantly with respect to the response at higher acidity and alkalinity. Moreover, Steininger[5] also observed an analogous depressing effect on pyrite in the presence of copper sulphate.

This depression was attributed[5] to the formation in solution of copper–collector hydroxylated complexes, whereas Girczys and co-workers[6] interpreted the phenomenon as being due to the different reaction kinetics between xanthate and the activated mineral surface in relation to the different form in which, at various pH values, the copper is present.

It is difficult to understand *a priori* how sphalerite and pyrite can be successfully separated at weak alkalinity by use of such reagents. Nevertheless, evidence from the industrial process highlights the need to determine, first, the floatability of each mineral at various solution pH values and with different concentrations of reagents to establish whether conditions do exist for separation and, if so, to identify the optimum field of application, and, second, to elucidate the mechanism that underlies the selectivity of the possible separation.

A systematic investigation was made into the objectives outlined above. The present paper is concerned with the results of a series of micro-flotation experiments conducted to determine the floatability of the pure minerals under different operating conditions. The findings indicate that sphalerite–pyrite separation can be achieved with careful adjustment of the flotation pH and with the appropriate choice of dosage and molar ratio between copper sulphate and sodium cyanide. In addition, an interpretation of the mechanism that governs the flotation response of both minerals at different pH values and sodium cyanide/copper sulphate ratios is proposed.

Materials and methods

In the experiments discussed here pure potassium ethyl xanthate (prepared by K & K Laboratories, Inc., U.S.A.) served as collector and reagent grade $CuSO_4 \cdot 5H_2O$, NaCN and HCl and NaOH as modulating agents and pH modifiers, respectively. The pure sphalerite and pyrite minerals were hand-sorted from samples supplied by Lula, Sardinia, and Gavorrano, Tuscany, mines, respectively.

Table 1   Chemical composition of the minerals used in experiments

Contents	Sphalerite, %	Pyrite, %
Zn	58.18	0.11
Fe	5.68	46.80
Cu	0.057	–
Pb	0.77	–
S	27.41	52.86
iep	4.5	6.5

From the chemical composition given in Table 1 it can be seen that the sphalerite used in the experiments was somewhat marmatitic, but for simplicity it is termed sphalerite. The value of the isoelectric point, determined with a Mark II Rank Bros. electrophoresis apparatus, is also given. Samples of both minerals were prepared by dry grinding in a porcelain mortar and the products were sized to −100 +200 mesh (Tyler). Immediately prior to flotation a 1.05-g sample of each mineral was conditioned for 3 min in an ultrasonic bath containing distilled water to remove any fines that adhered to the particle surface, screened at 200 mesh and washed with 200 ml of distilled water. Distilled water was used throughout; 197 ml of copper sulphate and/or sodium cyanide solution was prepared and the pH was adjusted to the desired value. The sample was added to this solution and conditioned for 1 min; 3 ml of potassium ethyl xanthate solution was then introduced to ensure a concentration of 2.10^{-5} M. The system was conditioned for 2 min, the pulp then being transferred to the cell. Flotation time was 1 min and a constant air flow of 75 cm³/min was maintained. At the end of each test the pH of the solution, termed the flotation pH, was measured and the floated material was collected, dried and weighed. A Pyrex injection-type Hallimond tube and a Beckman model Century SS 1 pH meter were used in the experiments.

Results

Experiments were conducted on both the sphalerite and pyrite minerals to determine the floatability as a function of pH under the following conditions: without modulation of

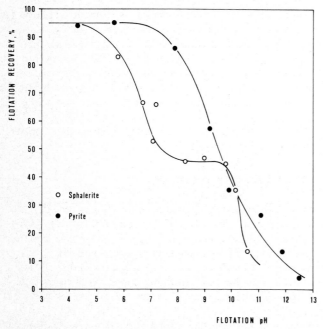

Fig. 1   Flotation recovery as a function of pH in presence of potassium ethyl xanthate (2×10^{-5} M)

collection, in the presence of sodium cyanide, in the presence of copper sulphate and in the presence of both sodium cyanide and copper sulphate.

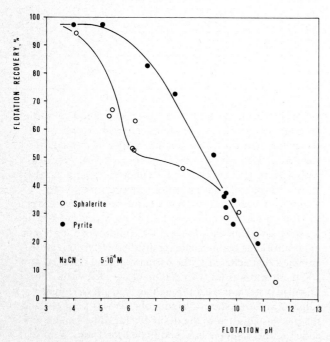

Fig. 2   Flotation recovery as a function of pH in presence of sodium cyanide (5×10^{-4} M) and KEX (2×10^{-5} M)

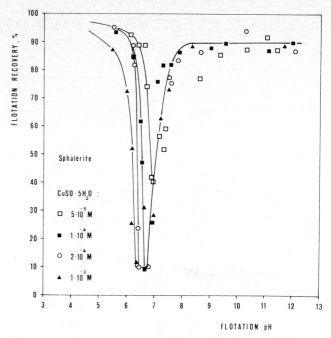

Fig. 3   Flotation recovery of sphalerite as a function of pH in presence of copper sulphate and KEX (2×10^{-5} M)

The flotation recovery of pyrite and sphalerite as a function of pH is shown in Fig. 1. Almost complete flotation of both minerals is obtained at acid pH, but recovery tends to decrease progressively with increasing pH values—almost linearly for pyrite and with a pronounced plateau for sphalerite at weakly alkaline pH.

Fig. 2 shows the effect of sodium cyanide at a concentration of 5×10^{-4} M on flotation response at various pH values. This reagent, as is well known, is a depressant of both minerals.

In Figs. 3 and 4 the variation in recovery of sphalerite and pyrite, respectively, is plotted as a function of pH and for various levels of addition of copper sulphate. At all $CuSO_4 \cdot 5H_2O$ concentrations tested the recovery of sphalerite, optimum at acid pH, decreased sharply at between pH 6 and 7. Above pH 7 recovery increased again,

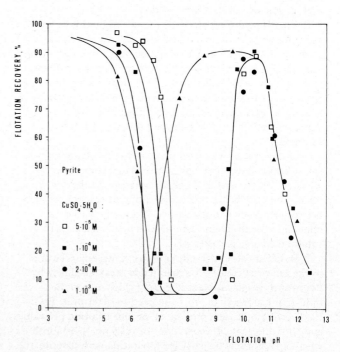

Fig. 4   Flotation recovery of pyrite as a function of pH in presence of copper sulphate and KEX (2×10^{-5} M)

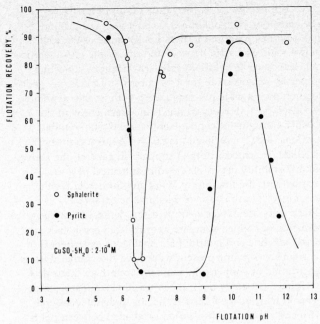

Fig. 5   Effect of pH on flotation recovery of sphalerite and pyrite in presence of copper sulphate (2×10^{-4} M) and KEX (2×10^{-5} M)

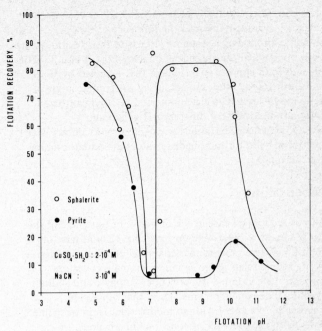

Fig. 7   Effect of pH on flotation recovery of sphalerite and pyrite in presence of copper sulphate (2×10^{-4} M), sodium cyanide (3×10^{-4} M) and KEX (2×10^{-5} M)

maintaining a constant high level in the alkaline range. The effect of variation in copper sulphate concentration seems to consist of a slight shift of the maximum depression point towards lower pH values with increasing concentrations.

By contrast, the corresponding curves for pyrite (Fig. 4) exhibit a different recovery pattern versus pH, at least for copper sulphate concentrations between 5×10^{-5} and 2×10^{-4} M. In regard to the latter, two regions of good flotation (pH < 6 and between 10 and 11) were observed, separated by the same number of depression regions.

For copper sulphate concentrations of the order of 10^{-3} M pyrite behaved akin to sphalerite.

The joint effect of copper sulphate and sodium cyanide was observed by varying concentrations between 5×10^{-5} and 10^{-3} M. The most significant data reported here are, in

fact, representative of the overall results obtained.

A comparison of the results obtained with pyrite and sphalerite is presented in Figs. 5–8 (2×10^{-4} M of $CuSO_4 \cdot 5H_2O$ and varying concentrations of NaCN). The results from the combined use of these reagents clearly depend on the molar ratio between the two: in particular, a substantial change in the flotation response of the two minerals is observed at sodium cyanide/copper sulphate concentration ratios higher than 3. At lower values cyanide alters the behaviour of activated sphalerite, inducing a drastic depression above pH 10.5. For pyrite, which already exhibits poor floatability in the absence of cyanide, at neutral or weakly alkaline pH, a further depression is observed throughout the range above pH 6.5, and the flotation achieved in the presence of copper sulphate alone

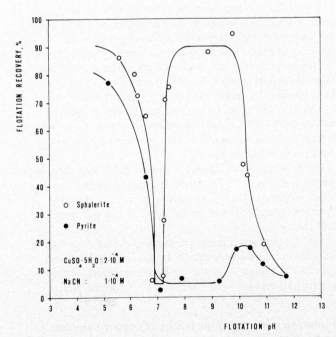

Fig. 6   Effect of pH on flotation recovery of sphalerite and pyrite in presence of copper sulphate (2×10^{-4} M), sodium cyanide (10^{-4} M) and KEX (2×10^{-5} M)

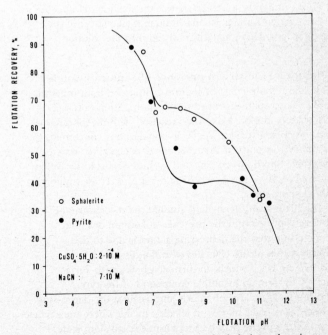

Fig. 8   Effect of pH on flotation recovery of sphalerite and pyrite in presence of copper sulphate (2×10^{-4} M), sodium cyanide (7×10^{-4} M) and KEX (2×10^{-5} M)

at pH 10–11 is effectively neutralized.

Excess cyanide minimizes the influence of copper sulphate, producing a response similar to those exhibited by both minerals in the absence of copper (Figs. 1 and 8). This phenomenon appears analogous to that reported by Wark and Sutherland,[7] who, by measuring the contact angle of copper-activated sphalerite immersed in ethyl xanthate solution, discovered at different pH values and $CuSO_4 \cdot 5H_2O$ concentrations an island of non-contact near neutral pH and for intermediate values of sodium cyanide concentration.

Discussion

As was mentioned earlier, the objective of this stage of the study sought to determine the existence or otherwise of conditions favourable to the separation of sphalerite from pyrite by modulating the action of xanthate collectors through the combined use of copper sulphate and sodium cyanide. The results obtained show that separation, impossible to achieve without modulation, is, in principle, possible in the presence of copper sulphate alone, in accordance with long-established industrial practice or in combination with sodium cyanide.

Variation of recovery with pH
It is well known that sphalerite and pyrite exhibit poor floatability with xanthates in the absence of an activator at neutral or alkaline pH. The iep of the sphalerite and pyrite samples used in the experiments were 4.5 and 6.5, respectively. Consequently, physical adsorption of the xanthate ion can be expected for both minerals at pH values lower than the iep where the surface is positively charged, whereas this is unlikely in alkaline media, where only chemisorption may take place. The data of Fig. 1 are in good agreement with these considerations. The plateau at pH 7–9.5 for sphalerite can be attributed to the presence of copper detected in the mineral (Table 1). In fact, in similar experiments on another copper-free sphalerite sample* a constant decrease in recovery was observed at alkaline pH—as for pyrite.

On the other hand, the different flotation response of the two Zn minerals at neutral or weakly alkaline pH appears to be in line with the particular influence (see later) of the copper ions deliberately introduced into the solution.

Flotation recovery in presence of sodium cyanide
The depressing effect of sodium cyanide on both minerals (Fig. 2) is usually ascribed to the competition between xanthate and CN^- ions in the reaction with metals present on the crystal surface. As far as sphalerite is concerned, the stability constants of the reactions between zinc and ethyl xanthate and between zinc and cyanide reported by Sillén and Martell[8] as $\log \beta_3 = 4.63$ and $\log \beta_2 = 11.07$ support this hypothesis.

Elgillani and Fuerstenau[9] studied the mechanism of pyrite depression in the presence of sodium cyanide, concluding that the depressing action is due to the combination of the CN^- ion with the dissolved Fe^{++} to form $Fe(CN)_6^{4-}$, which, in turn, combines with surface Fe^{+++} to form an insoluble compound of the type $Fe_4(Fe(CN)_6)_3$. This obviously implies that the depressing effect takes place mainly in alkaline media where the surface iron of the pyrite may be present in the trivalent state.

*Chemical analysis of this sample gave 64.7% Zn, 0.43% Fe, 0.13% Pb, 32.16% S and no Cu.

Flotation recovery in presence of copper sulphate
The activation of sphalerite by copper ions is a technique that is widely practised in flotation. Because of the well-known ionic exchange between the zinc of the crystal lattice and the copper in solution, sphalerite acquires collecting properties analogous to those of copper sulphides, i.e. good flotation over a wide pH range, even with weaker xanthates as collectors.[10] Moreoever, this is in agreement with the stability constants of copper–xanthate and zinc–xanthate reactions ($\log \beta_2 = 9.56$ and $\log \beta_3 = 4.63$, respectively[8,11]). The data presented in Fig. 3 support, in general, the above, but a floatability gap is observed near neutral pH—in keeping with the findings of Wark and Sutherland[7] and Steininger.[5] On the basis of alkalimetric titration experiments Steininger attributed this depression to the formation of copper–xanthate hydroxylated complexes at weakly alkaline and neutral pH. Analogous experiments in the framework of the present work have shown that during the titration of copper salts with ethyl xanthate the yellow precipitate, probably neutral copper ethyl xanthate, which forms in truly acid conditions, begins to dissolve around pH 6 and maximum dissolution is attained between pH 6 and 7.5. At higher values the neutral copper ethyl xanthate compound begins to precipitate again, reaching a maximum at pH 9. A similar effect was also observed in the micro-flotation experiments.

The formation of soluble copper–xanthate hydroxylated complexes of the type $Cu(OH)X$ therefore appears to be responsible for the depression of the mineral experimentally determined at near neutral pH.

Similar considerations hold for the flotation response of pyrite in the presence of copper (Fig. 4), but in this case, apart from the possibility of the formation of copper–xanthate hydroxylated compounds, there also exists that of the formation of soluble ferro-xanthate hydroxylated compounds of the $Fe(OH)_2X$ type, which might be responsible for pyrite depression even at weakly alkaline pH. The maximum solubility of such complexes would, according to the mechanism suggested, take place at pH between 7 and 9, at which, moreover, the presence of the ferric ion is possible.

Kakovsky and Arashkevich[12] and Sheikh and Leja[13] obtained direct evidence of the existence of a ferric hydroxyl–xanthate complex. The similarity, at pH < 10, between the flotation recovery curves of pyrite in the presence of high copper sulphate concentrations and those of sphalerite may be due to the similar surfaces of the two minerals resulting from the adsorption, also on pyrite, of large amounts of copper. Pyrite is therefore probably less sensitive to activation by copper than sphalerite. Bushell and co-workers[14] ascribed this phenomenon to the possible formation of a coating of $Fe(OH)_3$ creating a barrier to the adsorption of the copper ions.

Pyrite depression at strongly alkaline pH is therefore very probably caused by the extreme insolubility of this coating, which impedes adsorption (thereby preventing the good flotation typical of activated sphalerite in that pH range from being reproduced).

Fig. 5 summarizes the phenomena discussed regarding the effect of copper sulphate as a function of pH on both minerals at copper sulphate and potassium ethyl xanthate concentrations of 2×10^{-4} and 2×10^{-5} M, respectively.

Flotation recovery in presence of copper sulphate and sodium cyanide
The joint effect of the reagents NaCN and $CuSO_4 \cdot 5H_2O$ is a consequence of their opposing action on the mineral

surfaces. The activating effect of copper and depressing effect of cyanide have already been discussed. The simultaneous presence of both reagents in solution gives rise, as is known, to the formation of copper–cyanide complexes.[1] The reaction of a cupric salt with an alkali cyanide produces, initially, a cupric cyanide precipitate, which is rapidly transformed into cuprous cyanide, with elimination of cyanogen. A copper–cyanide complex is formed subsequently by dissolution of cuprous cyanide in the presence of excess cyanide. The overall reaction is represented by

$$Cu^{++} + 3CN^- \rightarrow Cu(CN)_2^- + \tfrac{1}{2}(CN)_2 \qquad (1)$$

For the solubility products of the complexes Cu^+ with S^{--} and CN^- Sillén and Martell[8,15] reported log values of -48.14 and -19.49, respectively. These values confirm, in agreement with industrial experience, that as they are able to compete with the surface sulphide ions in the reaction with copper ions cyanide ions are an effective deactivator of both sphalerite and pyrite.

The different response of these two minerals at pH 8–11 owing to the presence of both NaCN and $CuSO_4 \cdot 5H_2O$ (Figs. 6, 7 and 8) in comparison with copper sulphate alone (Fig. 5) seems to be controlled by the formation of the copper–cyanide complexes described above. With the appropriate choice of reagent concentration it is possible, theoretically—in relation to the different sensitivity of the two minerals to the activating effect of copper—to reduce the concentration of active copper ions to a level sufficient to promote activation and flotation of the sphalerite and insufficient to activate the pyrite.

Finally, the restoration of flotation recovery of both minerals to levels analogous to those achieved without modulation (Fig. 8) is again due to the interaction between copper and cyanide.

Bearing in mind the value of 2×10^{-24} reported by Vladimirova and Kakovsky[16] for the equilibrium constant of the complex $Cu(CN)_2^-$, it can be deduced that excess cyanide over total copper reduces the concentration of the cuprous and cupric ions to negligible values.

It is therefore understandable why, in the systems $ZnS–CuSO_4 \cdot 5H_2O–NaCN$ or $FeS_2–CuSO_4 \cdot 5H_2O–NaCN$, an excess of cyanide neutralizes the effects produced by the presence of copper (cf. Figs. 1 and 8). Reaction 1 shows that, stoichiometrically, $3CN^-$ groups are required to complex a Cu atom, which is in good agreement with the experimental results obtained.

Conclusions

The separation of sphalerite from pyrite with xanthates as collector seems possible both in the presence of copper sulphate alone at strongly alkaline pH (possibly > 11) and in the presence of a combination of copper sulphate and sodium cyanide at moderately alkaline pH (7.5–9.5). In the latter case the molar ratio between the two reagents must be contained within moderate values, in any case below 2, to enable a satisfactory activation of the sphalerite and at the same time a sure depression of the pyrite to be achieved.

The general applicability of the method awaits verification in a subsequent research stage with systematic experiments on a large number of industrial ores.

References

1. Gaudin A. M. *Flotation, 2nd edn* (New York: McGraw-Hill, 1957), 439.

2. Thorn C. Standard flotation separations. In *Froth flotation* Fuerstenau D. W. ed. (New York: AIME, 1962), 328–46.

3. Tveter E. C. and McQuiston F. W. Jr. Plant practice in sulfide mineral flotation. Reference 2, 382–426.

4. Antoniolli R. Caproni G. and Steri M. Die Flotation von Zinkblende bei niedrigem pH-Wert aus einem hochpyrithaltigen Monteponi Erz. *Erzmetall*, **25**, 1972, 281–7.

5. Steininger J. The depression of sphalerite and pyrite by basic complexes of copper and sulfhydril flotation collectors. *Trans. Am. Inst. Min. Engrs*, **241**, 1968, 34–42.

6 Girczys J. Laskowski J. and Lekki J. Copper activation studies with sphalerite. *Can. metall. Q.*, **11**, 1972, 553–8.

7. Wark I. W. and Sutherland K. L. Influence of the anion on air–mineral contact in presence of collectors of xanthate type and its consequent influence on differential flotation. *Tech. Publ. Am. Inst. Min. Engrs* 1130, 1939, 23 p.

8. Sillén L. G. and Martell A. E. Stability constants of metal-ion complexes—supplement no. 1. *Spec. Publ. chem. Soc., Lond.* no. 25, 1971, 865 p.

9. Elgillani D. A. and Fuerstenau M. C. Mechanisms involved in cyanide depression of pyrite. *Trans. Am. Inst. Min. Engrs*, **241**, 1968, 437–45.

10. Finkelstein N. P. and Allison S. A. The chemistry of activation, deactivation and depression in the flotation of zinc sulphide: a review. In *Flotation: A. M. Gaudin memorial volume* Fuerstenau M. C. ed. (New York: AIME, 1976), 414–57.

11. Perrin D. D. *Stability constants of metal-ion complexes* (Oxford: Pergamon, 1979).

12. Kakovsky I. A. and Arashkevich V. M. The study of properties of organic disulfides. In *Eighth international mineral processing congress, Leningrad, 1968* (Leningrad: Institut Mekhanobr, 1969), vol. 2, 300–14. (Russian text); Paper S8, 10 p. (English text)

13. Sheikh N. and Leja J. Evaluation of iron xanthates by Mössbauer spectroscopy. *Can. min. metall. Bull.*, **66**, Aug. 1973, 31 (abstract).

14. Bushell C. H. G. Krauss C. J. and Brown G. Some reasons for selectivity in copper activation of minerals. *Can. min. metall. Bull.*, **54**, 1961, 244–51.

15. Sillén L. G. and Martell A. E. Stability constants of metal-ion complexes. *Spec. Publ. chem. Soc., Lond.* no. 17, 1964, 754 p.

16. Vladimirova M. G. and Kakovsky I. A. Physicochemical constants characteristic of the formation and composition of the lowest cuprous cyanide complex. *Zh. prikl. Khim.*, **23**, 1950, 580–98. (Russian text)

Centrifuge study of use of sand and flocculants in consolidation of phosphatic clays

Brij M. Moudgil, John C. Ransdell and Bahar Hoghooghi

Synopsis
The disposal of phosphatic clays—a waste product of phosphate beneficiation—is a formidable task owing to their fine size and low self-weight consolidation of the clay particles. In this investigation the consolidation and dewatering behaviour of flocculated brown and blue phosphatic clays, and their mixture, was studied by use of centrifugation with and without tailings sand addition. It was determined that flocculation of the clays in several steps required less polymer dosage and yielded denser flocs than when all the polymer was added at once. It was, however, observed that the final consolidation with sand cap occurred to the same extent with and without the addition of the polymers. In general, blue clay consolidated to a lower degree than the brown clay. Filtration tests were also conducted on the flocculated clay samples. The results of the filtration tests as a comparable dewatering process were correlated with those obtained from the centrifugation studies.

Phosphatic clays are generated during hydraulic processing of the phosphate rock. Because of their poor settling and consolidation behaviour the clay slurries are currently stored in settling ponds surrounded by earthen dykes. An alternative to the present disposal practice is being sought by industry to reduce clay disposal costs.

The problematic behaviour of the phosphatic clays is attributed to the fine particle size and the lower self-weight consolidation forces. Over the years a number of techniques have been investigated to improve the settling and consolidation of the clays.[1-14] A potential approach involves dewatering the clays from an initial 4 wt% solids to 12–15 wt% solids and then either mixing them with tailings sand or capping the pre-thickened clays with tailings sand. A major difficulty to the development of a general solution is the site-specific nature of the clays. The clays from one mining area exhibit surface chemical properties different from those from another area. Generally, the phosphatic clays can be divided into two categories on a colour basis. Brown clays can be flocculated easily, but the bluish type requires much larger amounts of polymer to enable flocculation to be achieved, and flocculation of blue clays is not always possible.

At present anionic polyacrylamides and non-ionic polyethylene oxide are reported to be among the more effective flocculants of brown clays on a large scale. Good flocculation results in a considerable improvement in the settling rate; the effect of polymer addition on consolidation of the clays is not, however, completely known.

The objective of this study was to investigate the effect of polymers on the consolidation and dewatering behaviour of the brown and blue clays and their mixture; also, the effectiveness of sand capping and sand–clay mixing was investigated. As the time scale over which clay consolidation occurs in the field extends to several decades it is difficult to conduct laboratory experiments to simulate the field conditions. Centrifugation of the samples has, however, been reported to yield data that could be correlated with the time scale encountered in actual settling ponds.[15]

Centrifugation and filtration tests that represent comparable dewatering processes were conducted to investigate the consolidation of phosphatic clays. In both processes the fluid flows through a packed bed and the permeability of the bed is an important parameter.

Initial seepage forms an impervious clay layer that seals off the flow of water from the sides and bottom of the clay settling ponds. Vertical movement of water through the top clay layer and sand cap therefore becomes a rate-controlling parameter in further dewatering. Ideally, the clay layer that supports the sand cap should remain at 20 wt% solids until completion of the consolidation process. The filtration rate measurements through a 20 wt% clay bed are therefore expected to yield information regarding the flow of fluid from the top sand–clay layer. The effect of sand capping on the filtration through a 20 wt% clay solids bed was also examined.

It is suggested that the information generated by centrifugation tests should only be considered in relative terms because in these tests the water chemistry of the samples will not undergo the changes that would otherwise take place under natural settling conditions.

Experimental

Materials

Clays
Two clay samples of brown and blue colour were obtained from Occidental Chemical Co., White Springs, Florida. The specific surface area of the samples was determined by Quantasorb, with nitrogen as the absorbate, to be 113 and 157 m²/g for the brown and blue clays, respectively. By use of the X-ray sedigraph particle size was found to be 80% <0.3 μm for both clays. X-ray analysis revealed that the palygorskite content of the brown clay sample was higher than that of the blue clay sample. This was substantiated by SEM photomicrographs in which a relatively larger number of needle-shaped (palygorskite) particles was observed in the brown clay than in the blue.

Zeta-potential of the clays was determined with a Laser Zee meter (model 501) to be -24.0 ± 1.0 mV at pH 7.0 and at 2 x 10^{-3} kmol/m³ NaCl concentration.

Tailings sand
Tailings sand (–35 +150 mesh Tyler) was obtained from International Minerals and Chemical Corporation, Bartow, Florida.

Polymers
One non-ionic and two anionic polymers were selected on the basis of discussions with several chemical and phosphate mining companies. The characteristics of the polymers employed in this investigation are: polyethylene oxide (PEO)—a product of Union Carbide Corporation—is a non-ionic and partially hydrophobic polymer with a molecular weight of about 5 000 000; Nalco 7877, supplied by Nalco Chemical Co., is an anionic polyacrylamide in the form of an emulsion and is stated

to be moderately anionic; and Accophos 1250 (American Cyanamid Co.), also in the form of an emulsion, is characterized by the manufacturer as a moderately anionic polyacrylamide.

Inorganic reagents
NaCl, obtained from Fisher Scientific Co., was employed for adjustment of the ionic strength.

Water
Distilled deionized water with a specific conductivity of 1 μmho was used in this study.

Methods
All tests were conducted under neutral (natural) pH conditions of 7.3 ± 0.1 and at an ionic strength of 2×10^{-3} kmol/m^3 under room temperature (21 ± 1°C) conditions. Reproducibility of the consolidation and filtration results presented was within ±4%. The test procedures employed in this study are described below.

Flocculation tests
A 400-ml sample of a 2 wt% clay slurry was mechanically stirred by an impeller at 300 rev/min. A predetermined amount of a given polymer solution was added in a single dosage and the slurry was stirred for 30 s. The flocculated sample was allowed to settle for 2 h, at which time the supernatant was decanted.

Consolidation tests
A 40-ml sample of each flocculated clay was centrifuged at 900 g (2250 rev/min) for varying time intervals to enable the consolidation behaviour of the clay to be evaluated. After the samples had dewatered to a solids content at which the settled mass was capable of supporting a sand cap, enough tailings sand (−35 +150 mesh) to maintain a sand to clay ratio of 2 to 1 was gently placed over the settled clay and centrifugation continued at 2250 rev/min for further consolidation.

For flocculation of sand–clay mixture mechanical agitation speed was increased from 300 to 600 rev/min to keep the sand particles in suspension. The consolidation procedure was similar to that described above, but no sand capping was involved.

Filtration tests
Measurements of filtration rate were performed with an apparatus similar to that employed by LaMer and co-workers.[16] The flocculated samples were poured over a coarse Fisherbrand filter paper (7.0-cm diameter). The flocculated suspension was then filtered under a vacuum of 96 kPa (720 mm Hg) until a cake of 20% solids was obtained. The filtrate was then poured over the filter cake and the cake filtration rate was obtained by measuring the volume of filtrate collected as a function of time.

In another set of experiments a 2:1 weight ratio of sand to clay was applied over the cake to study the effect of sand addition on the filtration rates. This was done by sprinkling the sand over the cake uniformly and measuring the cake filtration rate as described above.

Results and discussion

The amounts of polymer used in this study (Table 1) were established on the basis of minimum dosage required for good visual flocculation and clarity of the supernatant. Blue clay required more flocculant than the brown. It should be stated that no effort was made to optimize the amount of polymer needed for flocculation. It was, however, observed that the nature of the flocs formed differed with the three polymers used in this study. The PEO resulted in large globular flocs, whereas those obtained with Nalco 7877 or Accophos 1250 were ellipsoidal in shape. The non-ionic PEO seemed to form flocs more rapidly than the two anionic polyacrylamides. The amount of polymer employed in industry is lower than was used in this study: this could be due to differences in (1) the clay–polymer mixing procedures and (2) the nature of the clays employed in this study.

As was stated earlier, pre-thickening of the clays is necessary before tailings sand is either mixed with the clays or placed over it as a cap. Centrifugation tests were conducted to determine the extent of dewatering that was required before a sand cap could be placed over the clay mass.

The results presented in Table 2 show that the blue clay samples, with or without the flocculant, had to be dewatered to a higher solids content (20 wt%) than the brown clay samples (15 wt%). The brown–blue clay mixture sample, flocculated with multi-stage polymer addition, mostly behaved in a manner similar to that of the brown clays. It appears that the brown clay flocs have higher shear strength than the blue clay flocs and are therefore able to support a sand cap at a lower solids content.

Effect of flocculation on clay consolidation
The amount of clay solids attained as a function of centrifugation time with and without flocculation is plotted in Fig. 1 for brown clay. The flocculated slurries attained a higher solids content than the unflocculated sample, PEO attaining the highest solids content among the three flocculants. This was also determined in the case of blue clays, although the degree of consolidation attained was lower. This improvement in the final solids could have been due to changes in the flow of water through the pores of the consolidated clay mass as a result of the polymer coating of the solids and residual polymer in the water. It should be noted that the results obtained in this study do not agree with those reported in the literature on the basis of jar tests of flocculated and unflocculated clays.[15] It is possible that the higher shear stresses experienced during centrifugation

Table 1   Minimum polymer required for flocculation (initial clay solids, 2 wt%)

System	Reagents, kg/t		
	PEO	Accophos 1250	Nalco 7877
Brown clay (single-stage addition)	1.0	2.0	3.5
Blue clay (single-stage addition)*	1.5	3.5	4.5
75% brown and 25% blue clay mixture (single-* and multi-stage addition)	—	—	1.5
75% brown and 25% blue clay mixture (multi-stage addition at 600 rev/min)	—	—	2.0

* Poor flocculation.

Table 2   Initial dewatering required to support sand cap

System	Clay solids after pre-thickening, wt%			
	Unfloc-culated	PEO	Accophos 1250	Nalco 7877
Brown clay (single-stage addition)	16	15	15	15
Blue clay (single-stage addition)	16	20	20	20
75% brown and 25% blue mixture (single-stage addition)	—	—	—	21
75% brown and 25% blue mixture (multi-stage addition at 300 and 600 rev/min)	—	—	—	15

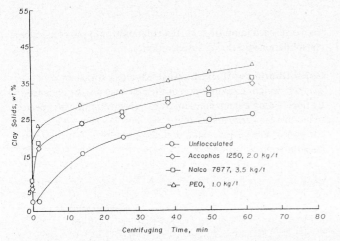

Fig. 1   Effect of flocculation on consolidation of brown phosphatic clay without sand cap

collapse most of the agglomerates and the slurry consolidates differently than in the jar settling test.

The brown clay exhibited a much faster filtration rate than the blue clay, and flocculation of both the blue or brown clay enhanced the filtration rate. These results (Fig. 2) support the centrifugation test data. The filtration rates of the PEO flocculated clays were, however, much faster than those of the other flocculated samples. This could be explained by the structure of flocs formed when the clays are flocculated with PEO.

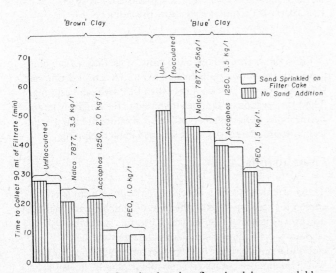

Fig. 2   Filtration of flocculated and unflocculated brown and blue phosphatic clays with and without sand addition

Effect of sand capping

Results plotted in Fig. 3 indicate that placing a sand cap on the pre-thickened clay enhances clay consolidation, this improvement in consolidation being seen both for brown and blue clays and for flocculated and unflocculated samples. Similar results were also observed in the filtration tests, sand addition on the filter cakes improving the filtration rate of the brown clay more than that of the blue clay or the blue–brown clay mixture. Consolidation of the blue clay and the blue–brown clay mixture, with or without flocculation, was similar.

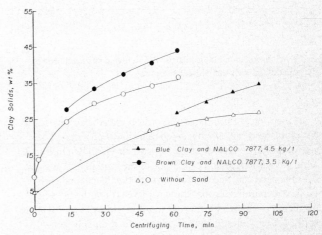

Fig. 3   Consolidation of flocculated brown and blue phosphatic clays with and without a sand cap

Sand addition, however, did not increase the filtration rate of the PEO-flocculated brown clay, whereas those flocculated with Nalco 7877 and Accophos 1250 demonstrated a significant increase in their filtration rates. This can also be explained by the nature of the flocs formed, which affected the filter cake structures. The flocs produced with PEO addition exhibited cohesiveness; smaller flocs aggregated to form large groups of flocs. As sand addition actually hindered the filtration rate it is possible that the sand layer further compresses the flocs together, producing a more compact, uniform bed and thereby reducing cake permeability. On the other hand, flocculation with Nalco 7877 and Accophos 1250 resulted in much smaller and less cohesive flocs. As a result, sand addition would not compress the flocs together; instead, it is possible that the sand grains would form 'channels' in the filter cake. This 'channelling' effect could explain the faster filtration rates of the samples flocculated with Nalco 7877 and Accophos 1250 on sand addition.

For the blue clay samples, which did not show any significant difference in consolidation or filtration behaviour on sand addition, the floc size was smaller than that obtained with brown clays.

Effect of aging on consolidation of flocculated clays

It was determined that aging the flocculated brown clays for 34 days had an adverse effect on the consolidation behaviour. On aging, the floc size had become smaller and a longer centrifugation time was required to pre-thicken the clays to 15 wt% solids. For example, for a freshly flocculated brown clay suspension a 2-min centrifugation was required for a solids content of 20 wt% to be attained; after aging, however, the clays reached a solids content of 15 wt% with a 30-min centrifugation.

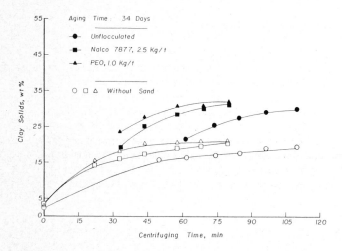

Fig. 4   Consolidation of flocculated, unflocculated and aged brown phosphatic clay with and without a sand cap

Consolidation of flocculated and unflocculated clays, with and without a sand cap, was observed to be lower on aging. The consolidation behaviour of aged brown clay is shown in Fig. 4 with and without a sand cap. Some of the sand placed as a cap over the aged clay had filtered through the flocculated clay mass, which indicates that the shear strength of the flocs had decreased on aging. This would result in a loss of vertical stress applied, thus yielding lower final consolidation. The zeta-potential measurements revealed that under the present experimental conditions the zeta-potential changed from –23.6 mV for the freshly prepared clay suspension to –32.2 mV after 34 days, with a shift in pH from 7.3 to 7.7 during the same period. Increase in charge density would inhibit consolidation, thus resulting in lower solids content. It is to be noted, however, that, even after aging, flocculated clays consolidated to a higher solids content, with and without a sand cap, than the unflocculated clay sample.

Effect of multi-stage addition of polymers

Two modes of polymer addition were tested—the single-stage and the multi-stage addition of the polymer, multi-stage flocculation resulting in a higher consolidation of the clay mixture (Fig. 5).

The filtration studies showed a decrease in the filtration rate of the clay mixtures with the multi-stage polymer addition. It is to be noted that the flocs produced in multi-stage flocculation were observed to be more compact and dense than those which were produced with the single-stage addition of the polymer. This could be due to the more homogeneous adsorption of the polymer on the clay particles in multi-stage flocculation.[17] It is, therefore, possible that the compact and dense nature of the

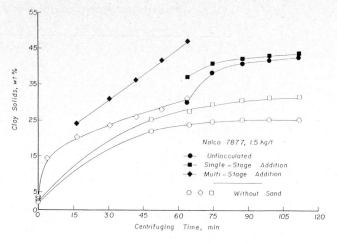

Fig. 5   Effect of flocculation method on consolidation of phosphatic clays mixture with and without sand cap

flocs produced in multi-stage flocculation would result in higher consolidation and slower filtration rates.

Consolidation of flocculated sand–clays mixture

The self-weight consolidation of the clays can also be enhanced by flocculating a sand–clays mixture. This technique is expected to modify the permeability of the clay bed as a consequence of entrapped sand particles and, therefore, results in more uniform consolidation.

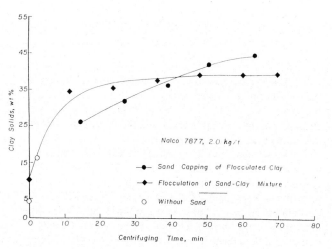

Fig. 6   Comparison of sand capping and sand–clay mixing on consolidation of flocculated phosphatic clays mixture

Fig. 6 shows that although the multi-stage flocculation of a sand–clays mixture exhibited a higher initial consolidation rate, the final consolidation was lower than that with sand capping. These observations might be attributed to the relatively larger permeability of flocculated sand–clays mixture but lower self-weight consolidation than that attained in sand capping.

Conclusions

The consolidation trends observed in the present study are similar to those reported on the basis of centrifuge modelling by other investigators.[15] This makes it possible to use the laboratory centrifuge in simulating the trends in the consolidation behaviour of clays over longer settling times, which has not been otherwise possible. It should, however, be noted that to simulate the consolidation under natural conditions centrifugation tests need to be conducted as a function of water chemistry of the clay suspensions.

The flocculant polyethylene oxide had the maximum effect on the consolidation behaviour of the clays. It should, however, be emphasized that because of the site-specific nature of the clays this might be true only for the samples that were employed in this investigation.

Multi-stage addition of the flocculant resulted in lower dosages in comparison with those of the single-stage flocculation. Sand capping of pre-thickened clays yielded higher consolidation, whereas flocculation of the sand–clays mixture resulted in a faster initial consolidation rate. Filtration rate measurements with a 20 wt% clay bed were compatible with the trends observed in consolidation studies under the different experimental conditions employed.

It was observed that the final consolidation did not depend significantly on the flocculation of the clays alone. The major advantage of the flocculation step, however, is that it enhances the settling rate, allowing the placement of sand over the clay in a shorter time than for the unflocculated clay. In this manner a degree of consolidation similar to that achieved without flocculation can be attained in a shorter time period. Thus, flocculation of the clays can improve the settling pond turnover rate.

To maximize the use of flocculants the clay slurries must be induced to reach the minimum weight per cent required to support the tailings sand cap before degradation of the polymer. In most cases this will mean that to optimize the effect of sand capping and the settling pond turnaround rate flocculation, sedimentation and hindered settling must occur within a short period of time—of the order of a few weeks.

Acknowledgement

The authors wish to thank Rob Pelick for help in experimentation and the College of Engineering–EIES (COE Funds) for partial financial support of this work.

References
1. Bromwell L. G. and Oxford T. P. Waste clay dewatering and disposal. In *Geotechnical practice for disposal of solid waste materials: proceeding of the conference, University of Michigan, June 1977* (New York: American Society of Civil Engineers, 1977), 541–58.
2. Keshian B. Jr. Ladd C. C. and Olson R. E. Sedimentation-consolidation behavior of phosphatic clays. Reference 1, 188–209.
3. Martin R. T. Bromwell L. G. and Sholine J. H. Field tests of phosphatic clay dewatering. Reference 1, 559–73.
4. Raden D. J. Dewatering phosphatic clay waste using the Enviroclear thickener. In *Consolidation and dewatering of fine particles: proceedings of conference, USBM, Tuscaloosa, Al., August 1982* (Tuscaloosa, Al.: U.S. Bureau of Mines, 1982), 205–24.
5. Lawver J. E. The clay waste problem in a nutshell. Reference 4, 225–48.
6. Taylor J. W. Thickening, disposal, dewatering consolidation of slimes from phosphate washeries in Florida. Reference 4, 249–64.
7. Moudgil B. M. Aggregation of phosphatic clay. Reference 4, 339–57.
8. Brierley C. L. and Lanza G. R. Microorganism research for dewatering phosphate clay wastes. Reference 4, 358–84.
9. Scheiner B. J. Smelley A. G. and Brooks D. R. Large scale dewatering of phosphatic clay waste from central Florida. *Rep. Invest. U.S. Bur. Mines* 8611, 1982, 11 p.
10. Lawver J. E. McClintock W. O. and Snow R. E. Beneficiation of phosphate rock: a state of the art review. *Minerals Sci. Engng*, **10**, 1978, 278–94.
11. Moudgil B. M. and Bunch J. P. Mined land reclamation by the Florida phosphate industry. *Trans. Am. Inst. Min. Engrs*, **260**, 1976, 187–91.
12. Somasundaran P. Smith E. L. and Harris C. C. Effect of coarser particles on settling characteristics of phosphate slurries. In *Proceedings first international conference in particle technology, Chicago, August 1973*, 144–50.
13. Moudgil B. M. *et al.* Field test of seepage technique for dewatering waste phosphatic clays. *Min. Engng, N.Y.*, **34**, March 1982, 297–301.
14. Moudgil B. M. Dewatering and consolidation of the Florida phosphatic clays. In *International symposium on recent advances in particulate science and technology, Madras, India, December 1982*, Preprint vol. II, D-13 to D-20.
15. Bloomquist D. Centrifuge modeling of large strain consolidation phenomena in phosphate clay rentention ponds. Ph.D. thesis, University of Florida, Gainesville, FL, 1982.
16. LaMer V. K Smellie R. H. and Lee P. Flocculation, subsidence and filtration of phosphate slurries. *J. Colloid Interface Sci.*, **11**, 1956, 711–9.
17. LaMer V. K. and Smellie R. H. Flocculation, subsidence and filtration. *J. Colloid Interface Sci.*, **12**, 1957, 230–9

Synthetic flocculants in the mineral processing industry—types available, their uses and advantages

M. J. Pearse

Synopsis

The types of dewatering equipment that utilize flocculants in the minerals industry are described and the general benefits of flocculant usage are highlighted. The chemical types of flocculants that are available to the minerals industry are described and some of their more important properties are discussed. A broad classification based on areas of usage in specific mineral processes and chemical composition–molecular weight is attempted. The classification covers metallurgical and industrial mineral processing, coal washing and hydrometallurgical processes.

Five specific examples illustrate the use of flocculants. In the first, plant thickening of a copper porphyry tailings is used to show how flocculants can help to save process water in a desert environment and how throughput can be increased, thereby saving capital expenditure on new equipment. An example of raw coal slurry thickening shows how 'thickener operating diagrams' help in the use of flocculants economically. High-capacity thickeners designed to use powerful flocculants are compared with conventional thickeners, coal tailings being used as an example. The advantages of the use of specially designed flocculants are illustrated by way of the Bayer alumina process, and the benefits to be gained from the use of flocculants in filtration are exemplified by vacuum filtration of froth-floated fine coal.

Since the introduction of synthetic flocculants into the minerals industry in the early 1950s their usage has grown, and continues to grow, considerably. The reasons for this sustained growth in usage include process advantages, environmental concern, a continual improvement in flocculants and the mining of leaner orebodies, which requires finer grinding and, hence, the necessity for better solid–liquid separation.

The main types of processes and equipment that utilize flocculants in the mineral processing, hydrometallurgical, industrial mineral and coal-mining industries are summarized in Table 1. A distinction is made between processes or units that often use flocculants, nearly always use flocculants or those associated with operations that rely on flocculation. It is noteworthy that the latest equipment (high-rate or high-capacity thickeners and filter-belt presses) depends on the powerful particle aggregation of modern synthetic flocculants.

The processing engineer is primarily concerned with process advantages and cost-benefits afforded by flocculants, some of the more relevant being the following: (1) rapid settling rates and filtration rates lead to smaller equipment installation or greater throughputs of existing units; (2) well-clarified overflows and filtrates prevent fines build-up in the mill, often alleviating deleterious effects in flotation or solvent extraction; (3) in arid desert-type climates process water recovery from tailings is essential and here high thickener underflows minimize water loss; (4) soluble values losses are minimized in CCD and CCF circuits at leach plants; and (5) efficient dewatering of concentrates ensures energy savings if thermal drying is involved, lower transport costs and, often, advantages in handling.

The present paper is less concerned with the mechanisms of flocculation, these having been published elsewhere,[1,2,3] than with the main chemical types of flocculants that are available to the minerals industry—to provide some guidance for effective application and to illustrate their effectiveness with practical examples. A broad classification is also put forward, based on ionic composition, molecular weight and areas of application in the industry.

Types of flocculants available

Synthetic flocculants are long-chain, predominantly linear, water-soluble polymers that can adsorb on to and cause aggregation of particles in suspension. Non-ionic, cationic and anionic types are available, the latter two often being referred to as polyelectrolytes. The majority of synthetic flocculants can be divided conveniently into two classes.

Class A flocculants

Class A flocculants are medium to high molecular weight (1–20 $\times 10^6$) bridging flocculants mainly based on acrylamide and its derivatives. The three ionic forms mentioned above are available.

Table 1   Use of flocculants in solid–liquid separation

Often used	Nearly always used	Always used
Conventional thickeners	Lamella clarifiers	High-rate or high-capacity thickeners
Conventional clarifiers	Solid-bowl centrifuges	Deep cone thickeners
RVF-drum, disc	CCD circuits	Filter-belt presses
Horizontal vacuum belts	CCF circuits	(multi-roll filters)
Pressure filters		
Settling lagoons/effluent treatment		
Clarification of underground water		

Non-ionic polyacrylamide

$$\left[\begin{array}{c} \text{CH} \quad\ \text{CH}_2 \\ | \\ \text{C}=\text{O} \\ | \\ \text{NH}_2 \end{array}\right]_n$$

Anionic forms are often co-polymers of acrylamide and sodium acrylate

$$\left[\left(\begin{array}{c} \text{CH}-\text{CH}_2 \\ | \\ \text{C}=\text{O} \\ | \\ \text{NH}_2 \end{array}\right)_x \left(\begin{array}{c} \text{CH}-\text{CH}_2 \\ | \\ \text{C}=\text{O} \\ | \\ \text{O}^-\text{Na}^+ \end{array}\right)_y\right] \quad n = x + y$$

Cationic examples are co-polymers of acrylamide and monomers, such as N, N-dimethylaminoethylmethacrylate or cationic Mannich reaction products of polyacrylamide. Cationic functional groups can be in the acid salt (protonated) form or as the quaternized product:

$$\left[\left(\begin{array}{c} \text{CH}-\text{CH}_2 \\ | \\ \text{C}=\text{O} \\ | \\ \text{NH}_2 \end{array}\right)_x \left(\begin{array}{c} \text{CH}_3 \\ | \\ \text{CH}_2-\text{C} \\ | \\ \text{C}=\text{O} \\ | \\ \text{O} \\ | \\ \text{C}_2\text{H}_4 \\ | \\ \text{N}^+ \quad \text{Cl}^- \\ \text{CH}_3 | \text{CH}_3 \\ \text{CH}_3 \end{array}\right)_y\right] \quad n = x + y$$

In both anionic and cationic types y can be varied from, say, 1 to 100% and a comprehensive spectrum of polymers from totally cationic through non-ionic to fully anionic can therefore be produced.

The degree of polymerization, n, can also be varied to produce a range of polymers of different average molecular weight. Thus, synthetic flocculants can be 'tailor-made' to suit virtually every pulp and slurry and dewatering duty. For pure polyacrylamide (monomer molecular weight $= 71$) of molecular weight 20×10^6 the $n = 282\,000$. The carbon–carbon bond length in the polymer 'backbone' is 1.54×10^{-10} m and, hence, the actual polymer chain, if fully extended, can be $43\ \mu\text{m}$ long! In solution, however, the polymer chain is substantially coiled, so the molecule size in any one dimension would be much less than this figure, but still of a considerable size.

Class A polymers are the most commonly encountered flocculants in the minerals industry, particularly the non-ionic and anionic types. These products are mainly available in the form of solids, emulsions and dispersions.

Class B flocculants

Class B flocculants are synthetic coagulants, sometimes referred to as 'primary coagulants' when used in conjunction with Class A anionic and non-ionic flocculants. These are of much lower molecular weight ($<5 \times 10^5$) and are highly cationic in nature. The products are generally supplied as 10–50% active solutions. The two main types available are polyamine quaternaries, e.g. poly (2-hydroxypropyl 1, 1,-N-dimethylammonium chloride)

$$\left[\begin{array}{c} \text{OH} \qquad\quad \text{CH}_3 \\ | \qquad\qquad | \\ \text{CH}_2-\text{CH}-\text{CH}_2-\text{N}^+ \\ \qquad\qquad\qquad | \\ \text{Cl}^- \qquad \text{CH}_3 \end{array}\right]_n$$

used extensively, for example, on U.S. coals as clarification aids, and poly(diallyldimethylammonium chloride) (poly-DADMAC), used, for example, for iron tailings clarification, particularly at high pH values.

Areas of flocculant application

As was indicated previously, flocculants are increasingly used on all types of mineral applications. Some examples of extreme conditions under which flocculants perform include those of highly caustic, hot Bayer process liquors, highly acidic copper and uranium leach liquors, saturated brines in the potash industry and hot acid black liquors of the TiO$_2$ sulphate process. Even coal washery waters contain several grammes per litre of dissolved calcium and sodium salts and base-metal flotation tailings are often high in lime content. At the other end of the scale low ionic strength slurries are encountered in some processes, e.g. sands and gravels.

Because of this highly variable environment in which efficient

Table 2 Areas of flocculant application in the minerals industry

Application	Non-ionic	Low anionic	Medium anionic	Medium-high anionic	High anionic	Low cationic	Medium cationic	High cationic
U/Cu/Co/Ni acid leach CCD	H	H					H	H
U acid leach CCF	M	M					M	M
U alkaline leach CCD				H				
U alkaline leach CCF				M				
Base-metal tailings T/C	H	H	H	H				
Pre-leach ground ores T/C	H	H	H	H				
Coal tailings T/C		H	H					
Coal-frothed fines F			M					
Electrolytic zinc–acid leach T/C	H	H			H			
Electrolytic zinc–neutral leach T/C	H	H	H					
Clayey coal tailings		H*						L
Iron ore tailings (pH 11) T/C		H*						L
Iron ore concentrate (pH 11) F								L
Bayer process red mud T/C						H		
Ni/Co alkaline leach T/C	H	H	H	H	H			
Barite/fluorite tailings	H	H	H					
Highly colloidal fraction in pulp T/C	H*	H*	H*			H	H	L
Potash tailings T/C	H	H	H	H				
High pH systems (pH>12) T/C						H		
Phosphate slimes/tailings T/C	H	H	H					
Sulphate process TiO$_2$ black liquor T/C							M	M
Sand and gravel slurries	H	H						

CCD, Countercurrent decantation; CCF, countercurrent filtration; H, high molecular weight (15–20 x 10^6); M, medium molecular weight (10 x 10^6); L, low molecular weight (<1 x 10^6); T/C, thickening/clarification; F, vacuum filtration.

* Used in combination with primary coagulant.

flocculation has to take place each manufacturer produces a wide spectrum of products. In addition, different types of dewatering equipment require a rather specific floc structure. For example, whereas a thickener might require a large, fast setting floc that collapses in the compression zone to give a high underflow concentration, a vacuum filter produces better performance with a smaller, stronger floc. Other cases in point are centrifuges where a shear resistant floc is required and filter-belt presses where the floc structure should be such as to allow rapid initial gravity drainage followed by progressive dewatering in the pressure/shear zones of the rollers. In addition to chemical composition, molecular weight plays a significant role in determining the properties of the floc structure formed. Further details of floc structure have been published elsewhere.[4]

As a very broad generalization, flocculants may be categorized in terms of areas of application according to Table 2.

Some important features of Table 2 are: (1) non-ionic and anionic Class *A* flocculants predominate in the mineral processing, coal and hydrometallurgical industries; (2) non-ionic flocculants are widely used in acidic pulps; (3) highly anionic flocculants are suitable for substantially alkaline pulps; and (4) medium molecular weight products are more suitable for vacuum filtration, high molecular weight flocculants predominating in sedimentation. Flocculants for centrifugation and pressure-belt filtration often fall into the latter category.

Examples of flocculant use in the minerals industry

Thickening/clarification (sedimentation)
In many cases the benefits of flocculant usage are self-evident: for example, with many slurries sufficient overflow clarity, settling rate and underflow density cannot be achieved without their use (synthetic flocculants can easily increase the natural settling rate by a factor of 10: this has an obvious effect on thickener size).

Thickening of copper porphyry flotation tailings
A 45-m diameter thickener treats 3000 t/day lime-coagulated flotation tailings. The available thickener area is 1534 m². The feed (30.0% w/w, 370 g/l solids; pulp sp. gr., 1.233; solids sp. gr., 2.7) thickens to about 65% w/w solids at a flocculant dose level of 10 g/t. The operation is steady under these conditions, but when higher underflow densities are sought the solids back up in the thickener. Talmage and Fitch unit area determinations (shown to be reliable on similar copper tailings) show the reasons for the thickener behaviour (calculations are given in Table 3). At a 3000 t/day feed rate and 10 g/t flocculant dosage the thickener is at capacity for an underflow density of 65% w/w solids. In times of water shortage underflow concentrations of 70% could easily be achieved by the use of more flocculant, which would allow greater water recovery for recirculation to the concentrator. Increasing underflow concentration from 65 to 70% w/w solids

has the effect of preventing the loss of nearly 18 000 m³ per month: this is significant in a desert environment.

In addition, an increase in the flocculant dosage from 10 to 15 g/t would, under normal conditions, allow an increase in thickener throughput of 600 t/day. The alternative to such an increase in throughput would be to build an extra 20-m diameter thickener (calculated from Table 3) and to use a 10 g/t flocculant dosage level on the total 3600 t/day of tailings.

It is interesting to compare the economics of retaining the present thickener at an elevated flocculant dosage with those for the construction of increased thickener capacity at the same flocculant dosage level. Present flocculant cost (10 g/t; 3000 t/day; 330 day/year) is £20 000 per annum; increasing the feed rate to 3600 t/day and the flocculant to 15 g/t produces an extra cost of £16 000 per annum (total flocculant, £36 000).

To build a 20-m diameter thickener with a heavy duty rate mechanism would require an approximate capital outlay of £170 000–£180 000. In addition, the extra flocculant would cost £4 000 per annum on to the original £20 000. Thus, the extra £12 000 in flocculant costs per annum offsets a capital expenditure of not far short of £200 000.

High-rate or high-capacity thickeners
The 'new-generation' thickeners are designed to exploit the benefits that can be achieved by the use of modern powerful flocculants. Such units include the Enviroclear thickener, the Eimco 'Hi-Capacity' thickener and the Dorr-Oliver 'Hi-Rate' thickener, which incorporates the 'Dynafloc' feedwell. The following example compares a conventional thickener and an Enviroclear thickener side by side treating an equal tonnage of coal tailings (470 t/day).

The feed pulp is approximately 5% w/w solids and the underflow discharge of both units is in the range 30–35% w/w solids. The conventional 13.7-m diameter thickener uses approximately 40 g/t flocculant to give a settling rate of about 6 m/h with an overflow or rise rate of about 2.4 m/h. The thickener unit area in this case is 0.32 m²/t/day, which is low for coal tailings. A 7-m diameter Enviroclear thickener does the same job with a dose level of 60–65 g/t flocculant. Upflow or rise rate is approximately 6.5 m/h and a settling rate of about 9 m/h would be appropriate. Unit area is calculated to be 0.12 m²/t/day.

The example above is a 'hard test' for a high-capacity unit, as the conventional thickener is being pushed to its limit and shows a low unit area for coal tailings thickening. Under more normal conditions (similar to those of the following example) there is no doubt that the 'new-generation' thickeners would show an even greater saving in diameter and installed unit area.

Thickening of raw coal slurry
This example illustrates the response of the parameters that determine thickening (settling rate, feed solids content, unit area) to flocculant dosage.

The actual installation has a 20-m diameter (314-m² area)

Table 3 Talmage and Fitch thickener areas for porphyry copper flotation tailings

Flocculant dosage, g/t	Underflow conc., % w/w	Unit area, m²/t/day	Thickener area required, m²						
			Thickener feed rate, t/day						
			2600	2800	3000	3200	3400	3600	3800
10	61.7	0.45	1170	1260	1350	1440	1530	1620	1710
	66.4	0.52	1352	1456	1560	1664	1768	1872	1976
	70.2	0.57	1482	1596	1710	1824	1938	2052	2166
15	61.7	0.35	910	980	1050	1120	1190	1260	1330
	66.4	0.43	1118	1204	1290	1376	1462	1548	1634
	70.2	0.48	1248	1344	1440	1536	1632	1728	1824

conventional thickener that discharges an underflow of about 34% solids w/w. The feed flow is reasonably constant at approximately 6800 m³/day, but the solids content of the feed varies considerably between 3.5 and 5.5% (this is fairly typical of a coal washery operation). Some data on the raw coal slurry are given in Table 4.

Table 4 Characteristics of raw coal slurry

*Solids content, w/w	4.48%
Solids content, w/v	45.8 g/l
Pulp sp. gr.	1.022
Solids sp. gr.	2.00
Ash content	58.7%
Slurry pH	7.20
Particle size, μm	
+ 250	0.4%
−250 + 125	1.3
−125 + 63	4.4
− 63	93.9

* Dilutions and concentration performed with plant water and by decantation.

Thickening characteristics for this slurry are shown in Figs. 1, 2 and 3. The Oltmann construction method was used to determine thickener unit areas. Without flocculant the thickener would be considerably undersized and overflow clarities would be poor. For this particular application a very high molecular weight medium anionic polymer produces the best results.

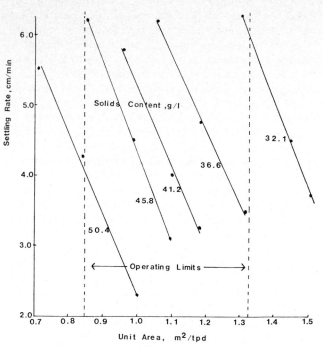

Fig. 2 Thickening of raw coal slurry (thickener operation diagram 2)

the most efficient manner. In the present example, at a steady flow rate of 6800 m³/day slurry, the required thickener area would be 1.32 m²/t/day for a slurry solids concentration of 35 g/l and 0.84 m²/t/day for a slurry with 55 g/l.

'Thickener operating diagrams' of this kind help to optimize the use of flocculants. Plant measurements of slurry specific gravity (as a quick method for determining solids concentration) and settling rate for a known flocculant dose level in a measuring cylinder indicate how to alter the polymer dose rate. Regular measurements of this kind can go a long way towards troublefree thickener operation by use of 'least-cost' flocculation.

Special flocculants for Bayer alumina process
After caustic digestion of bauxite the insoluble 'red mud' has to be separated efficiently from the valuable aluminate

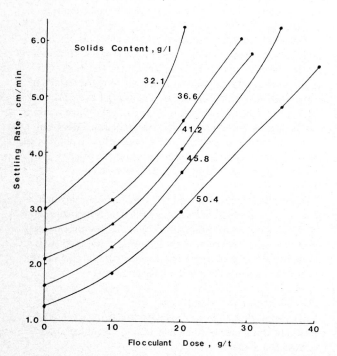

Fig. 1 Thickening of raw coal slurry (thickener operation diagram 1)

Initial settling rates as a function of flocculant dose level are shown in Fig. 1. The response is, as expected, more rapid for a dilute slurry. To achieve a given settling rate a higher unit dosage of flocculant (g/t) is required for the more concentrated slurries.

Figs. 2 and 3 show relationships between the required unit area, settling rate, feed solids concentration and flocculant dosage level. To keep within the operating limits of the thickener the flocculant dose rate has to be increased when the solids concentration of the slurry falls. This, in turn, increases the settling rate and the solids flux and decreases the unit area requirement. Conversely, when the solids concentration of the slurry increases adjustments can be made to use the flocculant in

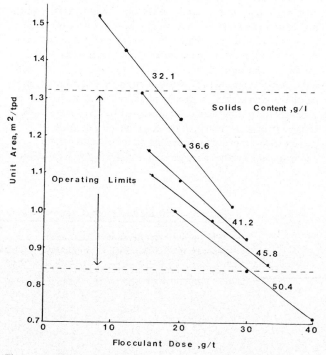

Fig. 3 Thickening of raw coal slurry (thickening operation diagram 3)

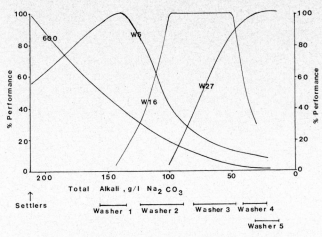

Fig. 4   Performance of Alclar flocculants on Bayer process pulps

liquor—achieved by primary decantation and counter-current washing. Special flocculants developed to work under high-temperature, highly caustic conditions aid immensely in the solid–liquid separation stages.

In addition, as one progresses from the primary decantation settler and down the CCD wash train the levels of total alkali, total caustic and soluble aluminate fall and in each unit the chemistry of the optimum flocculant changes. Fig. 4 shows the percentage performance (mainly based on settling rate) of four Alclar flocculants on the primary settlers and a five-unit wash train of a Bayer plant. The maximum performance of each flocculant can be correlated to the total alkali content of the liquor. For example, Alclar 600 is the product of choice for the primary settler, Alclar W5 is most suited to washer 1, Alclar W16 is best suited to washers 2 and 3, and Alclar W27 is the choice for washers 4 and 5.

Careful choice of these specialist flocculants contributes significantly towards maximum alumina recovery and minimum soda losses on a Bayer plant.

Fine coal filtration

It is common practice in many parts of the world to recover fine coal (–0.5 mm) by vacuum filtration (drum and disc). Flocculant filter aids are used widely in the United Kingdom to recover froth flotation concentrated fine coal, particularly on vacuum drum filters. Flocculant filter aids are generally of medium molecular weight to produce the type of floc structure most suitable for filtration, as was discussed in detail by Pearse and Allen.[4]

Flocculant filter aids generally increase the dry cake yields of rotary vacuum filters operating on frothed fines from about 2 kg/m^2 (without flocculants) to approximately 10–16 kg/m^2. A typical example, with the use of flocculant, would be a 56-m^2 filter operating at 1 rev/min and utilizing a 1/3 submergence producing 15–16 t/h dry cake (840 kg/m^2/h; 14 kg/m^2). Cake moisture contents usually range from 25 to 30%.

The filter leaf data of Table 6 illustrate the effectiveness of a particular filter aid (Magnafloc 1017) in improving filtration. Filter feed characteristics are given in Table 5.

Table 5   Frothed fines (clean coal) characteristics

Solids content, w/w	22.9%
Solids content w/v	233 g/l
Pulp sp. gr.	1.02
Solids sp. gr.	1.08
pH	7.4
Ash content	6.9%
Particle size, μm	
+ 1 mm	0.1%
–1 mm + 500	5.2
–500 + 250	13.4
–250 + 125	16.4
–125 + 63	15.5
– 63	49.4

Tests 1–9 show that the cake yield is increased progressively and considerably as the flocculant dosage is increased. All the cake moisture contents are lower when flocculant is used than

Table 6   Filter leaf data for vacuum filtration of frothed fines coal

Test no.	Flocculant dosage, g/t	Vacuum, in Hg	Pick-up time, s	Dry time, s	Dry cake yield, kg/m^2	Cake moisture, %	Cake porosity (voidage)
1	—	20	20	40	3.6	33.3	0.18
2	—	20	20	40	3.8	33.3	0.20
3	6.5	20	20	40	6.4	29.1	0.34
4	13.0	20	20	40	8.1	28.6	0.42
5	19.5	20	20	40	9.1	28.8	0.40
6	26.0	20	20	40	10.0	30.0	0.40
7	39.0	20	20	40	11.6	30.3	0.40
8	52.0	20	20	40	13.2	30.6	0.40
9	65.0	20	20	40	14.1	31.4	0.44
10	13.0	25	20	40	8.7	28.4	—
11	13.0	20	20	40	8.1	28.8	—
12	13.0	15	20	40	7.8	30.7	—
13	13.0	20	20	20	8.1	30.4	—
14	13.0	20	20	40	7.8	28.8	—
15	13.0	20	20	60	8.2	28.4	—
16	13.0	20	20	90	8.3	27.3	—
17	13.0	20	20	180	8.1	26.8	—
18	13.0	20	10	40	6.9	28.5	—
19	13.0	20	20	40	7.8	28.8	—
20	13.0	20	30	40	10.0	30.6	—
21	13.0	20	40	40	11.8	32.1	—
22	—	20	20	40	3.6	33.3	—
23	—	20	30	40	4.0	32.8	—
24	—	20	40	40	4.5	33.9	—

when it is not.[1,2] A moisture minimum is seen with 13–20 g/t
flocculant. Dosages greater than this range produce somewhat
higher moisture contents, mainly because of the increase in cake
thickness. Cake porosity (voidage) is shown for this range of
tests: this is not a particularly accurate measurement, but it does
illustrate the effect of flocculant producing a more porous cake.

Tests 1–12 show that the cake moisture content is not
benefited particularly by increases in vacuum from 20 to 25 in
Hg, but a reduction to 15 in Hg does show a considerable
deterioration.

Tests 13–17 show, as expected, that as the dry time is increased
at approximately constant pick-up, the cake moisture content
decreases. A cycle of 20-s pick-up and 40-s dry time appears to
be a fair optimum for a balance between high yield and low
moisture.

Tests 22–24 show that without the use of flocculant even
doubling the pick-up time does very little to increase the cake
yield markedly. Moisture contents of the untreated cakes are
high (32–34%). In contrast, tests 18–21, with flocculant at the
modest dosage level of 13 g/t, show much better pick-up, which
can be increased further by extending the pick-up time.
Moisture contents of the cakes are significantly lower for the
tests in which flocculant is used.

Particle size analyses of the formed filter cakes show, in part,
the mechanism by which flocculant filter aids produce such
spectacular effects in improving filtration.

The whole filter cake from test 23 (no flocculant) contains
39.9% of +63 μm material and 60.1% of –63 μm particles. In
comparison with the feed slurry (49–50% –63 μm) the filter picks
up a disproportionate amount of fines when flocculant is not
used. In contrast, the whole filter cake from test number 20,
which used 13 g/t flocculant, contained 51.6% +63 μm and
48.4% –63 μm particles: this is virtually identical to the feed
slurry particle size distribution. Thus, flocculation gives a
representative filter cake in terms of particle size compared with
the slurry—a prerequisite to continued and predictable high
porosity and permeability. Taking this a step further, the cakes
from test 24 (no flocculant) and test 21 (13 g/t flocculant) were
split approximately in half lengthways and each half was
analysed for particle size. With the unflocculated cake the top
half in contact with the filter cloth contained 56.6% –63 μm and
43.4% +63 μm particles, whereas the corresponding lower half
contained 72.6% -63 μm and 27.4% +63 μm material. Thus, in an
unflocculated filter cake the particle size distribution is uneven,
the majority of the fines being picked up towards the end of the
form time. This is contrary to popular belief, but indicates why
increasing the pick-up time on untreated slurry (tests 22–24)
does little to increase the filter yield. The flocculated filter cake
from test 21 showed 44.3% –63 μm and 55.7% +63 μm particles
at the top half of the leaf cake in contact with the filter cloth and
49.7% –63 μm and 50.3% +63 μm material in the bottom half,
i.e. a much more evenly distributed cake in terms of particle size.

Thus, one of the mechanisms by which flocculants produce a
more porous and permeable filter cake is by producing a more
even particle size distribution within the cake by preventing the
preferential pick-up of fines.

References
1.   Moss N. Theory of flocculation. *Mine Quarry*, **7**, May 1978, 57–61.
2.   Pearse M. J. and Barnett J. Chemical treatments for thickening and
filtration. In *Second World filtration congress, London, 1979* (Croydon:
Uplands Press, 1979), 333–54.
3.   Hunter T. K. and Pearse M. J. The use of flocculants and
surfactants for dewatering in the mineral processing industry. In
Preprints – XIV international mineral processing congress, Toronto, 1982,
session IX, pap. 11, 45 p.
4.   Pearse M. J. and Allen A. P. Chemical treatments for optimum
filtration performance. In *Filtech conference, London, 1981* (Croydon:
Uplands Press, 1981), 39–58.

Modified aldoxime reagents for the solvent extraction of copper

R. F. Dalton and G. W. Seward

Synopsis

Until about 1976 the commercial production of copper by solvent extraction was based entirely on the use of extractants of the aryl ketoxime type. These products, although acknowledged as being innovative at the time, lacked flexibility both in the range of feed solutions that could be treated and the size of plant that was required to operate with them.

More recently, the introduction of second-generation reagents based on formulations of the stronger hydroxy benzaldoximes, especially the ACORGA P5000 Series reagents, has led to major improvements in cost-effectiveness of the solvent extraction process and widened considerably the range of feed solutions that can be treated.

Further developments since the introduction of the original nonyl phenol modified ACORGA P5000 reagents have resulted in commercialization of other aldoxime-based reagents with alternative modifiers. As well as affecting the strength of the reagent, various modifiers have differing effects on other important properties of the extractant.

The way in which strip modifiers work and the properties, advantages and disadvantages of all types of modified aldoxime systems are discussed with a view to clarifying the picture for those who work in the field. Ultimately, the choice of reagent depends on that most suited to the particular feed conditions and the relative importance of various properties of the reagents herein discussed.

Historical perspective

The past five years have seen significant changes take place in the commercial application of solvent extraction to the production of copper, mainly because of the introduction of strong extractants based on formulations of aromatic hydroxy aldoximes with equilibrium modifiers.

Acorga Ltd., with the ACORGA P5000 Series, was the first company to market this development by ICI Organics Division with the commercialization of their reagents ACORGA P5300 and P5100 at the Arizona mines of Inspiration Consolidated Copper Co. and Kennecott, Ray Mines Division, in October, 1979, and February, 1980, respectively. More recently, Henkel Corporation followed this development with the introduction of their

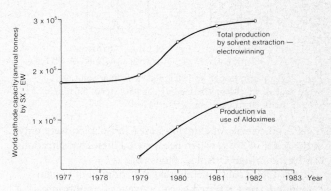

Fig. 1 Growth of world copper production by solvent extraction–electrowinning and proportion produced by use of aldoxime extractants

dodecylsalicylaldoxime range. Acorga has also introduced a further variant, PT5050. All of these 'second-generation' reagents, as they have become known, have notable advantages over the original ketoxime reagents, such as LIX64N (Henkel Corp.) and SME529 (Shell Chemicals), and their success is well illustrated by Fig. 1, which shows the increase that has occurred since 1979 in installed copper capacity that utilizes modified aldoxime extractants as compared to the total growth in copper capacity by solvent extraction–electrowinning over the same time period.

(I)   (II)

The considerable advantages of high strength, very fast kinetics, rapid phase separation and high copper–iron selectivity inherent in aromatic aldoximes such as ICI's P50 (I), the active component of Acorga extractants, compared to the ketoxime extractants (II) were recognized in the early 1970s, but a difficulty in commercialization of such a product lay in its relatively poor stripping when contacted with a typical spent electrolyte containing 30 g/l Cu^{2+} and 150 g/l sulphuric acid in the then existing plants. This resulted in poor utilization of the extractant and a low copper transfer efficiency, defined as the amount of copper transferred between loading and stripping stages as a percentage of the maximum copper loading capacity of the reagent. Typically, with the ketoxime reagents transfer efficiencies of 50–60% were obtained at organic to aqueous flow ratios that approximated to 1:1, whereas it was found that although aldoxime extractants were capable of producing very low copper raffinates in fewer stages,

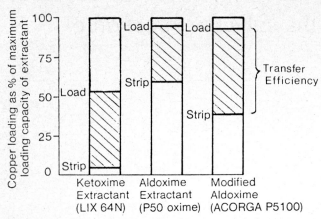

Fig. 2 Copper in loaded and stripped extractant solutions as percentage of stoichiometric loading capacity (feed, 3.0 g/l Cu^{++}, pH 2.0; strip, 30 g/l Cu^{++} and 150 g/l H$_2$SO$_4$)

transfer efficiencies of aldoximes used in isolation were only of the order of 30%, which necessitated high concentrations of reagent or high O/A flow ratios (Fig. 2).

It was found subsequently that the addition of certain compounds, now referred to collectively as equilibrium modifiers, would reduce the copper complexing power of the aldoxime by a degree dependent on the amount added. Further, the addition of moderate amounts of modifier gave a marked improvement in stripping and transfer efficiency, but with little change of performance under extraction conditions. The first commercial formulations to utilize this discovery were the ACORGA reagents P5100 and P5300, which are based on mixtures of P50 oxime with nonyl phenol. The reagent ACORGA P5100 is a strong reagent, but with a much better transfer efficiency (50–60%) than the unmodified aldoxime, and is capable of giving excellent copper recovery in purpose-built plants that employ relatively few extraction stages.

The effect of the combination of the advantages of high strength plus fast kinetics and phase separation of a modified aldoxime reagent over the earlier ketoxime extractants in reducing the size and capital cost of solvent extraction plants is most evident in comparing two plants that currently operate in Arizona, U.S.A., and with virtually identical copper cathode production capacities. The first, designed and built to run on the earlier ketoxime reagent, employs two parallel streams of solvent extraction, each containing four extraction and two strip mixer–settlers with a total settler area of 6600 m². The second plant, built in the late 1970s, and running on ACORGA P5100, utilizes only two extraction plus two strip mixer–settlers in a single stream with a total settler area of only 1935 m².

The extractant ACORGA P5300 contains a higher proportion of nonyl phenol modifier, and is hence a weaker extractant, though still somewhat stronger than the earlier ketoxime extractants. It enabled the very advantageous properties inherent in P50 aldoxime to be carried forward into a formulation that was fully compatible with the first-generation reagents and could be added as make up to existing plants designed to run on the earlier reagents, thus upgrading their performance over a period of time as more ACORGA P5300 was added.[1] Nonyl phenol, however, was found to cause an unacceptable degree of swelling of certain rubber components present in some of the earlier solvent extraction plants, and ACORGA PT5050 was developed partly to improve on this aspect. ACORGA PT5050 is based on a formulation of P50 aldoxime with tridecanol as modifier. Tridecanol itself gives virtually no swelling of nitrile rubber. A number of other effects were also observed on changing the modifier (see later).

The Henkel products LIX622 and LIX6022 are similarly stated to be based on formulations of an aldoxime (2-hydroxy-5-dodecyl-benzaldoxime) with tridecanol.[2] The modifiers themselves are not involved in interacting with the metal in these formulations but serve primarily to modify the strength of the aldoxime extractant. They are thus referred to here as *non-chelating* modifiers. Henkel have also recently introduced other formulations, which are stated to be simple mixtures of an aldoxime extractant with their earlier ketoxime formulations LIX64N and LIX65N.[2] It has been suggested that in these extractants the ketoxime acts in some way as a modifier for the salicylaldoxime on the strip side of the solvent extraction circuit.[3]

The ability of certain hydroxy aryl ketoximes to act as modifiers for aromatic aldoximes leads to a convenient classification of modifier types as (1) non-chelating equilibrium modifiers, e.g. tridecanol and nonyl phenol, and (2) chelating equilibrium modifiers.

The mechanism of reagent strength modification and the effect of various modifier systems on the properties of extractants are discussed later.

Equilibrium modifier effect

The major effect of the addition of a modifier to a strong aldoxime extractant is to cause some weakening of the extractive power of the metal complexing agent. For moderate amounts of modifier the effect is very pronounced under strip conditions, but the improvement in stripping that is obtained tails off asymptotically as more modifier is added. Under extraction conditions copper loadings are initially fairly insensitive to modifier concentration, but they begin to fall quite abruptly as modifier concentration is increased. Various compounds that have a modifying effect are quite different in the extent of that effect for a given weight of modifier—for example, tridecanol is a much stronger modifier than nonyl phenol (Fig. 3) and a similar modifying effect is obtained with the use of only about 40% by weight of the amount of nonyl phenol required.

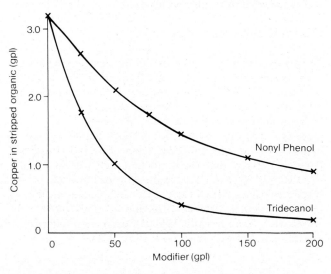

Fig. 3 Minimum copper concentration in stripped organic as a function of modifier concentration

It is evident immediately from curves of copper in loaded and stripped extractant solutions as a function of modifier content (Fig. 4) that there is a considerable gain in transfer efficiency by the addition of moderate amounts of modifier. The degree of modification—and, hence, transfer efficiency—of the formulation to be used must, of course,

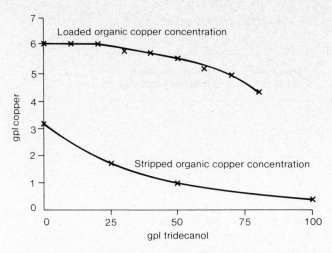

Fig. 4 Copper in loaded and stripped extractant solutions (50 g/l P50 oxime) as a function of tridecanol concentration

be set against other requirements, such as the overall copper recovery that is required.

Infrared spectroscopic studies have shown that nonyl phenol interacts with P50 oxime by a hydrogen bonding mechanism in which the proton in the oxime hydroxyl group forms a hydrogen bond with the acceptor oxygen atom in nonyl phenol.

In non-polar solvents, such as kerosene, P50 oxime is strongly associated into dimers (and possibly higher agglomerates) by intermolecular hydrogen bonding. Nonyl phenol has the dual effects of breaking up these dimers, thus giving a different ligand order dependence to the copper distribution, and of solvating the oxime extractant.[4] It can be shown that the more strongly solvated an extractant is in the organic phase the weaker it becomes as an extractant.[5] We have, however, found no evidence for any interaction between nonyl phenol and the copper complex of P50 oxime.

Although this effect has been studied and reported for mixtures of 2-hydroxy-5-nonylbenzaldoxime (P50) and nonyl phenol,[4] the proposed mechanism can be extended to embrace other oxygen-containing compounds that can associate with the oxime proton by hydrogen bonding. These compounds include esters, ketones, alcohols, ethers and other hydroxy aryloximes. It follows that, in the absence of steric effects, the hydrogen-bonding effect and, hence, degree of modification obtained with a particular compound will be a feature of the electron density on the acceptor oxygen atom in that compound with which a hydrogen bond is formed. Thus, aliphatic alcohols and ethers, which have a much higher electron density on the oxygen atom than phenols, are more powerful modifiers.

Confirmation that this mechanism can be extended to compounds other than nonyl phenol, and that there is indeed a correlation between degree of modification and the formation of a hydrogen-bonded species between the oxime and modifier, is provided by infrared spectroscopic studies

that involve mixtures of P50 oxime and both nonyl phenol and tridecanol as modifiers.

Infrared spectra were recorded in 0.1-mm cells for 5% solutions in hexane of 2-hydroxy-5-nonyl-benzaldoxime (P50) and of various concentrations of modifier. The spectra were recorded on a Perkin Elmer 580B infrared spectrophotometer combined with PE 3600 data station, which gave the facility for combining spectra additively. Spectra were also recorded for mixtures of 5% P50 oxime with various amounts of modifiers. The spectra for these mixtures were then compared with the combined spectra for the two components, any differences in the two sets of spectra being due to interaction between oxime and modifier.

The most obvious effect of modifier addition is a progressive decrease in the intensity of the free oximino OH band in the spectrum of the oxime at 3610 cm^{-1}. There is also, on adding modifier, the appearance of a band centred at 3350 cm^{-1} due to formation of a hydrogen-bonded complex between oximino –OH and modifier. This band increases in intensity with increasing concentration of modifier. From careful measurement of the optical densities of these bands for the various solutions estimates have been made of the relative amounts of different oxime species at various modifier concentrations (Table 1). Similar ratios of free monomeric oxime:dimer:hydrogen-bonded complex are obtained with solutions that contain about half the amount by weight of tridecanol of those modified with nonyl phenol.

For aryl ketoximes, which are themselves copper chelating compounds, it is believed that under extraction conditions both the aldoxime and ketoxime participate in the extraction of copper, either independently or, quite possibly, by also forming some mixed–ligand complex. It is suggested that under strip conditions more of the weaker ketoxime is displaced initially from the copper and then acts as a hydrogen-bonding modifier by associating with the aldoxime as it is stripped. A free hydroxy aryloxime can, of course, be viewed as merely another substituted phenol.

An interaction between the aldoxime and chelating ketoxime modifier has been confirmed—again by infrared spectroscopy.

Measurements of the infrared spectra of 0.075 M hexane solutions of P50 oxime, LIX64N, and mixtures of the two show an interaction between them by a hydrogen-bonding mechanism. The spectra show that at the same oxime concentrations solutions of LIX64N contain a higher proportion of dimer than solutions of the aldoxime (P50) used in the ACORGA P5000 reagents. A reduction in the intensity of the band at 3610 cm^{-1} for the 'free' non-hydrogen-bonded OH bond in the spectrum of a 1:1 mixture of the oximes in comparison with the combined spectra for the two individual components, together with the increase in intensity of a band centred at 3410 cm^{-1}, shows an increased degree of association in the mixture (Fig. 5).

Properties of equilibrium-modified formulations

In practical terms equilibrium modifiers can affect the following major properties of reagents: (1) shape and position of isotherms; (2) copper transfer efficiency; (3) copper recovery; (4) reaction kinetics; (5) selectivity; (6) phase disengagement; (7) hydrolytic stability; (8) effect on materials of construction; and (9) formation of crud and stable emulsions.

It is with due regard to this combination of properties

Table 1 Various hydroxyoxime species as a function of modifier concentration for 5% P50 oxime in hexane

Modifier	Monomeric oxime, %	Associated oxime, %	Oxime-modifier H-bonded complex, %
None	24	76	–
2% Nonyl phenol	21	56	23
4%	16	23	61
6%	11	9	80
8%	9	6	85
10%	8	4	88
1% Tridecanol	21	56	23
2%	17	29	54
3%	14	17	69
4%	12	11	77
5%	10	8	82

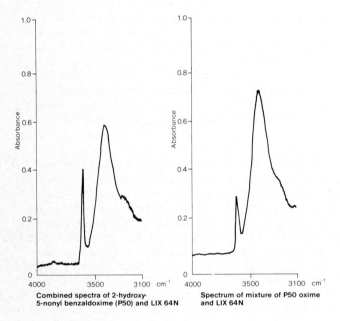

Combined spectra of 2-hydroxy-5-nonyl benzaldoxime (P50) and LIX 64N

Spectrum of mixture of P50 oxime and LIX 64N

Fig. 5 Infrared spectra

and the requirements of a particular solvent extraction circuit that appropriate reagent selection should be made, and against this background that the relative merits of various formulations are discussed.

Formulations based on mixtures of aldoximes with non-chelating modifiers exhibit many of the advantageous properties of the salicylaldoximes referred to earlier, with the added advantage that flexibility and variation of certain properties can be built in by appropriate choice of modifier and the amount of modifier in the formation.

Acorga's current product range is based on 2-hydroxy-5-nonyl-benzaldoxime (P50 oxime, mol wt 263), which is manufactured to a high degree of purity and available for use modified with 5-nonyl phenol, as in ACORGA P5100 and ACORGA P5300, or, alternatively, modified with tridecanol in ACORGA PT5050.

The method of numbering acting as a clear guide to the product formulation, the number '5' is used to identify with the ACORGA P5000 Series and the remaining three digits, when decimalized after the first, display the ratio of modifier in the formulation relative to the oxime: thus

P5100   equivalent to oxime : nonyl phenol ratio 1:1
P5300   equivalent to oxime : nonyl phenol ratio 1:3
PT5050 equivalent to oxime : tridecanol ratio 1:0.5

The range offered by Acorga is designed to cover all practical eventualities that arise in terms of feed solutions to be treated.[6] With moderate to strong feeds (3–20 g/l Cu) use of a strong extractant gives optimum copper recovery in the minimum number of extraction stages. At the weak end of practical use, however, when both the copper concentration and acidity of the feed are low, as is the case with many dump leaching operations, a weaker extractant that maximizes transfer efficiency may be a more economic proposition, particularly for older solvent extraction plants that were built with more than two extraction stages.[1]

Reagent formulations recently introduced by Henkel, Inc., and referred to earlier as containing a chelating modifier, bring together their original ketoxime reagents (LIX64N and LIX65N) and a salicylaldoxime (LIX860, 2-hydroxy-5-dodecylbenzaldoxime, mol wt 305). Such a combination is being marketed as LIX864, which contains a 1:1 combination of aldoxime and ketoxime.[3]

Although some of the properties of this combination are no doubt simply associated with the parent constituents, others, such as transfer efficiency, are claimed to be enhanced as a result of the ketoxime–aldoxime combination. The mechanism proposed by Henkel is as discussed earlier, the ketoxime acting under strip conditions in an analogous fashion to the non-chelating modifiers.[3]

The utility in ketoxime–aldoxime mixtures of this type lies not in any advancement in performance that they offer over aldoximes formulated with non-chelating modifiers but, essentially, in the convenience that they may offer to operators of existing plants who use first-generation ketoxime reagents to upgrade their operation. A number of plants are making use of this facility to upgrade the performance of their current ketoxime reagent.

The benefits that each plant is seeking vary from one to another, but they are primarily improved copper recovery and the ability to achieve increased production from existing plant by increasing copper tenor in the feed solution while maintaining a high copper recovery through the upgrading of the extractant to second-generation performance on addition of an aldoxime reagent.

To illustrate the options that the currently available ranges of reagents offer for upgrading to second-generation performance we have considered the upgrading of a plant originally designed to operate with a first-generation ketoxime extractant with three stages of extraction and two of stripping. The plant has been running with a feed of 3 g/l copper and 1 g/l iron at pH 2.0 and the composition of the spent electrolyte used for stripping is 30 g/l Cu^{2+} and

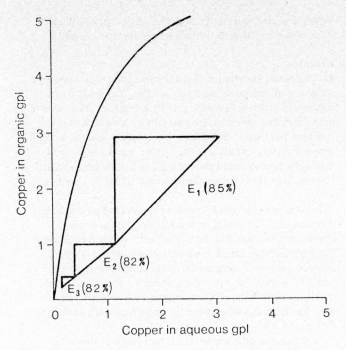

Fig. 6   Extraction of copper by 12 v/o LIX64N-HS in Escaid 100 (feed, 3.06 g/l Cu^{++}, 1 g/l Fe^{3+}, pH 2.0; strip, 30 g/l Cu^{++} and 180 g/l H_2SO_4)

180 g/l H_2SO_4. Consider the case in which the reagent in use is a commercial weak ketoxime extractant (LIX64N-HS) at a concentration of 12 v/o. The extraction isotherm for this situation is shown in Fig. 6 together with the stage to stage extraction profiles based on the average data accumulated from 12 samplings of a pilot-plant operation running under steady-state conditions. The bracketed values for stages E_1, E_2 and E_3 refer to the respective observed stage efficiencies. The raffinate achieved is 0.13 g/l Cu^{2+}, giving a copper recovery of 95.7%.

If, as a result of changes in the leaching conditions, it is possible to increase the copper concentration of the feed to 5 g/l, far more copper could be produced by the solvent extraction operation, provided that high copper recovery can be maintained. To do this the concentration of extractant must be increased, but the possibilities of maintaining copper recovery and producing a low copper concentration in the raffinate at higher feed concentrations with a weak ketoxime extractant are extremely limited because of the sensitivity of its extraction isotherm to the extra acid produced by removal of, say, 5 g/l Cu^{2+}. The situation is even more difficult if it is expected, as in one practical case, that the copper in the feed may go beyond 5 to, say, 7 g/l. An upgrading of the reagent in the system to second-generation performance is required therefore, and there are essentially two options, one of which uses a chelating modifier approach, the other relying on a linear progression towards second-generation performance by addition of an aldoxime–non-chelating modifier formulation.[1]

Option 1   Addition of aldoxime to weak ketoxime extractant to form chelating modifier–reagent system
The equivalent of 34 g/l 2-hydroxy-5-dodecylsalicylaldoxime was added to 12 v/o LIX64N-HS and a laboratory-scale continuous countercurrent solvent extraction circuit was operated under exactly the same conditions as the original LIX64N experiment described above, except that the concentration of copper in the feed was raised to 5 g/l. The

extraction isotherm for this system is shown in Fig. 7 with a McCabe–Thiele construction based again on the averaged values for numerous measurements of the various stage to stage concentrations. The bracketed values again refer to observed stage efficiencies. The average raffinate achieved was 0.13 g/l Cu^{2+}, as before.

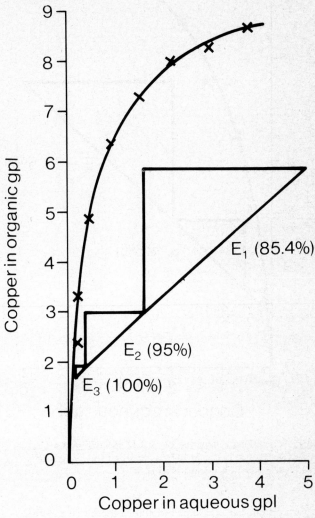

Fig. 7   Extraction of copper by 12 v/o LIX64N-HS plus 34 g/l of 2-hydroxy-5-dodecylbenzaldoxime in Escaid 100 (feed, 5.09 g/l Cu^{++}, 1 g/l Fe^{3+}, pH 2.0; strip, 30 g/l Cu^{++} and 180 g/l H_2SO_4)

Option 2   Addition of reagent containing non-chelating modifier (ACORGA PT5050) to resident weak ketoxime extractant
Allowing for the difference in molecular weights of the aldoximes, the weight of nonyl aldoxime in ACORGA PT5050 equivalent to 34 g/l of the dodecylaldoxime is 29.3 g/l. This required the addition of ACORGA PT5050 equivalent to a concentration of 6.4 v/o in the extractant solution. Again the laboratory-scale pilot plant was run for several hours to equilibrate with the 5 g/l Cu^{2+} feed and numerous samples were taken over a time period. The effect on the isotherms in this mixture is quite linear with respect to the amount of ACORGA PT5050 added, there being no synergism between the two reagents. The extraction isotherm is shown in Fig. 8 together with a McCabe–Thiele construction that represents the experimentally determined data as before. The net result in terms of copper recovery is effectively the same as that for the chelating modified system.

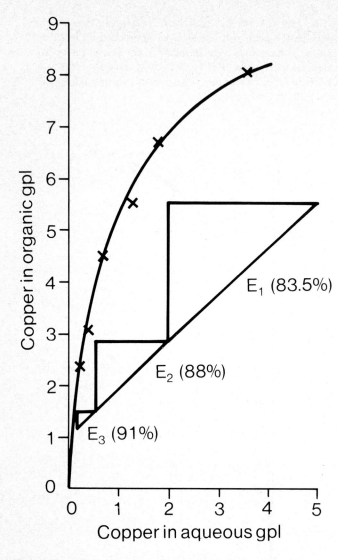

Fig. 8 Extraction of copper by 12 v/o LIX64N-HS plus 6.4 v/o ACORGA PT5050 in Escaid 100 (feed, 5.01 g/l Cu^{++}, 1 g/l Fe^{3+}, pH 2.0; strip 30 g/l Cu^{++} and 180 g/l H$_2$SO$_4$)

With option 1 it is assumed that after the initial addition of the aldoxime both to upgrade the reagent performance and to give the increased concentration of oxime required to deal with a 5 g/l copper feed, make-up of reagent would be with an approximately 1:1 molar ratio of aldoxime and ketoxime.

In option 2 the initial addition of 6.4 v/o ACORGA PT5050 does not necessarily represent the final stage of upgrading reagent performance. As reagent is lost from the system by entrainment, make-up with further quantities of ACORGA PT5050 leads progressively to a situation in which the plant is running almost entirely on this reagent: pilot trials have shown that a raffinate of 0.1 g/l copper can be produced from a 5 g/l copper feed at pH 2 with only 17 v/o ACORGA PT5050.

It may sometimes appear that on the basis of isotherms alone there may under certain circumstances be little to choose between one modifier system and another. Modifiers have different effects on various properties of reagent formulations, however, and this may have a considerable bearing on the final choice of reagent for a given application, particularly under more extreme conditions.

Consider, for example, a case in which the aqueous runoff from a leaching dump is at low temperature and heavily contaminated with iron. The effects of different modifiers on such properties as reaction kinetics, phase separation, and selectivity then become of considerable importance in the selection of the appropriate reagent.

Kinetics

It is common knowledge that the kinetics of extraction and stripping of certain hydroxy aldoximes, such as P50, are inherently much faster than for the ketoximes. The rates of extraction by ketoximes are basically so slow that it is common practice to add a kinetics synergist such as a small amount of an aliphatic hydroxyoxime, e.g. LIX63, as in LIX64N, and yet even the kinetics of this reagent are still considerably slower than the aromatic aldoximes, such as P50.

It is known that the addition of modifiers to aldoximes causes some retardation of the kinetics, but at normal operating temperatures the overall rates are still extremely fast and the retardation is of little consequence. Table 2, however, shows a comparison of the kinetic properties of a series of reagents at two temperatures (0 and 25°C). The molar concentration of the oxime in each reagent solution was the same (0.3 M) and the feed was 6 g/l Cu^{2+} and 3 g/l Fe^{3+} at pH 2.0.

The experimental methods for carrying out this comparison are as described elsewhere.[7] This collection of data clearly illustrates the superiority of the aldoxime extractants over a ketoxime even when, as in the case of LIX64N, it contains a kinetic modifier. The main point of interest, however, lies in the different effect between tridecanol and nonyl phenol on the kinetics under low-temperature conditions. Clearly, although still superior to the ketoxime reagent LIX64N-HS, the highly favourable kinetic properties of the nonyl phenol modified salicylaldoxime (ACORGA P5100) are considerably diminished at 0°C in comparison with the unmodified aldoxime reagent P50 oxime at 0°C, and with ACORGA P5100 at 25°C. On the other hand, the kinetics of the tridecanol-modified product ACORGA PT5050 are affected far less by low-temperature operation and it is only tridecanol-modified aldoxime reagents that seem best capable of giving good stage efficiencies at low temperatures.

There appears to be no kinetic synergism present in mixtures of aldoxime and ketoxime reagents, and at both temperatures the approach to equilibrium for a 1:1 mixture of P50 oxime and LIX64N-HS is slightly less than the average of the values for each component in the mixture.

Phase disengagement

Table 3 records phase separation data for a range of reagents at 0 and 25°C. Again, reagent concentrations are all at a total oxime content of 0.3 M, the feed 6 g/l Cu^{2+} and 3 g/l Fe^{3+} at pH 2.0, and the strip solution of 30 g/l Cu^{2+} and 150 g/l H$_2$SO$_4$. These data represent coalescence times recorded in a stirred vessel according to the standard procedures set out in Acorga technical literature.[7]

When considering the phase disengagement properties of reagents, static tests of this type can only act as a guide to performance. They do not provide design data from which equipment can be sized, as this can only really be obtained under continuous dynamic conditions in pilot-scale mixer-settlers, but such tests can provide useful comparative data on various reagents.

It is evident from these data, which formed the basis for an initial screening of reagents for low-temperature operation, that the tridecanol-modified aldoxime formulation ACORGA PT5050 is again considerably less susceptible to the effects of operating at lower temperatures. Under these conditions phase separation is considerably

Table 2 Rates of extraction and stripping for various reagents at 0 and 25°C

| Reagent | Approach to equilibrium,% | | | | | |
| | 0°C | | | 25°C | | |
	Extract 15 s	Extract 30 s	Strip 15 s	Extract 15 s	Extract 30 s	Strip 15 s
P50 oxime (C_9 aldoxime)	95.6	97.3	89.7	99.3	100	98
ACORGA P5100	61.0	64.4	72.6	91.0	96.2	99.4
ACORGA PT5050	81.0	85.6	90.6	95.2	96.5	100
LIX64N-HS	55.9	62.8	42.1	81.4	86.3	81.7
1:1 mixture of C_9 aldoxime(P50) and LIX64N-HS oxime	70.9	75.4	45.2	88.1	94.1	87.9
1:1 mixture of C_{12} aldoxime and LIX64N-HS	59.7	64.0	43.4	–	–	–

Table 3 Phase disengagement rates of various reagents

| Reagent | Phase disengagement, t_f, values, s | | | | | | | |
| | 0°C | | | | 25°C | | | |
	Ext. (Org)	Ext. (Aq)	Strip (Org)	Strip (Aq)	Ext. (Org)	Ext. (Aq)	Strip (Org)	Strip (Aq)
P50 oxime	80	71	24	104	61	45	97	44
ACORGA P5100	184	92	139	64	53	–	70	–
ACORGA PT5050	64	37	17	70	23	32	27	36
LIX64N-HS	226	98	217	108	82	36	128	54
1:1 mixture of P50 oxime and LIX64N-HS	122	92	241	112	54	36	100	49

faster than that of the nonyl phenol modified product, the aldoxime–ketoxime mixture, or, indeed, the kerosene solution of the aldoxime alone.

Selectivity

Selectivity of reagents is a function of both oxime and modifier type. It is also known to be influenced by such factors as degree of loading of reagent, length of contact (primarily in the mixer but also in the settler) and temperature. A simple procedure that displays both the influence of modifier type and that of copper loading on a reagent is to pre-load an organic phase with strip solution containing 40 g/l Cu^{2+} and 150 g/l H_2SO_4 contacted at O:A ratio of 1:1 for 3 min. After the phases have separated the organic is then contacted with a feed solution containing

1 g/l Cu^{2+} and 1.5 g/l Fe^{3+} at pH 2.0 at the following O:A ratios: 4:1, 2:1, 1:1 and 1:10.

After stirring for 15 min at ambient temperature samples are separated and the organic phase is filtered and analysed for Cu and Fe. Table 4 shows the results obtained by this procedure for 3.5 v/o P5100 and 3.5 v/o PT5050. Tridecanol appears to inhibit iron pick-up more than does nonyl phenol. Both extractants, however, show the influence of copper crowding, the rejection ratio progressively increasing as the reagent is more highly loaded with copper.

Data determined in this way do not, however, take into account the influence of the rate of extraction and stripping of impurity metals on the overall selectivity of the reagent for copper over other ions.

Selectivity data determined under equilibrium conditions

Table 4 Cu–Fe selectivity of ACORGA P5100 and PT5050

Reagent in Escaid 100	O:A ratio	Cu^{2+} extracted, g/l	Fe^{3+} extracted, g/l	Cu/Fe rejection ratio
3.5 v/o ACORGA P5100	4:1	1.11	0.0111	100/1
	2:1	1.35	0.0085	159/1
	1:1	1.75	0.0046	380/1
	1:10	1.95	0.0018	1083/1
3.5 v/o ACORGA PT5050	4:1	1.02	0.0075	136/1
	2:1	1.26	0.0051	247/1
	1:1	1.65	0.0009	1833/1
	1:10	1.96	0.0007	2800/1

as described above indicate that progressive addition of nonyl phenol to P50 oxime reduces the copper–iron selectivity and, thus, ACORGA P5100 appears to have better selectivity than P5300. At one location, however, the mine R & D laboratory found, after extensive pilot trials, that the higher proportion of nonyl phenol in the ACORGA P5300 formulation reduced the *rate* of iron pick-up, which resulted in a net improvement in the already excellent selectivity of P5100, and they decided to opt for ACORGA P5300 in the early years of their commercial operation. Only later did they move to ACORGA P5100 when a change in leaching methods produced a stronger feed solution.

An investigation conducted by Acorga and ICI into the problems associated with the presence of molybdenum in aqueous feed solutions to some copper SX plants revealed, among other things, that the first-generation ketoxime-based extractants, such as LIX64N, had a rejection ratio, as defined by the ratio of Cu loaded on the organic to Mo loaded on the organic, of virtually 1.0, thus making them quite unsuitable for use with copper feed solutions containing molybdenum on the grounds of selectivity. Salicylaldoximes also extract molybdenum, but to a much lesser degree, thus making salicylaldoxime formulations modified with non-chelating modifiers quite acceptable for such purposes.

organic reagents. If nitrile rubber is being used as a gasket, attack will only occur at the edges of contact and a certain degree of swelling is not necessarily bad as it ensures a better seal. In other situations, however, such as when nitrile rubber is being used as a pump gland liner or as a lining for mild-steel pipes and vessels, such attack should be avoided.

Table 6 displays the results after 20 weeks of volume swelling tests on a number of rubber materials in contact with a range of extractant solutions in Escaid 100. 25-mm discs of each material under test were suspended in each test solution at 40°C and withdrawn at regular intervals for determination of the volume swell. In each case swelling had virtually ceased after 20 weeks. Some earlier solvent extraction plants contained appreciable amounts of nitrile rubber in areas exposed to the organic reagent. As these plants have run for a number of years on LIX64N with no known problems with regard to materials of construction, LIX64N is taken as a reference point. The tridecanol-modified aldoxime extractant ACORGA PT5050 gives a degree of swelling of nitrile rubber of the same order as LIX64N at similar oxime concentrations and is therefore considered to be quite satisfactory in this regard. It is clear that natural rubber and styrene butadiene rubber (SBR) are unsuitable for use in solvent extraction plants because, unlike nitrile rubber, they give quite a high degree of

Table 5   Copper–molybdenum selectivity of various extractants

Reagent	Loaded organic		Stripped organic		Cu/Mo rejection ratio	Cu/Mo transfer ratio
	Cu, g/l	Mo, g/l	Cu, g/l	Mo, g/l		
16 v/o ACORGA PT5050	8.08	0.511	2.94	0.454	15.8	90.2
16 v/o ACORGA P5100	8.37	0.680	3.46	0.674	12.3	818
16 v/o LIX622	8.57	0.644	3.80	0.560	13.3	56.3
20 v/o LIX64N-HS	4.43	3.791	0.44	3.518	1.2	14.6

In continuous laboratory-scale countercurrent mixer–settler trials with two stages of extraction and two of stripping the nonyl phenol modified formulation ACORGA P5100 showed a lower degree of molybdenum transfer to the electrolyte circuit than either of the tridecanol-modified products (ACORGA PT5050 and LIX622) (Table 5). This appears to be due to the slow rate at which molybdenum is stripped from P5100, combined with a relatively low limiting concentration of molybdenum in the organic phase. Table 5 displays averaged data from numerous samplings during these trials. The aqueous feed solution contained 6 g/l copper and 0.5 g/l molybdenum and had a pH of 2.0. Stripping was with 30 g/l Cu^{2+} and 150 g/l H_2SO_4.

Effect of extractant formulations on materials of construction

In some circumstances the effect of reagents on certain materials of construction is an important consideration in the selection of an extractant. This is particularly true when for commercial and technical reasons an existing solvent extraction–electrowinning operation wishes to change or mix reagents. A material common to a number of solvent extraction plants is nitrile rubber, which has been shown to be susceptible to attack and swelling on contact with certain

Table 6   Swelling of various rubbers by reagents

Reagent solution	Increase in volume after 20 weeks, %			
	Natural rubber	SBR	Neoprene	Nitrile rubber
24% LIX64N	250	185	89	74
40% LIX64N	256	199	85	104
8% PT5050	246	181	92	59
22% PT5050	255	185	81	90
Escaid 100	221	168	39	2

swelling on contact with kerosene diluent alone, as well as a considerably higher swelling in contact with reagent solutions. Neoprene is almost as good as nitrile rubber in resistance to attack by reagent solutions, but it does give a considerably larger degree of swelling in contact with diluent, though not nearly as bad as that of natural rubber and SBR.

Hydrolytic stability

It is generally known that modifiers added to improve the stripping of aromatic aldoxime extractants cause an increase in the rate of degradation of the oxime by acid-catalysed hydrolysis. Several factors can cause an increase in the rate of hydrolysis of these reagents, such as the amount of modifier in the formulation. Increasing the temperature also increases the rate of hydrolysis markedly, as does increasing the acid concentration in the strip electrolyte.

It is assumed that hydrolysis takes place essentially in the strip mixers and the lifetime of reagents in practice is generally longer than that predicted by degradation tests in which reagents are stirred continuously with strip acid in laboratory experiments. Even so, to minimize costs as a result of loss of reagent the degradation rate must be acceptably slow under normal plant operating conditions. Laboratory experiments to investigate hydrolytic stability can therefore be very lengthy and there is a tendency to rely on results of accelerated degradation tests carried out at elevated temperature. This can give very misleading results, however, and great care should be taken in extrapolating the results to normal plant conditions. Table 7 shows rates of hydrolysis measured for different aldoxime formulations at 35°C, which is the recommended temperature for degradation tests. In each case the formulation contained a total of 0.38 M oxime extractant in Escaid 100, and after equilibration with strip acid was stirred continuously with fresh strip acid containing 150 g/l H_2SO_4 and 30 g/l Cu^{++}. In the aldoxime–ketoxime mixture the solution was 0.19 molar in each and the rate of hydrolysis refers to degradation of the aldoxime only.

Table 7   Initial degradation rate of aldoxime in different formulations

Reagent	Rate of loss of aldoxime at 35°C, % h^{-1}
ACORGA P5100	0.0092
1:1 mixture of C_9 aldoxime (P50) and aryl ketoxime (LIX64N)	0.0095
C_9 aldoxime (P50)	0.0041

The result for the rate of hydrolysis of the aldoxime–ketoxime mixture shows that it is quite incorrect to assume that hydrolysis of the aldoxime will be less in such formulations than in those which contain non-chelating modifiers, such as nonyl phenol and tridecanol. The rate of loss of the aldoxime in this formulation is comparable, in fact, with the rate of degradation of the aldoxime in ACORGA P5100, and is considerably faster than the degradation rate of P50 alone. This is perhaps not so surprising and is, in fact, quite consistent with the evidence presented earlier that under strip conditions the ketoxime functions as a substituted phenol.

Crud formation

An extensive study of crud generation in solvent extraction circuits[8] has shown that there are a number of causes and types of crud in solvent extraction systems. Crud is certainly not caused by the presence of modifiers and laboratory experiments have shown that quite severe crud can be generated by contacting real mine feed solutions with kerosene diluent alone. One of the main causes of crud is finely divided particles of such aluminosilicate minerals as mica and china clay suspended in the feed solution. These particles become trapped in the dispersion band and stabilize a flocculant oil–water *mélange* referred to as crud. The volume of crud generated by this cause does not seem

very sensitive at all to reagents or modifiers and just as much crud is generated on contacting feeds with kerosene alone.

Another cause of crud is believed to be precipitation in the dispersion of colloidal silica present in some siliceous feed solutions. These solutions are initially quite clear, but the silica precipitates on polymerization to a gel, which stabilizes a thick mayonnaise-like emulsion at the interface.

The generation of cruds of this type from colloidal silica seems more sensitive to a number of factors than the aluminosilicate particle stabilized crud—notably, reagent, diluent and age of feed solution—and has recently been reviewed by Ritcey.[9]

It has been suggested that interactions of colloidal silica with reagents and modifiers may be responsible for the generation of cruds in solvent extraction circuits.[2] Again, however, laboratory work has shown that this is not the dominant factor because of the readiness with which cruds are generated on contacting clear feeds that contain colloidal silica with diluents alone. Reagents and modifiers can have an effect on interfacial tensions and, thus, influence droplet size and entrainment and the addition of certain modifiers has, in fact, been advocated[9] as a means of overcoming crud problems due to the formation of emulsions.

Our own programme of experimental work with side by side comparisons with the use of real siliceous mine solutions showed very little difference between a number of reagents, including tridecanol-modified reagents and mixtures of aldoximes and ketoximes. Throughout this work, however, the nonyl phenol modified product ACORGA P5100 performed consistently well without the production of any stable emulsion bands, and there is clear evidence that nonyl phenol has a beneficial, but as yet unexplained, effect in suppressing the generation of cruds from colloidal silica. This is also consistent with practical experience of a number of plants that operate with Acorga nonyl phenol modified aldoxime extractants. In general these have been particularly clean operations with hardly any crud of this type, despite operating with highly siliceous feeds due to crysocolla in the orebody.

Conclusions

The use of such modifiers as nonyl phenol and tridecanol to improve stripping was a critical discovery in the commercialization of *o*-hydroxyaryloximes for the solvent extraction of copper. It enabled the harnessing of the excellent copper recovery capabilities of these strong extractants to practical situations and the formulation of a new range of extractants with greatly improved kinetics, selectivity and phase disengagement. The growth since 1979 of installed capacity for the production of copper by the solvent extraction process is entirely accounted for by the use of modified aldoxime extractants—mainly in new compact highly cost-efficient plants that recover copper from a wider range of feed concentrations than had been contemplated previously.

The recent use of ketoximes in admixture with aldoximes is not intrinsically different in mechanism or result from the use of mixtures of aldoximes with non-chelating modifiers. Both oximes contribute to the extraction of copper, the strength of the mixed reagent being intermediate between that of the two components. Under strip conditions, however, the readily liberated ketoxime acts as a substituted phenol in modifying the aldoxime by a hydrogen-bonding mechanism.

Various modifiers can have quite different effects on the properties of extractants, and the selection of a particular reagent depends on choosing that most appropriate to the feed solution and the particular local requirements.

References

1. Tumilty J. A. Dalton R.F. and Massam J. P. The Acorga P-5000 series: a novel range of solvent extraction reagents for copper. In *Advances in extractive metallurgy 1977* Jones M. J. ed. (London: IMM, 1977), 123–31.

2. Kordosky G. A. Sierakostki J. M. and House J. E. The LIX860 series: unmodified copper extraction reagents. Paper presented to ISEC '83: international solvent extraction conference, Denver, August 1983.

3. Kordosky G. A. Hein H. C. and McGowen E. J. The recovery of copper from sulphuric acid leach solutions: a state of the art look at reagents. Paper presented to II Symposium Nacional de Ingenieria Metalúrgica organizado por la Universidad Nacional Alcides Carron, Peru, 1983.

4. Dalton R. F. The effect of alkyl phenols on the copper transfer properties of the extractant Acorga P-1. In *ISEC 77, Toronto, 1977* (Montreal: Canadian Institute of Mining and Metallurgy, 1979), 40–8. (*CIM Spec. vol.* 21)

5. Morrison G. H. and Freiser H. *Solvent extraction in analytical chemistry* (New York, etc.: Wiley, 1957), 280 p.

6. Tumilty J. A. Seward G. W. and Massam J. P. The ACORGA P-5000 series in the solvent extraction of copper: performance characteristics and implications for plant economics. Reference 4, vol. 2, 542–51.

7. Acorga Ltd., c/o ICI PLC Organics Division, Manchester, England. Standard methods of test. *Mining Chemicals Tech. Inf. Sheet* MC 3.80.

8. Dalton R. F. Maes C. J. and Severs K. J. Aspects of crud formation in solvent extraction systems. Paper presented to Arizona Section of AIME, Tucson, Arizona, Dec. 1983.

9. Ritcey G. M. Crud in solvent extraction processing—a review of causes and treatment. *Hydrometall.*, **5,** 1980, 97–107.

Reagent selection for treatment of an Argentinian porphyry ore

J. P. Gil, P. E. Sarquís and J. A. Matar

Synopsis
The results of a study to determine optimum flotation conditions for the Bajo La Alumbrera ore are briefly described. To establish a reagent schedule batch tests were performed that compared copper–gold grades and recoveries and applied Klimpel's methodology as an aid in the assessment.

Different types, proportions and dosages of collectors, frothers and modifiers commonly used with such ores were tested. A combination of potassium amyl xanthate and isopropyl ethyl thionocarbamate collectors, plus lime for pH adjustment and pyrite depression, plus a mixture of alcohol and polyglycol frothers, produced the best results.

The Bajo La Alumbrera porphyry copper–gold deposit is located in the northwest of the Argentine Republic. After the completion of 19 000 m of diamond drilling the exploration stage is nearly completed. Estimated reserves are 576 000 000 t with 0.56% copper and 0.67 g/t gold. Of this total, 60% (average grade, 0.54% copper and 0.73 g/t gold) is planned to be mined by open-pit. In addition, the deposit has 61 000 000 t of surface ore with 0.19% copper and 0.47 g/t gold, which will be leached by heap cyanidation for gold recovery. Reserves estimation and pit design have made use of geostatistical methods and computerized calculations.

The Instituto de Investigaciones Mineras is carrying out an integrated study, at ground plan level, which includes reserve estimation, mining, metallurgical testwork, and feasibility studies. Beneficiation studies[1,5,6] at the Institute and in other laboratories[2,3,4] have shown that the ore is amenable to conventional flotation processing.

This paper deals with aspects of the study that were aimed at optimizing copper and gold flotation performance.

All work conducted to date has been at the laboratory bench-scale level. The most important operating conditions were analysed by direct comparison of grades and recoveries. The findings related to primary grinding, rougher flotation, regrinding of rougher concentrate, cleaning and losses of gold in the tails, are given here.

The effects of the type, proportion and dosage of collectors and frothers on the kinetics of gold and copper extraction were analysed by Klimpel's kinetic parameters method[14] and also by direct comparison of grades and recoveries. By locked-cycle tests[6] the response of various ore types to simulated continuous processing was evaluated under the best conditions determined in the previous studies.

The investigation was concentrated on copper and gold—the metals of greatest economic interest; those factors which affect molybdenum and silver recovery will be analysed later.

Samples

Three basic ore types were studied: samples that represent alteration facies (A, potassic zone; B, silicate zone; C, sericitic zone); composites representative of surface mineralization from various depths and with different grades and copper/gold ratios (E, F, G and H); and samples that represent primary mineralization (sulphides) in the central zone of the orebody with different copper and gold contents (I, J and K). Table 1 gives the chemical composition of these samples

Mineralogical composition

Mineralogical examination by transmitted light microscopy,[1,5,6] complemented by X-ray diffraction analysis,[1,5,6] demonstrated the presence of the following mineral species.
Copper minerals: chalcopyrite in grain sizes from 10 to 250 μm, chalcocite, covellite and minor quantities of oxidized primary minerals, including malachite, chrysocolla and digenite, mainly in the surface zone of the ore deposit. Chalcopyrite, the major economic copper mineral is frequently associated with and included in magnetite. When free it often lies interstitially between gangue.
Iron minerals: pyrite, magnetite, hematite, goethite and marmatite.
Precious metals: gold and silver. Gold was not observed in any sample by the above techniques, but studies with a X-ray microanalyser suggest that it is associated mainly with iron and copper sulphides and, in lesser proportions, with quartz.
Gangue minerals: quartz, feldspar and mica.
Others: particles of molybdenum, galena and sphalerite.

Table 2 gives percentage mineralogical analyses of the ore types.

Table 1   Chemical composition of samples for metallurgical testwork

Sample	Ore type	% Cu total	Ox. Cu, %	Au, g/t	Ag, g/t	Mo, %	Magnetite %
A	Primary potassic	0.55	0.027	0.7	2.0	0.001	6.8
B	Primary silicate	0.63	0.027	1.0	2.0	0.03	13.8
C	Primary sericitic	0.31	0.019	0.5	1.0	0.03	4.0
E	Secondary	1.28	0.12	2.0	3.0	0.002	13.6
F	Secondary	0.66	0.14	1.6	3.0	0.0001	3.8
G	Secondary	1.14	0.32	1.6	2.5	—	4.7
H	Secondary	0.70	0.11	1.1	2.0	—	5.3
I	Sulphide	0.98	0.03	1.5	2.0	0.0001	5.0
J	Sulphide	0.81	0.04	1.0	2.0	0.0004	3.1
K	Sulphide	0.63	0.05	0.7	2.0	0.001	6.7

Table 2   Percentage mineralogical composition

Ore type	Chalcopyrite	Covellite, digenite, chalcocite	Pyrite	Magnetite, hematite	Gangue
Primary potassic	1.4	0.1	2.9	6.8	88.8
Primary silicate	2.0	0.1	3.3	13.8	80.9
Primary sericitic	1.4	0.1	2.9	4.0	91.6
Secondary	1.8	0.2	3.6	13.6	83.3
Sulphide	1.9	0.1	3.5	12.0	82.5

Experimental procedures

Grinding
Samples (1 kg) were batch-ground in tap water in a laboratory rod-mill. In some tests a ball-mill was used.

Flotation
Flotation tests were conducted with the flowsheet presented in

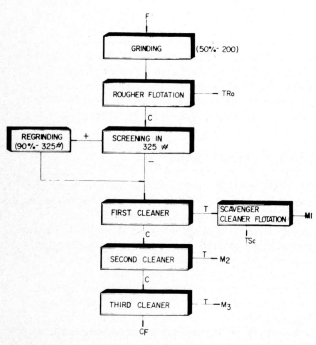

Fig. 1   Flowsheet for batch flotation test (F, feed; T, tails; C concentrate; TSc, scavenger tails; TRo, rougher tails; C_F, final concentrate; M1, M2, M3, middlings)

Fig. 1 in a Denver laboratory flotation machine to which a measuring and regulating air-flow system was attached.

Reagents
For more precise work[17] sparingly soluble in water collectors and frothers were added in drops from hypodermic needles. Xanthates were added in dilute solutions and lime as a solid. For sample C a dispersing agent (sodium silicate) and an organic product (Dowfax)[13] were used in some tests.

Chemical analyses
Concentrates and middlings were analysed volumetrically and by fire assay, the remaining products being assessed by atomic absorption spectrophotometry.

Regrinding
The rougher concentrate was screened on a 325 mesh sieve and the +325 mesh fraction was reground in a laboratory porcelain jar mill.

Other procedures
All tests were carried out under ambient conditions, no attempt being made to control temperature and with the use of tap water.

Experimental results and considerations

Operating conditions
From tests related to non-chemical operating parameters conclusions were drawn and, in turn, applied in the evaluation of the chemical reagents.

Primary grinding
From mineralogical examination it was determined that a very fine grind would be required to fully liberate chalcopyrite from the other mineral species. Nevertheless, in porphyry copper processing economic considerations frequently dictate the adoption of a relatively coarse primary grind, fine grinding being reserved for the treatment of the resultant rougher concentrate. To assess the situation tests over a range of possible primary grinds between 55 and 80% –200 mesh were carried out. Concentrates were cleaned directly without regrinding (Fig. 2).

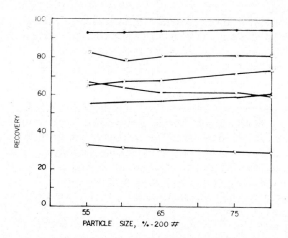

- ● ROUGHER CONCENTRATE, COPPER RECOVERY
- △ ROUGHER CONCENTRATE, GOLD RECOVERY
- ○ RECLEANER CONCENTRATE, COPPER RECOVERY
- ▽ RECLEANER CONCENTRATE, GOLD RECOVERY
- □ RECLEANER CONCENTRATE WITH MIDDLING CIRCULATION, COPPER RECOVERY
- × RECLEANER CONCENTRATE WITH MIDDLING CIRCULATION, GOLD RECOVERY

Fig. 2   Recovery, %, at particle size stated (rougher and recleaner concentrates)

Copper rougher recovery was relatively constant over the range tested, but gold rougher recovery increased gradually from 66 to 73% with decreasing particle size. Cleaner recoveries of both metals diminished with decreasing particle size, however, which confirmed the need for an intermediate concentrate regrinding stage. An economic analysis of the results indicated that a primary grind of 65% –200 mesh should offer the best results. This conclusion was applied later in closed cycle tests.

Rougher flotation

Besides grinding, stage addition of reagents and the effects of pH were investigated. Differences in the performance of collectors were noted as the number of reagent addition steps was increased. Table 3 gives results for one, two and three rougher flotation stages, which were preceded by separate addition and conditioning steps. The total reagent concentration remained constant. Stage feeding of reagents improved ultimate recovery.

Table 3 Effect of staged collector addition on rougher grade and recovery

Stages of collector addition	Grade		Recovery, %	
	Copper, %	Gold, g/t	Cu	Au
1	10.5	14.0	86.5	67.0
2	6.2	10.0	94.8	73.4
3	4.8	5.3	97.1	83.5

To analyse the influence of pH rougher tests were carried out with modification of this variable. Fig. 3 gives the effect of pH on copper and gold recovery as well as on copper grade. It shows a slight benefit in favour of maintaining the pH above 10.5, which can also be expected to assist in pyrite depression.

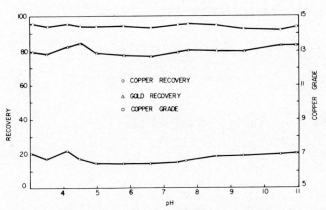

Fig. 3 Effect of pH on copper–gold grade, %, and recovery, %, in rougher concentrate

Regrinding

The mineralogical studies had indicated that a high degree of chalcopyrite liberation could only be obtained by fine grinding, and the primary grinding testwork had also shown the need for regrinding of the rougher concentrate prior to cleaner flotation. Tests to determine the amount of additional comminution required led to the adoption of a 95% –325 mesh size specification. Table 4 shows recleaner concentrate grades and recoveries with fine, coarse and no regrinding.

Table 4 Regrinding size versus final performance (sample A)

Regrinding	% –325 mesh	Grade		Recovery, %	
		Cu, %	Au, g/t	Cu	Au
No	29.9	14.0	16.0	63.2	55.0
Yes	65.0	23.9	24.1	64.0	57.0
Yes	94.0	27.2	30.2	76.1	61.0

Cleaner flotation

Testwork on reground rougher concentrates showed that three cleaning steps were necessary to yield a final product grade >20% Cu. It would also be advantageous to reduce the overall circulating loads by eliminating any feed back from the cleaning circuit to the rougher flotation and, accordingly a scavenger flotation step was introduced to treat the first cleaner tailing. Concentrate from this step would be recirculated to the regrind mill, the scavenger tailing forming a discardable reject product. The results of the introduction of this scavenger flotation operation are shown in Table 5.

Analysis of tailings losses

In all the samples studied it was noted that gold recovery was relatively low—only 65–75% in the final concentrate. With the use of bromoform and the Franz isodynamic separator mineralogical studies were performed on different tailing fractions to determine the nature of the tailings losses (Table 6).

Uniformly high copper recoveries are being achieved for all fractions coarser than 10 μm. The deterioration in the recovery of –10 μm copper is a customary consequence of the unfavourable flotation kinetics of such small particles.

Separations on the +37 μm particles show that 70% of the contained gold is finely disseminated in light silicate minerals, the remaining 30% being somewhat better liberated in the same light silicates or associated with iron oxides and unfloated sulphides. The bulk of the gold losses, however, occurs in the finer (–37 μm) fraction in which the flotation response of the gold is much worse than that of the copper, culminating in the 1.80 g/t Au loss in the –10 μm fractions. No mineralogical analysis was carried out on these fine fractions, but it would appear that the –10 μm gold-bearing particles exhibit very low flotation rates.

Flotation reagents selection

This study considered only those collectors and frothers which are commonly used in the treatment of copper sulphide ores.[7–13,15,16] The influence of type, combination and dosage has been determined by direct comparison of grades and recoveries and in special tests by a series of laboratory time–recovery experiments[14] (with calculation of associated R and K values, see later). The collectors studied were xanthates, dithiophosphates and thionocarbamates; a non-polar reagent (fuel oil) was included in each test. The frothers pine oil, synthetic alcohols, cresylic acid and polyglycols were tested. (Na ethyl xanthate, NaEX; isopropyl ethyl thionocarbamate, DTC; K amyl xanthate, KAX; mercaptobenzothiazole, R404; Na sec-butyl xanthate, SBX; alcohols, R70, R71A and MIBC; cresylic acid, CAc; pine oil, PO; and polyglycols, R65, DF250 and DF1012.)

Results from first evaluating method

Different collectors were tested independently and the joint effect of KAX and DTC in a 1:1 ratio (Table 7). The influence of dosage is shown in Table 8.

For the same dosage, slightly superior results were achieved with a 1:1 mix of KAX and DTC. Although KAX was more selective by itself, the resultant recoveries were slightly reduced. Increased dosage resulted in a better recovery. The use of a 1:2 mixture of DTC: KAX increased gold recovery by 5%.

Different types, concentrations and proportions of frothers were tested (Table 9).

Copper recovery varies directly with dosage of DF250, use of a DF 250–MIBC mixture significantly increasing copper and gold recoveries but at the marked expense of concentrate grade.

With another sample different mixtures of reagents were tested, the DF250–MIBC combination giving the most favourable results.

The modifying reagents that were tested were lime, in grinding and regrinding stages, sodium carbonate, in the cleaning stages

Table 5 Effect of scavenger flotation of first cleaner tailing on process metallurgy

First cleaner scavenger	Product	Wt%	Grade Cu, %	Au, g/t	Distribution, % Cu	Au
No	Concentrate	2.6	21.40	17.0	86.8	60.0
	Middlings 1,2,3	5.9	0.96	2.4	8.9	19.0
	Rougher tails	91.5	0.03	0.17	4.3	21.0
Yes	Concentrate	2.2	23.20	18.1	83.4	66.3
	Middling 1,2,3	1.9	2.86	2.84	8.7	8.9
	Scavenger tails	6.0	0.45	0.71	4.4	7.1
	Rougher tails	89.9	0.024	0.12	3.5	17.7

Table 6 Copper and gold distribution in products of tailings loss analyses

Product	Wt% Overall	Stage	Grade Cu, %	Au, g/t	Cu Overall	Stage	Au Overall	Stage
Tailings μm								
+74	44.7		0.02	0.12	36.1		20.5	
+37	24.7		0.02	0.12	19.9		11.3	
+20	14.8		0.02	0.25	12.0		14.2	
+10	9.8		0.026	0.34	10.1		12.6	
−10	6.0		0.09	1.80	21.9		41.3	
Feed	100.0		0.02	0.21	100.0		100.0	
Particles +37 μm Magnetics and sp. gr. higher than 2.85	14.1	20.3	0.06	0.18	33.6	60.0	9.5	29.8
Non-magnetics and sp. gr. lower than 2.85	55.3	79.7	0.01	0.10	22.4	40.0	22.3	70.2
Feed	69.4	100.0	0.02	0.12	56.0	100.0	31.8	100.0

Table 7 Effects of different collectors on rougher concentrate

Collector	Dosage, g/t	Grade Cu, %	Au, g/t	Recovery, % Cu	Au
KAX	50	9.15	11.8	94.0	74.5
R404	50	9.10	12.0	89.9	67.7
NaEX	50	10.90	10.1	87.0	59.3
SBX	50	11.00	13.5	86.9	64.5
KAX+DTC	25+25	6.20	10.0	94.8	76.0

Table 8 Effects of collector dosage on rougher concentrate

Dosage of collector, DTC + KAX	Grade Cu, %	Au, g/t	Recovery, % Cu	Au
50 + 50	6.2	10.5	94.8	78.7
30 + 30	5.9	10.2	92.5	73.4
20 + 20	6.4	10.4	86.5	71.9
30 + 60	13.9	18.0	87.0	84.0

as a partial substitute for lime, and sodiums cyanide, to aid in the separation of copper sulphides from pyrite (Table 10).

Partial substitution of sodium carbonate for lime and the use of cyanide both gave higher-grade concentrates, but adversely affected copper and gold recoveries.

Flotation reagents evaluation by Klimpel method

The evaluation of flotation batch test results by means of a kinetic parameter method allows separation of the effect of the

Table 9 Effects of type and concentration of frothers on rougher concentrate

Sample	Proportion	Reagent	Dosage, g/t	Grade Cu, %	Au, g/t	Recovery, % Cu	Au
A		DF250	20	7.6	8.6	87.8	70.1
		DF250	30	7.2	8.4	91.1	71.3
		DF250	40	7.7	9.1	93.3	71.3
	2:1	DF250+MIBC	10+10	4.8	5.3	97.1	83.5
H	2:1	DF250+MIBC	10+10	11.5	14.0	89.7	80.0
	2:1	MIBC+R70	10+10	9.0	11.1	92.5	82.5
	2:1	CAc+R70	10+10	9.6	10.4	93.2	79.8
	2:1	R71A+R70	10+10	11.6	16.6	86.7	74.9

Table 10 Results from tests with lime, soda ash and cyanide

Reagent	Dosage, kg/t	Grade Cu, %	Au, g/t	Recovery, % Cu	Au
Lime	2.8	18.0	13.8	89.0	60.0
Lime+soda ash	1.7 + 0.2	23.0	20.0	77.3	55.0
Cyanide	0.02	33.1	31.0	69.9	44.0

role of reagent type and concentration into two components—R, the ultimate equilibrium recovery at long flotation times, and K, the rate at which this potential value can be reached. Calculation of R and K was made with a model of the form

$$r = R \left\{ 1 - 1/Kt \left| 1 - e^{-Kt} \right| \right\}$$

where r is cumulative recovery at time t. The values of R and K are selected by non-linear optimization to yield the best match (least squares technique) between the calculated and observed recovery values over time (Fig. 4).

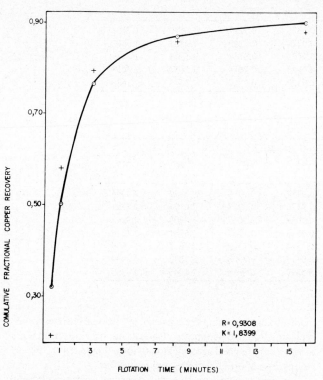

Fig. 4 Copper recovery versus flotation time (+ observed and O calculated recovery)

The reagents study was done on sample H, which is representative of the surface mineralization. Sample H exhibits a higher content of secondary copper minerals (oxidized) than the other samples, and shows correspondingly lower copper- gold recoveries and the highest reagent consumptions.

The *equipment, analytical and experimental techniques* were the same as those which were applied in the previous tests. The addition of reagents was performed in two stages—first, during grinding when the total amount of lime and the water insoluble fuel oil and thionocarbamate reagents were incorporated, and, second, during the 5-min conditioning period when the soluble KAX and frothers were added.

Cell level, sequence of froth extraction, and paddle depth were kept constant throughout the tests. The froth was extracted in five separate portions at 30 s, 1, 3, 8 and 15 min, respectively (Table 11).

To determine the estimated confidence limits for the calculated R and K parameters six tests (under the same conditions) were carried out, the following *results* being given

$$\bar{X}\,R\mathrm{Cu} = 0.9287 \pm 0.0086$$
$$\bar{X}\,R\mathrm{Au} = 0.7414 \pm 0.0186$$
$$\bar{X}\,K\mathrm{Cu} = 2.1526 \pm 0.2750$$
$$\bar{X}\,K\mathrm{Au} = 1.925 \pm 0.1786$$

The results of the collector evaluation tests are shown in Table 12. The collector combination that gave the highest recoveries was DTC–KAX (1:3) proportion; R and K are not conclusive, but in general agreement.

The results of the frother study are given in Table 13. An increased dosage of DF250 (tests 6 and 7) results in a better extraction of gold.

These results are in agreement with those given in Table 9. In addition, by direct comparison of grades and recoveries of the different combinations tested it is seen that the best results are those which correspond to test 12.

Comparison of R and K for tests 12 and 8 shows interesting results. The former has the highest R values, whereas the latter has the highest K values, which would indicate an important difference in the kinetic performance of these two frother mixtures.

Locked-cycle tests

On the basis of the conclusions of previous studies locked-cycle tests were carried out on the most important ore types. The methodology[13,17] applied is described in Fig. 5 and results are given in Table 14. Satisfactory final copper recoveries of 88–92% were obtained from all samples, reasonable gold recoveries (76–83%) were obtained from all samples except for ore C (60.9% Au recovery) and all concentrate grades exceeded 20% Cu, these products being suitable for smelter feeds.

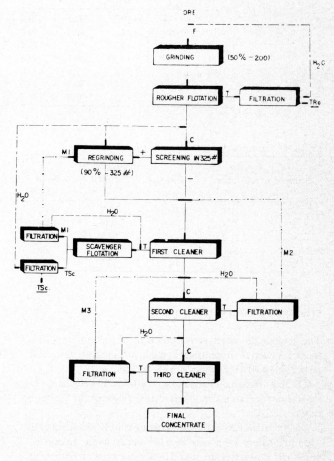

Fig. 5 Locked-cycle flotation tests

Table 11 Test programme for flotation reagents study by kinetic indexes

Test	Name	Collector Proportion	Dosage, g/t	Name	Frother Proportion	Dosage g/t
1	DTC+KAX	1:1	40	PO+R70	1:2	20
2	DTC+KAX	3:1	40	PO+R70	1:2	20
3	DTC+KAX	1:3	40	PO+R70	1:2	20
4	DTC+KAX	1:3	60	PO+R70	1:2	20
5	DTC+KAX	1:3	20	PO+R70	1:2	20
6	DTC+KAX	1:3	40	DF250+MIBC	1:1	15
7	DTC+KAX	1:3	40	DF250+MIBC	2:1	20
8	DTC+KAX	1:3	40	DF250+CAc	1:1	15
9	DTC+KAX	1:3	40	R71A+CAc	1:1	15
10	DTC+KAX	1:3	40	R71A+PO	1:1	15
11	DTC+KAX	1:3	40	R71A+R70	1:1	15
12	DTC+KAX	1:3	40	DF1012+MIBC	1:1	15

Table 12 Results of collectors evaluation

Test	Grade Copper, %	Gold, g/t	Recovery, % Copper	Gold	R Cu	Au	K Cu	Au
1	5.5	8.1	88.0	72.9	0.9378	0.7217	1.8399	1.7188
2	4.7	6.9	88.2	84.0	0.9270	0.8840	2.0204	1.6372
3	4.6	7.2	89.7	84.4	0.9403	0.8784	2.1205	1.6736
4	5.2	7.7	92.2	77.1	0.9548	0.7819	2.7437	2.3098
5	5.6	10.6	89.3	73.6	0.9328	0.7527	2.3347	2.1686

Table 13 Results of evaluation of frothers

Test	Grade Copper, %	Gold, g/t	Recovery, % Copper	Gold	R Cu	Au	K Cu	Au
6	6.4	10.2	90.5	73.2	0.9487	0.7596	2.8390	2.4594
7	6.0	11.1	90.3	80.0	0.9476	0.8237	2.6194	2.7284
8	5.8	10.2	90.2	78.4	0.9328	0.8002	3.2406	2.9245
9	7.2	13.9	89.1	75.8	0.9285	0.7767	2.5351	2.4346
10	7.7	13.1	89.4	70.8	0.9322	0.7322	2.4611	1.0899
11	6.7	13.0	90.3	79.6	0.9319	0.7958	2.7842	3.0909
12	5.4	7.8	91.6	84.5	0.9829	0.8814	2.8845	2.3355

Table 14 Summary of locked-cycle tests results

Sample	Grade Copper, %	Gold, g/t	Recovery, % Copper	Gold
A	25.3	33.0	91.2	77.7
B	21.8	26.5	90.5	83.4
C	21.6	17.2	87.9	60.9
H	24.1	25.3	89.6	76.6
K	23.1	19.2	92.5	78.1

Discussion of results

The flotation flowsheet developed for Bajo La Alumbrera allows the production of concentrates suitable for smelting, with final recoveries of 90% for copper and 75–80% for gold.

The most important variables were studied in detail and satisfactory operating conditions were defined for the various ore types.

An important part of the non-floating gold is contained in the −10 μm fraction, which exhibits a low flotation rate. In coarse sizes (+37 μm) losses are caused by association with both gangue minerals and unfloated sulphides.

The R and K parameter indexes method proved a useful tool for evaluation of the effects of type and concentration of collectors and frothers on the flotation of samples from the oxidized zone, enabling the effects of operational changes to be separated into two parameters. Conclusions obtained from these indexes were in good agreement with those suggested by direct comparison of product grades and recoveries.

The locked-cycle tests generally confirmed earlier results, with the bulk of the fine values contained in the middling products reporting in the final concentrates.

References
1. Matar J. A. Rudolph C. G. and Videla J. C. Estudio del beneficio de la mena de cobre y oro diseminado del yacimiento Bajo La Alumbrera. Instituto de Investigaciones Mineras, San Juan (IIM) *Informe* no. 113, 1976.
2. Tanen V. V. and Saari M. Report on preliminary concentration tests of La Alumbrera Cu–Au ore. Outokumpu Oy, Helsinki, 1977.
3. Bajon P. H. Estudio de orientación para la valorización del mineral sulfurado de cobre de La Alumbrera. Bureau de Recherches Géologiques et Minières, 1977.
4. Marubeni Corporation, Overseas Resources Research Department. Report of Alumbrera auriferous copper ore deposit in Argentina, 1977.
5. Gil J. P. Sarquís P. E. and Matar J. A. Continuación de los estudios de flotación del Cu–Au del yacimiento Bajo La Alumbrera. IIM, 1979.
6. Gil J. P. Sarquís P. E. and Matar J. A. Pruebas complementarias de flotación del mineral del yacimiento Bajo La Alumbrera. *IIM Informe* no. 171, 1982.
7. Crozier R. D. and Ottley D. J. Processing of copper sulphide ores: froth flotation reagents—a review. *Min. Mag., Lond.*, **138**, April 1978, 332–9.
8. Sutulov A. *Copper porphyries* (Salt Lake City: The University of Utah, 1974), 200 p.

9.   Glembotskii V. A. Klassen V. I. and Plaksin I. N. *Flotation* (New York: Primary Sources, 1963), 51–205.

10.   Cyanamid Company. *Mining chemicals handbook*, current edition.

11.   Booth R. B. and Freyberger W. L. Froth and frothing agents. In *Froth flotation, 50th anniversary volume* Fuerstenau D. W. ed. (New York: AIME, 1962), 258–76.

12.   Dudenkov S. V. Shubov L. Y. and Glazunov L. A. *Fundamentos de la teoría y la práctica de empleo de reactivos de flotación* (Editorial M.I.R., 1980), 252–9.

13.   Dow Chemicals Company. *Flotation fundamentals and mining chemicals*, current edition.

14.   Klimpel R. R. Selection of chemical reagents for flotation. In *Mineral processing plant design, 2nd edn* Mular A. L. and Bhappu R. B. eds (New York: Society of Mining Engineers of AIME, 1980), 907–34.

15.   Hoechst Company. *Flotation reagents*, current edition.

16.   Poling G. W. Reactions between thiol reagents and sulphide minerals. In *Flotation: A. M. Gaudin memorial volume* Fuerstenau M. C. ed. (New York: AIME, 1976), 334–63.

17.   MacDonald R. D. and Brison R. J. Applied research in flotation. Reference 11, 298–327.

Role of sodium sulphide, xanthate and amine in flotation of lead–zinc oxidized ores

A. M. Marabini, V. Alesse and F. Garbassi

Synopsis

The interaction of sodium sulphide and conventional collectors and cerussite and smithsonite has been studied by infrared spectrophotometry and X-ray photo-electron spectroscopy and by examination of the interaction equilibria. The effects of sulphidization differ for the two minerals. With cerussite hydroxy carbonate and sulphoxide forms occur with PbS.

Transformation of the lead carbonate to lead sulphide is incomplete, extending into the particles with the formation of a few dozen layers. For smithsonite a compact coating of ZnS a few monolayers thick is formed.

Xanthate reacts with the Pb^{++} ions of the cerussite, whether sulphidized or not, to form $Pb(EtX)_2$, but this adheres in a stable form only to the sulphidized surface. Amine is adsorbed on the sulphidized and non-sulphidized smithsonite probably in molecular dissolved form, but the presence of different amounts of hydroxyl species in the two cases confers different degrees of hydrophobicity on the surfaces.

The most common flotation technique for lead–zinc oxidized ores comprises sulphidization with Na_2S and treatment by conventional collectors—xanthate for lead oxides and amines for zinc. The first stage of the sulphidization process is particularly critical, efficiency depending on a wide range of variables that are very difficult to control.

Rey[1,2] was the first to tackle the problem of lead–zinc oxide ores. He attempted to interpret the numerous phenomena that are observed in the process to establish the best conditions for reagent usage, and his important work continues to provide a sound basis for those in this field.

Fleming[3] was the first, however, to study the sulphidization mechanism scientifically. Despite the limitations of the methods that were then available, Fleming's work marked a real step forward in the interpretation of the complex phenomena involved.

Only in recent time have Cases and co-workers,[4] by use of advanced techniques, found zinc sulphide on the surface of sulphidized smithsonite and demonstrated that Na_2S exerts a very strong activating effect on the adsorption energy of the amine.

The work that is reported here hinged around the use of direct methods of investigation by use of infrared spectrophotometry (IRS) and X-ray photo-electron spectroscopy (XPS) to ascertain the phenomena that occur on the surfaces of cerussite and smithsonite as a result of reaction with Na_2S and collector. The two minerals were examined by both techniques before and after reagent treatment to establish the nature and amount of elements present, the types of bond involved and the molecular structures to which they belong.

The quantities of reagent that were abstracted at equilibrium by both minerals under various operating conditions were also determined.

Experimental

Minerals

The pure cerussite and smithsonite samples that were used in the studies were obtained by repeated wet-treatment of ores from the San Giovanni and Buggerru–Caitas mines, Sardinia, respectively. That of cerussite graded 98% $PbCO_3$ and 2% PbS; that of smithsonite was 99.4% pure, the remainder being calcite. The pure samples were ground to some $10~\mu m$, the specific surface of the smithsonite (BET method) being $6.12~m^2g^{-1}$ and that of the cerussite $1.60~m^2g^{-1}$.

The feed for the flotation tests was obtained by mixing the two original ores from San Giovanni and Caitas (7.48% Zn–3.70% Pb).

Reagents

All reagents were of analytical grade (Carlo Erba, except for dodecylamine acetate (DAA)—a commercial grade product supplied by Anorgana GmbH.

Techniques and apparatus

For the IRS examinations the KBr pellet technique was used with a Perkin-Elmer model 580 B IR spectrophotometer fitted with a data station. The XPS examinations were made on a Physical Electronics model 548 X-ray photo-electron spectrometer fitted with a PDP 11/50 computer.

The samples were prepared by pressing the powder on a sheet of pure indium metal. The quantity of sodium sulphide used was determined by analysis of the sulphur content of the solution before and after contact with the mineral. The sulphur was determined by use of a Perkin-Elmer model 5500 inductive coupled plasma spectrophotometer (ICP) (radiation, λ, = 182.04 nm).

The amount of ethyl xanthate (EtX) adsorbed by the cerussite was determined by difference with a Perkin-Elmer model 330 ultraviolet–visible spectrophotometer. The quantity of DAA adsorbed by the smithsonite was also determined by difference by means of a salicylic aldehyde colorimetric method, the reading being performed by the spectrophotometer that was used for xanthate.

Sulphidization mechanism

Test procedure

The sulphidization tests for IRS and XPS analysis of the solid samples were performed by agitating 1 g of mineral for 15 min with 20 ml Na_2S solution at concentrations that varied from 0 to $16.25~g~l^{-1}$ and at three temperatures (20, 40 and 60°C). After conditioning, the solid was separated by centrifuging, washed twice with 20 ml water and again centrifuged. The mineral was then vacuum-dried at 60°C and stored in a vacuum-sealed flask. The sulphidization tests at acid pH were performed with saturated solutions of H_2S.

The equilibrium and abstraction rate tests were carried out in the same way but with 4 g of mineral and a Na_2S concentration between 10^{-2} and $1~g~l^{-1}$.

Cerussite

Results

IRS analysis

The infrared spectrum of cerussite treated with Na_2S and with H_2S is compared in Fig. 1 with the spectra of untreated cerussite, hydro-cerussite and galena. The ν_1, ν_2, ν_3 and ν_4 peaks characteristic of orthorhombic carbonates of the aragonite group[5,6,7] are very clear for the untreated cerussite. After treatment with sulphide, however, there is a decided weakening of these peaks, a spectrum forming that is very similar to that of

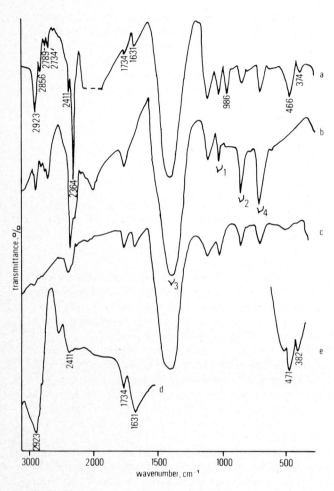

Fig. 1   Infrared spectra of lead minerals: (*a*) cerussite treated with 16.25 g l^{-1} Na_2S; (*b*) untreated cerussite; (*c*) cerussite treated with H_2S; (*d*) hydro-cerussite; (*e*) galena

the hydro-cerussite. The appearance of peaks characteristic of the galena and sulphoxide forms of lead[8] is also evident. The main changes due to sulphidization are the increase of the 2923–2856 and 2411–2364 cm^{-1} bands, attributable to OH ions; the decrease of the doublet 2789–2856, attributable to adsorbed water; the appearance of the peak at 1631 cm^{-1}, attributable to the Pb hydroxide and hydroxy carbonate forms, which are very evident in the hydro-cerussite; the appearance of a pronounced peak at 986 cm^{-1}, attributable to stretching of sulphoxide forms of the PbS_2O_3 type; and the appearance of peaks at 466 and 374 cm^{-1}, typical of galena. The peak at 466 cm^{-1} is particularly evident and clearly demonstrates the formation of PbS.

At acid pH values, resulting from the action of H_2S, there are no PbS peaks at 466 and 374 cm^{-1} and none attributable to PbS_2O_3 at 986 cm^{-1}.

XPS analysis

Pb, C, O and a minor amount of S are present on the surface of the untreated cerussite and the sulphidized mineral, but with marked differences in regard to species composition and concentration.

Tables 1 and 2 indicate the binding energies of the various elements and the energy intensities of the carbon and sulphur peaks, which are especially significant to the understanding of the phenomenon.

Fig. 2 shows the effects of the Na_2S concentration and temperature on the atomic ratios O/Pb and S/Pb. The Pb in the untreated sample has only one peak at 139.2 eV attributable to $PbCO_3$, whereas in the treated mineral this peak moves to lower values, sometimes to 137.7 eV, which is typical of PbS.[9,10] The higher values occur in the presence of H_2S at pH around 5, low Na_2S concentrations and high temperatures, whereas PbS formation is maximum, albeit below 80%, at higher sulphide concentrations and lower temperatures.

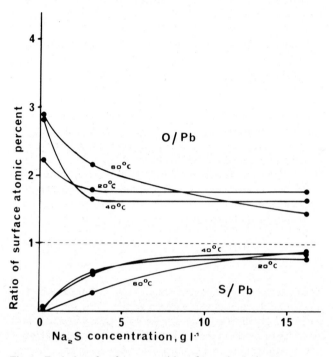

Fig. 2   Evolution of surface composition of cerussite during Na_2S treatment as a function of reagent concentration and temperature

At intermediate concentrations and temperatures the Pb binding energy is between that of the carbonate and the sulphide, though the presence of PbO, $Pb(OH)_2$ and $2PbCO_3 \cdot Pb(OH)_2$[11] cannot be excluded.

The carbon profile has three components— C_I, C_{II} and C_{III}. Excluding the first, C_I, as a result of the hydrocarbon carbon from normal contamination, there remain the C_{II} component at 286.7 eV attributable to C–OH and C=O bonds and the C_{III} component at 290.0 eV attributable to the carbonate group.

The carbonate peak decreases markedly after treatment, but does not disappear even at the highest reagent concentrations. The ratio of intensities for the C_{II} and C_{III} peaks increases with concentration of Na_2S and decrease in temperature: this indicates that surface sulphidization is never complete and that there is an increase in the intermediate carbon species characterized by the presence of C–OH and C=O bonds.

It is just possible to distinguish two components in the 531.4-eV oxygen peak—the first at 530.7 eV (attributable to the CO_3 group) and the other at 533.2 eV (owing to –OH ions or surface-adsorbed H_2O).

As a result of the action of sulphur the O peak intensity decreases markedly, falling to 531.6 and 530.5 eV, especially in samples in which PbS formation is evident: this indicates a diminution in the –OH groups owing to physically adsorbed water.

Table 1 XPS analysis of cerussite samples treated with Na_2S (binding energy of atom peaks)

Sample no.	Sulphidizing agent		Temperature, °C	Binding energy, eV						
	Type	Concn, g l^{-1}		O1s	Pb4f$_{7/2}$	S2p		Cl$_s$		
						S$_I$	S$_{II}$	C$_I$	C$_{II}$	C$_{III}$
1	—	—	—	531.4	139.2	163.1	—	284.9	286.7	290.0
2	Na_2S	0.325	20	531.0	138.6	161.5	—	285.0	287.5	289.8
3	Na_2S	0.325	40	531.8	139.6	160.7	162.5	284.9	286.6	289.2
4	Na_2S	0.325	60	531.9	139.5	160.9	163.0	285.3	287.2	289.7
5	Na_2S	3.25	20	530.5	137.8	159.8	161.8	284.4	287.5	289.8
6	Na_2S	3.25	40	530.5	137.9	159.5	161.8	285.3	287.2	289.5
7	Na_2S	3.25	60	531.0	138.1	160.5	162.5	285.3	287.3	290.0
8	Na_2S	16.25	20	530.5	137.6	158.8	160.6	284.8	287.9	290.5
9	Na_2S	16.25	40	530.5	137.4	158.5	160.9	285.3	287.1	289.6
10	Na_2S	16.25	60	530.5	137.5	159.3	161.4	285.2	288.2	291.3
11	H_2S	Saturated soln	20	531.9	139.6	162.7	—	285.3	287.1	289.8

Table 2 XPS analysis of cerussite samples treated with Na_2S (relative intensity of carbon and sulphur peaks)

Sample no.	Sulphidizing agent		Temperature, °C	Relative intensity				
	Type	Concn, g l^{-1}		C$_I$	C$_{II}$	C$_{III}$	S$_I$	S$_{II}$
1	—	—	—	20.9	31.1	48.0	—	—
2	Na_2S	0.325	20	45.9	23.2	30.2	100.0	—
3	Na_2S	0.325	40	30.4	24.2	45.5	61.5	38.5
4	Na_2S	0.325	60	32.1	11.3	56.6	21.4	78.6
5	Na_2S	3.25	20	45.4	38.5	16.1	55.7	44.3
6	Na_2S	3.25	40	30.9	22.4	46.7	19.2	80.8
7	Na_2S	3.25	60	27.2	25.4	47.4	69.0	31.0
8	Na_2S	16.25	20	62.3	27.2	10.5	25.3	74.7
9	Na_2S	16.25	40	42.0	40.6	17.4	24.6	75.4
10	Na_2S	16.25	60	59.2	31.9	8.9	22.1	77.9
11	H_2S	Saturated soln	20	34.2	16.4	49.4	100.0	—

The surface composition of the untreated sample, stripped of the contaminating effect, is $Pb_{0.87}C_{1.24}O_3$, which is sufficiently close to that expected for $PbCO_3$.

Sulphur is present in small quantities in the untreated samples (0.27%S) with a binding energy of 163.1 eV, which is attributable neither to PbS (160.7 eV) nor to oxygenated compounds, such as $PbSO_3$ or $PbSO_4$. It may be molecular sulphur, or even a compound of the PbS_2O_3 type (163.9 eV), according to Manocha and Park.[12]

Two quite distinct peaks occur after sulphidization, the more intense (at 161.1 eV) being attributable to PbS and the other (at 159 eV) being in line with that observed by Manocha and Park immediately after sublimation of a film of PbS and assumed to be elemental sulphur.

The presence of oxidized forms of sulphur different from sulphide is more evident with a decreased reagent concentration. For the sample treated with H_2S at pH 5 it is seen that, despite the marked presence of sulphur (not attributable, however, to PbS, at least as the predominant species), the treatment is not very efficient.

Equilibrium and abstraction rate
Fig. 3 indicates the quantities of S and Na_2S abstracted by cerussite at equilibrium at various Na_2S concentrations. The results can be represented approximately by a straight line with an equation of the Freundlich type:

$$\Gamma = Kc^{1/n}$$

where $1/n = 1.2$. The trend of the graph shows that the abstraction of sulphide from solution by cerussite is attributable to adsorption. The abstraction curve has three distinct regions and its trend is surprisingly like that of normal aliphatic surfactants. Interpretation of this curve shape is not easy, sulphur ions being fundamentally different from surfactant molecules.

A detailed study devoted entirely to this phenomenon would be needed to frame a hypothesis of the real significance of this trend. Since $1/n$ is greater than unity, however, it is reasonable to assume that the trend is attributable to the solvent action of the sulphide and the resulting diffusion of the reagent within the mass of the mineral, with the formation of many PbS monolayers.

From calculation of the number of S atoms that can be adsorbed on the (110) cleavage face of the cerussite at Na_2S concentration of 0.325 g l^{-1} and consideration of the results of the XPS analyses, which indicate that only 25% of the Pb atoms are sulphidized, it can be deduced that the lead sulphide coating may actually be the equivalent of 11 monolayers in thickness. This would explain the black colour of the cerussite particles after treatment in soluble sulphide.

The quantity of sulphur abstracted by cerussite as a function of time at a Na_2S concentration of 0.08 g l^{-1} was also determined. It is observed that adsorption is complete after only 30 s of conditioning. Such a high rate of adsorption suggests that direct chemical action must be involved.

Discussion of results
Taken as a whole, the results provide a very complete picture of the effects of sulphidization on cerussite, which can be summarized thus: a decrease but never total disappearance of the $PbCO_3$; the formation of two types of sulphur species due to PbS and the sulphoxide forms (elemental S and PbS_2O_3), with

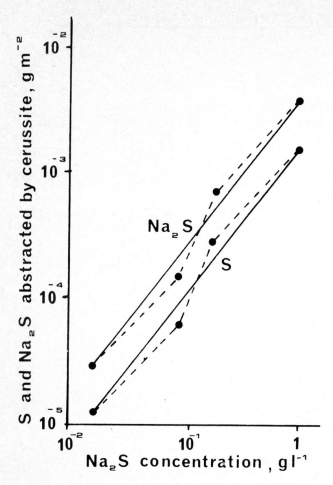

Fig. 3   Influence of concentration on abstraction of sulphide by cerussite

towards the formation of soluble hydroxide forms of the $Pb(OH)_3^-$ type, which predominate at Na_2S concentrations $>1 \, g \, l^{-1}$.

Fig. 4 illustrates the effect of Na_2S on pH with and without mineral present. The pH falls markedly in the presence of cerussite, revealing the high consumption of OH^- ions by the mineral employed in the two sets of tests described.

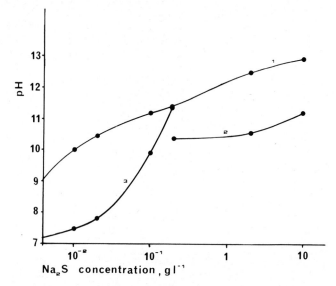

Fig. 4   Effect of Na_2S on pH with and without cerussite: 1, without mineral; 2, 1-g mineral, 20 ml; 3, 4-g mineral, 20 ml

a maximum occupation of 70–80% of the metal sites at very high Na_2S concentrations; energetic cleaning of physically adsorbed H_2O; a large increase in the hydroxy-carbonate species similar to hydro-cerussite already present prior to treatment or of Pb oxide–hydroxide forms; an essentially chemical-type adsorption with simultaneous solvent action on the mineral and penetration of the sulphidization into the crystalline mass with formation of an incomplete lead sulphide coating with a thickness equivalent to a few dozen monolayers; the generally deleterious effect of high temperatures; and the adverse effect of pH values below neutral.

When lead carbonate is immersed in water a series of chemical species is formed—carbonate, hydroxy-carbonate and hydroxide—the relative abundance of which depends on the solution equilibrium established in the Pb^{2+}-H_2O-CO_2 system. XPS and IRS analyses show that this happens to some extent even for untreated cerussite. The predominant species at a given pH is evident from inspection of the electrochemical diagram reported by Stumm and Morgan:[13] below pH 7.3 $PbCO_{3(s)}$ is the predominant species, whereas between that value and 12.5 the $2PbCO_3 \cdot Pb(OH)_{2(s)}$ or hydro-cerussite is dominant; above pH 12.5 the soluble species $Pb(OH)_3^-$ is dominant.

There is a large increase in alkalinity in the presence of sulphide, as is evident from the hydrolysis and dissociation reactions that occur when $Na_2S_{(s)}$ is dissolved in H_2O:

$$Na_2S_{(s)} + 2HOH \rightleftharpoons H_2S + 2OH^- + 2Na^+$$

$$H_2S \rightleftharpoons HS^- + H^+$$

$$HS^- \rightleftharpoons S^{--} + H^+$$

The equilibrium of the system thus shifts towards the formation of hydroxy-carbonate forms and, subsequently,

The formation of soluble Pb hydrate species explains the partial solvent action of the sulphide. This will be at a maximum with the highest accumulation of reagent, but it is possible even under normal flotation conditions. This solvent effect on the Pb^{++} ions is inevitably accompanied by adsorption of surface sulphur and by penetration of the sulphide into the crystal lattice. The formation of PbS occurs via the reactions

$$Pb^{++} + HS^- \rightleftharpoons PbS_{(s)} + H^+$$

$$Pb^{++} + S^{--} \rightleftharpoons PbS_{(s)}$$

The curve that illustrates abstraction of S from the solution at various reagent concentrations indicates a consumption in excess of that which can be explained purely by adsorption. The results obtained are broadly in line with some of the conclusions that were reached by Rey[14] and Fleming.[3] Rey also referred to the formation of a lead sulphide coating on the cerussite, emphasizing the inevitable penetration of the sulphide into the crystal lattice owing to the very porous nature of this mineral and the high alkalinity of the medium.

According to Fleming, the abstraction of sulphide by cerussite is due to chemical adsorption, the equilibrium of which can be represented by a Freundlich-type equation. He assumed, mainly on the basis of colour intensity, that the layer of Pb sulphide on the surface of the cerussite increases with concentration to reach a thickness of several thousand monolayers. In fact, however, the thickness is only of the order of a few dozen monolayers.

There is a very marked difference between Fleming's rate of reaction results and those which are reported here. According to Fleming, equilibrium is attained after about a 20-min conditioning with sulphide, whereas the present tests show that the reaction is already complete after 30 s, which is in more reasonable agreement with the suggestion that direct chemical combination is involved. The discrepancy in results may be due to the fact that in his rate of reaction tests Fleming employed a concentration one hundred times higher than that which was used here. It is possible that with such a high concentration the process of diffusion into the crystal results in a delay in the attainment of equilibrium conditions.

A further modification of the outermost sulphide layer in direct contact with the solution can be postulated, however, on the basis of the XPS results, which clearly reveal the presence of excess O along with S and the hydroxy-carbonate forms. This oxygen is attributable to the surface formation of sulphoxide compounds of the PbS_2O_3 type similar to those frequently encountered on galena exposed to oxygen-containing water.

Toperi and Tolun,[15] on the basis of electrochemical and thermodynamic studies, demonstrated the coexistence of hydrated oxidation products or basic lead thiosulphate, plumbite, beyond pH 10.7.

Eadington and Prosser[16] in their interpretation of the mechanism of sulphidization of galena by oxygen dissolved in water agreed that the initial products of oxidation are elemental S and $Pb(OH)_2$ that give rise to basic lead thiosulphate by further reaction in alkaline solution:

$$2PbS + 2H_2O + O_2 \rightleftharpoons 2Pb^{++} + 4OH^- + 2S^0$$

$$4Pb^{++} + 8OH^- + 4S^0 \rightleftharpoons 2PbS + PbO \cdot PbS_2O_3 \, x \, H_2O_{(s)} + (4-x)H_2O$$

The neutral sulphur atoms remain in the lead neutral lattice and, simultaneously, the lead sulphide surface loses new lead ions to the solution, which react again according to the first reaction. As a consequence, the outer crystal layers of lead sulphide become supersaturated with sulphur and both elemental sulphur and PbS_2O_3 are visible by XPS analysis.

Smithsonite

Results

IRS analysis
The infrared spectrum of smithsonite treated with Na_2S and H_2S is given in Fig. 5 with the spectra of untreated smithsonite, hydrozincite and sphalerite. The three characteristic peaks of calcite-type carbonates (ν_2, ν_3 and ν_4) are evident in the untreated smithsonite.[5,6,7] Broadly, there are no significant variations in the spectrum after sulphidization, as would be expected in that the bands of ZnS and $ZnCO_3$ are very similar. A slight increase in the hydroxide and hydroxy-carbonate forms is to be seen at the 1625 cm^{-1} peaks and a decided decrease of the bands due to water of adsorption at 2920–2850 cm^{-1}.

Treatment with H_2S leaves no trace of ZnS, but it does cause a marked diminution in the physically adsorbed H_2O.

XPS analysis
Zn, C and O occur on the surface of the untreated smithsonite, and the same elements plus S on the sulphidized samples. Tables 3 and 4 give the binding energies of the peaks of these elements and the intensities of the Gaussian components of the carbon peak.

The zinc peak at 1021.8 eV appears to be formed of a single component with a binding energy corresponding to that of $ZnCO_3$.[10] As expected, after sulphidization the binding energy remains more or less unchanged, the values for $ZnCO_3$ and ZnS being very similar. The shift of the Auger parameter $ZnL_3M_{4.5}M_{4.5}$[17] from 2009.7 to 2012 eV indicates, however, that the $ZnCO_3$ has been transformed into ZnS in accordance with published values.[9,10]

The carbon peak has a complex profile that can be resolved in three Gaussian components. The first C_I (at 285 eV) is certainly attributable to hydrocarbon carbon due to surface contamination and the third, C_{III}, (at 289.6 eV) to the carbonate species; the intermediate C_{II}, with a binding energy of the C–OH type, is probably due to surface hydration.

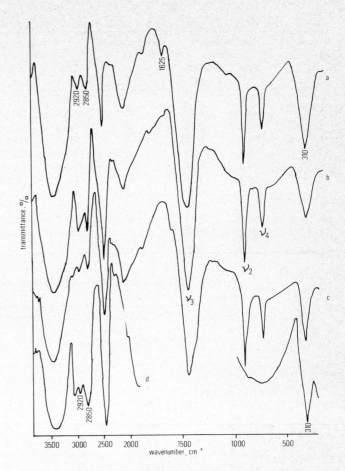

Fig. 5 Infrared spectra of zinc minerals: (a) smithsonite treated with 16.25 g l^{-1} Na_2S; (b) untreated smithsonite; (c) smithsonite treated with H_2S; (d) hydrozincite; (e) sphalerite

Treatment with Na_2S produces very important changes in the three species. The carbonate species is greatly reduced and, finally, disappears at reagent concentrations >16 g l^{-1}. The C_{II} component seems to increase, in particular, at low Na_2S values, though to a lesser extent than for cerussite.

The oxygen peak can be considered to consist of a single Gaussian component. The situation remains unchanged after treatment, except for a slight broadening at low reagent concentrations that is probably associated with the presence of various hydration forms.

The surface composition of the untreated smithsonite, stripped of the influence of carbon contamination, is $Zn_{0.85}C_{1.02}O_3$, which is very close to that expected for $ZnCO_3$. There is no sulphur on the untreated sample, but it is present on the sulphidized sample, there being a single component with a binding energy of 162.1 eV, corresponding to ZnS.

The efficiency of treatment with H_2S at a pH of about 5 is virtually nil, as is shown by examination of surface sulphur.

The O/Zn and S/Zn trends (Fig. 6) demonstrate that treatment efficiency increases with sulphide concentration and generally decreases as the temperature rises. At an initial sulphide concentration of 3.25 g l^{-1} one-half of the carbonate is transformed to sulphide at temperatures of 20 and 40°C, and at 60°C the figure is only 25%.

Equilibrium and abstraction rate
Fig. 7 illustrates the quantity of S removed from solution by smithsonite at various Na_2S concentrations at 20°C. The trend is linear in this case, too, and can be expressed by the Freundlich equation. As $1/n$ is about unity, it would appear that only surface adsorption is involved, accounting for all the abstracted sulphur. There is no likelihood of reagent being consumed in mineral dissolution, as occurs with cerussite.

129

Table 3   XPS analysis of smithsonite samples treated with Na$_2$S (binding energy atom peaks)

Sample no.	Sulphidizing agent Type	Concn, g l^{-1}	Temperature, °C	O1s	Zn2p$_{3/2}$	S2p	C$_I$	C1s C$_{II}$	C$_{III}$	Auger Zn parameter
1	—	—	—	531.6	1021.8	—	285.1	287.0	289.6	2009.7
2	Na$_2$S	0.325	20	531.8	1022.1	161.7	284.5	286.6	289.8	2010.1
3	Na$_2$S	0.325	40	531.5	1022.0	162.2	285.1	286.5	288.1–290.2	2009.8
4	Na$_2$S	0.325	60	531.7	1022.2	—	284.6	286.4	289.7	2010.3
5	Na$_2$S	3.25	20	531.1	1021.8	162.1	285.4	287.6	289.9	2012.5
6	Na$_2$S	3.25	40	531.8	1021.8	162.0	284.8	287.0	289.9	2010.9
7	Na$_2$S	3.25	60	531.7	1021.9	162.0	285.0	287.2	289.8	2009.9
8	Na$_2$S	16.25	20	531.7	1021.7	162.1	285.0	286.5	289.1	2012.4
9	Na$_2$S	16.25	40	531.8	1021.8	162.2	285.1	287.2	289.3	2012.2
10	Na$_2$S	16.25	60	531.7	1022.0	161.7	285.0	286.2	288.2–289.5	2012.6
11	H$_2$O	Saturated soln	20	531.1	1022.0	—	285.0	287.5	289.9	—

Table 4   XPS analysis of smithsonite samples treated by Na$_2$S (relative intensity of carbon peaks)

Sample no.	Sulphidizing agent Type	Concn, g l^{-1}	Temperature, °C	C$_I$	C1s C$_{II}$	C$_{III}$
1	—	—	—	47.4	4.5	48.1
2	Na$_2$S	0.325	20	30.9	23.1	46.0
3	Na$_2$S	0.325	40	28.9	19.6–12.9	38.6
4	Na$_2$S	0.325	60	31.4	22.9	45.7
5	Na$_2$S	3.25	20	59.6	29.7	10.7
6	Na$_2$S	3.25	40	45.3	32.2	22.5
7	Na$_2$S	3.25	60	49.7	13.1	37.2
8	Na$_2$S	16.25	20	56.8	20.9	22.3
9	Na$_2$S	16.25	40	57.6	28.3	14.1
10	Na$_2$S	16.25	60	42.6	33.6–15.7	8.1
11	H$_2$S	Saturated soln	20	40.3	8.5	51.2

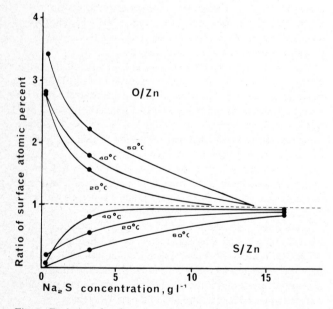

Fig. 6   Evolution of surface composition of smithsonite during Na$_2$S treatment as a function of reagent concentration and temperature

The thickness of the sulphide coating calculated for the (10$\bar{1}$1) cleavage face at a Na$_2$S concentration of 0.325 g l^{-1} is 1.1 monolayers, which is ten times less than that which forms on the cerussite.

The contact time tests with 0.08 g l^{-1} sodium sulphide show that sulphur abstraction ceases after a 30-s conditioning, as for cerussite. Hence, for smithsonite it is also possible to postulate adsorption mainly of the chemical type.

Discussion of results

The results for smithsonite can be outlined thus: total disappearance of the ZnCO$_3$ species; complete formation of a coating of ZnS alone, which occupies all the surface metal sites at very high Na$_2$S concentrations; energetic cleaning of adsorbed water; a slight increase of hydroxide and hydroxy-carbonate species under the outer layer of ZnS, similar to hydrozincite; mainly chemical-type adsorption with the formation of one monolayer of ZnS or a little more; the mainly deleterious effect of high temperatures; and the adverse effect of pH values below neutral.

Examination of the stability diagram of the Zn^{2+}–CO$_2$–H$_2$O[13] system shows that smithsonite is the predominant phase up to pH 8.5, hydrozincite, 2ZnCO$_3$·3Zn(OH)$_2$, between pH 8.5 and 11, and the insoluble hydroxide, Zn(OH)$_2$, is stable at pH >11.

The absence of soluble hydroxide complexes explains why with smithsonite there is none of the dissolution that is so clear with cerussite. The evidence of hydroxide and hydroxy-carbonate forms revealed by XPS and IRS analyses and the fact that they increase in the presence of Na$_2$S are explicable by the predominance of these species in an alkaline medium.

The layer of ZnS that forms by reactions similar to those described for Pb is ten times less thick than the cerussite. This difference too is connected with the lack of solvent action by the OH$^-$ ions from hydrolysis of the Na$_2$S.

The S abstraction curve is closer to that of simple adsorption and the rate of reaction is indicative of a truly chemical-type interaction.

Sulphoxide forms are not so evident, which means that the process of oxidation of the layer of ZnS in direct contact with the water is not as marked as for the PbS layer. It is known[10] that

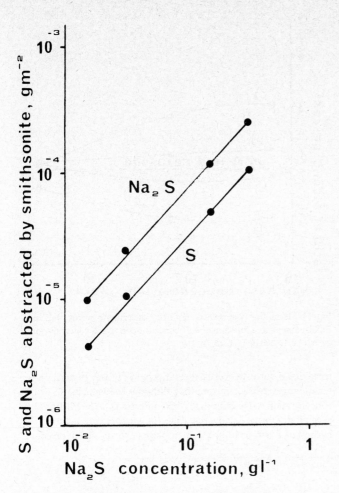

Fig. 7 Influence of concentration on abstraction of sulphide by smithsonite

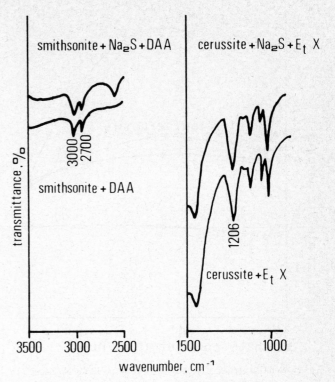

Fig. 8 Infrared spectra of smithsonite and cerussite treated with Na_2S and collectors

surface layers of ZnS change very slowly into sulphate after exposure to water and that the forms that do occur are essentially ZnO and $ZnSO_4 \cdot 7H_2O$ (both present in very small quantities).

In fact, the O/Zn value after sulphidization is very low in comparison with that of cerussite. Since the ZnS coating has a thickness of around one monolayer, the oxygen revealed by XPS is attributable to the underlying carbonates.

Collector action

Test procedure

The samples for IRS and XPS analyses were prepared by treating 1 g of mineral at room temperature with 20 ml of Na_2S solution at various concentrations and conditioning by agitation for 15 min. After centrifugation and separation of the liquid phase 20 ml of collector solution was added to the remaining solid. After a further 15-min conditioning, followed by centrifuging and washing, the solid was vacuum-dried at 60°C.

The tests to determine the quantity of collector adsorbed at equilibrium on 4-g mineral samples were performed in the same way.

Cerussite

Results

IRS analysis

The peak at 1206 cm^{-1} in the infrared spectrum (Fig. 8) clearly indicates the formation of similar quantities of Pb(EtX)$_2$[18] both on the sulphidized and untreated samples of cerussite. It cannot be established, however, whether the precipitate was entrained in

the mineral when it was separated from the liquid or whether it is present in the adsorbed state.

XPS analysis

After treatment with EtX the same elements are found on the surface of the cerussite as after sulphidization (O, Pb; S and C and traces of K), as would be expected in view of the elemental composition of the xanthate. Figs. 9, 10 and 11 indicate the O/Pb, S/Pb and C/Pb values as a function of EtX concentration at various Na_2S concentrations and in the absence of this reagent.

It would appear that the EtX produces no noteworthy effects on the surface of the unsulphidized cerussite, but a large increase in the O/Pb and C/Pb values is noted at intermediate reagent concentration—specifically, at 0.16 g l^{-1} Na_2S and 1.1 x 10^{-4} mol l^{-1} EtX.

The S/Pb value first decreases and then increases, reaching a maximum at a Na_2S concentration at 0.16 g l^{-1} that is attributable to the substitution of a pre-existing sulphide species. With EtX alone the small increase in the S/Pb value may be due to the slight adsorption of xanthate. At higher Na_2S concentration O/Pb and C/Pb tend to stabilize around constant values, which indicates a steady fall in the efficiency of the collector.

The binding energies of the elements remain more or less unchanged in comparison with those observed after sulphidization treatment alone; there is only minor variation in the binding energies of S and Pb after treatment with both reagents, which is attributable to the presence of Pb(EtX)$_2$.

By breaking down the peaks of the elements into the diverse Gaussian components and performing a stoichiometric calculation on the basis of their intensities it would be possible to identify exactly what molecular species are present. Even a preliminary analysis along these lines, however, reveals that because of the effect of both reagents, used individually and together, oxygen is always present in excess in comparison with that attributable to the PbCO$_3$.

If it is assumed that the hydroxide species observed are present as Pb(OH)$_2$, it is evident that there is an excess of O in all

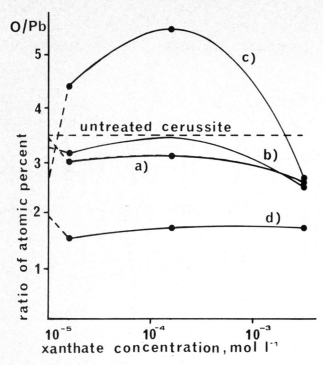

Fig. 9 Evolution of surface composition of cerussite during Na₂S and EtX treatment as a function of EtX concentration (Na₂S concentration, g l⁻¹: (*a*) 0; (*b*) 0.016; (*c*) 0.16; (*d*) 1.6)

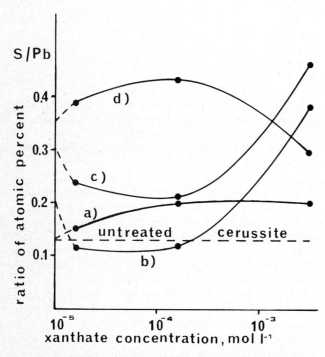

Fig. 10 Evolution of surface composition of cerussite during Na₂S and EtX treatment as a function of EtX concentration (Na₂S concentration, g l⁻¹: (*a*) 0; (*b*) 0.016; (*c*) 0.16; (*d*) 1.6)

cases. The relative quantities of hydroxide forms and of excess oxygen are ranked thus:

$$Pb(OH)_2 = \begin{matrix} \text{Treatment} \\ \text{with EtX} \end{matrix} > \begin{matrix} \text{Treatment} \\ \text{with Na}_2\text{S} \end{matrix} > \begin{matrix} \text{Treatment} \\ \text{with} \\ \text{EtX + Na}_2\text{S} \end{matrix}$$

$$\text{Excess O}_2 = \begin{matrix} \text{Treatment} \\ \text{with} \\ \text{EtX + Na}_2\text{S} \end{matrix} > \begin{matrix} \text{Treatment} \\ \text{with Na}_2\text{S} \end{matrix} > \begin{matrix} \text{Treatment} \\ \text{with EtX} \end{matrix}$$

Xanthate abstraction equilibrium

The quantity of xanthate abstracted from solution by Na₂S

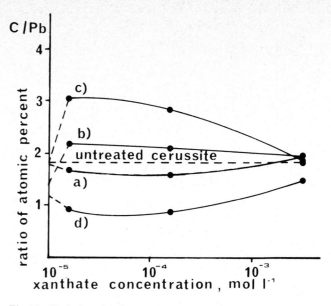

Fig. 11 Evolution of surface composition of cerussite during Na₂S and EtX treatment as a function of EtX concentration (Na₂S concentration, g l⁻¹: (*a*) 0; (*b*) 0.016; (*c*) 0.16; (*d*) 1.6)

treated and untreated cerussite is shown in Fig. 12. In both cases the quantity abstracted from the solution is the same in the concentration range examined: this indicates that the $Pb(EtX)_2$ precipitates forms equally regardless of whether carbonate or hydroxide forms or sulphide or sulphoxide forms are involved.

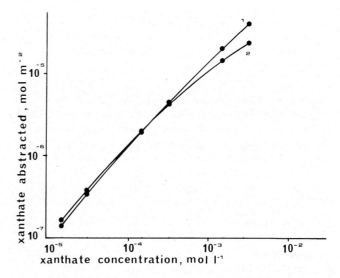

Fig. 12 Influence of concentration on abstraction of EtX by cerussite: 1, untreated mineral; 2, mineral treated with 1.6 g l⁻¹ Na₂S)

The quantity of xanthate abstracted from the solution in the two cases is, however, not the same as that actually absorbed, as is evident from the different surface compositions revealed by XPS analysis.

Discussion of results

The xanthate reacts with the surface Pb^{++} ions of the cerussite whether or not these are sulphidized. In both cases $Pb(EtX)_2$ is formed and the reaction goes ahead. The effect of this reaction as regards surface coverage is, however, different: the $Pb(EtX)_2$ is visible on the sulphidized surface but not on the untreated surface—indeed, XPS shows the atomic composition of the cerussite surface to be markedly different in the two cases.

On the non-sulphidized mineral the carbonate forms are quite evidently transformed to hydroxide forms, there is a small increase in sulphur and no rise in the C/Pb value—even, perhaps, a slight decrease. On the sulphidized mineral the xanthate causes a large increase in carbon, a rise in the O/Pb value and an evident decrease in that of the S/Pb. For the non-sulphidized mineral, therefore, apart from the pre-existing carbonate forms, there are hydroxide forms and also perhaps a very small xanthate species component, probably in the hydroxide form.[19] So far as the sulphidized mineral is concerned, the composition clearly indicates the presence on the surface of $Pb(EtX)_2$, formed at the expense, in particular, of the hydroxide and sulphoxide forms.

On the basis of these results the following reactions can be postulated in the two cases. For untreated cerussite the formation of $Pb(EtX)_2$, which precipitates in the bulk state

$$PbCO_3 + 2EtX^- \rightleftharpoons Pb(EtX)_2 + CO_3^{--}$$

and that of hydroxide and hydroxy-carbonate surface forms by reaction with the OH^- ions from hydrolysis of the EtX

$$PbCO_3 + 2OH^- \rightleftharpoons Pb(OH)_2 + CO_3^{--}$$

$$3PbCO_3 + 2OH^- \rightleftharpoons 2PbCO_3 \cdot Pb(OH)_2 + CO_3^{--}$$

and for sulphidized cerussite the presence of sulphoxide and hydroxide forms characteristic of the $PbS-O-H_2O$ system[15]

$$2PbS + H_2O + 4O \rightleftharpoons PbS_2O_3 + Pb(OH)_2$$

and reaction of the oxide species with the EtX^- ions and formation of $Pb(EtX)_2$ in the adsorbed state

$$PbS_2O_3 + 2EtX^- \rightleftharpoons Pb(EtX)_2 + S_2O_3^{--}$$

$$Pb(OH)_2 + 2EtX^- \rightleftharpoons Pb(EtX)_2 + 2OH^-$$

The existence of oxidized forms on the surface of the galena in water as the predominant species that causes the greatest uptake of xanthate has been stressed by many investigators.[20,21,22]

In fact, the reaction

$PbS + 2EtX^- \rightleftharpoons Pb(EtX)_2 + S^{--}$ is thermodynamically improbable in view of the solubility products of PbS (7×10^{-29}) and $Pb(EtX)_2$ (2.1×10^{-17}).

To conclude, although the reaction between surface Pb^{++} ions and EtX^- ions with the formation of $Pb(EtX)_2$ occurs with both the untreated and the sulphidized minerals, only sulphidization seems to ensure that the reaction product remains on the surface. This could be because of the different steric and thermodynamic compatibility of the reaction product with the structure of the underlying lattice.

Gaudin[23] emphasized the importance of the crystal-chemical resemblance of collector and mineral, ascribing the efficiency of xanthates on sulphidized minerals to this phenomenon.

For the untreated cerussite, there is probably steric and thermodynamic incompatibility between the solid carbonate and hydroxy-carbonate forms and the $Pb(EtX)_2$, so the connexion between substrate and coating may be fragile.

Comparison of the solubility products of the lattice species and the $Pb(EtX)_2$ indicates that the latter is 10^5 times less soluble than the compounds to which it should adhere. This condition is certainly unfavourable for stable adhesion of the reaction product to the mineral surface and it very likely causes a breakaway. This has been observed much more clearly for chelating agents,[27] their products of reaction with metals being characterized by extremely low solubility. Here the process of extracting the metal ions from the surface as chelates becomes so fierce as to cause corrosion in the true sense of the word.

The reverse situation occurs, of course, when the substrate is PbS. The solubility product of the $Pb(EtX)_2$ in this case is some ten times greater than the PbS, which is ideal for stable coating.

It is important to note the existence of an optimum Na_2S/EtX concentration above which adsorption of xanthate on the mineral surface decreases. The effect, which can be interpreted as competition between S^{--} and HS^- ions and EtX^- ions is similar to that encountered for galena.[24] Rey[14] stressed the basic importance of this phenomenon, suggesting the technique of small-stage additions of the sulphidizing agent.

Smithsonite

Results

IRS analysis
Examination of the infrared spectra of samples of Na_2S-treated and untreated smithsonite reveals the presence of CH_2 groups characteristic of the amine in both cases, owing to the action of the DAA (Fig. 8). An indication of the nature and quantity of the products of interaction can be obtained only by qualitative and quantitative analysis of the spectrum processed in an appropriate manner, but on the basis of the present highly reproducible results it can be postulated that the collector interacts equally whether sulphide is present or absent.

IRS, of course, does not provide information on whether or not this will continue to adhere to the mineral surface, since the technique involves the mass of the sample, including any precipitated compound that inevitably remains entrained when the solid is separated from the liquid.

XPS analysis
Nitrogen is present on the surface of the sulphidized and non-sulphidized samples after treatment with DAA.

As with cerussite, an attempt was made to correlate reagent concentrations and O/Zn, S/Zn and C/Zn values. It is observed, however, that the S/Zn and C/Zn, in particular, are affected by such marked inaccuracies that it is impossible to establish an unequivocal correlation between them and the variables examined. The O/Zn and N/Zn are within the margins of error of the method; the values for untreated smithsonite and for the mineral treated with 1.6 g l^{-1} Na_2S are plotted against DAA concentration in Fig. 13. After a slight initial decline the O/Zn gradually increases with collector concentration, whereas the N/Zn increases with DAA concentration in the absence of sulphide, but seems to remain constant or even to fall slightly when sulphide is present. It would appear, therefore, that sulphidization does not activate DAA adsorption. At low collector concentration adsorption

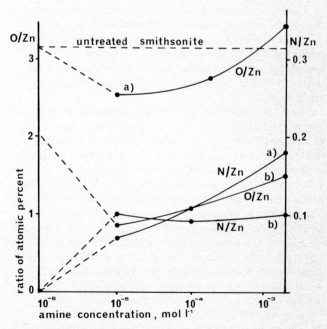

Fig. 13 Evolution of surface composition of smithsonite during Na_2S and DAA treatment as a function of DAA concentration (Na_2S concentration, g l^{-1}: (*a*) 0; (*b*) 0.016)

would seem to occur at the expense of surface oxygen, whether this is in the form of carbonate or hydroxide, as is apparent from the decrease in the O/Zn value, which begins to increase above a certain DAA concentration for both samples.

Table 5 Composition of smithsonite surface after treatment with high concentrations of Na_2S and DAA

Na_2S concn, $g\ l^{-1}$	DAA concn, $g\ l^{-1}$	C/Zn	O/Zn	S/Zn	N/Zn
—	—	2.27	3.53	—	—
16.25	—	1.64	0.88	0.95	—
—	0.2	7	4.73	—	0.36
16.25	0.2	7	1.83	1.08	0.36

Because of the relative lack of evidence on phenomena at low concentrations, the effect of both reagents individually and together was also examined at very high concentrations (Table 5). The most significant data are the very large increase in the C/Zn value in both cases, an increase in the O/Zn value in both cases and the appearance of N to the same extent on both surfaces.

It would therefore seem clear that sulphidization does not activate DAA adsorption by smithsonite. The increase in oxygen in both cases must be attributable to adsorption of oxidized surface species, the considerable excess of C being certainly due to the presence of the alkyl chain on the surface.

Adsorption equilibrium
The adsorption isotherms obtained for the treated and untreated minerals are illustrated in Fig. 14. Despite the inevitable limitation of the amine determination method, which prevents the investigation being extended to concentrations closer to real values, the results generally confirm those from the surface analysis and IRS.

The presence of Na_2S does not appear to increase the adsorption of DAA—indeed, at high amine concentrations it even seems to be deleterious.

Discussion of results
The amine is adsorbed in more or less equal quantities on the smithsonite in the untreated and sulphidized states since the final N/Zn and C/Zn values are quite similar. There is an increase in the O/Zn value in both cases. The final O/Zn value on the surface of the untreated smithsonite is some three times greater than on the sulphidized mineral, where the quantity of sulphur adsorbed during sulphidization remains virtually unchanged.

The DAA dissociates in water in three forms—ionically dissolved $RNH_{3(aq)}^+$—molecularly dissolved $RNH_{(aq)}$ and precipitated $RNH_{2(s)}$. As the dissociation constant of DAA is around 7.7, the ionic and molecular forms are present in equal quantities at that pH, the ionic form prevailing at lower values and the undissociated form at higher values, passing from the dissolved to the precipitated species as the pH increases above 10.5. Much attention has been paid to ascertaining the species that is actually responsible for the collecting action of the amine.[25,26] It is currently held that the effective agent that causes the coating of zinc minerals is the free amine. In fact, the best sphalerite recovery is at a pH value between 10 and 11[23] where, in effect, only the free amine is present.

Cases *et al.*[4] also reported that the optimum pH for the flotation of sulphidized smithsonite in the presence of DAA is 10, with a shift towards lower values in the presence of higher collector concentration.

Although the present study does not provide precise

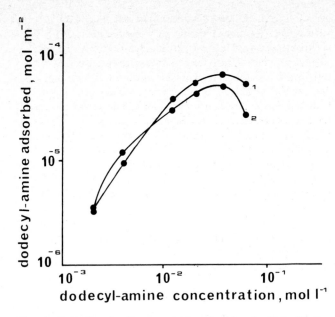

Fig. 14 Evolution of surface composition of smithsonite during Na_2S and DAA treatment as a function of DAA concentration

clarification of the various theories that have been put forward, it does allow some interesting points to be made.

First, since at the usual flotation pH (pH > 7) the RNH_3^+ is effectively absent, it seems justifiable to assume that the RNH_2 becomes attached to the surface zinc in both the $ZnCO_3$ and ZnS forms through complexation bonds. The increase in oxygen is probably attributable to the adsorption of hydroxyl ions on the surface of the two samples. These ions could bond to the surface zinc as complexes, where Zn could have a coordination number even greater than four, of the type[29]

$$CO_3\ or\ S - ZN \begin{matrix} CO_3\ or\ S \\ | \\ \vdots \\ | \\ CO_3\ or\ S \end{matrix} \cdots (NH_2R)_n \\ \cdots (OH)_n$$

They could also be present as zinc oxide–hydroxide species owing to the protonation reaction of DAA $RNH_3^+ \rightleftharpoons RNH_2 + H^+$ with a mechanism similar to that described by Healy and Moignard[27]

$$ZnCO_3 + 2H^+ + O \rightleftharpoons Zn(OH)_2 + CO_2$$

$$ZnS + 2H^+ + 2O \rightleftharpoons Zn(OH)_2 + S^0$$

Both the products of reaction would continue to adhere to the surface as an insoluble coating, coexisting with the long-chain amine groups.

The preponderance of hydroxide forms on the untreated smithsonite in comparison with that of the sulphidized variety could well render the surface dominantly hydrophilic, thus nullifying the hydrophobic effect of the long-chain amines.

Flotation cell tests

Procedure
The flotation cell tests were run on 500–800 g of ore, ground to $-150\ \mu m$, with use of a 2-1 capacity Humboldt–Wedag cell. The collectors used were AeroXanthate (AX) 350 (Cyanamid) and DAA (Anorgana); the frother was AeroFroth (AF) 65 (Cyanamid).

Results and discussion

Cell flotation tests were run on a lead–zinc oxidized ore at various Na_2S concentrations, conditioning times and pH values. The results obtained confirmed those of the basic studies described.

For cerussite (Fig. 15) there exists an optimum Na_2S concentration above which recovery falls off sharply. This finding is in agreement with the results of the XPS analysis in regard to the existence of an optimum Na_2S/EtX ratio related to the surface $Pb(EtX)_2$ content.

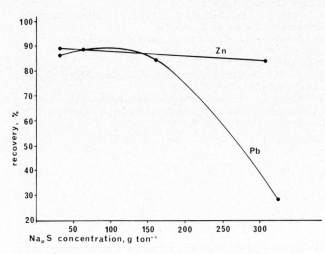

Fig. 15   Flotation of cerussite (pH 10; AX, $80\,g\,t^{-1}$; AF, $20\,g\,t^{-1}$; conditioning time, 2 min) and smithsonite (pH 10; DAA, $100\,g\,t^{-1}$; AF, $15\,g\,t^{-1}$; conditioning time, 2 min)

The optimum conditioning time is probably that at which the best compromise is attained between the quantity of sulphur ions adsorbed, the formation of sufficiently thick sulphidization layers and the occurrence of antagonistic processes, such as the dissolution of the mineral and, of course, competition of the S^{--} and HS^- ions of the Na_2S with the X^- ions in regard to surface Pb sulphide (Fig. 16).

For the smithsonite the conditions are less critical and variations in recovery are less sensitive to the effects of concentration and conditioning time. This is to be expected because of the less complex nature of the sulphidization phenomena—essentially, the formation of ZnS and the absence of antagonistic processes. A rise in pH from 8 to 12 leaves lead recovery virtually unchanged, but it produces a marked increase for smithsonite (Fig. 17).

An increase in alkalinity leaves the cerussite indifferent to the action of the xanthate collector—probably because the beneficial effect of the formation of a greater number of

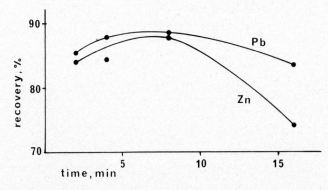

Fig. 16   Flotation of cerussite (pH 10; Na_2S, $160\,g\,t^{-1}$; AX, $80\,g\,t^{-1}$; AF, $20\,g\,t^{-1}$) and smithsonite (pH 10; Na_2S, $160\,g\,t^{-1}$; DAA, $100\,g\,t^{-1}$; AF, $15\,g\,t^{-1}$)

sulphoxide species, which are especially reactive with the xanthate, is accompanied by an increase in the dissolution of the mineral, which results in the consumption of hydroxyl ions.

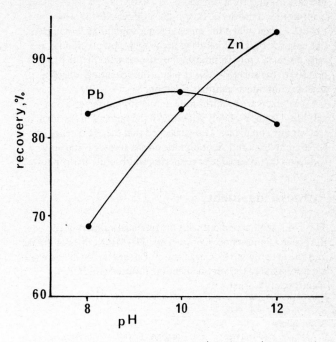

Fig. 17   Flotation of cerussite (Na_2S, $160\,g\,t^{-1}$; AX, $80\,g\,t^{-1}$; AF, $20\,g\,t^{-1}$; conditioning time, 2 min) and smithsonite (Na_2S, $160\,g\,t^{-1}$; DAA, $100\,g\,t^{-1}$; AF, $15\,g\,t^{-1}$; conditioning time, 2 min)

The fact that smithsonite recovery increases with pH seems to confirm that the free amine is the active species. The best Zn grade is obtained at pH 9–10, the $RNH_{2(aq)}$ form reaching its maximum concentration at that value.

Conclusions

Taken as a whole, the results obtained are in line with phenomena commonly observed during laboratory tests and plant operations. Hence, they provide an interpretation of fundamental mechanisms, especially those which concern sulphidization, based on direct investigations.

It should be borne in mind, however, that there exists a great variety of Zn–Pb oxide ores. As has also been noted previously,[30] these can occur in extremely complex forms, particularly in regard to the selected accessory minerals (iron oxides and hydroxides). It is evident, therefore, that the tests performed are of a purely indicative nature and do not reflect an actual processing plant operation.

Within these limitations the following conclusions may be drawn:

Carbonate, hydroxy-carbonate, hydroxide and physically adsorbed H_2O forms are present on the surface of cerussite and smithsonite immersed in water.

Na_2S markedly reduces the amount of physically adsorbed H_2O, transforms the chemical species present into PbS and ZnS and partly increases the hydroxide forms.

With intense Na_2S treatment the maximum degree of sulphidization achieved for cerussite is below 80%, but in smithsonite the transformation of surface carbonate forms to sulphide is complete.

In cerussite the sulphidization spreads into the mass of the mineral, causing partial dissolution of the outermost layers. The thickness of the final PbS layer is of the order of ten monolayers. For smithsonite the sulphidization does not involve dissolution, being limited to a monolayer or a little more.

For cerussite there is an optimum Na_2S concentration above which the quantity of $Pb(EtX)_2$ formed on the surface decreases. For smithsonite an increase in Na_2S concentration results in an increase in collector adsorption.

Xanthate reacts with the Pb ions of the cerussite to form $Pb(EtX)_2$, even when the mineral is not sulphidized, though in this case the $Pb(EtX)_2$ tends to break away and precipitate as a bulk product. Only sulphidization ensures that the $Pb(EtX)_2$ is bonded to the surface—this explains the activating role of sodium sulphide in xanthate flotation.

DAA interacts with smithsonite in the sulphidized and non-sulphized state, probably adhering to the mineral in the form of zinc–amine complexes. It is suggested that the coexistence of these complexes and zinc sulphide on the surface is the only condition that is capable of rendering smithsonite hydrophobic.

Acknowledgement

This work was carried out with the financial support of the European Commission (Contract no. 097-MPP). Special thanks must be extended to C. Cozza and P. Passariello for the care and attention paid to the very demanding infrared and ICP spectroscopy work.

References

1. Rey M. and Raffinot P. The flotation of oxidized zinc ores. In *Recent developments in mineral dressing* (London: IMM, 1953), 571–9.
2. Rey M. Memoirs of milling and process metallurgy: 1 — flotation of oxidized ores. *Trans. Instn Min. Metall. (Sect. C: Mineral Process. Extr. Metall.)*, **88**, 1979, C245–50.
3. Fleming M. G. Effects of soluble sulphide in the flotation of secondary lead minerals. Reference 1, 521–54.
4. Cases J. M. *et al.* Concentration par flottation d'un minerai d'oxyde de zinc et de plomb. In *Processing of oxidized and mixed oxide–sulphide lead–zinc ores: round table seminar, XIII international mineral processing congress, Warsaw, 1979* Laskowski J. ed. (Warsaw: Polish Scientific Publishers, 1979), 93–121.
5. White W. B. The carbonate minerals. In *The infrared spectra of minerals* Farmer V. C. ed. (London: Mineralogical Society, 1974), 227–84.
6. Angino E. E. The infrared spectra of some carbonate minerals. *Am. Miner.*, **52**, Jan. 1967, 137–48.
7. Adler H. H. and Kerr P. F. Infrared adsorption frequency trends for anhydrous normal carbonates. *Am. Miner.*, **48**, 1963, 124–37.
8. Leja J. Little L. H. and Poling G. W. Xanthate adsorption studies using infrared spectroscopy. *Trans. Instn Min. Metall.*, **72**, 1962–63, 407–23.
9. Wagner C. D. *et al. Handbook of X-ray photoelectron spectroscopy* (Eden Prairie, Minnesota: Perkin-Elmer Corp., 1979).
10. Brion D. Etude par spectroscopie de photoelectrons de la degradation superficielle de FeS_2, $CuFeS_2$, ZnS et PbS à l'air et dans l'eau. *Appl. Surface Sci.*, **5**, 1980, 133–52.
11. Pederson L. R. Two-dimensional chemical state plot for lead using XPS. *J. Electron Spectros. related Phenom.*, **28**, 1982, 203–9.
12. Manocha A. S. and Park R. L. Flotation related ESCA studies on PbS surfaces. *Appl. Surface Sci.*, **1**, 1977, 129–41.
13. Stumm W. and Morgan J. J. *Aquatic chemistry* (New York, etc.: Wiley, 1970), 187–8; 322–6.
14. Rey M. Flotation of oxidized ores of lead, copper and zinc. *Trans. Instn Min. Metall.*, **63**, 1953–54, 541–8.
15. Toperi D. and Tolun R. Electrochemical study and thermodynamic equilibria of the galena–oxygen–xanthate flotation system. *Trans. Instn Min. Metall. (Sect. C: Mineral Process. Extr. Metall.)*, **78**, 1969, C191–7.
16. Eadington P. and Prosser A. P. Oxidation of lead sulphide in aqueous suspensions. *Trans. Instn Min. Metall. (Sect. C: Mineral Process. Extr. Metall.)*, **78**, 1969, C74–82.
17. Garbassi F. XPS and AES study of antimony oxides. *Surface Interface Analys.*, **2**, no. 5 1980, 165–9.
18. Marabini A. and Cozza C. Determination of lead ethyl xanthate on mineral surface by IR spectroscopy. *Spectrochim. Acta, part B: Atomic Spectros.*, **38B**, 1983 supplement, 215.
19. Granville A. Finkelstein N. P. and Allison S. A. Review of reactions in the flotation system galena–xanthate–oxygen. *Trans. Instn Min. Metall. (Sect. C: Mineral Process. Extr. Metall.)*, **81**, 1972, C1–30.

20. Mielczarski J. *et al.* Investigations of the products of ethyl xanthate sorption on sulphides by IR-ATR spectroscopy. In *Thirteenth international mineral processing congress, Warsaw, 1979* Laskowski J. ed. (Amsterdam, etc.: Elsevier, 1981), 110–33.
21. Poling G. W. Reaction between thiol reagents and sulphide minerals. In *Flotation: A. M. Gaudin memorial volume* Fuerstenau M. C. ed. (New York: AIME, 1976), 334–63.
22. Mellgren O. and Subba Rau M. G. Adsorption of ethyl xanthate on galena. *Trans. Instn Min. Metall.*, **72**, 1962–63, 425–42.
23. Gaudin A. M. *Flotation* (New York: McGraw-Hill, 1957), 231–8.
24. Reference 23, 288–95.
25. Reference 23, 258–64.
26. Smith R. W. and Akhtar S. Cationic flotation of oxides and silicates. Reference 21, 87–116.
27. Healy T. W. and Moignard M. S. A review of electrokinetic studies of metal sulfides. Reference 21, 275–97.
28. Marabini A. M. Study of adsorption of salycilaldehyde on cassiterite. *Trans. Instn Min. Metall. (Sect. C: Mineral Process. Extr. Metall.)*, **87**, 1978, C76–8.
29. Pascal P. Complexes du zinc. In *Nouveau traité de chimie minérale, tome V* (Paris: Masson, 1962), 318–21.
30. Marabini A. M. La valorizzazione dei semiossidati di piombo e zinco caratterizzati da strutture complesse. Final report, European Commission contract 097-MPP, 1983.

Heat of reaction at solid–liquid interfaces in flotation of lead and zinc oxidized minerals

Paulo Massacci, Girolamo Belardi and Giuseppe Bonifazi

Synopsis
Smithsonite and cerussite from Sardinian ore deposits were introduced into aqueous systems characterized by the presence of the principal reagents (either alone or in combination) used in classical flotation techniques.

By means of a calorimetric LKB system the heat that was added to or subtracted from the biphase system was measured. In particular, the influence of various concentrations of sodium sulphide, pH and a cationic collector, such as dodecylamine acetate, was studied.

The heats and the kinetics of the sulphidization process were quantified and the differences between smithsonite and cerussite were noted. Besides the chemical adsorption of the sulphide ion on the smithsonite surface, a more complex phenomenon of adsorption on the cerussite surface was apparent.

The sulphidization conditions of the smithsonite surface below which there is maximum heat transfer in the reaction between the cationic collector (amine) and the sulphidized surface of the mineral were detected. From the results obtained modification of the traditional treatment processes for zinc oxidized minerals was proposed.

The treatment of lead and zinc oxidized minerals is difficult for two main reasons. First, because of the complexity of the ores that contain those mineral species, which, in turn, is due to the generally fine texture of the ore, which makes it difficult to obtain a high liberation degree, even after grinding down to flotation sizes; and the composition of the elementary mineral species, because of the presence of polluting or substituting elements in the crystal lattice in relation to the conditions of formation and to the type and extent of 'oxidation' of the primary minerals.

The second set of difficulties may be attributed to the poor selectivity of the treatment processes, which generally fail to yield the high grades and high metal recoveries comparable with those of traditional processes on the ores of the respective non-oxidized mineral species.

At the present state of knowledge, starting with the ores that can be liberated at flotation sizes, as was pointed out by Rey[1-5] the only industrial techniques that provide marketable products are those based on the preliminary sulphidization of the surfaces followed by flotation of the lead oxidized minerals with xanthate collectors and of the zinc oxidized minerals with primary aliphatic amine collectors, developed industrially since the 1950s.[6] Despite a great deal of research,[7,8,9] the sulphidization mechanism of mineral surfaces with Na_2S, NaSH and H_2S is not yet fully understood and, in particular, the action of the sulphide ion added to the solution on the adsorption of the various reactive collectors has still to be explained fully. Specifically there is difficulty in the evaluation of the adsorption mechanism of the amines on the zinc oxidized mineral surfaces.

Investigations[8,10] on the collector properties of the cation reagents in the flotation of calamines, and those carried out by Ghiani and Massacci[11] on the use of amine–xanthate molecular combinations in the flotation of calamine minerals, have identified the best modulation conditions for each technique, but

the study of collector adsorption on these minerals cannot be considered exhaustive in either quantitative or qualitative terms. Moreover, some experimental techniques, developed for the evaluation of phenomena at the interfaces, have opened up new investigation possibilities: of particular interest are techniques based on the measurement of energy exchange at the solid–liquid interface.[9,12-16]

The present paper aims to characterize adsorption phenomena of the modulating reagent and of the collector on lead and zinc oxidized mineral surfaces on the basis of calorimetric determinations.

Experimental methods

Investigated minerals
This study was conducted on lead and zinc oxidized minerals from Sardinian deposits. The zinc mineral is from the outcropping Buggerru–Caitas deposit. Samples of the ore—essentially smithsonite and calcite, seemingly without the presence of sulphides—were taken from an experimental mining study.

The lead mineral sample (from the S. Giovanni deposit) was taken during underground mining activities, the complex oxidized ore deposit being located above the natural hydrostatic level.

The sampled ores were beneficiated by means of hydrogravimetric techniques (superpanner), the pure minerals obtained passing through a large number of recleaning processes. It was particularly difficult to isolate the pure species for the lead mineral owing to the complex mineralogical combination of the ore available for the experiments. On the other hand, the pure minerals had to be isolated from the 'real' ores not only to enable the 'real' species to be identified but also to make it possible to transfer the experimental data to industrial processes, if appropriate. Microscopic and diffractometric analyses on the grains of the pure isolated minerals showed the results of the concentration operations to be quite satisfactory. Microscopic analyses showed that the zinc oxidized mineral sample consisted of individual crystals, either isolated or aggregated, all of which had the same characteristics. Diffractometric analysis revealed the presence of smithsonite alone. Microscopic analyses on the lead oxidized mineral sample revealed the presence of individual or geminate crystals that the diffractometric test proved to be cerussite. Furthermore, within some of the crystal relicts of lead sulphides that could not be removed were found.

X-ray fluorescence analysis also revealed the presence of traces of the following elements in the smithsonite: Fe, Ca, Cd, Mg, Pb, Ba, Hg and Mn; and in the cerussite traces of Fe, Mg, Zn, Ba, Ca and Hg. The presence of sulphur was more marked, albeit limited: this is probably due to the galena inclusions and to the trapping of S ions in the crystalline lattice of the cerussite.

Sample preparation
The pure species, isolated from the ores, were subjected to overgrinding to yield samples with a high specific surface. Specific surface determinations (B.E.T. method) with different

N_2/He ratios gave values of 7.00 m²/g for smithsonite and 1.76 m²/g for cerussite.

Experimental conditions

The study required the assessment of the heat released or acquired by the system, to which the mineral belonged, as a result of the following phenomena: hydration of the surface of the dry mineral, addition of sodium sulphide to the suspension of mineral dispersed in water and addition of amine to the suspension of mineral dispersed in water and/or previously conditioned with sodium sulphide.

The experimental conditions generally entailed the use of 0.4 g of mineral dispersed in a volume of distilled water so that the resulting suspension would have a final volume of 60 cm³, including the reagents added. Sodium sulphide and the amine were always added in the form of appropriately dilute solutions

and, in any case, their volume was negligible in comparison with that of the suspension (0.1 cm³ per addition to a maximum of 1 cm³).

Pure $Na_2S \cdot 7-9H_2O$ from Carlo Erba was used and a dodecylamine acetate produced by Anorgana GmbH. The pH of the mineral–water suspension was measured with a 4500 Beckmann pH meter with a 39.501 combined electrode; pH evolution with time was monitored by recording the values.

Measurement of reaction heat

The measurement of the heat acquired or released during the reactions, in the system consisting of the mineral, the water and, according to the molalities, the reagents used (sodium sulphide and amine), was made by means of an 8700 LKB calorimeter modified in the control thermostat circuit (dual adjustment), and by recording the physical parameters of the process (Fig. 1).

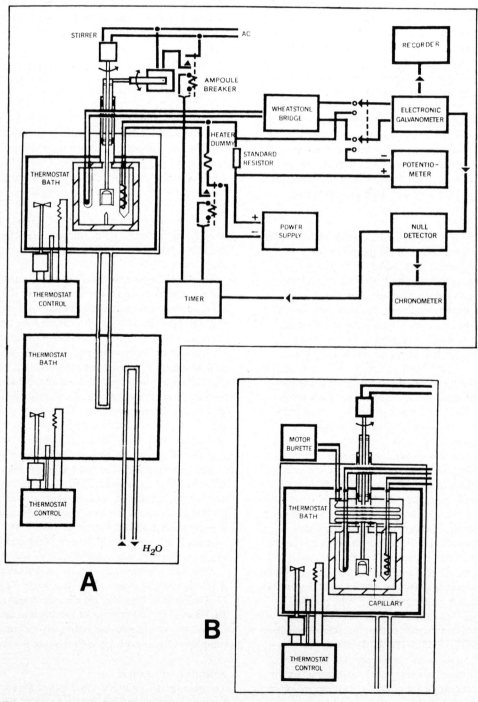

Fig. 1 Measurement system of heat of reaction: modified LKB 8700 calorimeter with double thermostation (A, breaking system of ampoule with solid; B, titration system)

The system illustrated in Fig. 1(A) was used for the hydration tests. The distilled water (60 cm³) was introduced into a reaction vessel (capacity, 100 cm³) immersed in a thermostatic bath. The water was constantly agitated during the tests by a stirrer, which held an ampoule with a capacity of 1 cm³. The mineral was placed inside the ampoule; steady state having been reached, the ampoule would be broken and the heat changes recorded.

Heat released into or subtracted from the system was recorded as variations of a resistance sensitive to the temperature variations of the same system. The resistance variations (and hence the variation of temperature and of the corresponding amount of heat) were measured by means of a Wheatstone bridge balanced with the aid of a zero instrument used at its boundary sensitivity (3 μV full scale). Between the released or acquired heat and the resistance variation in the reference sensor a correspondence was set up by introducing into the system a known amount of energy through a heater. Recordings of the measurements made it possible to describe the phenomena over time.

For the sulphide or amine adsorption tests the system described in Fig. 1(B) was used, with the same electronic hardware as shown in Fig. 1(A). The mineral (0.4 g) and the water (about 60 cm³) were introduced into a reaction vessel (capacity, 100 cm³) immersed in a thermostatic bath; the reagent (sodium sulphide or amine) was added in the form of dilute solutions, with successive additions (about 0.1 cm³) by means of titration (E 415 Metrohm Herisaw Multidosimat) through a Teflon tubing (capacity, 10 cm³) immersed in the same thermostatic bath.

The net heat that can be ascribed to the phenomenon was obtained from the energy measured during each experimental phase by subtracting the corresponding algebraic values of the heats deriving from the breaking of the ampoule and/or from the dilutions of the reagent solutions in the water contained in the reaction vessel.

Accordingly, all the measurements were taken twice, reproducing the same experimental conditions both with and without the mineral. The experimental tests were conducted at an initial temperature of 25° with a tolerance of 10^{-3}°C. For the maximum energy variation within the system after the reactions studied a temperature variation of 10^{-2}°C from the initial temperature was noted.

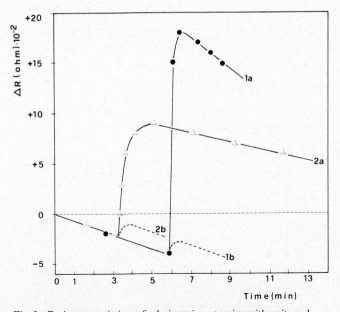

Fig. 2   Resistance variations of calorimetric system in smithsonite and cerussite wettability measurements: modified LKB 8700 calorimeter scheme (Fig. 1(A)) (1a, smithsonite in 60 cm³ H₂O; 1b, breaking of empty ampoule; 2a, cerussite in 60 cm³ H₂O; 2b, breaking of empty ampoule)

Experimental determinations

Measurement of heat of wetting
Three sets of determinations of the heat of wetting were carried out on the two minerals. The data obtained are presented in Fig. 2, which enables the assessment of the energy released by the water–solid system as well as the time required for the hydration process to be completed following the procedures described by Wadso.[17]

The following results were obtained (both exothermic):

$$W_{ad,s} = -136 \text{ mJ m}^{-2} \text{ (Smithsonite)}$$
$$W_{ad,s} = -136 \text{ mJ m}^{-2} \text{ (Cerussite)}$$

Fig. 2 also shows that the hydration rate is greater for smithsonite than for cerussite.

pH measurements showed there was a marked interaction between the smithsonite surface and the water with a marked rise in the pH induced by the immersed solid, which is in agreement with Morshak's[18] findings for carbonates.

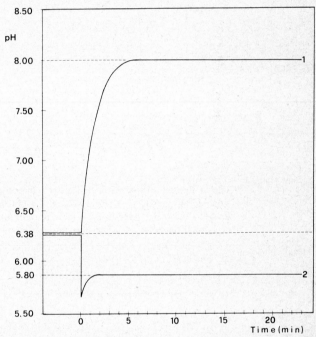

Fig. 3   Interaction of minerals with water: effect on pH (1, smithsonite, 0.4 g in 60 cm³ H₂O; 2, cerussite, 0.3 g in 60 cm³ H₂O)

The trend found for cerussite is typical of cases where lead sulphides are present (and/or lead sulphates) in the species isolated for the tests (Fig. 3).

Measurement of heat of sulphidization
The measurement technique (Fig. 1(B)) was used to determine the heat of sulphidization on the two minerals. Sodium sulphide was introduced into the reaction vessel in successive additions, the data obtained with these measurements being plotted in Fig. 4 (smithsonite) and Fig. 5 (cerussite).

For each sodium sulphide addition the heat measured was subtracted from the dilution heat of the sodium sulphide in the water and, hence, the data shown in Fig. 6 were obtained. Both cases were exothermic. The phenomenon appears to be described by an expression of the type

$$W_s = -k \, S^{1/n}$$

For the smithsonite the trend is linear. For the cerussite the trend of the phenomena may be represented, in the field studied,

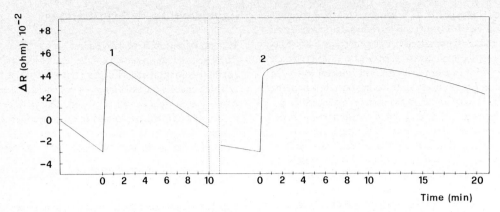

Fig. 4   Resistance variations of calorimeter in measuring sodium sulphide adsorption on smithsonite (sodium sulphide introduced into system by successive additions): modified LKB 8700 calorimeter scheme (Fig. 1(B)) (curves 1 and 2 refer, respectively, to measurements made at first and final addition of reagent: amount of heat and kinetics of adsorption phenomenon comparable in both cases)

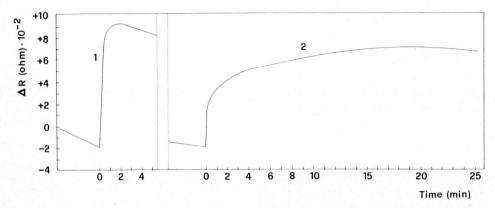

Fig. 5   Resistance variations of calorimeter in measuring sodium sulphide adsorption on cerussite (sodium sulphide introduced into system by successive additions): modified LKB 8700 calorimeter scheme (Fig. 1 (B)) (curves 1 and 2 refer, respectively, to measurements made at first and final addition of reagent: amount of energy and kinetics of adsorption phenomenon depend on amount of sodium sulphide present in solution)

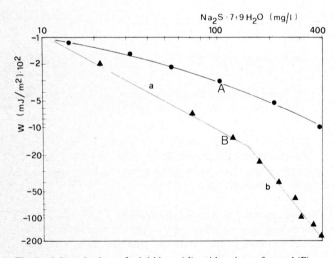

Fig. 6   Adsorption heat of sulphide on (A) smithsonite surface and (B) cerussite surface

by two branches of a curve; for each branch an expression of the following type holds true:

Branch a: $k = 7.944$ $1/n = 1.07$
Branch b: $k = 0.012$ $1/n = 2.36$

The foregoing remarks are confirmed by Fig. 7 and they substantially coincide with those inferred by Rey and Formanek[19] and Mitrofanov et al.[20,21] by use of other experimental procedures on the sulphidization of lead and zinc oxidized minerals and, in general, of carbonates.

With a given concentration of sodium sulphide in the

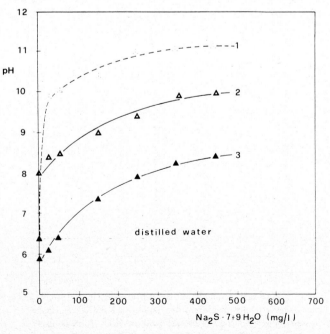

Fig. 7   pH of water–sulphide system in absence (curve 1) and presence of smithsonite minerals (curve 2) and of cerussite minerals (curve 3)

140

suspension the difference between the ordinates of the two sulphidization curves is in agreement with the observations of Rey and Raffinot[22] on the differences between sulphidization of the surfaces of the two minerals (smithsonite and cerussite).

The kinetics of the phenomenon therefore support the existence of mainly chemical adsorption phenomena in regard to smithsonite and, in regard to cerussite, of more complex interactions at the solid–liquid interface with the reagent added to the liquid phase.

occurs. In line with the observations of Cases et al.,[23] the sulphide appears to exert an activating action on amine adsorption. An interaction is apparent between the initial sodium sulphide concentration and the initial amine concentration on the heat. Fig. 9 shows that for a given initial concentration of amine its adsorption heat is represented as a function of sodium sulphide concentration and of the corresponding pH values. To obtain a significant reaction between the amine and the solid–liquid interface there must be sodium sulphide in the

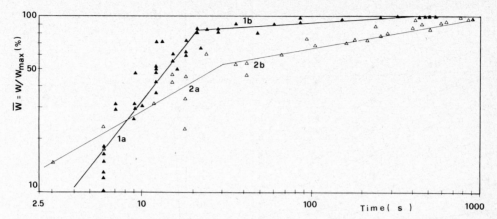

Fig. 8   Sulphidization heat as a function of time: ordinate represents cumulative values of energy released by solid–liquid system expressed as a percentage of overall amount of heat released during sulphidization reaction (1, sulphidization of smithsonite and 2, sulphidization of cerussite)

For the two minerals the kinetics of the sulphidization are shown in Fig. 8. In agreement with the studies of Mitrofanov et al.[20] on metal carbonates, the kinetics of the sulphidization reaction of the surfaces may reasonably be represented, at least for the initial stages of the process, by an equation of the type

$$\overline{W} = a\,\tau^{1/n}$$

where

$$\overline{W} = \frac{W}{W_{max}} \cdot 100$$

is the heat released by the solid–liquid system during the sulphidization reaction (as a percentage of the overall energy released);

$$\tau\,|\,s\,|$$

is the time from the start of sodium sulphide addition to the suspension, and a, b and $1/n$ are system-characteristic constants. For smithsonite these constants are (branch 1a, Fig. 8) $a = 1.824$ and $1/n = 1.260$, and for cerussite (branch 2a, Fig. 8) $a = 8.353$ and $1/n = 0.547$.

Measurements of heat of amine adsorption

First, the mineral was dispersed in water to which sodium sulphide was added until the desired concentration was reached within a range between 0 and 411.5 mg/l of $Na_2S \cdot 7$–$9H_2O$. Conditioning was conducted in the calorimetric reaction vessel, tightly sealed for the time required for conditions of thermal equilibrium to be reached. The amine was then introduced into the reaction vessel in successive additions. With each addition of amine the heat detected was subtracted from the heat of dilution of the amine in water characterized by an electrolytic composition equivalent to that of the corresponding adsorption test.

Amine adsorption at the solid–liquid interface, in the absence of sodium sulphide in the suspension, has been noted to be exothermic, but in the presence of a small concentration of sodium sulphide in the suspension an endothermic reaction

solution (and, hence, S^{--} ions adsorbed on the surfaces). Moreover, when the concentration of sodium sulphide is such that the pH value exceeds the 8.5–9.0 range there is a marked decrease in the heat evolved.

Sodium sulphide has a generally activating effect on amine adsorption at the mineral surface. Moreover, for high sodium sulphide concentrations there is a decrease in the heat evolved by the solid–liquid system in the interaction with the amine, and it can therefore be assumed that there is a decrease in the amount of amine adsorbed. In agreement with the studies carried out by Danilova[24] this may be related to the decrease in the concentration of RNH_3^+ ions in the area in which the pH is higher than 8.5. Such a pH value may indeed be reached in line with higher concentration values of the sodium sulphide. Indeed, Danilova[24] demonstrated that for initial concentrations of dodecylamine salt solutions lower than 100 mg/l (the field of interest of this study) the RNH_3^+ ion concentration remains virtually constant up to pH 8.5 and then gradually decreases, tending to zero for pH 10–11; for pH $>$9–10 there is a rapid growth in the undissolved RNH_2.

The results obtained in this study seem to show that maximum energy heat of interaction between the collector and the solid–liquid interface is ensured in the area in which the pH (in accordance with the sodium sulphide present) is lower than 9.0, the ionic form of the amine predominating.

Role of pH in amine adsorption

To verify the role of pH in the adsorption of the cation collector on the sulphidized smithsonite surfaces a series of tests was carried out to compare the heat with different sulphidization molalities. The first set of results was obtained by sulphidizing the surfaces and then adding the collector reagent (dodecylamine acetate) to the suspension without changing the solid–liquid dilution; the pH of the suspension then remained unchanged at 9.90 throughout the two conditioning phases.

The second set of results was obtained by sulphidization in a

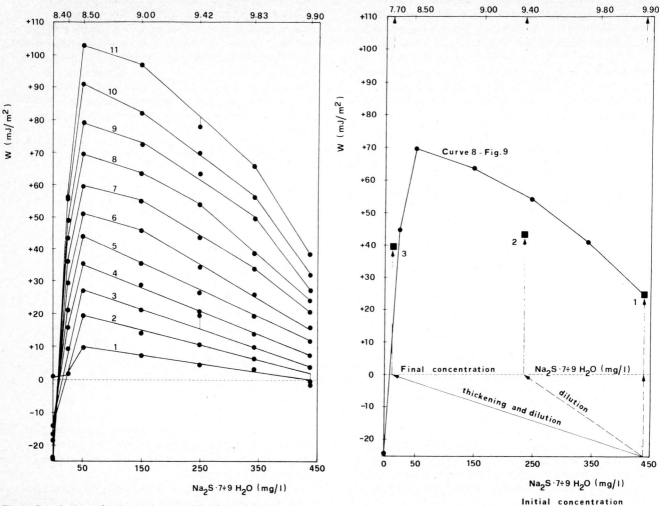

Fig. 9 Reaction heat of dodecylamine on smithsonite surface as a function of different sodium sulphide concentrations (curves 1–11 plotted for dodecylamine acetate concentrations in solution, respectively, equal to 0, 1.00, 1.99, 2.99, 3.98, 4.97, 5.95, 6.93, 7.91, 8.88 and 9.85 mg/l)

Fig. 10 Heat for dodecylamine on smithsonite in various modulation conditions of process (1, conditioning with sodium sulphide in 'highly' dilute suspension: solid, 0.4 g; water, 60 cm³; $Na_2S \cdot 7–9H_2O$, 550 mg/l; conditioning with amine: dodecylamine acetate, 7.91 mg/l; 2, conditioning with sodium sulphide in 'low' dilution suspension: solid, 0.4 g; water, 30 cm³; $Na_2S \cdot 7–9H_2O$, 440 mg/l; dilution of suspension with distilled water: water = 30 + 30 = 60 cm³; 3, conditioning with sodium sulphide in 'highly' dilute suspension: solid, 0.4 g; water, 60 cm³; $Na_2S \cdot 7–9H_2O$, 440 mg/l; thickening of suspension: water, (60-58) = 2 cm³; dilution of suspension with distilled water: water = (2+58) = 60 cm³; conditioning with amine: dodecylamine acetate, 7.91 mg/l)

'dense' suspension followed by dilution of the suspension and addition of the collector reagent; the pH of the suspension was found to be 9.90 for the first conditioning phase (sodium sulphide) and 9.40 in the second phase (amine added after dilution).

A third set of results was obtained by conditioning the mineral in a 'dilute' suspension at high sodium sulphide concentration followed by thickening by centrifugation of the solid with almost total elimination of the solution, the thickened solid then being dispersed in distilled water and, finally, conditioning with a collector reagent in a 'dilute' suspension; the pH was found to be 9.90 for the first conditioning phase with sodium sulphide and 7.75 in the final conditioning phase with amine.

The caption to Fig. 10 details the experimental molalities; heat changes in the solid–liquid systems are shown.

Preliminary sulphidization of the surfaces proved effective in determining the interaction between collector and solid–liquid interface. Moreover, with the same initial concentrations of sodium sulphide and dodecylamine acetate for each conditioning phase the heat evolved is higher when amine is introduced into a suspension in which the pH is low rather than high.

The experimental results also appear to support the views expressed above, as well as those which may be inferred from the work of Ghiani and Massacci,[25] on the collecting power of primary aliphatic amines in the flotation of various non-metallic minerals. The flotation action of primary aliphatic amines

appeared to be highest in the pH range at which the ionic form of the amines predominates.

Further investigation of this problem would require direct measurements of amine adsorption on the mineral surfaces. Because of the restricted sensitivity and reproducibility of known methods, such measurements would be extremely difficult. Tests are being conducted to extend the reliability of determinations of amine concentration in a solution before and after the collector has come into contact with the mineral.

Industrial applicability of experimental results

The results obtained point to the possibility of treating zinc oxidized ores by means of processes in which the conditioning phases with sodium sulphide and amine occur in ore pulps of differing densities. Thus, it may be possible to condition the ore with sodium sulphide in dense ore pulp to ensure maximum concentration of this reagent for improved sulphidization of the smithsonite surfaces. This conditioning phase must be followed by a dilution of the ore pulp before conditioning with amine so that the pH is as low as possible, thereby eliminating the unfavourable effects of a highly basic environment on the collector.

Acknowledgement

The work described was supported financially by the Italian Ministero della Pubblica Istruzione within the framework of research and development programmes in the area of raw materials that is also partly funded by the EEC. The authors wish to thank Vito Rustia for his contribution to the determination of some experimental parameters and Professor Anna Marabini, head of a similar research programme, for constructive discussions.

References

1. Rey M. Flotation of oxidized ores of lead, copper and zinc. *Trans. Instn Min. Metall.*, **63**, 1953–54, 541–8.
2. Rey M. Quinze années de flottation des calamines. *Revue Ind. minér.*, **47**, 1965, 105–20.
3. Rey M. *et al.* Recent research and developments in flotation of oxidized ores of copper, lead and zinc. *Colo. Sch. Mines Q.*, **56**, no. 3, July 1961, 163–75.
4. Rey M. *et al.* Quelques progrès récents dans la flottation des minerais oxydés de cuivre, de plomb et zinc. *Revue Ind. minér.*, **44**, 1962, 349–60.
5. Rey M. Flottation des minerais oxydès. *Ind. minér. – Les Techiques* no. 8-83, Oct. 1983, 375–82.
6. Société Minière et Métallurgique de Peñarroya SA. Italian Patent 478 943, 1953.
7. Rey M. Brandela M. and Sement E. Quelques études cinétiques sur la sulfuration des minerais oxydés du plomb en vue de leur concentration par flottation. In *36e Congrès intérnational de chimie industrielle volume II (Industrie chim. belge, **32**, numéro spécial, 1967)*, 276–80.
8. Rey M. Chataignon P. and Formanek V. The influence of certain inorganic salts on the flotation of lead carbonate. *Trans. Am. Inst. Min. Engrs*, **187**, 1950, 1126.
9. Fleming M. G. Effects of soluble sulphide in the flotation of secondary lead minerals. In *Recent developments in mineral dressing* (London: IMM, 1953), 521–54.
10. Formanek V. Contribution à l'étude des propriétés collectrices des réactifs de flottation cationiques. Reference 7, 179–88.
11. Ghiani M. and Massacci P. Miscele e associazioni molecolari ammine-xantati nella flottazione dei minerali calaminari. Paper presented to Symposium sull'arriochimento dei minerali dell' Associazione Mineraria Sarda, Cagliari-Iglesias, October 1965.
12. Cases J. M. Adsorption des tensio-actifs à l'interphase solide–liquide thermodynamique et influence de l'hétérogenéité des adsorbants. *Bull. Minéral.*, **102**, 1979, 684–707.
13. Prédali J. J. and Cases J. M. Thermodynamics of the adsorption of collectors. In *Tenth international mineral processing congress, London, 1973* Jones M. J. ed. (London: IMM, 1974), 473–92.
14. Mellgren O. Heat of adsorption and surface reactions of potassium ethyl xanthate on galena. *Trans. Am. Inst. Min. Engrs*, **235**, 1966, 46–60.
15. Mellgren O. and Ramachandra Rao S. Heat of adsorption and surface reactions of potassium diethyldithiocarbamate on galena. *Trans. Instn Min. Metall. (Sect. C: Mineral Process. Extr. Metall.)*, **77**, 1968, C65–71.
16. Mellgren O. *et al.* Thermochemical measurements in flotation research Reference 13, 451–72.
17. Wadso I. Calculation methods in reaction calorimetry. *Sci. Tools*, **13**, no. 3 1966, 33–9.
18. Morshak F. An investigation of the pHs of mineral suspensions. *Kolloid. Zh.*, **12**, no. 1 1950. (Russian text)
19. Rey M. and Formanek V. Some factors affecting selectivity in the differential flotation of lead–zinc ores, particularly in the presence of oxidized lead minerals. In *International mineral processing congress, London, 1960* (London: IMM, 1960), 343–53.
20. Mitrofanov S. I. *et al.* An investigation of the sulphidization of oxide minerals. *Sb. nauch. Trud. gos. nauchno-issled. Inst. tsvet. Metall.* no. 10, 1955, 7–29. (Russian text); *Chem. Abstr.*, **50**, 1956, 16598f.
21. Mitrofanov S. I. Kushnikova V. G. and Frumkina R. A. The problem of flotation of oxidized lead minerals. *Sb. nauch. Trud. gos. nauchno-issled. Inst. tsvet Metall.* no. 10, 1955, 41–51. (Russian text); *Chem. Abstr.*, **50**, 1956, 15367a.
22. Rey M. and Raffinot P. The flotation of oxidized zinc ores. Reference 9, 571–6.
23. Cases J. M. *et al.* Concentration par flottation d'un minérai d'oxyde de zinc et de plomb. In *Processing of oxidized and mixed oxide–sulphide lead–zinc ores: round table seminar, XIII international mineral processing congress, Warsaw, 1979* Laskowski J. ed. (Warsaw: Polish Scientific Publishers, 1979), 93–121.
24. Danilova E. V. Physico-chemical properties of laurilamine as flotation reagent. *Sb. nauch. Trud. gos. nauchno-issled. Inst. tsvet. Metall.* no. 1, 1952. (Russian text); Referred to in Klassen V. I. and Mokrousov V. A. *An introduction to the theory of flotation* (London: Butterworths, 1963), 493 p.
25. Ghiani M. and Massacci P. Contributo alla conoscenza del potere collettore delle ammine alifatiche primarie nella flottazione di alcuni minerali non metallici. *Resoconti dell' Associazione Mineraria Sarda*, **73**, April 1968.

New reagents in coal flotation

J. S. Laskowski and J. D. Miller

Synopsis
The main difference between mineral processing and coal preparation is usually claimed to be the extent of comminution. Grinding is very important in a mineral processing plant, but is not found in a coal preparation plant. In run-of-mine coal a large proportion of both coal and shale is already sufficiently liberated to permit immediate concentration. Coal separation then consists mostly of gravity concentration and, to some extent, flotation of natural fines. Screening and solid–liquid separations are auxiliary processes that complete the coal preparation process.

Mechanization of mines and friability of the coal were, in the past, claimed to be mostly responsible for increasing the amount of fines in the raw coal. As a way of increasing the recovery, re-crushing and re-concentration of middlings has become a common practice. So far this approach has been typical for a metallurgical coal but, because of their value and environmental regulations, thermal coal fines have progressively been cleaned also. This trend is expected to continue, especially for coals with a high content of sulphur. The development of flotation technology and other cleaning techniques able to deal with fine particles will then continue to increase, irrespective of the rank of coal.

Two main problems—flotation of low rank and/or oxidized coals and selective separation of pyrite from coal—are considered.

Emulsion flotation of coal

The complexities of particle–bubble attachment—the basis for any flotation separation—are well known and seem to involve the following forces:[1-4] coulombic, which arise from the electrical double layer and are generally repulsive in nature and operative at a film thickness of 2000 Å; dispersion, which are based on the well-developed DLVO theory involving London–Van der Waals attractive forces (dispersion forces generally predominate over 50 to 1000 Å and have second-order dependence on separation dispersion); and structural, which arise owing to specific effects of the solid on the water molecule (through hydrogen bonding or hydration effect) in the interfacial region of 100 Å and are an exponential function of the separation distance.

These forces will determine the hydrophobic character of the surface (both the rate and equilibrium position for bubble attachment). In emulsion flotation the complexities are even greater as a fourth phase must be considered.[5]

One of the major, long-established applications of emulsion flotation is in the flotation of coal. In this process an apolar, water-insoluble, oily hydrocarbon is used as a collector and a water-soluble surfactant is used as a frother. Dispersion of the water-insoluble hydrocarbon oil is a critical issue in the achievement of improved flotation efficiency.

Liquid-phase dispersion
In conventional froth flotation water-soluble collectors must adsorb on the mineral to make its surface hydrophobic. The feature that makes emulsion flotation differ from conventional flotation is the presence of a collector in the form of oil droplets, which collide with mineral particles, followed by adhesion. The process is based on selective wetting; therefore, oil droplets can adhere only to the particles that are hydrophobic to some extent.

Three main factors can be claimed to be mainly responsible for the surface properties of coal particles:[6,7] hydrocarbon skeleton (related to the rank), oxygen functional groups and inorganic impurities. Subbituminous coals and/or weathered coals contain sufficient oxygen to become significantly hydrophilic and difficult to float.

As was shown by Sun and co-workers,[8] water-insoluble collectors that are emulsified (for example, by ultrasonic treatment) are more effective in the flotation process. An emulsified collector provides much higher coal recoveries: without emulsification such recoveries cannot be achieved, even after very lengthy conditioning of the reagents with the pulp. Sun and co-workers also showed that emulsification is facilitated in the presence of emulsifying agents.

Brown[9] showed that metallurgical coals can be easily floated with a small amount of one flotation reagent only; low reagent consumption apparently corresponds to the high native hydrophobicity. For low rank coals—that is, the coals containing a greater amount of oxygen—flotation with the use of one universal reagent is poor. This is especially clear from the example given by Klassen.[10]

In this example flotation of medium volatile metallurgical coal with 2.5 kg/t of medium tar oil yielded 71.7% concentrate with an ash content of 4.5%. The ash content of the tailings was 63.9%. Flotation of lower rank, high volatile, bituminous coal with the use of the same 2.5 kg/t of tar oil provided only 38.9% yield of concentrate (3.9% ash) and 61.1% of tailings containing 23.2% of ash. In this case flotation was obviously very poor, but proved to be quite successful when an additional reagent was properly selected. With the use of 2.5 kg/t of tar oil and 0.6 kg/t nonyl alcohol even in the flotation of that lower rank coal the yield of concentrate was 79.1% (4.1% ash), the tailings containing 62.1% ash. These results strongly reinforce the observations of Sun and co-workers.[8]

To study the attachment of oil droplets to coal particles, and the spreading of the oil over the wet coal surface, Burkin and Bramley[11,12] measured the zeta-potential of the droplets and the particles and used the DLVO theory to characterize the interaction process. Their results clearly suggest that the collision of the droplet and the particles can lead to attachment only if the kinetic energy of approach between them is larger than the energy of repulsion. Their work revealed that some surface-active agents (for example, Lissapol NBD) can drastically improve the flotation process, and that this effect is accompanied by a decrease in the zeta-potential value of interacting coal and oil particles.

The effect of the frother-type surfactants on flotation with the oily collector was demonstrated and explained by Melik-Gaykazian and co-workers (Fig. 1). Frother adsorbs at the oil–water interface, lowering its surface tension and improving emulsification. It also adsorbs at the coal–water interface,[14,15,16] however, and through interactions of adsorbed molecules at both the oil–water and coal–water interfaces facilitates attachment of oil droplets to coal particles. This approach depends, however, on the coal surface properties and the concentration of frother.

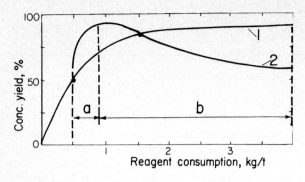

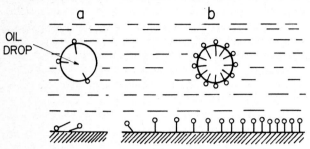

Fig. 1   Flotation of coal under various conditions: 1, flotation with kerosene; 2, flotation with kerosene and *n*-octyl alcohol. After Melik-Gaykazian and co-workers[13]

An opposite effect can be expected at high frother concentrations.

It was reported that contact angles do not change appreciably with MIBC addition, but the rate of attachment increases

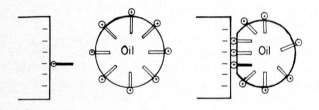

a) Penetration model for low CTAB conc.

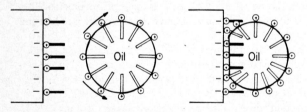

b) Sweeping-penetration model for medium CTAB conc.

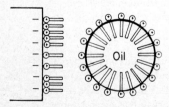

c) No adhesion possible at high CTAB conc.

Fig. 2   Schematic model of oil drop–mineral particle adhesion. Long-chain ions adsorbed at mineral interface are identical to those at oil interface and blacked out to clarify model. After Mackenzie[17,18]

significantly, induction times being reduced from 1 min to less than 3 s.[16]

A similar approach was adopted by Mackenzie,[17,18] who, through electrokinetic measurements, explained the effect of various ionic surfactants on the stability of oil in water emulsions and that of such stabilized emulsions on the flotation (Fig. 2).

In this respect the results that were reviewed recently by Tyurnikova and Naumov[19] are extremely interesting. They found that such surfactants as alkyl sulphates greatly improve the degree of dispersion of oil emulsions and, at the same time, the stability of the oil attachment on to coal particles increases in their presence. They also reviewed publications on the effect of ethyl, propyl and butyl oxides on the emulsion flotation of coal.

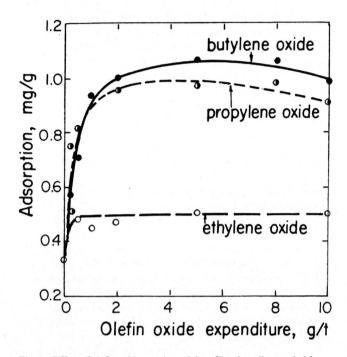

Fig. 3   Effect of olefin oxide on adsorptivity of heating oil on coal. After Tyurnikova and Naumov[19]

The amount of fuel oil abstracted by coal particles was found to increase clearly if the coal had previously been treated with these oxides (Fig. 3). It seems, then, that the specific olefin oxide adsorption on coal results in a greater stability of the adsorptive bond of the hydrocarbons on the coal surface. These substances also increase the degree of dispersion of oil in water emulsion.

Further, they have established that normal paraffins show very minor changes in their collecting properties as a result of ethylene oxide addition. Perceptible variations could only be detected for the higher molecular weight members of the *n*-paraffin homologues (with decane and dodecane 9–11% improvement was observed). The most dramatic changes occurred on flotation with naphthenic and aromatic hydrocarbons. This also indicates the possibility of reactions between the hydrocarbon and the olefin oxides, as it is known that as far as the reactivity towards molecular oxygen is concerned, the hydrocarbon groups can be arranged in the order $CH > CH_2 > CH_3$.

For example, such oxidation reactions as

$$H_2C-CH_2 + C_6H_6 \rightarrow$$

can lead to the formation of products that are surface-active. It has not been established whether the beneficial effect of olefin oxides on the emulsion flotation of coal is connected with the adsorption of these substances at the coal–water and oil–water interfaces that facilitate oil drop attachment to coal surface, or whether it is caused by the products of the reaction between olefin oxides and hydrocarbons used in the emulsion flotation. Nevertheless, these results indicate that either olefin oxides directly, or the condensation products of olefin oxides, adsorb specifically on the coal surface and strongly stabilize adhesion of oil drops to the coal surface. In this way these reagents *promote* the emulsion flotation of coal.

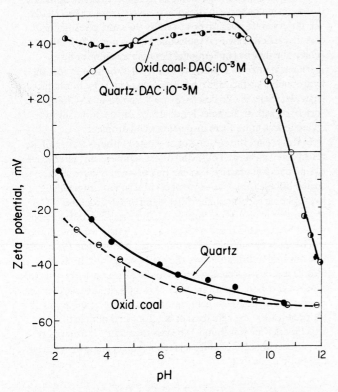

Fig. 4   Effect of pH and 10^{-3} M DAC on zeta-potential of oxidized coal (HVA-bituminous vitrain), quartz. After Wen and Sun[21]

It has been known since the early publication by Sun[20] that amines can efficiently float oxidized coal. Wen and Sun[21] showed that amines adsorb on oxidized coal and drastically change the zeta-potential value of coal particles from initially negative to positive values (Fig. 4). Thus, the cationic surfactants, such as amines, can serve as oxidized coal flotation *promoters* if used in a small amount together with a non-polar oil collector.

Wen and Sun[22] have also shown through the zeta-potential measurements that kerosene droplets carry a negative electrical charge in water practically over the whole pH range (Fig. 5) and therefore should be an inferior flotation collector—especially for oxidized coals—to the mixture of No. 2 and No. 6 fuel oils, which is positively charged in the pH range below 5. A generalized zeta-potential–pH curve for various coals is shown in Fig. 6.[23]

Furlong and Aston[24] investigated the adsorption of alkyl aryl phenol ethoxylates,

$$C_9H_{19} - \langle \bigcirc \rangle - O(CH_2CH_2O)_nH$$

on hydrophilic and hydrophobic surfaces. They have shown that these substances adsorb on both substrates, but the adsorbate–adsorbent affinity was higher for the hydrophobic solid.

It seems that similar agents were used to promote floatability of low rank coals by Sablik[25] (Fig. 7).

The results on the industrial use of promoters, for obvious

reasons, are not very detailed. Nimerick[26] discussed the use of so-called froth conditioning reagents developed to enhance the floatability of highly oxidized coals. The hydrogen/oxygen ratio was used in this study to characterize coal surface properties: if above 20, the coal is easy to float; when less than 20 the coal is hard to float. Conditioners, such as DOWELL Froth

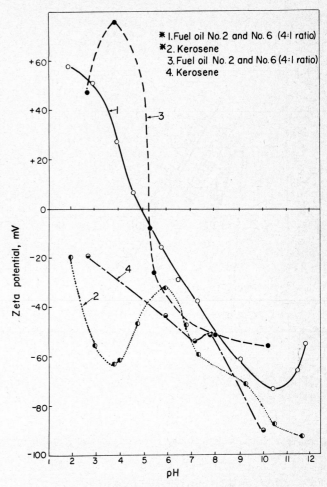

Fig. 5   Zeta-potential–pH of kerosene or fuel oil in water emulsion droplets.* After Wen and Sun[22]

Conditioner M-210, were developed to treat such oxidized coals. Comparative tests were conducted with the use of diesel oil–alcohol mixtures. A typical reagent blend consisted of 9.5 parts diesel, 4 parts glycol ether frother and 1.5 parts conditioner. From this study, they claimed that for one of the coals tested with the use of 0.32 kg/t of reagent (two parts diesel to one part frother) the recovery was 63.4%—in comparison with 87% recovery when the diesel oil contained 10% conditioner and the diesel/frother ratio was the same.

Scanlon *et al.*[27] clearly stated that to obtain high flotation recoveries it is important not only to have hydrocarbon oil collector but to ensure that the collector or collector–frother system is efficiently broken down to a sufficiently small droplet size. They also pointed out that because many fine coal flotation circuits do not provide for the effective conditioning of the hydrocarbon oil, the use of certain surface-active promoters can help to increase the abstraction of the oil collector on to the coal surface. The promoter, American Cyanamid Accoal 4433, was used in amounts slightly greater than 10% with respect to the amount of kerosene.

Another coal flotation promoter described in the literature is Nalcoal 8882.[28] Comparison of the available data indicates that the dose of the promoter is approximately 10% of the amount of the oily collector.

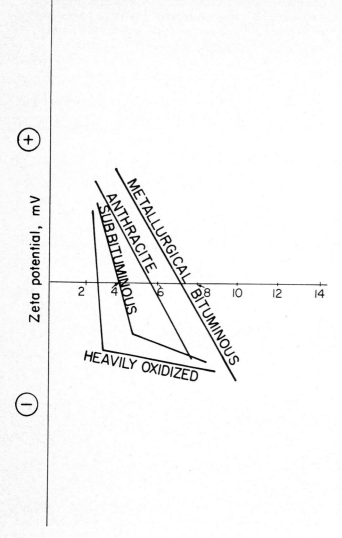

Fig. 6   Zeta-potential–pH curves for various coals

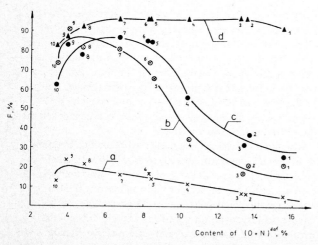

Fig. 7   Effect of conditions on floatability, F, of various coals: a, natural floatability of –0.3 +0.2 mm size fractions without reagents in Hallimond tube; b, floatability of –0.3 +0.2 mm coal in presence of 1 mg of fuel oil/g of coal in Hallimond tube; c, floatability of –0.5 mm coal in subaeration cell with fuel oil (collector) and long-chain alcohols (frother) (proportion of collector to frother 9:1) and d, as c but with the following composition of reagents used: 76% fuel oil, 20% alcohols and 4% EKT (promoter). After Sablik[25]

Gas-phase dispersion

The separation efficiency obtained with the direct addition of insoluble reagents may be affected by irreversible abstraction, poor froth control and high reagent consumption as a result of inadequate dispersion of these insoluble reagents. In molybdenite flotation it was observed that wetting and spreading of vapour oil was highly dependent on oil droplet size. The addition of Syntex, a sulphonated surfactant, sometimes increases the dispersion of these oil droplets and increases the flotation.[29] Similarly, for martite flotation it was observed[30] that by decreasing the average diameter of the oil droplets from 12.0 to 4.4 μm, an increase in flotation recovery from 53.5 to 69.0% was observed. It was also observed by the same investigators[30] that dispersion of neutral molecular oil was not sufficiently achieved either by conventional flotation machine or by mechanical mixers. Traditionally, the oil is thought to coat the hydrophobic surface of a particle and extend its hydrophobic character. Selective coalescence of oil droplets at a hydrophobic surface or with air bubbles is not always satisfactory, however, owing to lack of uniform dispersion of oil droplets.

In this regard the creation of oil-coated bubbles by gas-phase transport of an aerosol of the oil offers an interesting alternative to conventional practice.[31] It can be imagined that for an oil-coated bubble the coalescence of oil film and attachment at a hydrophobic surface might differ significantly from the attachment of an oil-free bubble. Under these circumstances it would be expected that London–van der Waals attractive forces will be more favourable for an oil-coated bubble than for an oil-free bubble. In the latter case the mass and polarizability of an air bubble can be neglected, whereas in the former case these factors should contribute significantly. For example, in the case of a Coal Basin sample the attachment time for an oil-free bubble was of the order of 100 ms, whereas for an oil-coated bubble the attachment time was found to be less than 5 ms. Furthermore, the oil-coated bubble exhibits greater contact angle than the oil-free bubble (Table 1).

Table 1   Hydrophobic character of Coal Basin sample for different bubble types

Bubble type	Attachment time, ms	Contact angle, degrees
Oil-free	>100	35–45
Oil-coated	< 5	55–60

The concept of flotation by gas-phase transport of atomized, water-insoluble reagents, such as oily promoters, has been tested for several systems—coal, tar sand and copper porphyry ore. Basically, the technique involves atomization of oily reagents into

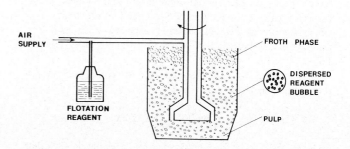

FLOTATION CELL
GAS PHASE TRANSPORT OF REAGENT

Fig. 8   Schematic representation of gas-phase transport of flotation reagents[31]

148

the gas stream. Under these circumstances an aerosol is introduced into the flotation cell so that, initially, the oil is dispersed within the gas phase (continuous with respect to the oil) and the gas is dispersed within the slurry (continuous with respect to the aerosol). A schematic diagram of such a technique is presented in Fig. 8. The atomized oil droplets coalesce on the bubbles' surfaces and create oil-coated bubbles.

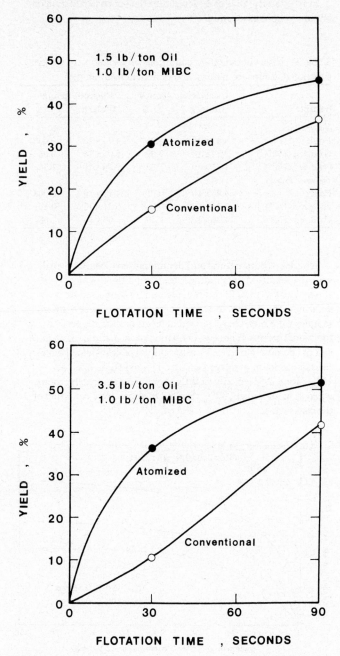

Fig. 9   Comparison of flotation response for Beaver Creek thickener underflow[31]

Experimental results for the thickener underflow from the preparation plant operated by Beaver Creek Coal, Price, Utah, are shown in Fig. 9. This sample contains 60 wt% below 38 μm material and has an ash content of about 33-38%. The rate of flotation by gas-phase transport is significantly faster than that for conventional oil addition to the slurry. Moreover, the froth formation by atomization was consistent and uniform—a very desirable feature from a plant operation point of view.

The bubble attachment process at the surface of hydrophobic particles appears to involve the coulombic, dispersion and structural forces. In this regard it might be expected that oil-coated bubbles would behave differently than oil-free bubbles and gas-phase transport in essence allows for the creation of such

bubbles. It has been shown for oil-coated bubbles that the attachment process involves the coalescence of oil films and that the hydrophobicity of the system differs significantly from the normal situation.

Coal desulphurization: reverse flotation

Two-stage reverse flotation of pyrite from coal was developed during the past decade as a possible process strategy for improved desulphurization of fine coal.[32,33] In essence, the first stage of the reverse flotation process is conventional flotation, which takes advantage of the coal particles' natural hydrophobicity and during which coal is floated away from hydrophilic gangue material (shale, clay and some pyrite). The second stage involves flotation of pyrite particles remaining in the first-stage clean coal product with use of a sulphydryl collector, such as xanthate, and an organic colloid depressant, such as dextrin. The selectivity that can be achieved with the reverse flotation strategy is reflected by the sensitivity of the flotation response of both minerals to dextrin addition (Fig. 10).[34] (Coal depression occurs at dextrin concentrations of 1.0 mg/l, corresponding to less than 10% surface coverage,[35] whereas pyrite with xanthate as collector is only modestly affected at 100

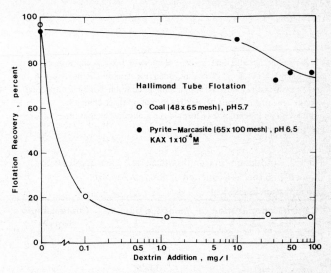

Fig. 10   Pyrite and coal recovery as a function of dextrin addition[38]

mg/l. Clearly, there is a large window for selectivity between the two components.)

Adsorption phenomena at coal surface
Organic colloids, such as dextrin, are typically used as coal depressants. Dextrin, $(C_6H_{10}O_5)_n$, is a water-soluble polymer with a molecular weight that ranges from 800 to 79 000. These higher branched polymeric carbohydrates are composed of dextrose units (Fig. 11). Even at a dextrin concentration of 1.0 mg/l, corresponding to about 10% surface saturation, coal depression occurs.[35] The hydrophilic character of the coal under these circumstances seems to be due to kinetic rather than thermodynamic considerations, as revealed by induction time and contact angle measurements presented in Table 2.[36] Surface saturation occurs at 600 mg/l and at such high surface coverage attachment does not occur.

Adsorption density and thermochemical measurements suggest that dextrin adsorption by coal occurs by hydrophobic bonding.[35] The same adsorption phenomenon previously had been suggested for the dextrin–molybdenite system.[37] In fact, it seems that dextrin adsorption by naturally hydrophobic solids is independent of the solids' chemical composition. Coal (hydrocarbon), molybdenite (sulphide) and talc (silicate)—all

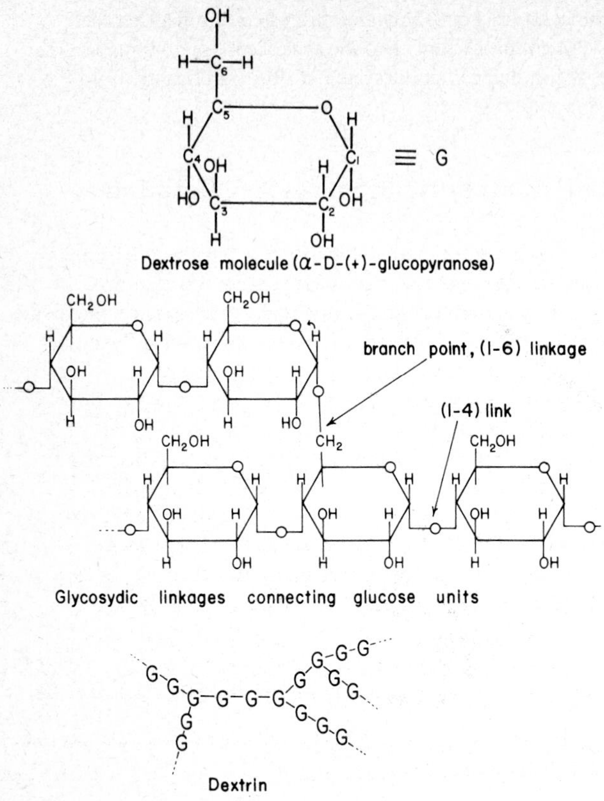

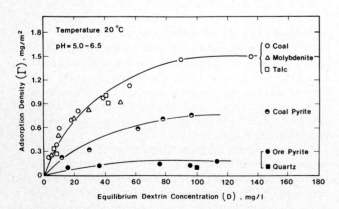

Dextrose molecule (α-D-(+)-glucopyranose)

≡ G

Glycosydic linkages connecting glucose units

Dextrin

branch point, (I-6) linkage

(I-4) link

Fig. 11 Starches and dextrins are polymers of dextrose monomeric units linked through 1–4 glycosidic joints (for straight chains) and 1–6 joints (for branch chains). In starches linear components have molecular weights reaching millions. In dextrin formation these chains are fragmented and recombine to form lower molecular weight molecules of highly branched structures[35]

Table 2 Induction time and contact angle measurements for Illinois No.6 coal as a function of dextrin (Amaizo 1706) concentration at pH 6.0[36]

Dextrin concentration, mg/l	Induction time, s	Contact angle degrees
0	3	40
1	25–36	36
10	30–45	33
60	300	31
80	360	29
600	No contact possible after 20 min	

naturally hydrophobic minerals—exhibit the same adsorption isotherm, in contrast to hydrophilic solids (Fig. 12).[38] Of course, such coincidence of the isotherms would not be expected, as a

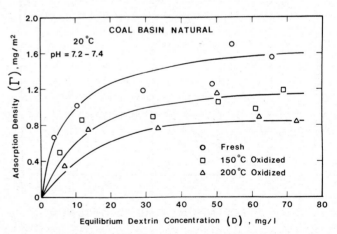

Fig. 12 Adsorption of dextrin by both hydrophobic and hydrophilic solids at 20°C and pH 5–6.5[38,39]

general rule, and may occur because the surface charge appears to be similar, as reflected by a zeta-potential of –40 mV under these pH conditions. The hydrophobic bonding adsorption reactions have been shown to have a heat of adsorption of about –0.5 kcal/mole of dextrose monomer and a free energy of adsorption of about –5.0 to –5.5 kcal/mole of dextrose monomer.[35]

Further study[39] has considered the effect of coal oxidation on organic colloid adsorption.

Table 3 Effect of oxidation conditions on formation of oxygen functional groups for natural and demineralized samples

Sample	Carboxylic groups mole/g	O,%	Phenolic groups mole/g	O,%
Natural				
Fresh	3.43×10^{-6}	0.01	4.73×10^{-6}	0.008
Oxidized (150°C)	2.84×10^{-5}	0.09	5.05×10^{-5}	0.08
Oxidized (200°C)	4.31×10^{-4}	1.38	9.76×10^{-4}	1.56
Demineralized				
Fresh	3.43×10^{-6}	0.01	4.73×10^{-6}	0.008
Oxidized (150°C)	2.45×10^{-6}	0.008	6.24×10^{-5}	0.1
Oxidized (200°C)	4.34×10^{-4}	1.39	1.05×10^{-3}	1.68

Samples of both natural and demineralized Coal Basin coal were dry-oxidized under atmospheric conditions in an oven at 150 and 200°C for 8 h; titration techniques were used to determine the content of active oxygen groups. These oxidized samples were then characterized in terms of their oxygen functional groups (Table 3). Oxidation of the natural (6.5% ash) and the demineralized (0.5% ash) samples of coal yielded almost the same amount of oxygen groups. Dry oxidation in air at 150°C for 8 h raised only slightly the content of oxygen groups, whereas oxidation at 200°C resulted in appreciable oxidation of the coal surface.

Fig. 13 Adsorption of dextrin by natural coal sample from Coal Basin seam at pH 7.2–7.4 and different levels of oxidation[39]

Adsorption of dextrin by the natural and demineralized coal samples is shown in Figs. 13 and 14, respectively, adsorption decreasing with increased oxidation in both cases. This supports strongly the hypothesis that adsorption of dextrin on naturally hydrophobic solids occurs via hydrophobic interactions, as discussed in conjunction with the results presented in Fig. 12. The isotherms presented in Figs. 15 and 16 follow the Langmuir equation

$$\frac{(D)}{\Gamma} = \frac{1}{\Gamma_0 K} + \frac{(D)}{\Gamma}$$

where

$$K = \exp(-\Delta G^0/RT)$$

from which the free energy of adsorption was determined to be from –5.2 to –5.8 kcal/mole dextrose monomer, which agrees well with the –5.0 to –5.5 kcal/mole of dextrose monomer determined previously.[35]

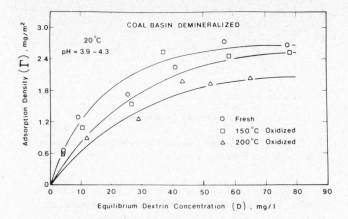

Fig. 14   Adsorption of dextrin by demineralized coal sample from Coal Basin seam at pH 3.9–4.3 and different levels of oxidation[39]

Hydrophobic bonding usually arises from the tendency of non-polar groups of organic molecules to adhere to one another in a polar aqueous environment.[40] The free energy change corresponds to the removal of a non-polar group from its aqueous environment and the resulting Van der Waals bonding between the non-polar group and the hydrophobic surface. In fact, the attraction of non-polar groups (such as hydrocarbon chains) for one another is small[41] and plays only a minor role in the adsorption process. The major contribution to the energetics

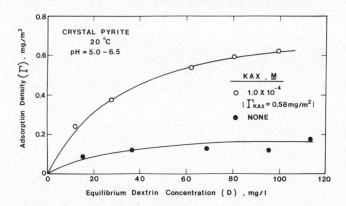

Fig. 15   Effect of potassium amyl xanthate on dextrin adsorption by crystal pyrite[38]

of adsorption probably arises from the change in the nature of the hydrogen bonds of the structured water molecules near the non-polar surface.[42] The total free energy change for the removal of a non-polar CH_2 unit from the aqueous phase into a non-polar environment has been estimated to be 600–800 cal/mole of CH_2 groups.[43] The magnitude of the experimental adsorption free energy, –5.2 to –5.8 kcal/mole, of dextrose monomer for the dextrin–coal system, suggests that the adsorption involves hydrophobic bonding between the non-polar groups of the dextrose monomeric unit and the coal surface, the polar groups directed away from the surface producing a hydrophilic surface state. The hydrophobic bonding of a dextrose unit to the coal surface could involve as many as six CH groups, which would correspond to an adsorption free energy of –4.8 kcal/mole of dextrose monomer—similar to the experimental adsorption free energies.

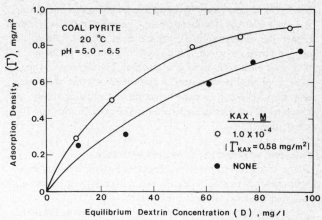

Fig. 16   Effect of potassium amyl xanthate on dextrin adsorption by coal pyrite[38]

The parking area for the dextrose monomer with the distorted ring parallel to the surface was estimated from a molecular model to be 50 Å^2, which would correspond to a maximum loading at saturation of 3.3 x 10^{-10} mole of dextrose monomer/cm^2. Experimentally, the apparent maximum surface saturation can be found to be about 1 x 10^{-9} mole dextrose monomer/cm^2 for the natural sample at pH 7.2–7.4 and 1.7 x 10^{-9} mole dextrose monomer/cm^2 for the demineralized sample at pH 3.9–4.3. These calculations suggest that the dextrose monomer is orientated in a different position at the surface or, in fact, some monomers (two out of three) do not bond at the surface.

Further detailed examination of the adsorption isotherms shows that adsorption by the demineralized samples (Fig. 14) is approximately twice the adsorption density of the corresponding natural samples (Fig. 13). This reflects the increased hydrophobicity of the demineralized samples owing to the removal of hydrophilic mineral matter components.

It is also to be noted that the pH of the suspension in the dextrin adsorption tests was in the range of pH 7.2–7.4 for natural samples and pH 3.9–4.3 for the demineralized samples. The difference in pH values occurs because the demineralized sample consists of the coal in its protonated form. The natural coal sample at pH 7.2–7.4 is negatively charged, whereas the demineralized sample at pH 3.9–4.3 is at its iep. This circumstance may also contribute to the higher adsorption density of dextrin on the demineralized coal. More recent work has shown that the pH effect on dextrin adsorption is not particularly significant and the increased adsorption stems from increased hydrophobicity as a result of demineralization.

The independence of dextrin adsorption by coal on pH suggests that the hydrophobic character of the coal should also be independent of pH. Contact angle measurements (equilibrium measure of hydrophobicity) support this inference (Table 4). Induction time measurements (kinetic measure of hydrophobicity) are dependent on pH, however, and the flotation rate would be expected to reveal a pH-dependence.[44] Indeed, such results have been reported.[7]

Table 4   Hydrophobic character of Coal Basin coal as described by induction time and contact angle measurements for selected pH values

System pH	Induction time, ms	Contact angle, degrees
4.3 (iep)	75	40
5.6	100	40
7.2	116	40

In summary, the experimental results generally confirm the notion that dextrin adsorbs by hydrophobic interactions at the coal surface. Removal of hydrophilic mineral matter sites from the coal surface by demineralization increases the level of dextrin adsorption, as was expected, whereas an increase in the acidic oxygen functional groups of the coal by controlled oxidation decreases the level of dextrin adsorption. The increase in the number of polar oxygen sites, as quantified in terms of carboxyl and phenol content, causes a reduction in the hydrophobic character of the coal and a decrease in the extent of dextrin adsorption.

Adsorption phenomena at pyrite surface

In the absence of sulphydryl collector ore–pyrite exhibits very little tendency to adsorb dextrin, whereas coal–pyrite shows an intermediate tendency to adsorb dextrin (Fig. 12).

Strong adsorption of sulphydryl collectors, such as xanthate, occurs at the pyrite surface and the consumption of xanthate may be complete, given an excess of oxygen and sufficient time. It is expected that such a hydrophobic surface should adsorb dextrin (which it does) and become hydrophilic (which it does not, at least not at modest levels of dextrin). This co-adsorption phenomenon has been studied to some extent.[38]

The adsorption isotherms for the dextrin–crystal pyrite system with and without potassium amyl xanthate are shown in Fig. 15. It is probable that in the absence of xanthate the low adsorption of dextrin by crystal pyrite occurs through hydrogen bonding between the hydroxyl groups of the dextrin polymer and surface oxygen sites. A significant increase of dextrin adsorption occurs, however, when potassium amyl xanthate is added to the system. In this regard it is important to recall that, in the absence of dextrin, xanthate adsorption by pyrite is quite strong and, essentially, goes to completion, forming the neutral molecular, dixanthogen oil, at the pyrite surface.[45] A similar xanthate adsorption phenomenon occurs in the presence of dextrin, resulting in co-adsorption of xanthate and dextrin (Fig. 15). The adsorption of dextrin in the presence of xanthate is thought to be due to hydrophobic bonding between the non-polar portion of the dextrin and the dixanthogen oil that forms on the pyrite surface. Alternatively, the co-adsorption phenomenon may be of heterogeneous nature with patches of dixanthogen and dextrin. For such a situation bubble attachment would occur at the macroscopic areas of dixanthogen predominance.

The adsorption isotherms for the dextrin–coal pyrite system are shown in Fig. 16. The dextrin–coal pyrite system exhibits a higher dextrin adsorption density than that of the dextrin–crystal pyrite system. This result is not surprising as the coal pyrite is not completely liberated and may be associated with a small amount of locked coal, which results in a slightly hydrophobic character for the coal pyrite; thus, 'partial' hydrophobic bonding is suggested as the mechanism for the adsorption of dextrin by coal pyrite. An increase of dextrin adsorption density in the presence of amyl xanthate is also observed for coal pyrite—again as a result of the formation of the hydrophobic dixanthogen oil on the coal pyrite surface. It is important to note that although co-adsorption occurs, the adsorbed dextrin does not significantly affect the floatability of pyrite in the range of concentrations of dextrins used in this study (Fig. 10). This behaviour gives the basis for the two-stage reverse flotation process. Again, the reason for the observed flotation response can be explained by imagining that either the dixanthogen oil wets the hydrophilic dextrin site at the pyrite surface, thereby presenting a hydrophobic character, or the dixanthogen exists in patches on the pyrite surface, as explained previously.

Bench-scale flotation

Preliminary tests to determine the effectiveness of canary dextrins as coal depressants have been reported for Lower Freeport and Illinois No. 6 coals.[36] Figs. 17 and 18 summarize

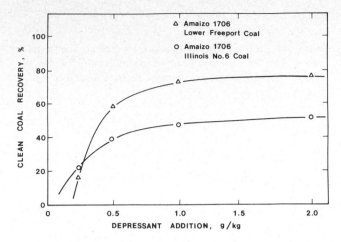

Fig. 17 Effect of depressant (Amaizo 1706) addition on recovery of clean coal for two different coal seams[38]

the preliminary results that were obtained with a specific canary dextrin (Amaizo 1706). The reverse flotation response of the Illinois coal is contrasted with the Lower Freeport coal: the response is similar for both coals. As can be seen from Figs. 17 and 18, the best pyritic sulphur rejection is obtained at a depressant addition between 500 and 1000 g/t. Previous studies[35] of the amyl xanthate flotation response of pure pyrite samples in a Hallimond cell showed that some depression occurred at an organic colloid (dextrin) addition of about 100 mg/l (Fig. 10). The corresponding Amaizo 1706 addition equivalent to this particular concentration is shown by the arrows in Fig. 18 and is in the region of addition at which the pyritic sulphur content of the clean coal is beginning to increase significantly.

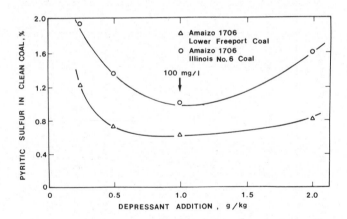

Fig. 18 Effect of depressant (Amaizo 1706) addition on pyritic sulphur content of clean coal product for two different coal seams[38]

Factorially designed experiments evaluated the significance of collector level, depressant level and pH. The effect of pH was found to be not particularly significant, the important variables being collector and depressant additions. Based on these results, the predicted response for the Illinois No. 6 coal can be represented by grade–recovery curves in Fig. 19. The response is similar for different levels of collector (amyl xanthate) addition. The best pyritic sulphur rejections with respect to collector additions are shown by the arrows in Fig. 19. These predictions indicate that the depressant addition for the best pyritic sulphur rejection is between 500 and 1000 g/t, as was mentioned above. Furthermore, for the best pyritic sulphur removal, decreasing the amount of depressant addition was found to be most effective, as opposed to increasing the amount of collector addition. The trend to use a smaller amount of depressant to achieve the pyritic sulphur removal can be explained in terms of

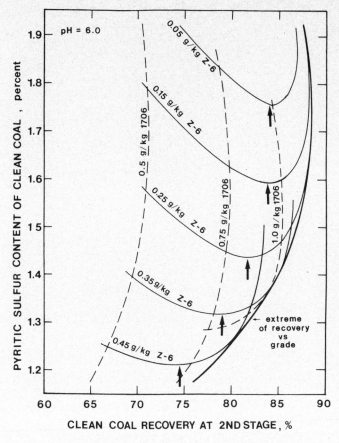

Fig. 19   Plot of recovery versus grade in second stage at different levels of Z-6 and Amaizo 1706 for Illinois No. 6 coal[38]

the co-adsorption of collector (xanthate) and depressant (dextrin).

By this method it was judged that the best combination of collector and depressant for this sample of Illinois No. 6 would be 410 g/t amyl xanthate and 680 g/t dextrin (Amaizo 1706).[36] The result of this combination should produce a second-stage clean coal recovery of 70% and a clean coal product with a pyritic sulphur content of 1.22%. This collector addition, which is significantly larger than is normally found in traditional sulphide ore flotation systems, arises because of the low per cent solids and represents a major operating cost.

Summary

The results discussed clearly show the importance for dispersion of water-insoluble oily collectors to achieve satisfactory flotation. Such dispersion can be accomplished in the suspension or by gas-phase transport. Improved wetting by oil can be achieved by specific additives, such as olefin oxides. Emulsion flotation of difficult to float coals can be quite effective by proper selection of oily collectors and modifiers to facilitate the attachment of oil droplets to coal particles.

The two-stage reverse flotation has been shown to be an interesting approach for coal desulphurization. Selectivity is governed by dextrin adsorption on to coal through hydrophobic bonding. In one particular case (Illinois No. 6 coal) the use of 410 g/t amyl xanthate (pyrite collector) in combination with 680 g/t dextrin (Amaizo 1706, coal depressant) produced a second-stage clean coal with a pyritic sulphur content of 1.22% at a coal recovery of 70%.

The new types of reagents and their use that have been discussed include coal flotation promoters and depressants. Both of these reagents have been shown to be very important in the further development of coal flotation technology.

References

1.   Derjaguin B. V. and Dukhin S. S. Kinetic theory of the flotation of fine particles. In *Thirteenth international mineral processing congress, Warsaw, 1979* Laskowski J. ed. (Amsterdam, etc.: Elsevier, 1981), vol. 1, 21–62.
2.   Blake T. D. and Kitchener J. A. Stability of aqueous films on hydrophobic methylated silica. *J. chem. Soc. Faraday Trans. I*, 68, 1972, 1435–42.
3.   Derjaguin B. V. and Churaev N. V. Structural component of disjoining pressure. *J. Colloid Interface Sci.*, 49, 1974, 249–55.
4.   Laskowski J. Particle–bubble attachment in flotation. *Minerals Sci. Engng*, 6, 1974, 223–35.
5.   Plaksin I. N. ed. *Physico-chemical principles of the action of apolar collectors in flotation of ores and coals* (Moscow: Izd. Nauka, 1965). (Russian text)
6.   Laskowski J. Surface chemistry aspects of fine coal beneficiation. In *First Meeting of the Southern Hemisphere on mineral technology, Rio de Janeiro, 1982*, preprints, vol. 1, 59–69.
7.   Rosenbaum J. M Fuerstenau D. W. and Laskowski J. Effect of surface functional groups on the flotation of coal. *Colloids Surfaces*, 8, 1983, 153–74.
8.   Sun S. C. Tu L. Y. and Ackerman E. Mineral flotation with ultrasonically emulsified collecting reagents. *Min. Engng, N.Y.*, 7, July 1955, 656–60.
9.   Brown D. J. Coal flotation In *Froth flotation. 50th anniversary volume* Fuerstenau D. W. ed. (New York: AIME, 1962), 518–38.
10.   Klassen V. I. *Coal flotation* (Katowice: Slask, 1966). Translated from Russian into Polish by J. Laskowski.
11.   Burkin A. R. and Bramley J. V. Flotation with insoluble reagents, part I. *J. appl. Chem.*, 11, 1961, 300–9.
12.   Burkin A. R. and Bramley J. V. Flotation with insoluble reagents, part II. *J. appl. Chem.*, 13, 1963, 417–22.
13.   Melik-Gaykazian V. I. Plaksin I. N. and Voronchikhina V. V. *Dokl. Akad. Nauk SSSR*, 173, no. 4 1967, 883–6. (Russian text)
14.   Frangiskos N. Z. Harris C. C. and Jowett A. The adsorption of frothing agents on coals. Paper presented to Third international congress on surface active substances, Köln, 1960.
15.   Fuerstenau D. W. and Pradip. Adsorption of frothers at coal/water interfaces. *Colloids Surfaces*, 4, 1982, 229–43.
16.   Miller J. D. Lin C. L. and Chang S. S. MIBC adsorption at the coal/water interface. *Colloids Surfaces*, 7, 1983, 351–5.
17.   Mackenzie J. M. W. Electrokinetic properties of nujol-flotation collector emulsion drops. *Trans. Am. Inst. Min. Engrs*, 244, 1969, 393–400.
18.   Mackenzie J. M. W. Interactions between oil drops and mineral surfaces. *Trans. Am. Inst. Min. Engrs*, 247, 1970, 202–8.
19.   Tyurnikova V. I. and Naumov M. E. *Improving the effectiveness of flotation* (Stonehouse, Glos., England: Technicopy Ltd., English edition, 1981), 229 p.
20.   Sun S. C. Effects of oxidation of coals on their flotation properties. *Trans. Am. Inst. Min. Engrs*, 199, 1954, 396–401.
21.   Wen W. W. and Sun S. C. An electrokinetic study on the amine flotation of oxidized coal. *Trans. Am. Inst. Min. Engrs*, 262, 1977, 174–80.
22.   Wen W. W. and Sun S. C. An electrokinetic study on the oil flotation of oxidized coal. *Separation Sci.*, 16, 1981, 1491–521.
23.   Parfitt G. and Laskowski J. Electrokinetics of coal/water suspensions. In *Interfacial phenomena in coal technology* Botsaris G. D. and Glazman M. eds (New York: Marcel Dekker Inc., in preparation).
24.   Furlong D. N. and Aston J. R. Adorption of polyoxythylated nonyl phenols at silica/aqueous solution interfaces. *Colloids Surfaces*, 4, 1982, 121–9.
25.   Sablik J. The grade of metamorphism of Polish coals and their natural and activated floatability. *Int. J. Mineral Process.*, 9, 1982, 245–57.
26.   Nimerick K. H. Characterization of coals responding to froth conditioning. Paper presented to SME–AIME Fall Meeting, Honolulu, September 1982, Preprint 82–377.
27.   Scanlon M. J. *et al.* Flotation promoters improve fine coal recovery. *World Coal*, Feb. 1983, 54–6.
28.   Beardsley J. A. Chemical boosts prep plant coal recovery. *Coal Min. Process.*, July 1978, 63–4.
29.   Hoover R. M. and Malhatra D. Emulsion flotation of molybdenite. In *Flotation: A. M. Gaudin memorial volume* Fuerstenau M. C. ed. (New York: AIME, 1976), vol. 1, 485–505.
30.   Glembotskii V. A Dmitrieva G. M. and Sorokin M. M. Nonpolar flotation agents. Academy of Sciences of the USSR, translated for the U.S. Department of Energy and National Science Foundation, 1970.
31.   Miller J. D. and Misra M. Flotation separation with gas phase transport of atomized oil droplets. Paper presented to Fine Particle Society, Honolulu, Hawaii, August 1983.
32.   Miller K. J. and Baker A. F. Flotation of pyrite from coal. *Tech. Progr. Rep. U.S. Bur. Mines* 51, 1972, 7 p.

33. Miller K. J. Flotation of pyrite from coal: pilot plant study. *Rep. Invest. U.S. Bur. Mines* 7822, 1973, 15 p.

34. Miller J. D. Radiotracer measurements of the adsorption of organic colloid by coal. In *Proceedings of the August 1979 Rindge coal cleaning conference* (Washington, D.C.: NSF, DOE and Engineering Foundation, 1982), 30.

35. Haung H. H. *et al.* Adsorption reactions in the depression of coal by organic colloids. In *Recent developments in separation science* (West Palm Beach, Florida: CRC Press, 1978). vol. 4, 115–33.

36. Lin C. L. Characterization of pyrite in reverse flotation products. M. S. thesis, University of Utah, Salt Lake City, 1982.

37. Wie J. M. and Fuerstenau D. W. The effect of dextrin on surface properties and the flotation of molybdenite. *Int. J. Mineral Process.*, **1**, 1974, 17–32.

38. Miller J. D. Lin C. L. and Chang S. S. Coadsorption phenomena in the flotation of pyrite from coal by reverse flotation. *Coal Preparation*, **1**, 1984, 21–38.

39. Miller J. D. Laskowski J. S. and Chang S. S. Dextrin adsorption by oxidized coal. *Colloids Surfaces*, **8**, 1983, 137–51.

40. Némethy G. and Scherage H. The structure of water and hydrophobic bonding in proteins, III. The thermodynamic properties of hydrophobic bonding in proteins. *J. phys. Chem.*, **66**, 1962, 1773.

41. Parsegian V. A. and Ninham B. W. Toward the correct calculation of van der Waals interactions between lyophobic colloids in an aqueous medium. *J. Colloid Interface Sci.*, **37**, 1971, 332–41.

42. Tanford C. T. *The hydrophobic effect: formation of micelles and biological membranes* (New York: Wiley, 1973), 240 p.

43. Reynolds J. A. Bilgert D. B. and Tanford C. Empirical correlation between hydrophobic free energy and aqueous cavity surface area. *Proc. natn. Acad. Sci. U.S.A.*, **71**, no. 8 1974, 2925.

44. Laskowski J. and Iskra J. Role of capillary effects in bubble–particle collision in flotation. *Trans. Instn Min. Metall. (Sect C: Mineral Process. Extr. Metall.)*, **79**, 1970, C6–10.

45. Haung H. H. and Miller J. D. Kinetics and thermochemistry of amyl xanthate adsorption by pyrite and marcasite. *Int. J. Mineral Process.*, **5**, 1978, 241–66.

Criteria for selection of activated carbon used in carbon-in-pulp plants

J. S. J. Van Deventer

Synopsis

With the introduction of the carbon-in-pulp process to the gold mining industry an abundance of activated carbon products has come on the market. The chemical and physical properties of these carbons vary considerably from soft but highly active carbons to hard but relatively inactive carbons.

A dual-rate kinetic model is proposed to simulate the adsorption of gold on activated carbon. In this model the carbon is divided into two interconnected regions with different kinetic characteristics. The Freundlich isotherm is shown to adequately predict equilibrium adsorption of gold on all the carbons investigated. Kinetic parameters are estimated from batch kinetic experiments and used to formulate selection criteria.

Coal-based extruded carbons, coconut shell carbons and peach pip carbons are compared on the basis of abrasion-resistance, equilibrium loading and kinetic and elution performance. Some carbons are shown to have high equilibrium loadings, but relatively slow kinetics.

Activated carbon was introduced in about 1880 as an adsorbent for the recovery of gold and silver from cyanide solutions. Although it was a strong competitor for zinc precipitation during the early years of the cyanidation process, it soon lost ground owing to the lack of a suitable means of stripping adsorbed gold from loaded carbon.

It was not until the 1950s that Zadra[1] and Zadra and co-workers[2] at the U.S. Bureau of Mines developed a method for the elution of gold and silver from activated carbon. The development of granules of hard activated carbon during the Second World War allowed its direct use in the cyanide pulp, thereby avoiding the costly filtration step. This so-called carbon-in-pulp (CIP) process was first applied on a commercial scale at the Homestake mine in South Dakota.[3] Since then numerous CIP plants have been constructed in North America,[4] Australia,[5] the Soviet Union[6] and South Africa.[7] Menne[7] estimated that in South Africa alone CIP circuits with a total capacity of 4 700 000 t/month will be operational by the end of 1985.

Fig. 1 outlines the various unit operations of a typical CIP circuit. The flowsheet consists primarily of (a) pre-screening of pulp at 0.6 mm, (b) adsorption of dissolved gold by activated carbon in tanks, (c) interstage screening at 0.85 mm, (d) stripping of the gold from the loaded carbon, (e) recovery of the gold from the eluate by electrowinning and (f) regeneration of the eluted carbon to remove adsorbed organic contaminants.

Activated carbon is produced commercially from a variety of carbonaceous materials, such as coconut shells, wood, fruit pips, peat, sugar and bituminous coal. The physical and chemical properties of activated carbon are influenced by the conditions of activation as well as the source material. For the CIP process it is essential to use an activated carbon that is abrasion-resistant to minimize the production of carbon fines that can result in gold losses. To allow for efficient carbon/pulp separation by screening the carbon should be relatively coarse, but simultaneously have sufficient activity.

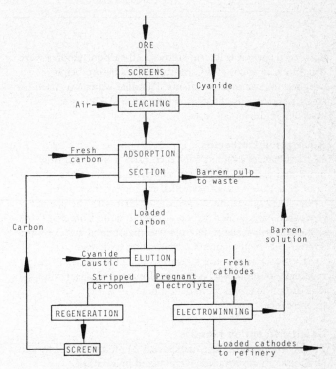

Fig. 1   Schematic flowsheet for typical CIP circuit

Since the introduction of the CIP process, however, activated carbon products have flooded the metallurgical market. These products have varied considerably from soft but highly active carbons through to hard but less active carbons. The selection of an activated carbon to be used in a CIP plant can significantly influence plant performance. The objectives of this paper are to compare the physical and chemical properties of a few carbon products and to lay down broad criteria for the selection of such carbons on the basis of a kinetic model for the adsorption of gold on activated carbon.

Experimental

Materials

All adsorption studies were conducted with potassium aurocyanide as adsorbate, and different carbons as adsorbents. The carbon samples were screened to remove the -600-μm fraction. Table 1 gives information about the carbons used, which were supplied by Gencor Group Laboratories (East), Springs, South Africa. Most of the carbons revealed a distribution of particle sizes between 600 and 2800 μm, which was determined by screening. Only the median particle size for each carbon is shown in Table 1. Some of the carbon was ground to -75 μm for use in the

Table 1 Details of activated carbons

Carbon sample	Name	Starting material	Median particle size, mm	Apparent density, kg/m³
A	Degussa	Coconut shell	1.77	530
B	Norit	Coal, extruded	1.79	640
C	Brazilian origin	Coconut shell	1.85	970
D	Sutcliffe Speakman	Coconut shell	2.00	890
E	Experimental	Peach pips	1.34	776
F	Sentrachem experimental	Coconut shell	1.60	1036
G	Haycarb	Coconut shell	1.83	1070
H	Experimental	Coal, extruded	2.75	770
I	Le Carbonne G210 AS	Coconut shell	1.84	930

powdered carbon isotherm studies. All carbon samples were dried in an oven at 150°C for three days before being weighed for use in experiments. Distilled water was used in all experiments. A constant temperature of 23°C was maintained during all tests.

Adsorption isotherms

Isotherms were evaluated for each carbon by contacting powdered carbon and different initial concentrations of gold cyanide solution in bottles rolled for longer than three weeks. Previous studies[8] have shown that with the use of powdered or granular carbon a single unique isotherm is obtained for a system. The pH was maintained at 8.5 by the addition of small amounts of potassium hydroxide or hydrochloric acid to the mixtures. The gold tenor of the resultant solutions was determined by atomic absorption and carbon loadings were determined by X-ray fluorescence.

Batch adsorption kinetics

Preconditioned granular carbon and 2 l of standard solution of potassium aurocyanide were mixed in a baffled cylindrical batch reactor by a six-blade Heidolph variable-speed stirrer. A stirring speed of 170 rev/min was maintained during all experiments. Solution samples (2 ml) were taken periodically during a batch test and analysed for gold by atomic absorption. The pH was maintained at 8.5.

Elution tests

Granular carbon samples (2 g) were loaded by contacting them with 2 l of solution containing 40 g Au/m³ for three weeks. Carbon loadings were then calculated by analysing the solution for gold. The carbon samples were then washed with distilled water and added to a boiling 1 l solution containing 1% KOH and 0.5% KCN. The mixture was refluxed for 2 h and small samples were withdrawn periodically for gold analysis.

Abrasion tests

A 3-l vessel fitted with baffles and a Heidolph two-blade impeller was used in a standard test to determine carbon abrasion. A total of 100 g of carbon (particle size distribution between 1 and 2.8 mm) was made up to 2 l with water. Initial conditioning was done at 800 rev/min for 3 h, after which the −1-mm fraction was screened out. Conditioning was continued for another 5 h, after which a second −1-mm fraction was removed. The impeller speed was then reduced to 400 rev/min and agitation was continued for a further 24 h. The third −1-mm fraction was then calculated as a percentage of the original carbon

mass and reported as the daily attrition loss.

Adsorption model

Peel and co-workers[9,10] and Weber and Liang[11] have used dual-rate kinetic models to describe the adsorption of various phenols in fixed beds of activated carbon. Most researchers in the field of water treatment have, however, used a single-rate model, which has resulted in a systematic lack of fit in some batch kinetic analyses.[12] In this paper a simplified driving force dual-rate model for the adsorption of gold on activated carbon is proposed. Fig. 2 depicts the physical representation of the model.

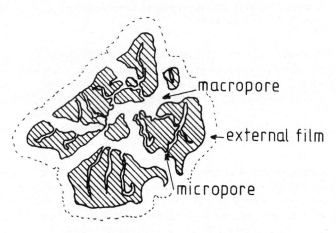

Fig. 2 Conceptual representation of carbon pore structure

The carbon is partitioned into a fast-adsorbing macropore region and a slow-adsorbing micropore region. These two regions are interconnected and homogeneously distributed through the carbon. It is not possible to specify *a priori* the relative proportions of the two regions. Gold cyanide entering the macropores from the liquid phase first has to diffuse through an external boundary layer. It is assumed that the adsorption reaction is not rate-controlling. A surface diffusion mechanism is assumed to be responsible for transport in the macropore region. The rate of diffusion beween macropore and micropore regions is described by a linear driving force expression.

The liquid phase material balance is★

$$V \frac{dc}{dt} = -\frac{6k_f W}{\bar{d}_p \rho_c}(c - c_s) \tag{1}$$

★Definitions of the symbols used in this paper are given on page 160.

156

The material balance for the macropore region is

$$\alpha W \frac{\partial q_m}{\partial t} = W\alpha \frac{D_m}{r^2} \frac{\partial}{\partial r} \left(r^2 \frac{\partial q_m}{\partial r} \right) - k_{mb} W (q_m - q_b)$$

(2)

Vermeulen[13] showed that the surface diffusion model may be approximated by a quadratic driving force expression, which was also used by Peel and Benedek[14] in the modelling of fixed-bed adsorbers. Equation 2 then becomes

$$\alpha W \frac{dq_m}{dt} = \frac{6 k_m W}{\bar{d}_p} \left(\frac{q_s^2 - q_m^2}{2q_m} \right) - k_{mb} W (q_m - q_b)$$ (3)

The material balance for the micropore region is

$$W(1 - \alpha) \frac{dq_b}{dt} = k_{mb} W(q_m - q_b)$$ (4)

It is assumed that no accumulation occurs at the carbon–liquid interface, so the transport rates across the external particle surface may be equated by

$$\frac{k_f}{\rho_c} (c - c_s) = k_m \left(\frac{q_s^2 - q_m^2}{2q_m} \right)$$ (5)

The equilibrium that exists at the solid–liquid interface is described satisfactorily by the Freundlich isotherm

$$q_s = AC_s^n$$ (6)

The set of equations (equations 1, 3, 4, 5 and 6) that comprises the batch kinetic solution was solved by use of a fourth-order Runge–Kutta routine with a time-step promotion. Initial guesses of the future values of q_s and c_s were calculated by linear extrapolation of the change over of the previous time interval. Midtime interval surface concentrations were obtained by averaging present and future values of c_s and q_s. A *regula falsi* solution of equations 5 and 6 then improved guesses of future surface concentrations. The solution converged when no improvement in the value q_s could be obtained, and was iterative at each point in time. The film transfer coefficient, k_f, was estimated from a plot of ln c versus t for batch data obtained during the first few minutes of adsorption. By use of the batch kinetic model in a Powell regression algorithm the values of α, k_m and k_{mb} that gave the best fit to the experimental data were estimated.

Results and discussion

Equilibrium adsorption

Table 2 shows fitted A and n values for different carbons. The Freundlich isotherm fitted experimental equilibrium data for all carbons with a regression coefficient of at least 0.99. With powdered carbon equilibrium was practically obtained after three weeks. It has been shown previously[8] that crushing carbon has a slight effect on the surface area. The use of powdered carbon in the evaluation of these isotherms seems justified.

In the determination of the AARL k-value,[15] which should have the same empirical meaning as A in this paper, an adsorption period of only 17 h is allowed before equilibrium behaviour is assessed. Cho and co-workers[16] allowed only 4 h for equilibrium. True equilibrium is not necessarily attained in these tests and, therefore, such kinetic factors as degree of agitation and carbon particle size become important in the determination of equilibrium parameters. Only the degree of activation will influence A and n values in this study.

Both A and n values should be considered in the evaluation of the equilibrium performance of a carbon. Carbon samples, A, C, E and G do not reveal sufficiently high activity to be used in CIP plants, but cost considerations may justify their use in some operations. Coal-based extruded carbons B and H both have superior equilibrium performance.

Loading kinetics

Table 2 shows kinetic factors k_f, k_m, k_{mb} and α for different carbons. The film transfer coefficient, k_f, gives an indication of the sensitivity of a carbon to changes in stirring speed. A relatively low value of k_f indicates a higher degree of film diffusional resistance, as for carbon H. In an earlier paper[17] it was shown that the value of k_f is dependent on the degree of particle suspension. When the particle surface is relatively free the dependence of k_f on stirring speed is small. Because k_f controls the initial adsorption period it cannot be used individually to judge kinetic behaviour.

The macropore pseudo mass-transfer coefficient, k_m, is a function of the initial rapid uptake period only and the

Table 2 Adsorption equilibrium and kinetic parameters, elution performance and abrasion-resistance of different carbons

Carbon	A	n	$k_f \cdot 10^5$, m/s	$k_m \cdot 10^9$, m/s	$k_{mb} \cdot 10^7$, s^{-1}	α	Elution factors, % Kinetic	Elution factors, % Equilibrium	Daily attrition loss, %
A	20	0.30	5.80	4.17	2.50	0.98	42	98	0.84
B	42	0.12	8.71	3.94	3.67	0.89	43	97	0.17
C	28	0.21	18.32	6.94	6.67	0.87	57	99	0.79
D	40	0.11	13.60	11.39	21.67	0.69	62	100	0.26
E	28	0.18	9.59	5.69	26.67	0.71	49	97	1.08
F	40	0.13	34.82	10.00	35.00	0.68	66	100	0.39
G	27	0.16	11.29	7.50	33.33	0.70	55	99	0.33
H	42	0.12	2.57	2.50	31.67	0.99	38	98	0.26
I	40.5	0.11	5.43	11.94	21.67	0.44	59	100	0.24

inter-regional rate coefficient, k_{mb}, is a function of the slow, long-term uptake. Initially, surface diffusion in the macropores is rate-controlling, restricted diffusion in the micropores controlling the subsequent slow approach to equilibrium. α gives an indication of the fraction of adsorptive capacity available as macropores. Although an activated carbon usually reveals a continuum of pore sizes, this dual-rate approach was found to adequately describe adsorption kinetics under different conditions (Figs. 3–11). The solid lines represent model predictions calculated by use of the parameters of Table 2.

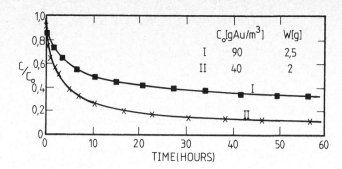

Fig. 7   Batch kinetic results for experimental peach pip carbon

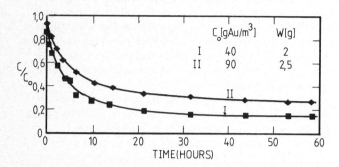

Fig. 3   Batch kinetic results for Degussa coconut shell carbon

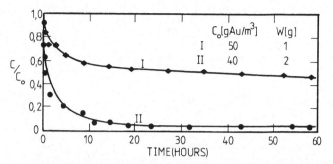

Fig. 8   Batch kinetic results for Sentrachem experimental coconut shell carbon

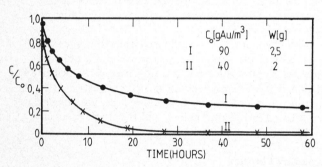

Fig. 4   Batch kinetic results for Norit coal-based extruded carbon

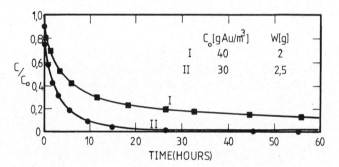

Fig. 9   Batch kinetic results for Haycarb coconut shell carbon

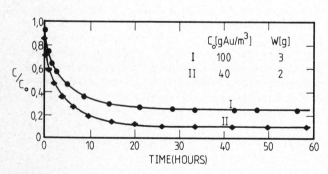

Fig. 5   Batch kinetic results for coconut shell carbon of Brazilian origin

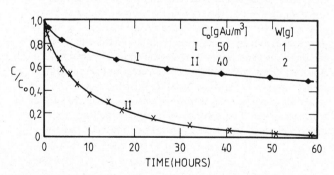

Fig. 10   Batch kinetic results for experimental coal-based extruded carbon

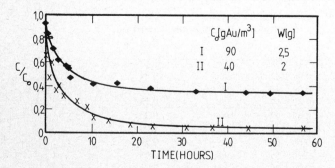

Fig. 6   Batch kinetic results for Sutcliffe Speakman coconut shell carbon

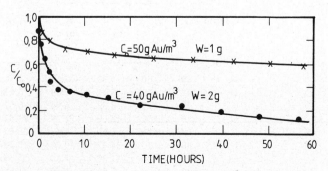

Fig. 11   Batch kinetic results for Le Carbonne G210 AS coconut shell carbon

Carbons A and H have α values close to unity, so restricted diffusion does not actually control the approach to equilibrium in these carbons. Carbons B and H reveal relatively slow macropore uptake, although their equilibrium loading behaviour is satisfactory. Carbons A, B and C show not only slow micropore uptake and high α values but also relatively slow macropore uptake. Carbons D, F and I show not only high equilibrium loadings but also high values for k_m and k_{mb}.

Particle size
Fig. 12 shows the effect of different particle sizes on the adsorption kinetics of Le Carbonne G210 AS. Particle size inversely affects the rate of diffusion into the macropore

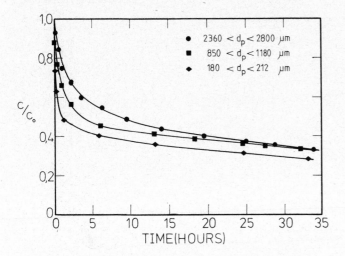

Fig. 12 Effect of carbon particle size on batch adsorption kinetics for Le Carbonne G210 AS ($c_0 = 50$ g Au/m³; $W = 2$ g)

region, so particle size distribution has a more significant effect on kinetics during the early adsorption period: in view of this, carbon sizes should be as small as possible. To ensure effective carbon-in-pulp separation, however, particle sizes should be well above 0.8 mm, which is usually the mesh size of interstage screens.

Elution tests
The theoretical concepts that govern elution of gold from loaded carbon are not as well understood as the adsorption process. No kinetic or equilibrium models have yet been formulated to enable elution behaviour to be predicted. It seems as if the standard commercial elution procedures[4] are all designed to shift the loading equilibrium, so gold desorbs from the carbon to re-establish a new equilibrium. Because of this lack of fundamental understanding simple elution factors are proposed to evaluate elution behaviour:

$$\text{Kinetic factor} = \frac{c(t = 10 \text{ min})}{c(t = 90 \text{ min})} \qquad (7)$$

$$\text{Equilibrium factor} = \frac{c(t = 90 \text{ min})V}{q(t = 0)W} \qquad (8)$$

Elution results are shown in Table 2. All carbons were found to be completely eluted after 90 min. Only carbons A, B and H reveal relatively slow elution kinetics.

Attrition-resistance
Table 2 shows the estimated daily attrition loss of the carbons. This test had an acceptable reproducibility and,

although it is not necessarily representative of actual carbon losses in a CIP plant, it is designed to yield a relative hardness factor. Menne[18] used a similar test to simulate plant-scale attrition. This test still does not predict carbon lost by gasification in the regeneration kiln.

Carbons A, C and E are relatively soft, and also show low equilibrium loadings. Carbon G is hard, but has a relatively lower equilibrium loading than abrasion-resistant carbons D, F and I. Both extruded carbons B and H have high attrition resistance.

Selection criteria
The following criteria for the selection of activated carbon are considered to represent adequate plant performance:

> $A > 30$ and $n > 0.1$
> $k_m > 6 \times 10^{-9}$ m/s
> $k_{mb} > 2 \times 10^{-6}$ s⁻¹ if $\alpha < 0.85$
> k_{mb} not specified if $\alpha \geqslant 0.85$
> Elution kinetic factor > 0.85
> Equilibrium kinetic factor $> 95\%$
> Daily attrition loss $< 0.45\%$

These criteria serve only as a guideline and should not be considered as entirely rigorous for all applications. The simultaneous requirement for activity and abrasion-resistance may not be important in some applications. Only carbons D, F and I satisfy all these criteria adequately. Carbon G may be considered as a runner-up. Although carbon I is most widely used in South African CIP plants, carbons D and G are also used on full-scale plants.

Conclusions

The proposed dual-rate kinetic model adequately predicted gold loading on activated carbon. Equilibrium behaviour of all the carbons was accurately described by the Freundlich isotherm. Coal-based extruded carbons revealed excellent equilibrium behaviour, but slow adsorption kinetics. Most of the carbons tested showed acceptable elution behaviour. An attrition test was capable of ranking the carbons according to their attrition-resistance.

Acknowledgement

Gratitude is expressed to the Anglo American Research Laboratories, whose financial support made this research possible. The X-ray fluorescence assays of the carbon conducted by the Council for Mineral Technology are gratefully acknowledged.

References
1. Zadra J. B. A process for the recovery of gold from activated carbon by leaching and electrolysis. *Rep. Invest. U.S. Bur. Mines* 4672, 1950, 47 p.
2. Zadra J. B. Engel A. L. and Heinen H. J. Process for recovering gold and silver from activated carbon by leaching and electrolysis. *Rep. Invest. U.S. Bur. Mines* 4843, 1952, 32 p.
3. Hall K. B. Homestake uses carbon-in-pulp to recover gold from slimes. *World Min.*, **27**, no. 12, Nov. 1974, 44–9.
4. Dahya A. S. and King D. J. Developments in carbon-in-pulp technology for gold recovery. *CIM Bull.*, **76**, Sept. 1983, 55–61.
5. McDonald N. W. The influence of the carbon-in-pulp process on the metallurgy of gold by reference to Australia. In *Proceedings twelfth CMMI Congress, Johannesburg, 1982* Glen H. W. ed. (Johannesburg: South African Institute of Mining and Metallurgy, 1982), vol. 2, 563–7.
6. How concentrators use carbon in pulp to recover byproduct gold. *World Min.*, **30**, no. 9, Aug. 1977, 56–9.

7.   Menne D. Optimization of full-scale circuits for the carbon-in-pulp recovery of gold. Reference 5, vol. 2, 569–74.
8.   Peel R. G. and Benedek A. Attainment of èquilibrium in activated carbon isotherm studies. *Environm. Sci. Technol.*, **14,** Jan. 1980, 66–71.
9.   Peel R. G. and Benedek A. Dual rate kinetic model of fixed bed adsorber. *J. Environm. Engng Div. A.S.C.E.*, **106,** no. EE4, Aug. 1980, 797–813.
10.   Peel R. G. Benedek A. and Crowe C. M. A branched pore kinetic model for activated carbon adsorption. *A.I.Ch.E.J.*, **27,** Jan. 1981, 26–32.
11.   Weber W. J. and Liang S. A dual particle-diffusion model for porous adsorbents in fixed beds. *Environm. Progr.*, **2,** no. 3, Aug. 1983, 167–75.
12.   Crittenden J. C. and Weber W. J. Model for design of multi-component adsorption systems. *J. Environm. Engng Div. A.S.C.E.*, **104,** no. EE6, Dec. 1978, 1175–95.
13.   Vermeulen T. Adsorption and ion exchange. In *Chemical engineers' handbook, 5th edn* Perry R. H. and Chilton C. H. eds (New York, etc.: McGraw-Hill, 1973), 16-19.
14.   Peel R. G. and Benedek A. A simplified driving force model for activated carbon adsorption. *Can. J. chem. Engng*, **59,** Dec. 1981, 688–92.
15.   Davidson R. J. and Strong B. The recovery of gold from plant effluent by the use of activated carbon. *J. S. Afr. Inst. Min. Metall.*, **83,** Aug. 1983, 181–8.
16.   Cho E. H. Dixon S. N. and Pitt C. H. The kinetics of gold cyanide adsorption on activated carbon. *Metall. Trans.*, **10B,** 1979, 185–9.
17.   Van Deventer J. S. J. Kinetic models for the adsorption of gold onto activated carbon. Paper presented to Mintek 50, Sandton, South Africa, March 1984.
18.   Menne D. Predicting and assessing carbon-in-pulp circuit performance. In *Preprints—XIV international mineral processing congress, Toronto, 1982,* session II, pap. 5, 19 p.

Nomenclature

A, n Parameters in Freundlich isotherm

c Gold concentration in solution, g Au/m³

$\bar{d}_p$ Median carbon particle diameter, m

D_m Surface diffusion coefficient in macropore region, m²/s

k_f External film transfer coefficient, m/s

k_m Macropore pseudo mass-transfer coefficient, m/s

k_{mb} Inter-regional rate coefficient, s⁻¹

q Gold loading on carbon phase, g Au/kg

r Radial variable, m

t Time, s

V Solution phase volume, m³

W Mass of carbon, kg

α Fraction of total adsorptive capacity available in macropores

ρ_c Apparent carbon particle density, kg/m³

Subscripts

b Micropore region

m Macropore region

mb Between macro- and micropore region

0 Initial

s Carbon–solution interface

Mineral flotation with hydroxamate collectors

D. W. Fuerstenau and Pradip

Synopsis
A summary of the published results on the flotation response of various minerals to hydroxamate collectors is presented. New results are given for the adsorption/flotation behaviour of barite, bastnaesite, calcite and chrysocolla with hydroxamate. For almost every mineral there is a characteristic maximum at about pH 9 for both adsorption and flotation response with hydroxamate. This peak has been interpreted in terms of two mechanisms of adsorption—co-adsorption of ions and molecules at the interface near the pK of the collector and, in cases that involve hydrolysing metal ions, reaction of the corresponding metal hydroxy complexes at the surface. A generalized model distinguishes between surface reaction and chemisorption of inorganic reagents and collectors that adsorb at a mineral surface.

One of the requirements of a flotation collector is that it should be highly selective to the mineral species that are being separated from the associated gangue minerals. In various mineral systems conventional flotation collectors, such as fatty acids and xanthates, do not separate the minerals effectively. Chelating agents have been proposed as an alternative reagent so that their highly specific adsorbate–adsorbent interactions can be exploited to yield better flotation selectivity. The utility of chelating agents in flotation systems was first demonstrated quite early in this century. Vivian,[46] for example, floated cassiterite by use of ammonium nitrosophenyl hydroxylamine; three years later, Holman[19] reported the results of the flotation of nickel oxide ores with dimethylglyoxime and suggested the use of taurine for oxidized lead ores. Gutzeit[18] presented a detailed study on the applications of a variety of chelating agents in flotation. De Witt and von Batchelder[8] and Ludt and De Witt[26] suggested the possibility of using oximes as collectors for copper minerals. More recently, Usoni and co-workers[45] reported on the use of cupferron with fuel oil for a wide variety of minerals, including pitchblende and pyrochlore. Rinelli and Marabini[39] have also done extensive work on the flotation of lead–zinc oxide/sulphide ores with oxime (8-hydroxyquinoline) and fuel oil. The latest study by Nagaraj and Somasundaran[29] has clearly established the collecting properties of various hydroxy oximes in copper mineral flotation.

Hydroxamic acids belong to a family of chelating agents that have been tried extensively in mineral flotation. The existence of hydroxamic acids has long been known[48] and the first mineral processing application of hydroxamates appears to have been proposed in 1940 when Popperle[34] obtained a patent in Germany for the use of hydroxamic acids or their salts as collectors in the flotation of ores. In 1965 Peterson et al.[33] used octyl hydroxamate as a collector for chrysocolla and, later, Fuerstenau and co-workers[14] studied the possibility of floating iron ores with the same collector. These two applications were patented in the U.S.A. in 1969.[13] Russian researchers[4,17] presented their results on several minerals and ores with the reagent IM-50, which had been developed at the Mekhanobr Institute in Leningrad (a mixture of alkyl hydroxamic acids and their salts containing 7–9 carbon atoms). Rosenbaum[40] used hydroxamates for cassiterite flotation; Evrard and De Cuyper[11] floated various copper–cobalt oxide ores with alkyl hydroxamates having 8, 12 and 14 carbon

atoms together with xanthate collectors; and Koltunova and co-workers[21] reported the flotation of quartz and microcline with potassium octyl hydroxamate. Kiersznicki and co-workers[20] also used potassium hydroxamate as collector in the flotation of oxidized Zn–Pb ores. In our laboratories various studies have been made with hydroxamate collectors in the flotation of hematite,[38] pyrolusite,[31] chrysocolla and, most recently, rare-earth bastnaesite ores.[36] The objective of this paper is to establish the conditions under which hydroxamate collectors adsorb on various minerals to cause flotation. The results of new studies on the uptake of hydroxamate and its effect on the flotation behaviour of sparingly soluble minerals, barite, bastnaesite and calcite, are presented. The flotation response of various minerals was reviewed and the results of the extensive review are summarized. Because chrysocolla appeared to deviate from the general pattern of flotation response with hydroxamate as collector, a series of flotation tests was carried out with chrysocolla to clarify the behavioural pattern.

Hydroxamic acids and their metal complexes

Hydroxamic acid is the name given to N-alkyl derivatives of hydroxylamine:[1]

$$H - N - OH$$
$$\mid$$
$$R - C = O$$

On the other hand, they can also be regarded as N-hydroxy derivatives of acid amines or as oximes of carboxylic acids.[1] The substitution of one or both hydrogen atoms by hydrocarbon or alkyl groups yields compounds with the general formula[1]

$$R_1 - N - OH$$
$$\mid$$
$$R_2 - C = O$$

where R_1 = H, phenyl, o-tolyl, m-tolyl, p-tolyl, etc., and R_2 consists of carboxylic or aliphatic acid derivatives. Hydroxamic acids contain the bidentate group

$$\begin{array}{cc} OH & O \\ \mid & \parallel \\ -N & -C \end{array}$$

through which are formed the metal complexes of hydroxamic acids:

$$n \begin{bmatrix} R_1 - N - OH \\ \mid \\ R_2 - C = O \end{bmatrix} + M^{n+} \rightarrow \begin{bmatrix} R_1 - N - O \\ \mid \\ R_2 - C = O \end{bmatrix}_n M + nH^+ \tag{1}$$

The formation of metal chelates via this mechanism has long constituted the basis of a wide variety of analytical methods for various metal ions in solution. This mechanism has been confirmed by infrared and ultraviolet spectral studies.[6]

The thermodynamic dissociation constants, K_a, of hydroxamic acids, HA, are defined by the reaction

$$HA \rightleftharpoons H^+ + A^-$$

$$K_a = \frac{[H^+][A^-]}{[HA]} \qquad \frac{\gamma H^+ \gamma A^-}{\gamma HA} \qquad (2)$$

where γ represents the respective activity coefficients in solution. The pK_a values of some hydroxamic acids (pH where ionization is 50%) have been determined by several workers by pH, potentiometric and spectrophotometric techniques. The results of measurements for a variety of hydroxamic acids compiled by Chatterjee[6] indicate that hydroxamic acids are, in general, weak donors. N-arylhydroxamic acids are even weaker donors than simple aromatic hydroxamic acids owing to intramolecular hydrogen bonding. It has also been found that unsaturated N-arylhydroxamic acids are stronger donors than the corresponding saturated compounds. More recently, Ryaboi and co-workers[41] reported the pK_a values of alkylhydroxamic acids and certain derivatives of acetohydroxamic acid (Table 1 lists some of their reported values for aliphatic hydroxamic acids).

Table 1 pK_a values for alkylhydroxamic acids at 20°C[41]

Compound	Sample, g	Ionic strength	pK_a In water	pK_a In 50% ethanol
$CH_3CONHOH$	0.0375	0.01	9.42 ± 0.03	10.70 ± 0.02
		1.0	8.75 ± 0.03	
$C_5H_{11}CONHOH$	0.0655	0.01	9.64 ± 0.01	10.93 ± 0.05
		0.1	9.47 ± 0.05	
$C_6H_{13}CONHOH$	0.0725	0.01	9.67 ± 0.01	11.02 ± 0.02
		0.1	9.49 ± 0.2	
$C_7H_{15}CONHOH$	0.0795	0.01	9.69 ± 0.01	11.01 ± 0.04
		0.1	$9.55 \pm 0.01^*$	
		0.5	8.91 ± 0.03	
		1.0	8.69 ± 0.05	
		3.0	8.66 ± 0.03	
$C_8H_{17}CONHOH$	0.0865	0.01		10.98 ± 0.03
$C_9H_{19}CONHOH$	0.0935	0.01		$10.93 \pm 0.03†$

$^*pK_a = 9.44 \pm 0.03$ at 25°C, 9.14 ± 0.03 at 50°C and 9.03 ± 0.04 at 65°C.
$† pK_a = 10.43 \pm 0.02$ in 15% ethanol at $I = 0.1$.

The stability constants for metal hydroxamates have been summarized by Schwarzenbach and Schwarzenbach[43] and are given in Table 2. The weakest complexes are those with alkaline-earth metal cations (Ca^{2+}, Ba^{2+}, etc.). Complexes formed with such transition elements as Nb, Ti, V, Mn, Zr, Hf and Ta have somewhat greater stability. Rather strong complexes are formed with the highly charged rare-earth elements and aluminium: the strongest complexes are formed with Fe^{3+} and probably with Ta^{5+} and Nb^{5+}. It is also suggested that the differences in stability

Table 2   Stability constants for metal hydroxamates at 20°C and $I = 0.1$ ($NaNO_3$)[43]

Cation	$\log K_1$	$\log K_2$	$\log \beta_2$	$\log K_3$	$\log \beta_3$
H^+	9.35				
Ca^{2+}	2.4				
Fe^{2+}	4.8	3.7	8.5		
La^{3+}	5.16	4.17	9.33	2.55	11.88
Ce^{3+}	5.45	4.34	9.79	3.0	12.8
Sm^{3+}	5.96	4.77	10.73	3.68	14.41
Gd^{3+}	6.10	4.76	10.86	3.07	13.93
Dy^{3+}	6.52	5.39	11.91	4.04	15.95
Yb^{3+}	6.61	5.59	12.2	4.29	16.49
Al^{3+}	7.95	7.34	15.29	6.18	21.47
Fe^{3+}	11.42	0.68	21.1	7.23	28.33

constants of complexes formed with the lattice cations of minerals to be separated are much greater for hydroxamic acids than for carboxylic acids (fatty acids).

Experimental materials and methods

Materials

Barite samples from Kings Creek, South Carolina, were obtained through Ward's Natural Science Establishment, New York. These samples were washed in triple-distilled water and ground to the desired size. Calcite samples from Kansas were also obtained through Ward's, New York, the preparation being the same as for the barite. A hand-picked sample of pure bastnaesite from Mountain Pass, California, analysing 57.4% REO (rare-earth oxides; theoretical composition of pure crystal 75%), was used in the adsorption and flotation experiments. The specific surface areas of the ground mineral samples, which were evaluated by the BET adsorption method with nitrogen gas, were found to be 1.73, 2.15 and 2.4 m^2/g for the bastnaesite, barite and calcite powders, respectively. Chrysocolla samples for the flotation tests were obtained from Miami, Arizona, through Dr. J. M. Wie (the material contained a small amount of malachite also). All the reagents that were used in the experiments were analytical grade chemical reagents. The hydroxamate collector was synthesized in the laboratory by combining the stoichiometric amounts of hydroxylamine hydrochloride and methyl octanoate in methyl alcohol solutions, as described below.

Preparation and characterization of alkyl hydroxamate

Potassium octyl hydroxamate was prepared in the following manner. One mole of KOH (56 g) in 140 cm^3 methyl alcohol was combined with 0.6 mole of hydroxylamine hydrochloride (42 g) in 240 cm^3 of methyl alcohol with constant stirring. After cooling the solutions to 10°C to effect complete precipitation of KCl, the solution was filtered. To the filtrate 0.33 mole (53 g) of methyl octanoate was added periodically while the solution was being agitated. The agitation was continued for 4-5 h at 40°C. Methyl alcohol was added periodically to compensate for the loss of liquid because of evaporation. The overall reaction is

$$CH_3(CH_2)COOCH_3 + NH_2OH.HCl + KOH \rightarrow$$
Methyl octanoate   (3)
$$CH_3(CH_2)_6CONHOK + KCl + H_2O + CH_3OK$$
Potassium octylhydroxamate

The mixture was then cooled to 0°C to effect the precipitation of hydroxamate, which was subsequently purified by recrystallization from hot methyl alcohol solution. The purification step was carried out three times to ensure the purity of the sample.

The product obtained by this procedure was analysed chemically for various elements (C, H, O, N and K). Previous researchers did not report chemical analyses of the material. The data in Table 3 show that the product thus obtained is a mixture of hydroxamic acid and its potassium salt. Even after repeated purification the analysis showed reproducible results. The composition compares very well with the analysis expected if the product were 50% salt (potassium octyl hydroxamate) and 50% acid (octyl hydroxamic acid).

The infrared spectrum of the synthesized product, which compares very well with the published spectra,[32,37] shows a broad band around 1650 cm^{-1} that corresponds to the amide I band (C=O stretching). Other important bands occur at 3000 cm^{-1} (C-H stretching), 3250 cm^{-1} (N-H stretching), 1570 cm^{-1} (amide II band), 1000 cm^{-1} (C-H out of plane vibrations) and 980 cm^{-1} (N-O stretching), and the C-N bond frequency at 1320 cm^{-1}.

The ultraviolet spectrum of the synthesized product exhibits a

Table 3 Chemical analysis of synthetic potassium octyl hydroxamate

Elements	Theoretical composition		Actual analysis of synthetic product		
	K-octyl hydroxamate	50% hydroxamic acid 50% octyl hydroxamate	Batch I	Batch II	Batch III
C	48.7	53.8	53.8	53.95	54.01
H	8.12	9.27	9.0	9.32	9.13
O	16.24	17.97	—	—	—
N	7.1	7.86	7.35	7.88	7.89
K	19.8	10.95	10.6	10.5	11.5

Potassium octyl hydroxamate, $CH_3(CH_2)_6CONHOK$.
Hydroxamic acid (octyl), $CH_3(CH_2)_6CONHOH$.

peak at 188 nm that can also be used for calibration and analysis of hydroxamate in solution. This peak is characteristic of the

$$\begin{array}{c} O \quad H \\ \parallel \quad | \\ -C-N-H \end{array}$$

group, which exhibits a peak at 188 nm for polyacrylamide also.[35] This method can be used only in the absence of electrolyte solution since KNO_3 and $NaNO_3$ solutions have peaks that interfere with the amide peak. For the adsorption studies in the present work another spectrophotometric method was used, as is mentioned below.

Hallimond tube flotation

A Hallimond tube was used for small-scale flotation experiments. A 1 g sample was conditioned in 100 cm³ of suspension for 15 min and floated for 2 min. Nitrogen gas was used at a constant flow rate of 60 cm³/min. The conditioning of the minerals was done separately in a shaker to avoid attrition in the Hallimond tube during conditioning.

Adsorption experiments

The adsorption of potassium octyl hydroxamate under various conditions was estimated by determining the difference in the concentration of the surfactant in solution before and after adding the solid minerals. The experiments were conducted in 50 cm³ polyethylene bottles. The solid/liquid ratio (by weight) was 1:20 for barite, 1:10 for calcite and 1:100 for bastnaesite, unless otherwise indicated. The conditioning times were selected for each mineral system according to the kinetics of collector adsorption for the three minerals.[36] The conditioning was carried out in polyethylene bottles while they were rotated in a shaker for predetermined times required for equilibrium. The supernatant, after equilibrium had been achieved, was centrifuged twice in a SORVALL superspeed centrifuge for 20 min at 12 500 rev/min. The concentration of hydroxamate in solution was measured by the well-known spectrophotometric method with ferric perchlorate.[36]

Results and discussion

Fig. 1 presents the results of the flotation of chrysocolla with potassium octyl hydroxamate as a function of pH at various additions of the collector. The characteristic peak at pH 6 for this mineral has been reported previously[33]—a peak that coincides with the pH of maximum concentration of $CuOH^+$ species in bulk solution. Figs. 2, 3 and 4 illustrate the observed trends in adsorption and flotation response for bastnaesite, calcite and barite, respectively. Sharp peaks at pH 9 can be directly correlated with the maximum in flotation recoveries for both barite and calcite. The plateau in flotation recovery in the range pH 5–9.5 for bastnaesite also coincides with the adsorption results at a similar collector concentration.

This characteristic peak at around pH 9.5 for hydroxamate adsorption and flotation has been reported by several other

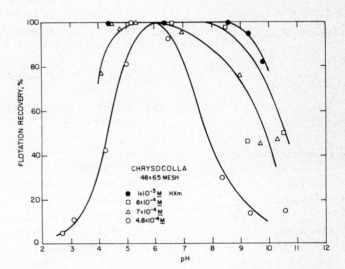

Fig. 1 Effect of pH on flotation of chrysocolla at various hydroxamate additions

investigators with such minerals as hematite,[15,37] rhodonite,[32] huebnerite, fluorite and malachite[4] and pyrolusite.[31]

A brief summary of these adsorption and flotation results with hydroxamates on various minerals is presented in Table 4. It is interesting to note that, with the exception of chrysocolla and pyrochlore, all investigations (on minerals with pzc from pH 2 to pH 10 and above) show that hydroxamate adsorption and flotation exhibit peaks around pH 9 ± 0.5. This value also happens to be the range of pK usually reported for hydroxamic acids: this coincidence has often been offered as one of the explanations for the observed peaks. Table 4 also shows that adsorption at the solid–liquid interface correlates quite well with the more complicated (solid–liquid–gas) flotation response for

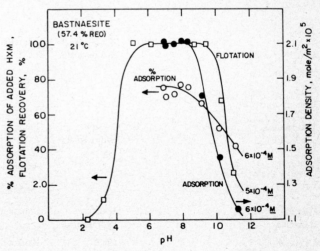

Fig. 2 Correlation of adsorption with flotation results for bastnaesite

Table 4   Summary of studies on hydroxamate collectors in the flotation of various minerals

Mineral	pzc pH	Reagent	Method of investigation	pH of optimum recovery or maximum adsorption	Effect of increasing temperature	Reference
Hematite, Fe_2O_3		K-octyl hydroxamate	Flotation	9.0	Increase in recovery (25–50°C)	15
Hematite, Fe_2O_3	8.2	K-octyl hydroxamate	Oil extraction, micro-flotation, contact angles with air/oil	8.0–8.5	—	38
Hematite, Fe_2O_3	8.2	K-octyl hydroxamate	Adsorption	8.5	Increase in adsorption (20–61°C)	37
γ-MnO_2	5.6	K-octyl hydroxamate	Flotation	9.0	—	31
γ-MnO_2	5.6	K-octyl hydroxamate	Adsorption	9.0	Increase in adsorption (20–40°C)	31
Rhodonite, $(Mn,Fe,Cu)SiO_3$	2.8	K-octyl hydroxamate	Flotation	9.0	—	32
Chrysocolla, $CuSiO_3.2H_2O$	2.0	K-octyl hydroxamate	Flotation	6.0	Increase in recovery (22–49°C)	32, 33
Chrysocolla, $CuSiO_3.2H_2O$	—	K-octyl hydroxamate	Flotation	6.0	—	Present work
Malachite, $Cu_2CO_3(OH)_2$	7.9	K-octyl hydroxamate	Flotation	6–10 plateau 9.5 at 10^{-4}M	—	24
Malachite, $Cu_2CO_3(OH)_2$	7.9	K-octyl hydroxamate	Adsorption	9, adsorption below 5	—	24
Chrysocolla/ malachite/ azurite	—	C6-C9 hydroxamate	Flotation	6.5–9.5 for good flotation; best in plant at 7.5–8	—	47
Pyrochlore, $NaCaNb_2F(CO_3)_6$	—	IM-50 (C7-C9)	Flotation	6.0	—	4
Fluorite, CaF_2	—	IM-50	Flotation, adsorption	8.5 8.5	— —	4
Huebnerite, $MnWO_4$	—	IM-50	Flotation, adsorption	9.0 9.0	— —	4
Barite, $BaSO_4$	10	K-octyl hydroxamate	Flotation	9.5	Increase in recovery (20–50°C)	36
			Adsorption	9.0	Increase in adsorption (21–61°C)	36
Calcite, $CaCO_3$	10	K-octyl hydroxamate	Flotation	9.5, also recovery below 8	Increase in recovery (20–50°C)	36
			Adsorption	9.5, also adsorption below 8	Increase in adsorption (21–61°C)	36
Bastnaesite, $(Ce,La)FCO_3$	9.5	K-octyl hydroxamate	Flotation	Plateau 5–9,	Increase in recovery (20–50°C)	36
			Adsorption	plateau, adsorption decreases above 8.5	Increase in adsorption (21–41°C)	36
Quartz/ microline	2.0	K-octyl hydroxamate	Flotation	1.5	—	21
Oxidized Zn–Pb ores		C6, 8 hydroxamate	Flotation	—	—	20

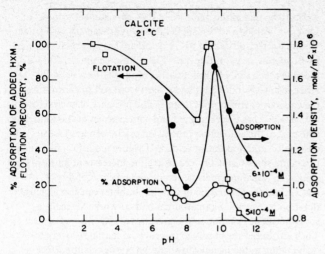

Fig. 3   Correlation of adsorption with flotation results for calcite

cases in which such studies have been carried out. Third, an increase in temperature is invariably accompanied by an increase in adsorption densities and in flotation recoveries of the mineral under consideration. This appears to be a general trend for all so-called chemisorbing collectors—notably oleate. Various infrared studies have established quite conclusively that hydroxamates do chemisorb at mineral–water interfaces.[24,31,32,37]

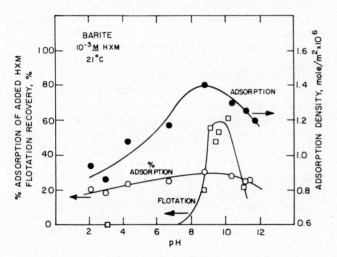

Fig. 4.   Correlation of hydroxamate adsorption with flotation results for barite

The interactions of hydroxamic acid derivatives with various mineral surfaces are strongly dependent on pH and, to some extent, also on the physico-chemical characteristics of the mineral–water interface. In the interpretation of these results one must consider the surface chemical properties of the adsorbent and the solution properties of the organic collector, with special reference to its chelation characteristics.

Since various cation species are chelated to the hydroxamate anions or neutral molecules, a study of the surface products can confirm the chelation reaction. Infrared studies of the minerals very conclusively demonstrate the formation of corresponding metal hydroxamates at the surface. The infrared absorption bands with fluorite that had been conditioned in hydroxamate solutions in the 1520–1530 and 1620 cm^{-1} frequency range coincide with those in the calcium hydroxamate spectrum and exhibit a considerable shift in comparison with the hydroxamic acid absorption bands.[4] The infrared spectrum of ferric oxide conditioned with hydroxamate exhibits a distinct peak at 1600 cm^{-1}, which indicates the presence of ferric trihydroxamate chelate at the interface.[37] Ferric hydroxamate complexes can also

attach to mineral surfaces and cause the flotation of minerals that contain no cations which are capable of reacting with hydroxamate anions or neutral molecules.[21] The chemisorption of hydroxamate in copper minerals and minerals that contain Mn^{+2} ions has also been confirmed by infrared studies.[24,31] The difficulties in removing the adsorbed species further substantiate a chemisorption mechanism. Furthermore, electrokinetic investigations[31,37] also suggest strong chemisorption in that there is a distinct shift in the isoelectric point of the minerals in the presence of hydroxamates, as would be expected in chemisorbing systems.

Coming back to the major question as to the cause of the maximum in the pH for flotation response with hydroxamate as collector, two different phenomena may have a role—hydrolysis of lattice cations in the mineral and ionization of the collector. For example, the work of Fuerstenau and co-workers[15,32] indicated that the adsorption in numerous anionic collector systems can be characterized by a mechanism of adsorption through hydrolysable cationic species. The cations hydrolyse in solution to various hydroxy complexes and then readsorb at the interface and assist collector adsorption. For example, solution equilibria for Fe^{++}, Mn^{++} and Pb^{++} show that the maximum concentration of corresponding $FeOH^+$, $MnOH^+$, and $PbOH^+$ ions occurs at pH 8.5–9.[32] An interesting substantiation of this mechanism is the adsorption of hydroxamate on chrysocolla. Chrysocolla floats best at pH 6—the pH value at which $CuOH^+$ species is maximally present (see Fig. 1), as was first suggested by Peterson et al.[33]

Raghavan and Fuerstenau[38] postulated a combination of adsorption–surface reaction mechanisms in which hydroxamic acid molecules take part in the reaction. In this mechanism dissolved hydroxylated species are not considered. Although the adsorption of oleate is usually described as a chemisorption process, Ananthpadmanabhan and co-workers[2] have suggested that the pH of maximum flotation for hematite corresponds to the pH at which acid–soap species ($RCOOH \cdot RCOO^-$) are maximum. The reasons for high surface activity of these species were not given. Furthermore, there is no evidence on the associative properties of hydroxamate collectors in aqueous solution, whereas strong evidence exists to suggest that hydroxamate ions adsorb through chemical interaction.

Around the pK of the collector the co-adsorption of neutral hydroxamate species may occur together with the chemisorbed hydroxamate anions. It is quite probable that the maximum in flotation recovery and adsorption of hydroxamates is due to the enhanced activity of hydroxamate at the surface as a result of this ion/molecule adsorption, both of which can form stable metal chelates.

Another notable feature of hydroxamate flotation systems is the effect of temperature on the flotation response of various minerals. All the studies on this aspect of hydroxamate flotation have shown an enhancement of both collector adsorption and flotation recoveries at elevated temperatures (Table 4). This behaviour appears to be common to all chemisorbing-type collector systems. First, an increase in the equilibrium adsorption density of collectors at high temperatures may be related to the endothermic nature of the adsorption reaction at the interface. Positive enthalpies and entropies have been observed in such systems.[36,37] Second, since adsorption may occur through the formation and adsorption of metal hydroxy complexes (or precipitation at the interface), an increase in the solubility of the minerals at elevated temperatures would also contribute towards enhanced adsorption. Third, elevated temperatures can also affect the kinetics of all thermally activated sub-processes, such as bubble–particle collision and attachment involved in flotation, and, hence, higher recoveries are expected at elevated temperatures.

Somewhat similar to the flotation behaviour of chrysocolla at

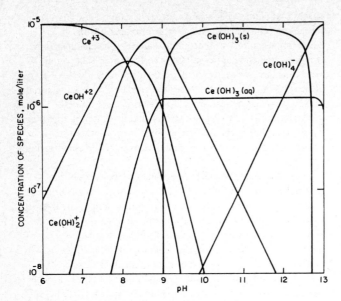

Fig. 5   Aqueous solution equilibria for Ce at 10^{-5} M total solution concentration

higher collector concentrations, the flotation and adsorption results with bastnaesite indicate a plateau in the pH range 5–9.5, this range increasing slightly as the concentration of hydroxamate is increased in solution. Bastnaesite contains lanthanum and cerium as its major cation constituents—ions that strongly hydrolyse in aqueous solution. Figs. 5 and 6 show the concentration of various solution species for cerium and lanthanum, respectively, based on data obtained from Baes and Messmer.[3] At 10^{-5} mole/l total concentration, in the range of observed plateau M^{+++}, $M(OH)^{++}$ and $M(OH)_2^+$ predominate in the bulk. It seems that these species may participate in the

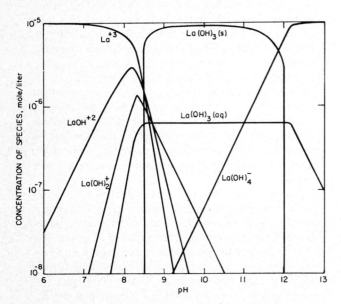

Fig. 6   Aqueous solution equilibria for La at 10^{-5} M total solution concentration

hydroxamate adsorption process. Above pH 9 a sharp drop in the concentration of these hydroxy complexes is observed, which also coincides with the observed drop in adsorption and flotation. It is clear that neither $Ce(OH)_3$ or $La(OH)_3$ assists in adsorption and flotation nor $Ce(OH)_4^-$ or $La(OH)_4^-$.

The sharp peak observed for barite in the flotation and adsorption experiments is not easily explainable. The limited data that are available for bulk Ba^{++} aqueous chemistry indicate that at pH 9 $BaOH^+$ is in negligible amount. The only possibility

seems to be that in the presence of CO_2 some other barium species is formed and is responsible for hydroxamate adsorption. The characteristic peak at pH 9 for calcite has also been observed by Bogdanov et al. for fluorite.[4] The solution equilibria for Ca^{++} indicate that a $CaOH^+$ peak occurs only at pH 13 or so in the absence of CO_2, but CO_2 plays a significant role in controlling the aqueous chemistry of calcite.[16] The presence of such species as $CaHCO_3^+$ has been reported and some species of this kind may take part in the adsorption process on calcite. An increase in adsorption and flotation at acidic pH values tends to substantiate this claim since $CaHCO_3^+$ concentration increases at lower pH values. In flotation experiments the enhanced solubility of $CaCO_3$ and the generation of CO_2 gas bubbles can also increase flotation recoveries. Sampatkumar and co-workers[42] made a study of calcite flotation in the presence of CO_2 instead of air. They attributed the observed improved flotation recovery to carbonation inducing a positive charge on the calcite surface through such reactions as the adsorption of $CaOH^+$, $CaHCO_3^+$, etc.

Further comments on adsorption mechanisms

Several mechanisms have been postulated in the literature, together with supporting evidence, to explain the interaction of chelate-type collectors with a surface. Here, we propose three routes or mechanisms by which a chelating collector, such as hydroxamate, can adsorb at a mineral surface.

The chemical interaction of hydroxamate at mineral–water interfaces may take place by *chemisorption*, where the reagent covalently bonds with metal cations that do not move from their lattice position, or by *surface reaction*, where the reagent bonds with metal cations that move from their lattice position to a region adjacent to the surface in the interface. Hydroxamate collector or similar reagent–mineral interactions can be summarized for sparingly soluble salt minerals according to reactions that are outlined in Fig. 7. In these reactions a metal ion Me^{++} to the left of the dotted line designates that it is in its lattice position; a metal ion Me^{++} to the right of the dotted line indicates that the ion is considered to have moved from its lattice position.

Ideally, collector uptake by chemisorption is desired since

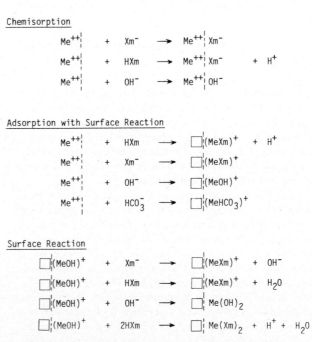

Fig. 7   Schematic representation of interaction between sparingly soluble minerals and chemically bonding reagents, differentiating between chemisorption and surface reaction mechanisms

adsorption would then be limited to a monolayer. Examples are given in Fig. 7 for the adsorption of the hydroxamate ion and the hydroxamic acid molecule. If adsorption takes place with surface reaction, however, the metal chelate is then formed adjacent to the surface—a process that could result in multilayer formation.

Eisenlauer and Matijevic,[10] who made a detailed study of the interactions of hydroxamic acid species with hematite, found some dissolution of ferric ions from the hematite particles on the addition of DFOB (desferrioxamine-B, a trihydroxamic acid chelating molecule) to the suspension. This can be interpreted in terms of DFOB preferentially leaching out some of the surface iron as $Fe(HA)_3^+$ complexes that go into solution or, in other words, a process of adsorption with surface reaction.

Inorganic anion adsorption with surface reaction can assist or may be a necessary step in the process of collector uptake in many cases. This may well be the reason why metal ion hydroxylation appears to be so effective in flotation with chemisorbing collectors: the hydroxyl ions first adsorb, displacing the metal ion from its lattice position, where the collector can then exchange with the surface hydroxyl, as illustrated by the surface reaction shown in Fig. 7. The adsorption/flotation behaviour of minerals in this system can be interpreted in terms of the reactions given in Fig. 7, which may either foster or compete with the collector adsorption reaction. The general maximum in flotation that occurs around pH 9—that is, at the pK of the hydroxamate collector—may result from co-adsorption phenomena, namely the co-adsorption of neutral hydroxamic acid molecules and hydroxamate anions. It is quite likely that the maximum in flotation recovery and hydroxamate adsorption is due to the enhanced activity of hydroxamate at the surface as a result of combined ion/molecule adsorption, both of which can form chelates. Other examples of this phenomenon have been noted. Fuerstenau[12] had earlier postulated the possibility of neutral amine molecules co-adsorbing at the quartz–water interface around the pK of the amine collector, which results in a sudden jump in adsorption/flotation for amine systems.

Multilayer adsorption in these systems may occur through hydrogen bonding, as shown in (1) below, or, more probably, may result from hydrophobic bonding through the hydrocarbon chains, as shown in (2). This mechanism had been suggested earlier by Raghavan and Fuerstenau[38] for hematite and octyl hydroxamate.

Another mechanism exists to explain multilayer formation—formation of trihydroxamate complexes by reaction with neutral hydroxamic acid species to release H^+ ions. The possibility of cerium and lanthanum forming trihydroxamate complexes in solution was reported by Chatterjee.[6] The surface reaction example given in Fig. 7 shows that the pH should decrease as a consequence of adsorption. At higher temperatures we observed a decrease in equilibrium pH after adsorption on bastnaesite had taken place.

Summary

The results of a detailed study of the adsorption of hydroxamate and the flotation behaviour of barite, bastnaesite and calcite are presented; they correlate well. In addition, a review of the flotation/adsorption behaviour of hydroxamate collectors and
other minerals has been summarized. Because the published results on the flotation behaviour of chrysocolla appeared to deviate from the common pattern observed with hydroxamate as collector, additional flotation studies were carried out with a sample of chrysocolla as a function of pH and collector concentration. Based on the results presented in this paper and in earlier studies, a general chemisorption/surface reaction mechanism is postulated to explain the mechanism of uptake of chemisorption-type collectors on minerals, including the sparingly soluble salt-type minerals.

A characteristic feature of hydroxamate collector systems is the observed maxima in flotation and adsorption behaviour at approximately pH 9, the pK_a of the collector. It is postulated that this maximum is primarily related to two phenomena—co-adsorption of neutral hydroxamic acid species with the corresponding hydroxamate anions near the pH of the pK_a and increase in the reactivity of surface metal ions through surface hydrolysis (that is, through surface reaction, which displaces the metal ions from their lattice position) or the re-adsorption of metal hydroxy complexes at the surface. Both phenomena could enhance the uptake of hydroxamate. Multilayer uptake can occur by the formation of surface compounds or by co-adsorption through hydrophobic or hydrogen-bonding phenomena. Hydroxamates belong to the family of chelating-type reagents that chemisorb or participate in surface reactions at mineral–water interfaces, as confirmed by various infrared studies and electrokinetic investigations.

Acknowledgement

The authors wish to thank the National Science Foundation for the support of this research, which was initiated by a grant from the Molybdenum Corporation of America. Pradip is grateful for a University of California Fellowship grant during the course of this work. Discussions with S. Chander and R. Urbina are also acknowledged.

References
1. Agarwal Y. K. Hydroxamic acids and their metal complexes. *Russian chem. Rev.*, **48**, no. 10 1979, 948–63.
2. Ananthpadmanabhan K. Somasundaran P. and Healy T. W. Chemistry of oleate and amine solutions in relation to flotation. *Trans. Am. Inst. Min. Engrs*, **266**, 1979, 2003–9.
3. Baes C. F. Jr. and Messmer R. E. *The hydrolysis of cations* (New York, etc.: Wiley, 1976), 512 p.
4. Bogdanov O. S. *et al.* Hydroxamic acids as collectors in the flotation of wolframite, cassiterite and pyrochlore. In *Tenth international mineral processing congress, London, 1973* Jones M. J. ed. (London: IMM, 1974), 553–64.
5. Bogdanov O. S. *et al.* Reagents chemisorption on minerals as a process of formation of surface compounds with a coordination bond. In *Proceedings of the 12th international mineral processing congress, 1977* (São Paulo, Brazil: D.N.P.M., M.M.E., 1982), vol. 2, 280–303.
6. Chatterjee B. Donor properties of hydroxamic acids. *Coordination Chem. Rev.*, **26**, 1978, 281–303.
7. De Witt C. C. and von Batchelder F. Chelate compounds as flotation reagents. *J. Am. chem. Soc.*, **61**, 1939, 1247–50.
8. De Witt C. C. and von Batchelder F. Normal oximes as flotation reagents. *J. Am. chem. Soc.*, **61**, 1939, 1250.
9. Dutt N. K. and Seshadri T. Chemistry of lanthanons—XXIV: formation constants or rare earth complexes with N-benzoyl N-phenylhydroxylamine (BHPA). *J. inorg. nucl. Chem.*, **31**, 1969, 3336–8.
10. Eisenlauer J. and Matijevic E. Interactions of metal hydrous oxides with chelating agents, II. α-Fe_2O_3-low molecular and polymeric hydroxamic acid species. *J. Colloid Interface Sci.*, **75**, no 1 1980, 199–211.
11. Evrard L. and De Cuyper J. Flotation of copper–cobalt oxide ores with alkylhydroxamates. In *Proceedings 11th international mineral processing congress, Cagliari, 1975* (Cagliari: Istituto di Arte Mineraria, 1975), 655–69.
12. Fuerstenau D. W. Correlation of contact angles, adsorption density, zeta potentials, and flotation rate. *Trans. Am. Inst. Min. Engrs*, **208**, 1957, 1365–7.

13. Fuerstenau M. C. and Peterson H. D. U.S. Patent 3 438 494, 1969.

14. Fuerstenau M. C. Miller J. D. and Gutierrez G. Selective flotation of iron oxide. *Trans. Am. Inst. Min. Engrs*, **238**, 1967, 200–3.

15. Fuerstenau M. C. Harper R. W. and Miller J. D. Hydroxamate vs. fatty acid flotation of iron oxide. *Trans. Am. Inst. Min. Engrs*, **247**, 1970, 69–73.

16. Garrels R. M. and Christ C. L. *Solutions, minerals, and equilibria* (San Francisco: Freeman, Cooper and Co., 1965), 450 p.

17. Gorlovskii S. I. *et al.* Improvement in concentration technology of some rare metal ores, based on taking advantage of complexing alkyl hydroxamic acids peculiarities of action. In *Eighth international mineral processing congress, Leningrad, 1968* (Leningrad: Institut Mekhanobr, 1969), vol. 1, 398–413. (Russian text); Paper D3, 9 p. (English text)

18. Gutzeit G. Chelate-forming organic compounds as flotation reagents. *Trans. Am. Inst. Min. Engrs*, **169**, 1946, 272–86.

19. Holman B. W. Flotation reagents. *Trans. Instn Min. Metall.*, **39**, 1929–30, 588–642.

20. Kiersznicki T. Borkowski J. and Majewski J. Flotation enrichment of oxidized zinc–lead ore. *Rudy Metale Niezel.*, **26**, Dec. 1981, 640–3. (Polish text)

21. Koltunova T. E. Bogdanov O. S. and Poroshina A. N. Effect of iron salts on the flotation of quartz by hydroxamic acids and their salts. *Obogashch. Rud*, **23**, no. 3 1978, 12–16. (Russian text)

22. Kragten J. *Atlas of metal–ligand equilibrium in aqueous solutions* (New York: Halsted Press, 1978), 781 p.

23. Kulkarni R. D. and Somasundaran P. Kinetics of oleate adsorption at the liquid/air interface and its role in hematite flotation. In *Advances in interfacial phenomena of particulate/solution/gas systems; applications to flotation research* Somasundaran P. and Grieves R. B. eds (New York: American Institute of Chemical Engineers, 1975), 124–33. (*AIChE Symp. Series* no. 150, vol. 71)

24. Lenormand J. Salam T. and Yoon R. H. Hydroxamate flotation of malachite. *Can. metall. Q.*, **18**, 1979, 125–9.

25. Liu C. Y. and Sun P. J. Studies of rare earth metal complexes of hydroxamic acids. *J. Chinese chem. Soc.*, **22**, 1975, 317–30.

26. Ludt R. W. and De Witt C. C. The flotation of copper silicate from silica. *Trans. Am. Inst. Min. Engrs*, **184**, 1949, 49–51.

27. Marabini A. M. and Rinelli G. Flotation of pitchblende with a chelating agent and fuel oil. *Trans. Instn Min. Metall. (Sect. C: Mineral Process. Extr. Metall.)*, **82**, 1973, C225–8.

28. Mukherjee P. The nature of the association equilibria and hydrophobic bonding in aqueous solutions of association colloids. *Adv. Colloid Interface Sci.*, **1**, 1967, 241–75.

29. Nagaraj D. R. and Somasundaran P. Chelating agents as collectors in flotation: oximes–copper minerals system. Paper presented to AIME annual meeting, New Orleans, 1979. Preprint 79-76.

30. Nagaraj D. R. and Somasundaran P. Chelating agents as flotaids: LIX®–copper minerals system. *Recent Developm. Separation Sci.*, **7**, 1979, 81–93.

31. Natarajan R. and Fuerstenau D. W. Adsorption and flotation behavior of manganese dioxide in the presence of octyl hydroxamate. *Int. J. Mineral Process.*, **11**, 1983, 139–53.

32. Palmer B. R. Gutierrez G. B. and Fuerstenau M. C. Mechanism involved in the flotation of oxides and silicates with anionic collectors, parts 1 and 2. *Trans. Am. Inst. Min. Engrs*, **258**, 1975, 257–60.

33. Peterson H. D. *et al.* Chrysocolla flotation by the formation of insoluble surface chelates. *Trans. Am. Inst. Min. Engrs*, **232**, 1965, 388–92.

34. Popperle J. German Patent 700 735, 1940, referred to in reference 11.

35. Pradip. The adsorption of polyacrylamide polymeric flocculants on apatites. M.S. thesis, University of California, Berkeley, 1977.

36. Pradip. The surface properties and flotation of rare-earth minerals. Ph.D. thesis, University of California, Berkeley, 1981.

37. Raghavan S. and Fuerstenau D. W. The adsorption of aqueous octylhydroxamate on ferric oxide. *J. Colloid Interface Sci.*, **50**, no. 2 1975, 319–30.

38. Raghavan S. and Fuerstenau D. W. On the wettability and flotation concentration of submicron hematite particles with octylhydroxamate as collector. Reference 23, 59–66.

39. Rinelli G. and Marabini A. M. Flotation of zinc and lead oxide–sulphide ores with chelating agents. Reference 4, 493–521.

40. Rosenbaum A. Hydroxamsäuren als Sammler für Zinnstein. *Freiberger Forschungsh.* A455, 1969, 35–45.

41. Ryaboi V. I. Shenderovich V. A. and Strizhev E. F. Protolytic dissociation of alkylhydroxamic acids and their derivatives. *Zh. fiz. Khim.*, **54**, no. 5 1980, 1279–81. (Russian text); *Russian J. phys. Chem.*, **54**, no. 5 1980, 730–1.

42. Sampatkumar V. Y. Mohan N. and Biswas A. K. Fundamental studies on the role of carbon dioxide in a calcite flotation system. *Trans. Am. Inst. Min. Engrs*, **250**, 1971, 182–6.

43. Schwarzenbach G. and Schwarzenbach K. Hydroxamatkomplexe I. Die Stabilität der Eisen (III)-Komplexe einfacher Hydroxamsäuren und der Ferrioxamins B. *Helv. chim. Acta*, **46**, 1963, 1390–408.

44. Somasundaran P. The role of ionomolecular surfactant complexes in flotation. *Int. J. Mineral Process.*, **3**, 1976, 35–40.

45. Usono L. Rinelli G. and Marabini A. M. Chelating agents and fuel oil, a new way to flotation. Paper presented to AIME Centennial annual meeting, New York, 1971. Preprint 71-B-10.

46. Vivian A. C. Flotation of tin ores. *Min. Mag., Lond.*, **36**, June 1927, 348–51.

47. Weibai Hu. Personal communication, 1980

48. Yale H. L. The hydroxamic acids. *Chem. Rev.*, **33**, 1943, 209–56.

49. Zimmels Y. Lin I. J. and Friend J. P. The relation between stepwise bulk association and interfacial phenomena for some aqueous surfactant solutions. *Colloid Polymer Sci.*, **253**, 1975, 404–21.

Application of hydroxamic acid and hydroxamic–xanthate collector system in metal ore flotation

Kong Dekun, Chen Jingqing and Zhou Weizhi

Synopsis
The properties and synthesis of hydroxamic acids with different non-polar groups are described, emphasis being placed on the commercial product of hydroxamic acid with 7–9 carbon atoms (AHA). In terms of its molecular structure, an attempt is made to explain the superiority of hydroxamic acid over fatty acid in regard to selectivity and collectivity.

In a commercial flotation test AHA was used with xanthate to treat a copper oxide of the skarn type rather than xanthate alone. The total reagent consumption was reduced significantly and the copper recovery increased. Production practice has confirmed that the AHA–xanthate collector system can both collect malachite and pseudo-malachite. Satisfactory results have also been obtained in the flotation of a refractory pelitic copper oxide ore with the AHA–xanthate collector system.

The successful use of hydroxamic acids to obtain a high-grade rare-earth concentrate and other applications on rare metal bearing complex ores are also described briefly.

As an analytical reagent hydroxamic acid has long been applied and its properties and preparations have been reported.[1] Much research has been conducted abroad into the application of hydroxamic acid in mineral flotation. The NM-50 reagent has been used in the Soviet Union as a collector for wolframite, cassiterite and rare metal ores.[2,3] In the U.S.A. flotation tests were conducted on chrysocolla and hematite with octyl hydroxamate[4,5] and Belgian workers reported on the recovery of copper-cobalt oxides with lauryl hydroxamate and amyl xanthate.[6] Alkyl hydroxamic acid has been studied as a collector for oxidized ores in China since the late 1960s. It was put into operation in the 1970s and was subsequently applied commercially for the beneficiation of copper oxide and rare-earth ores. Thereafter, some hydroxamic acids with different non-polar groups were synthesized and investigated (naphthenic, oleoyl, tallol, abietic and salicyl hydroxamic acid).[7]

Properties and preparations of hydroxamic acids

Hydroxamic acid may be considered to be in equilibrium with several other tautomeric forms.[8]

$$\bar{R}-C=N\rightarrow O \rightleftharpoons R-C=NOH \rightleftharpoons R-C-N-OH \rightleftharpoons R-C-NH_2\rightarrow O$$

$$\qquad (IV) \qquad\qquad (II) \qquad\qquad (I) \qquad\qquad (III)$$

Structure II is termed 'hydroximic acid'; structures I and II can form four- or five-member cyclic metal chelates of the O–O type or N–O type.

$$R-C-N-H \qquad R-C-N-OH \qquad R-C=N$$

Chelates with high stability constants are formed when complexed with ferrous, non-ferrous and rare metals, whereas those with low stability constants are formed when complexed with the alkali and alkali-earth metals of gangue minerals. For instance, the stability constants (lgk) of hydroxamates with two carbon atoms for Cu^{++} range from 7.9 to 2.4. Those of acetic acids, however, range from 1.89 to 1.24.[9] The former difference is more than eight times the latter—a determining factor in the selective collectivity of hydroxamic acids for copper oxide ore.

In regard to the molecular structure of

$$R-C-N-OH$$

a π_4^6 conjugating system has a configuration of π-electrons offered by C—O and unshared electron pairs from N—O. The shift of the electron density leads to the polarization of OH and NH bonds, so hydroxamic acid possesses a certain degree of acidity. Nevertheless, it is less acidic than fatty acid, the electronegativity of O connecting with carbonyl being stronger than that of N in the hydroxamic group. Thus, hydroxamic acid possesses a partly covalent character and tends to form biased covalent chemical adsorption with such transition metals as Ta, Nb, Fe and Cu.

In line with the theory that collectors belong to Lewis bases and metallic minerals Lewis acids, fatty acid is classified as a hard base, whereas hydroxamic acid is an intermediate base and can complex not only with such hard acids as Fe^{+++} and rare-earth ions but also with such soft or intermediate acids as Cu^{++} and Sn^{++++}. Hence, it can collect various metallic oxide ores.

Since the degree of ionization of hydroxamic acid is smaller, its melting point is generally higher than that of fatty acid with the same carbon atoms, the electric dissociation constants being five orders lower than those of fatty acids.

Hydroxamic acid can be oxidized into fatty acid by oxidants and reduced into amides by reductants.

$$2RCONHOH + 2[O] \rightarrow 2RCOOH + N_2O + H_2O$$
$$RCONHOH + 2[H] \rightarrow RCONH_2 + H_2O$$

In the promotion of the inorganic acid and base it can hydrolyse into fatty acid.

$$RCONHOH + H_2O \rightarrow RCOOH + NH_2OH$$
$$RCONHONa + H_2O \rightarrow RCOONa + NH_2OH$$

At high temperature isocyanate is formed.

$$RCONHOH \xrightarrow{\Delta} [RC-N\subset] \rightarrow R-N=C=O$$

169

To the fatty acids that are liable to be esterified, such as C_{7-9} fatty acid, oleic salicylic acid, preparation from ester and hydroxamine is preferred.

$$RCOOH + CH_3OH \xrightarrow[\Delta]{H_2SO_4} RCOOCH_3 + H_2O$$

$$RCOOCH_3 + (NH_2OH)_2 \cdot H_2SO_4 + 4NAOH \rightarrow$$

$$2RCONHONa + CH_3OH + Na_2SO_4 + 4H_2O$$

$$\xrightarrow{H_2SO_4} 2RCONHOH$$

When tallol, naphthenyl and abietic hydroxamic acids are synthesized acyl chlorides and hydroxyamine are used.

$$3RCOOH + PCl_3 \rightarrow 3RCOCl + H_3PO_3$$

$$2RCOCl + (NH_2OH)_2 \cdot H_2SO_4 + 6NaOH \rightarrow$$

$$2RCONHONa + 2NaCl + Na_2SO_4 + 6H_2O$$

$$\xrightarrow{H_2SO_4} RCONHOH$$

Hydroxyamine sulphate used in industrial production is synthesized by sodium nitrite, ammonia–water and sulphur dioxide—a water solution with 10–14% hydroxamine sulphate and 10–15% of sodium sulphate and ammonium sulphate. The molar ratio of ester to hydroxyamine sulphate to sodium hydroxide is 1:0.6:6.0. To eliminate the harmful effects of Fe^{+++} 10% Na_2S solution is added when the reaction mixture is neutral in terms of the theoretical amount calculated by the equation equation

$$2Fe^{+++} + 3Na_2S \rightarrow Fe_2S_3\downarrow + 6Na^+$$

In this way all Fe^{+++} in the reaction mixture can be precipitated to ensure the production of pure hydroxamic acid. The commercial product AHA is a dark red waxy solid, sometimes in liquid form, of specific weight 0.94. It is sparingly soluble in water, but easily soluble in alcohol, ketone and hydrocarbon

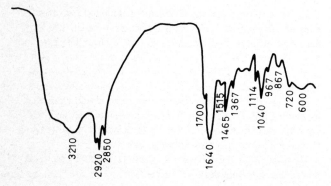

Fig. 1   Infrared spectrum of AHA

oils. Its sodium salt, SAHA, a dark red viscous liquid highly soluble in water, is not so stable as the acid form and it should not be stored for more than one year. Quality data are shown in Table 1 and the infrared spectrum of AHA is shown in Fig. 1. It may be regarded as being non-toxic or low in toxicity.

Application of AHA in metal ore flotation

Because AHA can form strong complexes with a number of metal ions, efforts have been made to apply it as a collector for different minerals. It has been used in some flotation plants or tested semi-commercially with success.

Flotation of copper oxide ores

The copper ore tested emanates from a skarn-type copper oxide deposit with a high iron content. The iron minerals are hematite, limonite and magnetite, and the copper minerals are mainly malachite with small amounts of azurite, pseudo-malachite, native copper and cuprite. There are traces of sulphides. When butyl xanthate was used alone in flotation large quantities of sulphidizers and pine oil were required.

Research into the SAHA–xanthate collector system, followed by semi-commercial tests, has resulted in a successful industrial application, the new collector system enjoying such advantages as high flotation rate, steady process, reduced reagent consumption (reagent cost 15% lower) and, hence, lower flotation cost.[10] Flotation results are shown in Table 2.

The final concentrate consists of a rougher concentrate and the concentrate obtained after cleaning the scavenger froth. Generally, pulp pH is controlled between 8.5 and 9.5. At pH >9.5 the Fe collected increases markedly and at pH <8 low copper recoveries are obtained.

Because the copper concentrate grade is not satisfactory further studies were carried out. Test results indicate that under the synergistic action of combined collectors the copper concentrate grade can be increased to 25% by use of the AHA–xanthate mixed reagent. In particular, in the treatment of the high pseudo-malachite ore the AHA–xanthate collector system yields a significant increase in copper recovery (Table 3).

Some highly pelitic and oxidized copper mineral is also present in this orebody, and in addition to the intergrowth of copper and iron, copper is associated with gold and silver. The flotation effect of the conventional xanthate–sulphidizer system is not efficient. When AHA–xanthate is applied, Au, Cu and Fe concentrates can be recovered at the same time. The overall recovery of the valuable constituents is shown in Table 4.

Another highly siliceous pelitic copper oxide ore (2.7% Cu) contains 20–25 wt% of –0.015 mm slime fraction (metal distribution in ore, 25–30%). When floated with butyl xanthate and sodium sulphide the copper concentrate grade and recovery are rather low, but with the use of AHA–xanthate the grade rises to 25–30% with a recovery of 65–70%.[11] The results of a small-scale pilot test (1.2 t/24 h) gave a copper concentrate grade of 28.3% with 69.7% recovery after rougher flotation, two cleaning and two scavenger stages.

Flotation practice in regard to oxidized copper ores has shown that the application of the AHA–xanthate collector system has advantages over the use of xanthate alone. These may be attributed to their synergistic effect. Co-adsorption is assumed to occur on the surface of copper mineral, forming a xanthate-AHA-Cu complex, which enhances the cross-sectional width of the polar function, enlarges the covered mineral area and imparts a reasonably high floatability to the mineral.

Flotation of light rare-earth-bearing ore

A rare-earth-bearing iron ore from Baotou mine in China contains mainly bastnaesite and monazite, with abundant fluorite and iron minerals. Beneficiation with conventional fatty acid collectors failed to yield high-quality rare-earth concentrate, but the application of hydroxamic acids gave a high-grade product by flotation. Strong depressants, such as sodium silicate and fluorosilicate, were used for the gangue minerals (Table 5).[12]

Flotation of Ta–Nb-bearing mineral

A medium-size columbite-bearing granitic deposit in south China is badly effloresced, with the result that a large quantity of slime is produced (grain size, 87% 0.04 mm; assay, 0.037% Nb_2O_5). Conditioning of the pulp with sodium silicate and

Table 1　Quality data of commercial products of AHA and SAHA

Name	Nitrogen content, %	AHA (SAHA) content, %	Water content, %	Fatty acid content, %
AHA with 7–9 C atoms	>5.3	>60	<15	<15
AHA with 5–9 C atoms	>5.8	>60	<15	<15
SAHA with 7–9 C atoms	>2.0	>26	55±3	<13
SAHA with 5–9 C atoms	>2.2	>26	55±3	<13

Table 2　Flotation results from SAHA combined with butyl xanthate

Test scale	Reagent consumption, g/t				Flotation index, %		
	Na$_2$S	Butyl xanthate	SAHA	Pine oil	Feed assay	Concentrate assay	Recovery
Bench	5500	800		150	5.88	17.85	91.69
	2500	300	300	80	5.85	17.03	92.84
	2500		600	80	5.85	17.11	90.56
Commercial (500t/24 h)	5500	750		600	4.42	10.38	90.07
	2500	300	300	100	4.44	14.37	89.90
Plant practice (2000t/24 h)	8133	1327		950	3.05	12.37	77.97
	3969	422	275	325	3.46	10.60	83.32

Table 3　Flotation results from AHA–xanthate system with combined collectors

	A (malachite-bearing)	B (containing malachite and pseudo-malachite)
Grade, %	3.74	3.50
Degree of ore oxidation, %	96.52	97.73
Single collector system		
Cu conc. grade, %	17.11	19.30
Cu conc. recovery, %	75.60	55.37
Xanthate–AHA collector system		
Cu conc. grade, %	24.58	26.25
Cu conc. recovery, %	83.96	78.70

sodium hydroxide to pH 8.5 and primary flotation with AHA and transformer oil (2:1) yields a final upgraded concentrate assaying 40.26% Nb_2O_5 with a recovery of 75%. In the pilot-plant test the flotation feed is a product from the high-intensity magnetic separation (grade, 0.23% Nb_2O_5).

After the addition of sodium hydroxide, sodium silicate and AHA–diesel oil at pH 6.5-7.5 rougher and scavenger flotation was conducted. The Nb concentrate was obtained after five cleaning stages at pH 2.5-3 in an oxalic acid medium (Table 6).

In treating this type of fine-grain columbite AHA alone is not as competitive as when it is used in combination with non-polar oils—when mixed with the non-polar oil, the AHA reagent will disperse better and can exert its function to the fullest possible extent.

Conclusions

The molecular structure of hydroxamic acid is such that it can form strong complexes with most of the valuable metallic oxide

Table 4　Performance of AHA–xanthate collector system in flotation of complex copper ore with high iron content

	Au–Cu conc.	Cu conc.	Total	Cu middlings	Cu tailings	Feed
Yield, %	0.68	3.52	4.20	10.54	85.26	100.00
Assay						
Cu, %	23.02	39.26	36.64	1.85	0.67	2.30
Fe, %	28.44	13.38	15.81	38.80	46.71	44.57
Au, g/t	108	5.0	21.68	0.60	0.30	1.29
Ag, g/t	340	140	172.4	15	4.4	12.6
Recovery, %						
Cu	6.81	59.93	66.74	8.46	24.80	100.00
Fe	0.43	1.06	1.49	9.17	89.34	100
Au	59.74	14.32	74.06	5.14	20.80	100
Ag	18.36	39.12	57.48	12.55	29.97	100

Table 5 Semi-commercial test results of flotation of rare-earth gravity concentrate with AHA

Sample	I	II
Feed assay, %	22.71	24.04
Conc. assay, %	60.67	61.64
Conc. recovery, %	56.41	62.94
Middlings assay, %	36.93	41.55
Middlings recovery, %	33.47	26.21
Total recovery, %	89.88	89.15

Table 6 Pilot test (110 kg/h) results for columbite flotation by AHA and diesel oil

Product	Yield, %	Nb$_2$O$_5$ Assay, %	Recovery, %
Flotation conc.	0.765	22.37	74.45
Flotation middlings	5.899	0.630	16.20
Flotation tailings	43.34	0.023	9.35
Feed (rougher conc. from magnetic separation)	100.00	0.230	100.00

minerals. Under the action of combined collectors it yields much better selectivity and collector power than fatty acid.

In the treatment of Ta–Nb-containing ores or hematite hydroxamic acid is always combined with hydrocarbon oils to increase its dispersivity and improve its foaming properties and the quality of the concentrate. In copper oxide ore flotation more effective results can be obtained by use of the AHA–xanthate collector system with the appropriate modifiers.

Further studies on hydroxamic acid and the variety of AHA-combined reagents will increase the scope of application of hydroxamic acids in the field of flotation.

References
1. Yale H. L. The hydroxamic acids. *Chem. Rev.*, **33**, 1943, 209–56.
2. Gorlovskii S. I. *et al.* Improvement in concentration technology of some rare metal ores, based on taking advantage of complexing alkyl hydroxamic acids peculiarities of action. In *Eighth international mineral processing congress, Leningrad, 1968* (Leningrad: Institut Mekhanobr, 1969), vol. 1, 398–413. (Russian text); Paper D3, 9p. (English text)
3. Bogdanov O. S. *et al.* Hydroxamic acids as collectors in the flotation of wolframite, cassiterite and pyrochlore. In *Tenth international mineral processing congress, London, 1973* Jones M. J. ed. (London: IMM, 1974), 553–64.
4. Peterson H. D. *et al.* Chelating agents — a key to chrysocolla flotation by the formation of insoluble surface chelates. *Trans. Am. Inst. Min. Engrs*, **232**, 1965, 388–92.
5. Fuerstenau M. C. Miller J. D. and Gutierrez G. Selective flotation of iron oxide. *Trans. Am. Inst. Min. Engrs*, **238**, 1967, 200–3.
6. Evrard L. and De Cuyper J. Flotation of copper–cobalt oxide ores with alkylhydroxamates. In *Proceedings 11th international mineral processing congress, Cagliari, 1975* (Cagliari: Istituto di Arte Mineraria, 1975), 655–69.
7. Song Wen Cai. Study of THA—a collector for difficult to treat oxide ores. In *Proceedings of the second mineral processing reagent congress of China Metal Society, Beijing, 1982*. (Chinese text)
8. Coutts R. J. Hydroxamic acids. *Can. J. Pharm. Sci.*, **2**, 1967, 1–8.
9. Sillén L. G. and Martell A. E. Stability constants of metal-ion complexes. *Spec. Publ. chem. Soc., Lond.* no. 17, 1964, 279.
10. Research Team of Guangzhou Institute of Non-ferrous Metals. The commercial test of floating Tong-Lu-Shen copper oxide ore with hydroxamate and xanthate. *Non-ferrous Metals, Beijing*, no. 6 1973. (Chinese text)
11. Zhou Weizhi. Research on the direct flotation of Shi-Lu copper oxide ores. *Min. Metall. Engng, Changsha*, **3**, no. 3 1983, 16–21. (Chinese text)
12. Research Team of Guangzhou Institute on Non-ferrous Metals. Study and practice on the flotation of rare earth-bearing ores and niobium ferrous ores with hydroxamic acids. *Non-ferrous Metals, Beijing*, no. 1 1977. (Chinese text)

New phosphoro-organic collectors for flotation of non-sulphide minerals

I. L. Kotlyarevsky, I. S. Alferiev, A. V. Krasnukhina, V. D. Pomazov and N. V. Egorov

Synopsis

A new class of efficient collectors for the flotation of non-sulphide ores has been developed. The collectors are diphosphonic acids of various structures. On the basis of this investigation the Flotol-7,9 collector was developed, produced on a commercial scale and applied successfully in the concentration of cassiterite and fluorite ores.

The general trend in the processing of mineral raw materials is the increase in the proportion of finely disseminated ores that pose difficulties in regard to beneficiation and the decrease in the valuable component content. As conventional methods and reagents are inefficient for the flotation of such materials, the search for new and efficient reagents remains an urgent problem.

In the Soviet Union the new phosphoro-organic chelate-forming compounds based on diphosphonic acid derivatives have been proposed as collectors as a result of investigation of the peculiarities of the collecting action of various compounds. The reagents are efficient in the flotation of cassiterite, fluorite, phosphorites, tungsten minerals and certain oxidized minerals of non-ferrous metals.

The investigation of the collecting action and practical application of a number of diphosphonic acid derivatives for the concentration of various types of mineral raw materials are considered.

Cassiterite flotation

In selective cassiterite flotation the basic problems arise in the processing of ores with a high content of tourmaline, ferric oxides and quartz associated with ferric oxides, with which finely disseminated cassiterite occurs. Phosphonic acids have been proposed as the most effective collectors for these types of ore.[9,10,11] With this class of compound only non-substituted monophosphonic acids have been studied, the best results being obtained with β-styrylphosphonic acid (SPA).

Only recently have diphosphonic acids been known as collectors. The investigation that was undertaken by the authors made it possible to establish that certain diphosphonic acid derivatives are efficient collectors for cassiterite, floating it with high selectivity in the presence of the complex minerals mentioned above.

Methods for the production of a series of functionally substituted diphosphonic acids have been developed and their synthesis has been accomplished. The effects of structure, length and nature of the radical, as well as the close environment of a disphosphonic group, on the collecting properties of the synthesized compounds have been studied. The aim of the investigation was to select a collector structure that was optimally efficient and amenable to synthesis on a commercial scale.

Comparative tests of reagents were carried out with a sample of a cassiterite–sulphide–silicate (tourmaline) type of ore. The ore contained 0.7% cassiterite, about 46% tourmaline, 45% quartz, 1% ferrous hydroxide and 6% sulphides. The cassiterite flotation feed was a finely ground ore (<0.1 mm). The removal of sulphides and classification in a hydrocyclone (>0.01 mm) preceded flotation.

A comparative evaluation of reagent efficiency was carried out. It was found that a number of synthesized compounds show a marked improvement over the best of the standard collectors, β-styrylphosphonic acid, in terms of efficiency. Although SPA provides the maximum four- to fivefold tin concentration ratio, the application of, say, 1-hydroxyoctylidene-1,1-diphosphonic acid, $C_7H_{15}C(OH)(PO_3H_2)_2$, results in a fourteen- to fifteenfold tin concentration ratio at 80% recovery per operation. Both collectors float cassiterite in a slightly acid medium and their selectivity increases two- to threefold in the presence of fluorides and fluorosilicates (Fig. 1).

The results obtained testify to the obvious advantage of the new collector over SPA: with comparable reagent consumption (200–250 g/t) and identical recovery (80–85%) the tin content in the concentrates obtained with 1-hydroxyoctylidene-1,1-diphosphonic acid is four to five times higher. Moreover, a forty- to fiftyfold tin concentration ratio is achieved with a single flotation stage with the use of fluorides as regulators (cf. the eight- to tenfold concentration ratio with SPA).

Study of the collecting efficiency of the compounds synthesized has shown that it changes within a wide range, depending on the size and structure of the hydrocarbon radical (clearly illustrated for 1-hydroxyalkylidene-1,1-diphosphonic acids in Fig. 2).

Thus, in the row of compounds with an unbranched aliphatic radical the collecting efficiency first increases, as the hydrocarbon radical lengthens from C_5 to C_8, and then decreases with further increase of radical length. With the C_{15} radical the compound is, in practical terms, inefficient as a collector (obviously, with increasing radical length the solubility of the collector complexes with polyvalent cations present in the pulp decreases, and the collector is bound in the volume of the solvent).

Compounds with a branched, cyclic or aromatic radical are much less effective as collectors than those with a normal radical with the same number of C atoms, i.e. the decisive factor is the overall length of a radical.

For most of the compounds that were investigated the effect of the close environment of a diphosphonate group on the collecting properties of the 1,1-diphosphonic acids is rather weak: this is clearly due to the screening of the bulky diphosphonate group.

Often, the change of the functional group has a lesser influence on flotation efficiency than the change of the total chain length. Thus, the transition from 1-hydroxyalkylidene-1,1-diphosphonic acids $(R-C(OH)(PO_3H_2)_2)$ to isomeric alkoxymethylene diphosphonic acids $(RO-CH(PO_3H_2)_2)$ results in a certain rise in the efficiency of the isomeric compounds, which is

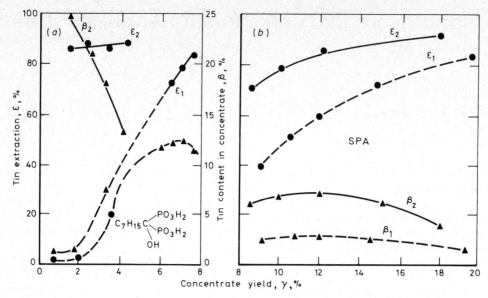

Fig. 1   Concentration ability, $\varepsilon = f(\gamma)$ and $\beta = f(\gamma)$ with $C_7H_{15}C(OH)(PO_3H_2)_2$ (a) and SPA (b) as collectors (β_1 and ε_1, broken curves, without depressant; β_2 and ε_2, unbroken curves, with 200 g/t NaF)

most probably caused by the general lengthening of the hydrocarbon chain owing to the incorporation of an oxygen atom.

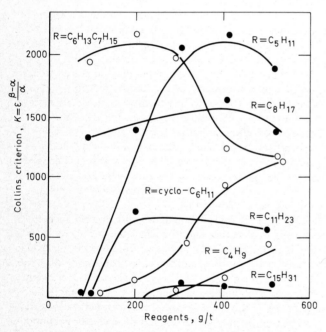

Fig. 2   Results of comparative tests of 1-hydroxyalkylidene-1,1-diphosphonic acids, $RC(OH)(PO_3H_2)_2$ with various alkyl chain lengths (Collins criterion, $K, = \varepsilon \frac{\beta - \alpha}{\alpha}$, where α is tin content in ore, %, β is tin content in concentrate, %, and ε is tin extraction, %)

In comparison with their oxygen analogue, alkyl(aryl)thioethylidene-1,1-diphosphonic acids, $(RSCH_2CH(PO_3H_2)_2)$, float cassiterite with higher selectivity: other factors being equal, they yield an improvement of 1.2 to 1.5 fold in the concentrate grade. These diphosphonic acid derivatives are, however, characterized by excessive sensitivity to the state of the surface of cassiterite particles to be floated. Films and micro-inclusions of ferrous oxides and other minerals result in a decrease in cassiterite floatability. For such cassiterite-bearing ores these reagents are less efficient than their oxygen analogues.

The 1-aminoalkylidene-1,1-diphosphonic acids, $R-C(NH_2)(PO_3H_2)_2$, studied are less effective in their selectivity than 1-hydroxyalkylidene-1,1-diphosphonic acids with the same length and structure of the radical; this must be ascribed to the positive charge on the amino group. In the order of aminodiphosphonic acids it is observed that the transition from 1-aminoalkylidene to N-alkylaminomethylene $(RNHCH(PO_3H_2)_2)$ and 2-(N-alkyl)aminoethylidene-1,1-diphosphonic acids $(RNHCH_2CH(PO_3H_2)_2)$ is connected with the further decrease in reagent selectivity, obviously due to the change of amino group basicity, which increases in this order. Aminodiphosphonic acids exhibit anomalous sensitivity to fluorides, as revealed in the decrease in tin recovery. The depressing action of fluorides increases in the order given. 2p-tolylaminoethylidene-1,1-diphosphonic acid is an exception, always exhibiting sensitivity to fluorides despite the low amino group basicity.

The introduction of ureide and thioureide groups $(R^2-NH-C-NR^1-)$ into 1,1-diphosphonic acids had no
$$\underset{O(S)}{\overset{\|}{}}$$
appreciable effect on their collecting efficiency in cassiterite flotation. These groups do not obviously promote fixing of the reagents on the surface of the mineral complex investigated. Considerable differences for thioureide derivatives of methylenediphosphonic acid should be expected in the flotation of minerals containing components more amenable to coordination with sulphur. In particular, the above-mentioned diphosphonic acid derivatives display considerable differences in complex formation with divalent copper salts in the volume of the solution.

Alkyl-imino-bis(methylphosphonic) acids were the only representatives of diphosphonic acids with non-heminal positions of the phosphonate groups. Such an alteration of the molecule geometry has not changed their efficiency as collectors significantly. Although they are more effective than isomeric 1-amino- and N-alkylaminoalkylidene-1,1-diphosphonic acids, they are worse than the best representatives of 1,1-diphosphonic acids.

The collectors based on diphosphonic acid derivatives

were founded on established principles. The reagent's molecule had both a polar part, capable of fixing on the surface of the mineral, and an apolar part, which imposed hydrophobic properties on the collector surface film.

A fundamentally novel approach was proposed that provides for the separation of these two functions and the creation of a two-component collector. The first component was aimed at fixing on the mineral surface, whereas the second was intended to make the surface film hydrophobic. Specific interaction is required between the components—for example, the formation of donor–acceptor π-complexes.

Such a separation of collector functions between two components increases the feasibility of flotation regulation and may be useful when conventional collectors are inefficient—for example, in processing materials with a high content of slime fractions <0.01 mm in size.

Taking into account the selective fixing of the compounds with the 1,1-diphosphonate group on the cassiterite surface, this group was taken as basic to the selection of components selectively interacting with the mineral.

1,1-diphosphonic acids containing an electron-acceptor group have been synthesized:

$$N \overset{+}{\underset{}{N}} - CH_2CH \begin{array}{c} PO_3H^- \\ PO_3H_2 \end{array} \quad (1)$$

$$O_2N - \underset{NO_2}{\overset{NO_2}{\bigcirc}} - NH - CH \begin{array}{c} PO_3H_2 \\ PO_3H_2 \end{array} \quad (2)$$

$$\underset{O_2N}{\overset{O_2N}{\bigcirc}} - CONH - CH \begin{array}{c} PO_3H_2 \\ PO_3H_2 \end{array} \quad (3)$$

$$O_2N - \underset{NO_2}{\overset{NO_2}{\bigcirc}} - S - CH_2CH \begin{array}{c} PO_3H_2 \\ PO_3H_2 \end{array} \quad (4)$$

Special investigation showed that such compounds can actually fix on the cassiterite surface.

Various low polar π-electron-donor compounds were used as hydrophobic components:

$$(5)$$

$$(6)$$

$$(7)$$

$$(8)$$

$$(9)$$

Mixture
$R = CH_3, C_2H_5, C_3H_7, C_4H_9, (CH_3)_2CHCH_2$

$$(10)$$

For correlation with flotation experiments the stability constants of certain molecular complexes of electron-acceptor and electron-donor components were measured. The measurements are accomplished by the spectrophotometric method in ethanol solution at 20°C. Stability constants ($l\,mol^{-1}$) are given in Table 1.

Table 1

| Acceptor | | | | |
Donor	(1)	(2)	(3)	(4)
(5)	—	—	0.23	—
(6)	0.2	0.54	0.65	0.93
(7)	—	—	0.40	0.72
(8)	—	—	—	2.26
(9)	—	—	—	2.38
(10)	—	—	—	0.85

The investigations that were carried out verified the viability of the idea of using two-component collectors for flotation. The relevant selection of the donor–acceptor combination provides results identical to the best that were obtained with ordinary collectors based on diphosphonic acid derivatives. The donor–acceptor complex stability is one of the major influences on flotation efficiency. In a system with the same donor the flotation efficiency and the stability of the donor–acceptor complex change sympathetically. It is, however, impossible to evaluate the efficiency of one or the other reagent combination by taking into account complex stability alone. Of major importance are the donor aggregate state, the degree of dispersion of its emulsion and the dispersion of the air bubbles, as well as pulp density and the conditions of its interaction with the reagents. At present, two-component collectors are still of theoretical interest and must be the subject of special study.

In further investigation of this approach special attention should be paid to other principles of achieving the specific interaction between the components with the aim of reducing the cost of the reagents, which are expensive and difficult to obtain, and of strengthening the bonds.

After the results obtained had been analysed a class of 1-hydroxyalkylidene-1,1-diphosphonic acids was taken for commercial production. Besides being efficient collectors, certain representatives of this class are guaranteed by the ready availability of inexpensive domestic raw material. The methods of synthesis developed are simple and reliable.

Synthesis of a commercially available collector has been accomplished, the main active compounds of the collector being 1-hydroxyalkylidene-1,1-diphosphonic acids with 7–9 C atoms. This collector was called Flotol-7,9.

In terms of efficiency Flotol-7,9 is not inferior to the previously studied compounds of the class of 1-hydroxyalkylidene-1,1-diphosphonic acids and is considerably better than collectors known in the world industry (Table 2).

concentrate was 7.5–8.0% Sn, the scavenger concentrate had a 25–30% content of tin at 70–75% recovery from the cassiterite flotation feed.[12]

The following characteristics of the new reagent should be mentioned.

Flotol-7,9 exhibits a wide range of differentiation in terms of collecting properties for cassiterite and rock-forming minerals and floats various samples of natural cassiterite (from colourless to dark in colour) with equal efficiency.

Its advantages over β-styrylphosphonic acid and sulphosuccinamate-type reagents are apparent in the flotation of ores that contain tourmaline, ferrous oxides and garnet. As for ores of simpler composition, the above advantages are equally significant.

The 'unavoidable' ions of the pulp, except trivalent iron and aluminium, have but negligible effect on cassiterite flotation with Flotol-7,9.

Under ideal conditions of mono-mineralic flotation in the mineral–distilled water–collector system maximum cassiterite floatability (as well as maximum of collector adsorption) is observed in the pH range 2.5–3.0. In ore flotation processes the maximum shifts to pH 4.5–5.0. The results of the investigations indicate that this is connected to the presence of cations and hydrolysed trivalent iron and aluminium in the pulp; they suppress cassiterite flotation in the acid medium by virtue of the formation of poorly soluble complexes with Flotol-7,9. The suppressing effect of

Table 2   Results of comparative collector tests

| Collectors | Tin content, % | | Tin recovery, % | Concentration ratio |
	Flotation feed	Concentrate		
Flotol-7,9	0.56	25.6	82.7	45.7
p-tolylarsonic acid	0.56	8.4	82.9	15.0
β-styrylphosphonic acid (SPA)	0.56	5.8	82.0	10.3
Mixture of alkylhydroxamic acids C_7–C_9 (IM50)	0.56	2.2	79.0	3.9
Tetrasodium salt of N-octadecyl-N-sulphosuccinoyl- aspartic acid (Aerosol-22)	0.56	2.3	83.0	4.0

Development of Flotol-7,9 has opened up new opportunities in the practical application of flotation in the processing of complex ores with tourmaline and ferrous oxide contents.[8,12] The flotation process for these ores with use of known reagents is schematically complex and unstable and the results obtained do not always satisfy processing requirements.

The new reagent makes it possible to increase the process selectivity (by three to ten times) and to simplify the technological scheme of cassiterite flotation by eliminating the number of rougher concentrate scavenging stages; it provides reliability and good modelling of the process. This is verified by the long-term commercial application of Flotol-7,9 for cassiterite flotation from the slimes of a gravity process treatment of cassiterite–sulphide–silicate (tourmaline) ores. The slimes contained 0.4–0.45% tin. The flowsheet included sulphide flotation, primary flotation, controlled cassiterite flotation and a single-stage scavenging of the rougher concentrate. The grade of the rougher

iron and aluminium may be eliminated with proper adjustment of the pH of the medium, collector consumption and the addition of fluoride or fluorosilicate of alkali metals. This does not, however, influence the high reagent selectivity because Flotol-7,9 occupies a special place among the known collectors. Flotol-7,9 is of both practical and scientific interest for study of the mechanism of collecting action of reagents in the flotation of non-sulphide minerals.

The practical use of Flotol-7,9 is not limited to cassiterite flotation, various other efficient applications of this collector having been found (of special interest is the selective flotation of calcium-bearing minerals).

Flotation of fluorite ores

The selective separation of the fluorite–calcite mineral complex is another unique property of Flotol-7,9. The floatability of calcium-bearing minerals in the presence of

Flotol-7,9 decreases in the order fluorite > phosphorite $\approx$ apatite > scheelite > calcite. Among the minerals investigated fluorite reveals the highest floatability. In the flotation of mono-mineralic fractions the Flotol-7,9 concentration necessary for effective fluorite flotation is lower by two orders than that in the flotation of other minerals. Fluorite floatability remains rather high in a wide range of medium pH values from acidic to alkaline. In this connexion the fluorite present in tin ores may be selectively floated in a slightly alkaline medium with low collector consumption and a negligible loss of tin with the fluorite concentrate. Fluorite flotation from silicate–fluorite ores is very effective with Flotol-7,9. The flotation of these ores with conventional fluorite collectors (higher carboxylic acids) does not, however, cause any particular problems.

Carbonate–fluorite (calcite–fluorite) ores are known to be rather difficult in this respect, carboxylic acids being efficient for their flotation. Flotation of fluorite from calcite-bearing ores with the use of carboxylic acids is carried out at 50–80°C according to an elaborate flowsheet with multiple scavenging stages.[13] For the final finishing of the rougher concentrate to a commercial grade, steaming ($t = 80$–90°C) at a high concentration of sodium silicate and sodium fluosilicate or acidic leaching is used.

Flotation of these ores with Flotol-7,9 is carried out according to a simple scheme, including pulp agitation with regulators and a collector, primary and control flotation and two to three scavenging stages of the rougher concentrate without heating of the pulp.

At Soviet plants the operational data shown in Table 3 have been obtained in the processing of finely disseminated calcite–fluorite ore with Flotol-7,9 (mineral liberation was achieved by grinding 92–94% of the ore to 0.04 mm):

Table 3

Consumption of Flotol-7,9, kg/t	0.25–0.30
Addition of inorganic regulators, kg/t	0.5
Fluorite content in ore, %	34–36
Fluorite content in concentrate, %	93–95
Calcite content in ore, %	8–14
Calcite content in concentrate, %	1.0–1.5
Silicon dioxide content in concentrate, %	<1.0
Fluorite recovery, %	78–80

The application of Flotol-7,9 made possible the elimination of heating at the flotation stage and a twofold reduction in heat consumption, the exclusion of the use of the oleic acid and Na_2SiF_6, simplification of the flotation scheme and an improvement in working conditions.

Flotation of phosphorite ores

Flotol-7,9 was tested for the concentration of sheet phosphorite ores at the laboratory and semi-commercial scales. The subject of the investigation was a finely disseminated ore of complex mineral composition that was difficult to concentrate.[14] In processing such ores with collectors based on aliphatic acids the recovery of phosphorus pentoxide did not exceed 65–68%; carboxylic acid collectors are sensitive to fine slimes.

With Flotol-7,9 it is possible to float phosphorite without prior desliming with 100% grinding to <0.071 mm (95% grinding to <0.16 mm with carboxylic acids). High operating data are achieved in flotation of phosphorites with Flotol-7,9 from ores of various mineral compositions: the

flotation of ore with 16–20% P_2O_5 gives a concentrate of 24–25% P_2O_5 at 80–90% recovery.

With Flotol-7,9 phosphorite concentrates with 35–40% P_2O_5 are obtainable; the engineering and economic expediency of producing a rich concentrate should, however, be considered in every particular case, account being taken of the reduction in recovery. Flotol-7,9 may also be used successfully in processing apatite ores, which are difficult to treat with other reagents.

Diphosphonic acids are used equally for tungsten minerals (scheelite, hübnerite, wolframite) and for the separation of oxidized minerals from lead and zinc.

Synthesis of collectors

Synthesis of 1-hydroxyalkylidene-1,1-diphosphonic acids is effected by introducing carboxylic acids into the reaction with phosphorus trichloride and water and subsequent hydrolysis of the polycondensed products obtained, with water in excess:

$$R-COOH \xrightarrow{PCl_3,\ H_2O} R-CO \left[O-\underset{\substack{| \\ R\ O}}{\overset{\substack{PO_3H_2\ \ OH \\ \diagdown\ \diagup}}{C}}-P \right]_n OH \xrightarrow{H_2O} R-C \underset{OH}{\overset{PO_3H_2}{\diagup\diagdown PO_3H_2}}$$

$R = C_4H_9 \div C_{15}H_{31},\ (C_3H_7)CH,\ cyclo\ C_6H_{11}$

The yield of the desired compounds was 67–84% in the case of normal radicals and 16–19% for α-branched radicals. Synthesis of 1-alkoxyalkylidene-1,1-diphosphonic acids was carried out by introducing carbonic acid esters (formates and acetates) into the reaction with phosphorus trioxide in an aproton solvent in the presence of BF_3, with subsequent acidic hydrolysis of the products obtained:

$$R^1O-\underset{R^2}{\overset{|}{C}}=O \xrightarrow[\text{(2)}H_2O\ (HCl)]{\text{(1)}P_4O_6\ (BF_3)} R^1O-\underset{R^2}{\overset{|}{C}} \overset{PO_3H_2}{\diagup\diagdown PO_3H_2}$$

$R^1 = C_4H_9$ to C_6H_{13}; $R^2 = H,CH_3$

The reaction proceeds under mild conditions (20–50°C); the introduction of formates ($R^2 = H$) results in high yields (70–80%), whereas that of amyl acetate ($R^2 = CH_3$) gives only 13%. In the latter case considerable dealkylation of the alkoxy group takes place and an appreciable amount of 1-hydroxyalkylidene-1,1-diphosphonic acid is formed.

Attempts to obtain 1-alkoxyalkylidene-1,1-diphosphonic acids in the reaction of carboxylic acid esters with a mixture of phosphorus trichloride and phosphoric acid failed. With formates the yield of the desired compounds did not exceed 15–20%, and the attempts with acetates failed completely.

1-aminoalkylidene-1,1-diphosphonic acids and alkylaminomethylenediphosphonic acids were obtained by the methods described previously.[15]

$$R-CN \xrightarrow{H_3PO_3\ PBr_3} R-\underset{NH_2}{\overset{}{C}} \overset{PO_3H_2}{\diagup\diagdown PO_3H_2}$$

$R = C_5H_{11}$ to $C_{11}H_{23}$

$$R-NH-CH=O \xrightarrow{\text{H}_3\text{PO}_3, \text{PCl}_3} R-NH-CH \underset{\text{PO}_3\text{H}_2}{\overset{\text{PO}_3\text{H}_2}{<}}$$

$$R = C_5H_{11} \text{ to } C_7H_{15}$$

Arylsulphonyl aminomethylene diphosphonic acids were obtained by introducing aminomethylene- and methylaminomethylene diphosphonic acids in a water–dioxane medium into the reaction with arylsulphochlorides in the presence of triethylamine at 0–5°C:

$$R-NH-CH \underset{\text{PO}_3\text{H}_2}{\overset{\text{PO}_3\text{H}_2}{<}} \xrightarrow[\text{Et}_3\text{N}]{\text{ArSO}_2\text{Cl}} ArSO_2-\underset{R}{\underset{|}{N}}-CH \underset{\text{PO}_3\text{H}_2}{\overset{\text{PO}_3\text{H}_2}{<}}$$

$$R = H.CH_3 ; Ar = p\text{-}CH_3C_6H_4, \beta\text{-}C_{10}H_7$$

The yield of the sulphonyl derivatives with $R = H$ was high ($>80\%$), whereas with $R = CH_3$ it was only 5%—probably owing to the difficulties of rendering the secondary amino group sulphonic.

A high yield of ureidic and thioureidic derivatives of the methylenediphosphonic acid was obtained as a result of interacting the corresponding isocyanates or isothiocyanates with triethylammonium salts of amino- and methylaminomethylene diphosphonic acids in aqueous methanol:

$$R^1-NH-CH \underset{\text{PO}_3\text{H}_2}{\overset{\text{PO}_3\text{H}_2}{<}} \xrightarrow[\text{Et}_3\text{N}]{R^2-N=C=O(S)} R^2-NH-\underset{\underset{O(S)}{\|}}{C}-\underset{\underset{R^1}{|}}{N}-CH \underset{\text{PO}_3\text{H}_2}{\overset{\text{PO}_3\text{H}_2}{<}}$$

$$R^1 = H.CH_3 ; R^2 = C_6H_5CH_2, \alpha\text{-}C_{10}H_7, C_7H_{15}$$

Unlike the previous reaction, this reaction proceeds quite smoothly in the case of a secondary amino group as well.

An interesting method of synthesizing potential collectors has been developed on the basis of nucleophilic addition to vinylidene-diphosphonic acid. When necessary, the method can be carried out readily on a commercial scale, as the above acid may be obtained by dehydration of an easily available 1-hydroxyethylidene-1,1-diphosphonic acid. Thus, the addition of aliphatic and aromatic amines to vinylidene-diphosphonic acid gives 2-N-alkyl(aryl)-aminoethylidene-1,1-diphosphonic acids:

$$CH_2=C \underset{\text{PO}_3\text{H}_2}{\overset{\text{PO}_3\text{H}_2}{<}} \xrightarrow{R-NH_2} R-NH-CH_2CH \underset{\text{PO}_3\text{H}_2}{\overset{\text{PO}_3\text{H}_2}{<}}$$

$$R = C_5H_{11}, C_7H_{15}, C_9H_{19}, p\text{-}CH_3C_6H_4$$

The reaction proceeds in highly polar protonic media (water, acetic acid) at 100–120°C and gives a high yield of the desired products of addition (75–93%).

As for amines, alcohols can be introduced into the reaction with vinylidene-diphosphonic acid:

$$CH_2=C \underset{\text{PO}_3\text{H}_2}{\overset{\text{PO}_3\text{H}_2}{<}} \xrightarrow{ROH} RO-CH_2CH \underset{\text{PO}_3\text{H}_2}{\overset{\text{PO}_3\text{H}_2}{<}}$$

$$R = C_4H_9, C_5H_{11}, \text{cyclo-}C_6H_{11}$$

The interaction results in 2-alkoxyethylidene-1,1-diphosphonic acid with a 50–70% yield. The reaction proceeds in an excess of the corresponding alcohol as solvent at 100–120°C.

Thiols proved to be much more reactive than alcohols in the reaction of nucleophilic addition to vinylidene-diphosphonic acid. The introduction of both aliphatic and aromatic thiols into the reaction with the triethylammonium salt of vinylidene-diphosphonic acid in acetic acid at 100–120°C results in about 100% yield of 2-alkyl- or arylthioethylidene-1,1-diphosphonic acids:

$$CH_2=C \underset{\text{PO}_3\text{H}_2}{\overset{\text{PO}_3\text{H}_2}{<}} \xrightarrow[\text{Et}_3\text{N}, \text{CH}_3\text{COOH}]{RSH} R-S-CH_2CH \underset{\text{PO}_3\text{H}_2}{\overset{\text{PO}_3\text{H}_2}{<}}$$

$$R = C_3H_7, C_4H_9, (CH_3)_2CHCH_2, C_6H_5CH_2, p\text{-}CH_3C_6H_4, \beta\text{-}C_{10}H_7$$

Alkyl-imino-bis (methyl phosphonic) acids are synthesized by the established method[16]

$$R-NH_2 \xrightarrow[\text{HCl}]{\text{H}_3\text{PO}_3, \text{CH}_2\text{O}} R-N \underset{\text{CH}_2\text{PO}_3\text{H}_2}{\overset{\text{CH}_2\text{PO}_3\text{H}_2}{<}}$$

$$R = C_5H_{11} \text{ to } C_{16}H_{33}$$

Picrylaminomethylenediphosphonic acid (2) was obtained with a yield close to 100% as a result of the interaction of picryl chloride and aminomethylenediphosphonic acid in a water–dioxane solution in the presence of triethylamine at 0–5°C.

Similarly, 3,5-dinitrobenzoylaminomethylene-diphosphonic acid (3) was obtained with a 65% yield under the same conditions by acylating aminomethylene-diphosphonic acid with 3,5-dinitrobenzoylchloride.

2-Picrylthioethylidene-1,1-diphosphonic acid (4) was obtained with a 68% yield by the interaction of tributylammonium salt of 2-mercaptoethylidene-1,1-diphosphonic acid with picryl chloride in a dioxane–tetrahydrofuran mixture at 0°C.

$$H_2N-CH\Big\langle\begin{array}{l}PO_3H_2\\PO_3H_2\end{array}\xrightarrow[Et_3N]{2,4,6-(O_2N)_3C_6H_2Cl}O_2N-\underset{NO_2}{\overset{NO_2}{C_6H_2}}-NH-CH\Big\langle\begin{array}{l}PO_3H_2\\PO_3H_2\end{array}\qquad(2)$$

$$H_2N-CH\Big\langle\begin{array}{l}PO_3H_2\\PO_3H_2\end{array}\xrightarrow[Et_3N]{3,5(O_2N)_2C_6H_3COCl}(O_2N)_2C_6H_3-CONH-CH\Big\langle\begin{array}{l}PO_3H_2\\PO_3H_2\end{array}\qquad(3)$$

$$HS-CH_2CH\Big\langle\begin{array}{l}PO_3H_2\\PO_3H_2\end{array}\xrightarrow[Bu_3N]{2,4,6-(O_2N)_3\ C_6H_2Cl}O_2N-\underset{NO_2}{\overset{NO_2}{C_6H_2}}-S-CH_2CH\Big\langle\begin{array}{l}PO_3H_2\\PO_3H_2\end{array}\qquad(4)$$

All compounds have been recovered separately in the form of free acids or their salts, their individuality and structure being reliably proved by analytical methods, thin-film chromatography, PMR and NMR (^{31}P) spectroscopy.

Production of Flotol-7,9

The technology of Flotol-7,9 production takes full account of the relevant requirements and has the characteristics of simplicity, efficiency and lack of wastage. The raw material for Flotol-7,9 production is phosphorus trichloride (inexpensive and produced on a large scale in all developed countries) and a mixture of synthetic carboxylic acids of the C_7–C_9 fraction obtained by oxidation of paraffins. The substitution of the inexpensive mixture of carboxylic acids for an individual caprylic acid does not in any way influence either the yield of the desired mixture of 1-hydroxyalkylidene-1,1-diphosphonic acids or the quality of the collector obtained. The process is performed in standard enamelled steel reactors and does not require any special equipment. Although the production of the collector is currently a batch process, it is so simple that the unit may be run by a single worker. Raw material consumption per ton of 100% collector is 0.5 t of synthetic carboxylic acids C_7–C_9 and 1.1 t of phosphorus trichloride. The temperature range of the process is 25–140°C and the pressure range is -0.8 to 2 atm. The only by-product is hydrogen chloride, which is readily extracted from primary material admixtures and after water absorption it gives pure hydrochloric acid ready for use. The yield of 33% hydrochloric acid is 2.5 t/t of 100% Flotol-7,9. Flotol-7,9 may be produced in the form of a dry powder of 90% purity or 50% water solution. The latter, after an addition of usual inhibitors of acid corrosion, may be transported and stored in steel containers. The storage time of both dry and liquid Flotol-7,9 is unlimited; in the latter case corrosion is reliably eliminated. In both forms Flotol-7,9 is non-combustible and low in toxicity. Research is being undertaken in the U.S.S.R. to develop the continuous technology of Flotol-7,9 production. The task is, however, not simple.

References

1. Krasnukhina A. V. et al. Russian Patent 406 575, 1974.
2. Krasnukhina A. V. et al. Russian Patent 497 788, 1977.
3. Krasnukhina A. V. et al. British Patent 1 469 894, 1975.
4. Pol'kin S. I. Russian Patent 523 714, 1977.
5. Krasnukhina A. V. et al. Russian Patent 605 638, 1978.
6. Krasnukhina A. V. et al. Russian Patent 638 378, 1979.
7. Alferiev I. S. et al. Russian Patent 1 022 970A, 1983.
8. Krasnukhina A. V. Kotlyarevsky I. L. and Alferiev I. S. Improvements of technological schemes and tin metallurgy (Novosibirsk: Central Scientific Research Institute of the Tin Industry, 1981), 38–45. (Russian text)
9. Collins D. N. Investigation of collector systems for the flotation of cassiterite. Trans. Instn Min. Metall. (Sect. C: Mineral Process. Extr. Metall.), 76, 1967, C77–93; Collins D. N. et al. Flotation of cassiterite: development of a flotation process. Trans. Instn Min. Metall. (Sect. C: Mineral Process. Extr. Metall.), 77, 1968, C1–13.
10. Kirchberg H. et al. Probleme der Zinnsteinflotation und der Zinnbestimmung. Freiberger Forschungsh. A455, 1969, 61 p.
11. Wottgen E. and Luft D. Reagenzien für die Zinnsteinflotation. Bergakademie, 22, 1970, 472–7.
12. Kotlyarov V. G. et al. Improvements in the technology of slurry concentration and introduction of the flotation of cassiterite. Res. Rep. Central Scientific Res. Inst. Tin Industry, Novosibirsk, no. 6 1977, 34–7. (Russian text)
13. Allen G. E. and Allen G. E. U.S. Patent 3 430 765, 1965 and 3 536 193, 1969.
14. Ratobyl'skaya L. D. Boyko N. N. and Kozheynikov A. O. Beneficiation of phosphate (Moscow: Nedra, 1979), 261 p. (Russian text)
15. Plöger W. et al. Herstellung von 1-Aminoalkan-1,1-diphosphonsäuren. Z. anorg. allg. Chem., 389, 1972, 119–28.
16. Moedritzer K. and Irani R. R. The direct synthesis of α-aminomethylphosphonic acids. J. org. Chem., 31, 1966, 1603–7.

Novel solvent extractants for recovery of copper from chloride leach solutions derived from sulphide ores

Raymond F. Dalton, Raymond Price, Peter M. Quan and Brian Townson

Synopsis

Hydrometallurgical processes, particularly those which are based on chloride leaching systems, occupy a leading position in the rapidly developing technology aimed at the recovery of the contained non-ferrous metals from the so-called complex sulphide ores. A major problem common to many such processes is their inability directly to produce high-purity copper without the need for subsequent refining stages. ICI Organics Division has developed a series of novel solvent extractants for copper from chloride media that provide the enabling technology to overcome this problem: they function by a chemical principle that is novel in the field of solvent extraction of copper

$$2L_{(Org)} + Cu^{2+}_{(Aq)} \rightleftharpoons L_2CuCl_{2(Org)}$$

and are capable of transferring large amounts of copper without the need for pH control or adjustment and with very high selectivity over a wide range of metals and metalloids. Further, they demonstrate excellent extraction and strip kinetics, possess good phase-disengagement properties and have high hydrolytic stability, thus matching the criteria against which solvent extractants are judged. These properties permit the very efficient recovery of copper from chloride leach solutions and the production of raffinates with very low concentrations of copper. This facilitates the subsequent recovery of zinc and of silver from the leach solutions. Flowsheets that incorporate this development are discussed and the results of the application of this novel technology to leach solutions derived from complex concentrates are presented.

Complex ores have been defined recently[1] as those ores from which it is difficult to recover one or more selective products of acceptable quality and economic value with minimal losses and at reasonable cost. The so-called complex sulphide ores, which are fine-grained, intimate associations of chalcopyrite ($CuFeS_2$), sphalerite (ZnS) and galena (PbS) freely disseminated in the dominant pyrite (Fe_2S) or pyrrhotite ($Fe_{1-x}S$) and which frequently contain valuable amounts of silver and, in some cases, gold, fall clearly[2] within this definition. For this reason their development to date has been on a small scale, despite their high mean metal contents (0.3–3% Cu, 0.3–3% Pb, 0.2–10% Zn, 30–100 g/t Ag, and 0.1 g/t Au), their worldwide distribution and their obvious importance [2–9] as a reserve of non-ferrous metals. Recently, however, the growing scarcity of easily worked minerals has led to an ever-increasing interest in their exploitation and their treatment for the recovery of the contained metals is an area of burgeoning research.[1–19]

The pyridine carboxylic ester extractant (CLX-20) is the subject of patents and patent applications filed in the name of Imperial Chemical Industries PLC in major mining countries. It is available from Acorga, Ltd., as ACORGA CLX-20. The word ESCAID is a trade mark, the property of EXXON Corporation, U.S.A. The word ACORGA is a trade mark, the property of Acorga, Ltd., Bermuda.

The various process options[2,3] for the recovery of the contained metal values from complex sulphide ores are broadly summarized in outline in Fig. 1. By definitition[1] the production of individual concentrates by differential flotation is unattractive,[2,3,6–9,20] not least because the normal standards of purity that are usually required for smelter operations are far from being met by the various concentrates. This is compounded by the frequent presence of arsenic, antimony, mercury, etc., in the concentrates. Further, losses of metal values to other concentrates and to tailings represent a substantial waste of resources and loss of revenue.

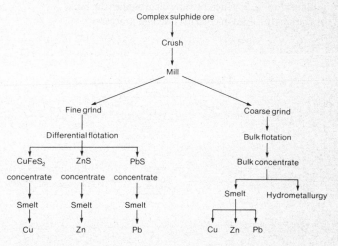

Fig. 1 Process options for treating complex sulphide ores

The production of bulk concentrates is, therefore, a much more attractive proposition in economic terms, but transfers the problem of metals separation to a later stage in the overall process. This cannot be achieved by conventional pyrometallurgical processing[2,10] and bulk concentrates can only be treated successfully[3,6] in smelter complexes of the Dowa or Boliden types. These have highly sophisticated flowsheets and have taken many years to develop. New smelter complexes of these types would be very difficult to justify commercially at prevailing metal prices and would be quite unsuitable for relatively small deposits of complex sulphide ores.[3,6]

Recent years have, therefore, seen a vast increase in research on hydrometallurgical processes for the treatment of bulk concentrates, this option offering the most promise[2] for the successful exploitation of complex sulphide deposits. A wide variety of such processes has been described and, although these have frequently related to only one metal—usually copper—they have recently been reviewed[2,3,6,20] in the light of their potential or real application to bulk complex sulphide concentrates.

The technology encompasses a wide variety of leach regimes, of which chloride-based systems[7,10–15,17,21–38] are by far the most popular. Ferric chloride, cupric chloride and mixtures of these reagents are favoured leachants because of their high leaching efficiency, the rapid rate of the leaching reactions (equations 1 and 2) and the fact that sulphur is liberated in the elemental form.

$$CuFeS_2 + 3\,FeCl_3 \rightarrow CuCl + 4FeCl_2 + 2S \qquad (1)$$

$$CuFeS_2 + 3\,CuCl_2 \rightarrow 4\,CuCl + FeCl_2 + 2S \qquad (2)$$

Corrosion problems associated with chloride media have been overcome[10,20] by the use of such modern materials of construction as fibre-reinforced plastic, polypropylene and butyl rubber, and chloride hydrometallurgy has recently been described[20] as the logical choice for the treatment of unconventional concentrates that smelters cannot handle and as being particularly suitable for on-site refining of copper for small-tonnage operations in remote areas.

The very high efficiency of chloride leaching systems does, however, bring problems in its train. Many minor metals present in complex sulphide concentrates—arsenic, antimony, bismuth, mercury, cadmium, selenium, manganese, etc.—are leached very effectively.[10] Frequently, they appear[3,10] in the copper product, necessitating expensive fire- and electrorefining stages to produce a marketable product. Further, silver, which is often present at economically viable levels in complex sulphide concentrates, is co-deposited[3,10,13,20,27] with the copper and must be recovered. These problems are illustrated in the circuit outlined in Fig. 2, which broadly incorporates the basic operations involved in chloride leaching processes.

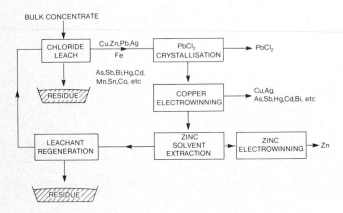

Fig. 2   Outline circuit for chloride hydrometallurgical treatment of bulk concentrates

Solvent extraction is now widely recognized as a means of producing pure copper electrolytes and in certain chloride-based processes[8,11,12,13,15,16,33,34] the problem of copper purity has been overcome by this technology. Of necessity, this is invariably based on the commercially available o-hydroxyaryl oxime reagents and is, therefore, limited by their operating parameters. The performance of these reagents is governed by the equilibrium

$$2RH_{(Org)} + Cu^{2+}{}_{(Aq)} \rightleftharpoons R_2Cu_{(Org)} + 2H^+{}_{(Aq)}$$

$$K = \frac{[R_2Cu]\,[H^+]^2}{[Cu^{2+}]\,[RH]^2}$$

$$= \frac{D\,[H^+]^2}{[RH]^2}$$

$$D = \frac{K\,[RH]^2}{[H^+]^2} \quad \propto \frac{1}{[H^+]^2}$$

from which it can be seen that the distribution of copper between the organic and aqueous phases, D, is inversely proportional to the square of the hydrogen ion concentration in the aqueous phase. With the exception of the Minemet Recherche process,[15,16,33,34] the practical result of this is that only limited amounts of copper can be transferred unless the pH of the aqueous solution is controlled at the extraction stage. This

problem is compounded by the very high activity of hydrochloric acid in concentrated chloride media[19] (Fig. 3), with the result that one of the attractions of chloride leaching—the ability to produce concentrated solutions—is negated. The problem is alleviated in the Minemet Recherche process by air-blowing the extraction mixers to oxidize the copper to the cupric state, thus consuming the acid liberated during the exchange reaction. Even in this case, however, the copper content of the leach solution cannot be reduced to a very low level and silver recovery remains a problem.

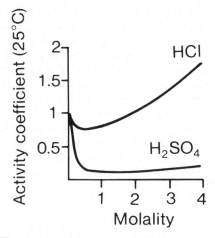

Fig. 3   Relationship between activity coefficients and molality of hydrochloric and sulphuric acids[19]

The clear need that was recognized by ICI to permit the attractions of chloride hydrometallurgy to be exploited to the full was a solvent extractant capable of extracting copper from concentrated aqueous chloride solutions with high efficiency without the need for pH adjustment or control and with very high selectivity over a wide range of metals and metalloids. This would not only permit the *direct* production of pure copper but also, as a result of the very low copper content of the raffinate from the solvent extraction stage, facilitate both the recovery of silver by cementation and the subsequent solvent extraction of zinc since high selectivity for zinc over copper would no longer be required in this operation (Fig. 4).

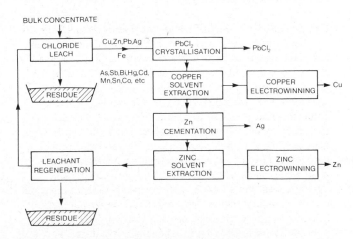

Fig. 4   Modified outline circuit for chloride hydrometallurgical treatment of bulk concentrates

It was with this objective in mind that ICI embarked on a programme of research that culminated in the novel pyridine carboxylic ester solvent extractant for copper from chloride media known for short as CLX-20 (formerly[21,39,40] DS5443). This reagent functions by a chemical principle that is entirely novel in the field of solvent extraction of copper and its mode of action is governed by the equilibrium

$$2L_{(Org)} + Cu^{2+}_{(Aq)} + 2Cl^-_{(Aq)} \rightleftharpoons L_2CuCl_{2(Org)}$$

$$K = \frac{[L_2CuCl_2]}{[L]^2[Cu^{2+}][Cl^-]^2}$$

$$= \frac{D}{[L]^2[Cl^-]^2}$$

$$D = K[L]^2[Cl^-]^2$$

Distribution of copper between the organic and aqueous phases, D, is formally proportional to the square of the chloride ion concentration in the aqueous phase, and the extraction process takes place at high chloride ion concentration and the stripping process at lower chloride ion concentrations. This approach utilizes the high chloride ion concentration of the leach liquor as the driving force for copper transfer. The latter is, therefore, effectively independent of pH and, in marked contrast to the o-hydroxyaryl oxime extractants, it is unnecessary to exercise careful control over this function to achieve efficient copper transfer. Further, selectivity for copper over a wide range of metals and metalloids is high. Thus, the reagent has immediately obvious potential for improving the overall efficiency and economics of chloride-based hydrometallurgical processes for the treatment of sulphidic copper ores in general.[40] A number of criteria must be met, however, by a successful solvent extractant and these, together with their impact on plant operation, are set out in Table 1.[41]

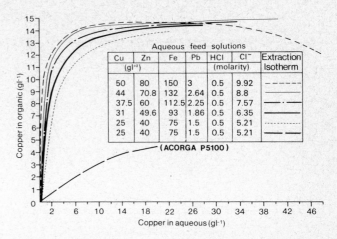

Fig. 5 Extraction isotherms for 26 v/o ACORGA CLX-20 in Escaid 100 and equimolar solution of ACORGA P5100 against aqueous copper chloride solutions

generated with an equimolar solution of Acorga P5100 in Escaid 100 against the least concentrated aqueous solution is included in Fig. 5 to show the very marked difference in the extraction performance of the two types of reagent under these conditions. The shapes of the series of CLX-20 isotherms show it to be a strong extractant and demonstrate the effect of increasing chloride ion concentration in the aqueous feed solution. The shape of the isotherm generated by use of a feed with very high concentrations of copper (50 g/l) and iron (150 g/l) and chloride ion (9.92 M) is unusual in that copper concentration in the organic phase rises to a maximum as 0:A ratios are progressively

Table 1   Relationship between extractant properties and plant design and performance

Extractant property	Effect on plant
Strength	Number of stages; amount of extractant required
electivity	Purity of electrolyte; quality of cathodes
olubility	Volume of organic solvent, therefore size of plant
peed	Stage efficiency or size of mixer
eparation	Size of settler
tability	Loss of extractant, therefore running cost
ynthesis	Consistent reagent quality, consistent plant performance
ystem	Good interfacing with rest of circuit

One objective of the present paper is to describe the properties of CLX-20 in relation to these key factors. Although the chemistry of the extraction and stripping processes of this reagent is different from that of the o-hydroxyaryl oxime extractants, and it is designed for a different application, comparisons have been made, where possible, with the well-established ACORGA P5100, the latter providing a convenient reference point in solvent extraction circuit design and operation.

Strength

The 'strength' of a solvent extractant relates to its ability to transfer metal, in this case copper, and is conveniently described by means of its extraction and strip isotherms. Fig. 5 depicts the extraction isotherms generated at room temperature for a 26 v/o solution of CLX-20 in Escaid 100 against various aqueous solutions selected to simulate those achievable[42] by ferric chloride leaching of complex sulphide concentrates. (Complex sulphide concentrates were employed in preference to chalcopyrite concentrates in this work to demonstrate the performance of the reagent under the most rigorous conditions likely to be encountered in practice.) An extraction isotherm

decreased to a certain point, but then falls at very low 0:A ratios. The explanation for this is that under the latter conditions some iron is extracted into the organic phase as the ion pair $(LH)^+[Fe^{III}Cl_4]^-$, thus depressing the uptake of copper.

This phenomenon is a reflection of the coincidence of several effects under these extreme conditions. The first of these arises from the liganding character of CLX-20—the very property on which its performance as an extractant hinges. A ligand is, by definition, any molecule or ion that can function as the donor partner in the formation of a coordinate bond with a metal ion. Implicit in this definition is the requirement that the ligand have at least one pair of electrons available for donation to the metal ion. The ability to provide a pair of electrons also describes compounds that function as Lewis bases and, not surprisingly, many ligands have a high affinity for protons. Both metal ions and protons are Lewis acids in that they are capable of accepting a pair of electrons and one of the major problems encountered in the development of CLX-20 was the achievement of very high selectivity for copper ions over protons. Despite the success in solving this problem, CLX-20 is a very weak Bronsted base and some protonation of the reagent can occur under extreme conditions (Fig. 6). These are the very conditions encountered in the generation of the CLX-20 extraction isotherm for a 50 g/l copper, 150 g/l iron, 9.92 M

183

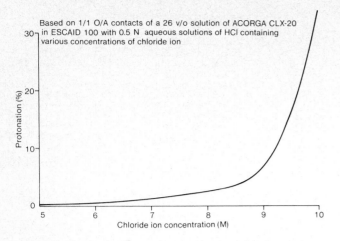

Fig. 6 Protonation of ACORGA CLX-20 as a function of chloride ion concentration

chloride feed where the second effect comes into play—the very high activity of hydrogen ions in concentrated chloride solutions (Fig. 3).[19]

The third effect arises from the fact[43] that equilibrium 3, which lies far to the left in dilute solutions, moves dramatically to the right in solutions that contain high concentrations of chloride ions.

$$Cu^{II} + Fe^{II} \rightleftharpoons Cu^{I} + Fe^{III} \tag{3}$$

The direct consequence of this and the liganding ability of chloride ions is that solutions such as that used in the generation of the particular isotherm contain the anionic chloro complex $[Fe^{III}Cl_4]^-$, some of which is extracted into the organic phase as the ion pair $(LH)^+[Fe^{III}Cl_4]^-$. The relationship between ligand protonation and iron extraction can clearly be seen from a comparison of Figs. 6 and 7.

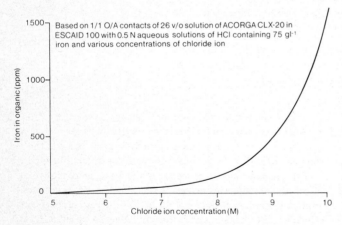

Fig. 7 Extraction of iron by ACORGA CLX-20 in relation to chloride ion concentration

In practical terms, although this imposes some restrictions on the feed solutions with which the reagent can be used, Fig. 6 shows that only solutions in excess of 8–9 M in chloride ion are excluded.

Fig. 8 depicts the strip isotherm generated with a 26 v/o solution of CLX-20 in Escaid 100 loaded to 14.45 g/l with copper and an aqueous strip solution with 25 g/l copper as chloride and 5.5 g/l hydrochloric acid: the concentration of copper in the organic medium can be reduced to very low levels under these conditions.

These results give some indication of the potential of CLX-20 to treat concentrated copper chloride feed solutions, but even more convincing are the results of a laboratory-scale trial in a

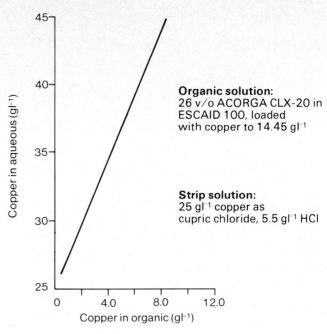

Fig. 8 ACORGA CLX-20 strip isotherm

continuous countercurrent mixer–settler unit. This was carried out with a synthetic leach solution, selected as being representative of the type of solution achievable[42] by ferric chloride leaching of a complex sulphide concentrate, which was 8 M in chloride ion and contained 40 g/l copper, 64 g/l zinc, 120 g/l iron, 2.5 g/l lead and 18 g/l hydrochloric acid. CLX-20 was employed as a 26 v/o solution in Escaid 100 and the synthetic strip solution contained 25 g/l copper as chloride and 5.5 g/l hydrochloric acid. Two stages of extraction and two stages of strip with O:A ratios of 4.25 and 1.61, respectively, gave a raffinate with only 0.4 g/l copper and an 'advance electrolyte' with 40 g/l copper. The relevant extraction and strip isotherms, together with McCabe–Thiele constructions, are shown in Fig. 9. This demonstrates very effectively the ability of CLX-20 to recover copper very efficiently from a concentrated feed solution without the need for pH control or adjustment. Thus, in the circuit outlined in Fig. 4 solvent extraction with use of CLX-20 with a feed solution that contains 40 g/l copper produces a raffinate with only 0.4 g/l copper, which greatly facilitates silver recovery and subsequent zinc solvent extraction.

The extraction of copper from chloride medium by CLX-20 is dependent not only on chloride ion concentration in the aqueous phase but also on temperature. Fig. 10 shows the results of equilibrating 26 v/o CLX-20 in Escaid 100 with equal volumes of aqueous solutions that contain 25 g/l copper as chloride, 3.65 g/l hydrochloric acid and the required amount of calcium chloride to give total chloride ion concentrations of 1.0, 2.5, 5.0, 7.5 and 10 molar, respectively, at various temperatures between 20 and 70°C. From this it can be seen that extraction efficiency decreases with temperature over the whole range of chloride ion concentrations and this is reflected in the extraction isotherms shown in Fig. 11. These were generated over the range 20–60°C with a 26 v/o solution of CLX-20 and an aqueous solution that was 5.21 M in chloride ion and contained 25 g/l copper and clearly show the adverse effect of increased temperature. The stripping process, however, improves with increasing temperature: this is well illustrated by the strip isotherms depicted in Fig.12, which were generated over the range 10–40°C with a 26 v/o solution solution of CLX-20 loaded to 13.79 g/l with copper and a strip solution with 25 g/l copper as chloride and 5.5 g/l hydrochloric acid.

Maximum efficiency in terms of copper recovery would be achieved by carrying out the extraction process at low

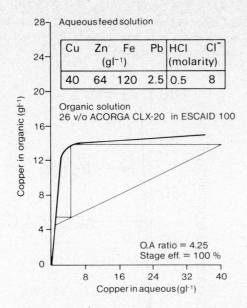

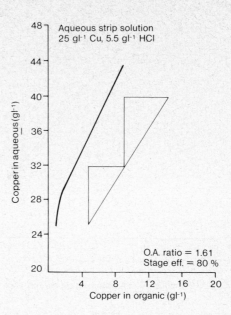

Fig. 9   ACORGA CLX-20 versus 40 g/l copper–8M chloride feed and 25 g/l copper strip solution: operating conditions

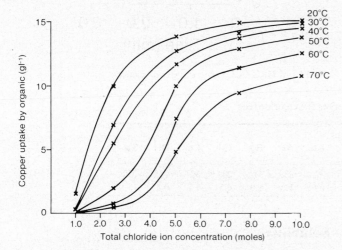

Fig. 10   Effect of temperature and chloride ion concentration on extraction of copper by ACORGA CLX-20

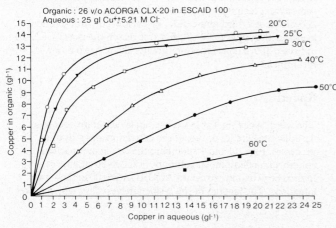

Fig. 11   Effect of temperature on extraction isotherms of ACORGA CLX-20

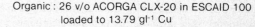

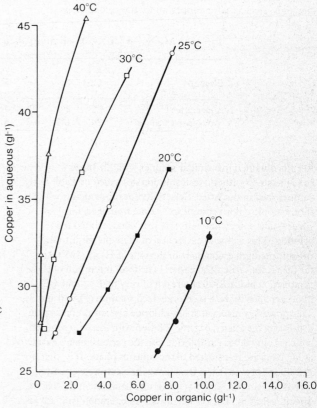

Fig. 12   Effect of temperature on strip isotherms of ACORGA CLX-20

temperature and the strip process at an elevated temperature. This may not, however, always be convenient and McCabe–Thiele data have been computed by use of the sets of isotherms shown in Figs. 11 and 12 to determine the relationship between copper recovery and temperature when the latter is the same in both operations. Fig. 13 indicates that although the optimum operating temperature is 29°C (96.5% copper recovery)

for these particular feed, organic and strip solutions, copper recovery exceeds 94% over the range 20–36°C.

Selectivity

In the context of chloride leach solutions derived from complex sulphide concentrates high selectivity over a wide range of metals and metalloids is essential since such solutions contain many elements the presence of which in a copper electrolyte is

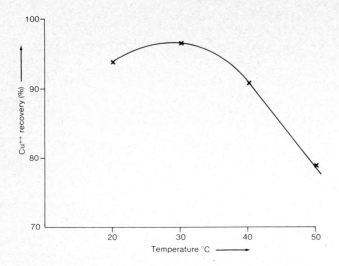

Fig. 13 ACORGA CLX-20 : effect of temperature on copper recovery

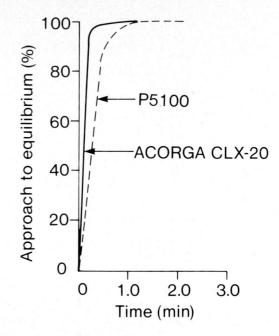

Fig. 14 ACORGA CLX-20 : extraction kinetics

O:A ratio (32.1) are detailed in Table 3. The versatility of CLX-20 with regard to the range of feed solutions with which it can be employed is readily apparent.

highly undesirable. The performance of CLX-20 in this respect is illustrated by the results quoted in Table 2. These were generated by use of CLX-20 to treat the synthetic leach solution described in Table 2 under continuous conditions in a laboratory-scale mixer–settler unit that incorporated an electrowinning cell. They are therefore representative of the system at equilibrium and serve very effectively to demonstrate the high selectivity for copper under these conditions.

Table 2   ACORGA CLX-20: selectivity data versus 5 M chloride feed

Element	g/l			ppm							
	Cu	Fe	Zn	Pb	Ag	As	Hg	Cd	Co	Bi	Sb
Aqueous feed	25	69	30	164	32	239	37	23	30	135	159
'Advance electrolyte'	39	0.5	0.2	1.5	0.6	1.2	1.0	0.5	1.1	0.3	13

Results obtained in a similar manner with the more concentrated synthetic feed solution described in Table 3 are summarized in the latter. Selectivity for those metals which form anionic chloro complexes—zinc, iron, lead and silver—falls somewhat with this very concentrated feed solution. This is due to extraction of these metals into the organic medium as ion pairs of the type $(LH)^+_{(m-n)}[M^nCl_m]^{(m-n)-}$ for the reasons discussed earlier. The most important of these is protonation of CLX-20 as a result of very high activity of hydrogen ions in the 8 M chloride feed solution (Figs. 6 and 3). This process is reversed at low chloride concentration and on contacting the loaded organic solution with the strip solution, which is only 0.94 M in chloride ion, the various metals extracted as ion pairs are transferred to the aqueous phase. It is, therefore, possible to prevent their transfer to the electrolyte circuit by means of a simple, single-stage scrub operation on the loaded organic solution. The results of such an operation with advance electrolyte to scrub the loaded organic solution at a very high

Solubility

No solubility problems were encountered in extended continuous operations under the conditions described earlier and Escaid 100 solutions of CLX-20 loaded with copper to 14.5 g/l showed no precipitation on prolonged storage at 0°C. Slow deposition of a third phase did, however, occur with solutions loaded with copper to 20 g/l. For this reason the use of CLX-20 in Escaid 100 at concentrations greater than 26 v/o is not recommended.

Speed

The word 'speed' in Table 1 is used in an alliterative sense to describe the kinetics or rate of the extraction and stripping processes. Figs. 14 and 15 compare the rate of approach to equilibrium of equimolar solutions of CLX-20 and the o-hydroxyaryl oxime extractant ACORGA P5100 in these two situations. The kinetics of the former are very fast, which makes

Table 3   ACORGA CLX-20: selectivity data versus 8 M chloride feed with and without scrubbing of loaded organic phase

Element	g/l				ppm						
	Cu	Fe	Zn	Pb	Ag	As	Hg	Cd	Co	Bi	Sb
Aqueous feed	40	120	64	2.4	40	480	50	50	40	40	240
'Advance electrolyte' (no scrub)	40	0.95	0.5	9 ppm	0.4	13	4	0.3	0.2	1.0	55
'Advance electrolyte' (with scrub)	40	0.06	0.03	0.25 ppm	0.23	1.0	0.3	<0.1	<0.2	<0.5	9.5

it difficult to generate meaningful results under the customary test conditions employed to measure the kinetics of the *o*-hydroxyaryl oxime reagent. The results displayed in Figs. 14 and 15 were obtained under strictly comparable conditions with an unbaffled cylindrical reaction vessel and a stirrer speed such that stirring was just sufficient to achieve mixing of the aqueous and

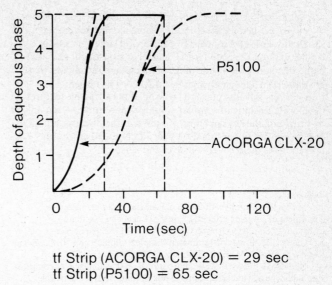

tf Strip (ACORGA CLX-20) = 29 sec
tf Strip (P5100) = 65 sec

Fig. 17   ACORGA CLX-20 : phase-disengagement properties, strip

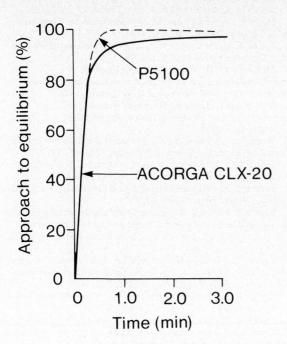

Fig. 15   ACORGA CLX-20 : strip kinetics

organic phases. These data serve to illustrate the very fast kinetics of CLX-20.

Separation

The term 'separation' is also used in an alliterative way in Table 1 and describes the rate at which the organic and aqueous phases disengage after they have been contacted in the extraction and stripping operations. Figs. 16 and 17, respectively, illustrate the rates of phase disengagement of CLX-20 and ACORGA P5100 in these two situations. The results were obtained under stricly comparable conditions with equimolar solutions of the two reagents in Escaid 100 with the 25 g/l copper feed and strip solutions described earlier. They clearly demonstrate the rapid phase-disengagement properties of CLX-20 and its superiority over ACORGA P5100 in this particular system. It should be noted, however, that the results obtained with the latter are

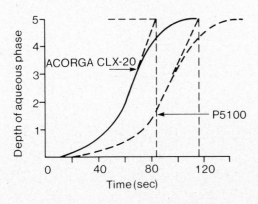

tf Ext (ACORGA CLX-20) = 84 sec
tf Ext (P5100) = 116 sec

Fig. 16   ACORGA CLX-20 : phase-disengagement properties, extraction

inferior to those achieved with this reagent in aqueous sulphate medium—the system for which it was designed.

Stability

Accelerated degradation tests on CLX-20 in which an Escaid 100 solution of the reagent was stirred continuously with an aqueous solution containing 50 g/l copper, 150 g/l iron, 35 g/l zinc and 38 g/l hydrochloric acid at 50°C showed it to be remarkably stable under these severe conditions. After 40 days more than 98% of the reagent remained unchanged and phase-disengagement properties were unimpaired.

System

The term 'system' relates to the overall hydrometallurgical process from concentrate to metal, embracing leaching, solvent extraction electrowinning and leachant regeneration stages, all of which must be mutually compatible.

$$\text{(1) } CuFeS_2 + 3FeCl_3 \rightarrow CuCl + 4FeCl_2 + 2S \qquad (4)$$

$$\text{(2) } CuFeS_2 + 4FeCl_3 \rightarrow CuCl_2 + 5FeCl_2 + 2S \qquad (5)$$

Most of the chloride-based hydrometallurgical processes that have been devised for the treatment of copper-containing sulphidic concentrates operate in a regime designed to produce a leach solution with cuprous (equation 4) rather than cupric chloride. This provides a feed that is unsuitable for CLX-20, but a relatively minor modification to the stoichiometry of the leaching operation (equation 5) permits the generation of the appropriate cupric feed. This has been proved[42] with a complex sulphide concentrate and the derived leach solution has been used to demonstrate[40] the ability of CLX-20 to produce an electrolyte suitable for the direct electrowinning of high-purity copper.

Conclusions

The results presented here describe the properties of the novel copper extractant CLX-20 in relation to the well-established criteria (Table 1) against which the performance of a solvent extractant is judged and the impact of these on the chloride-based hydrometallurgical treatment of complex sulphide concentrates. So far as the vital requirements common to *all* types of solvent extractant are concerned—solubility, speed, separation, stability and synthesis—the properties of the reagent are excellent. Of the remaining 'S's, strength and selectivity relate directly to the system or specific application for which the reagent is designed. The requirements regarding strength and selectivity defined by the chloride system are that the extractant should be capable of efficiently transferring large amounts of copper without the need for pH control or adjustment and with high selectivity over a wide range of metals and metalloids: these are more than adequately met by CLX-20. The reagent thus permits full advantage to be taken of the attractive features of chloride leaching of complex sulphide concentrates—not only by providing the key enabling step towards the direct production of high-purity copper but also by facilitating such other vital operations as the recovery of silver and zinc.

References

1. Shank J. R. Complex minerals in Canada. Paper presented to Treatment of complex minerals: Canada/European Economic Community Seminar, Ottawa, October 12–14, 1982. Paper A1.
2. Cases J. M. Finely disseminated complex sulphide ores. In *Complex sulphide ores* Jones M. J. ed. (London: IMM, 1980), 234–47.
3. Barbery G. Fletcher A. W. and Sirois L. L. Exploitation of complex sulphide deposits: a review of processing options from ore to metals. Reference 2, 135–50.
4. Fontanillo P. Motta F. and Espeso G. Sulphide ores in Spain. Reference 1, paper C1.
5. D'Oliveira Sampaio A. A. R and D structure and programmes for complex minerals in Portugal. Reference 1, paper D1.
6. Barbery G. Complex sulphide ore processing: recent developments in France. Reference 1, paper I1.
7. Boe G. H. Krogh S. and Ydstie B. Notes on the treatment of complex sulphide ores. Paper presented to 111th AIME annual meeting, Dallas, 1982.
8. Nogueira E. D. *et al.* The Comprex process: non-ferrous metal production from complex pyrite concentrates. Reference 2, 227–33; Nogueira E. D. The Comprex process for treating complex sulphide ores. Reference 1, paper M1.
9. Strauss G. K. and Gray K. G. Complex pyritic ores of the Iberian Peninsula and their beneficiation, with special reference to Tharsis Company mines, Spain. Reference 2, 79–87.
10. Andersen E. *et al.* Production of base metals from complex sulphide concentrates by the ferric chloride route in a small, continuous pilot plant. Reference 2, 186–92.
11. Campbell M. C. and Ritcey G. M. Applications of chloride metallurgy to base-metal sulphide and uranium ores at CANMET. In *Extraction metallurgy '81* (London: IMM, 1981), 76–90.
12. Ritcey G. M. Lucas B. H. and Price K. T. Extraction of copper and zinc from chloride leach liquors resulting from chlorination roast–leach of fine-grained sulphides. In *ISEC '80: proceedings international solvent extraction conference Liège, September 1980*, vol. 3, session 18: base metals, pap. 80-71, 10 p.
13. Ritcey G. M. Lucas B. H. and Price K. T. Evaluation and selection of extractants for the separation of copper and zinc from chloride leach liquor. *Hydrometall.*, **8**, 1982, 197–222.
14. Everett P. K. The Dextec copper process. Reference 11, 149–56.
15. Demarthe J. M. Gandon L. and Georgeaux A. A new hydrometallurgical process for copper. In *Extractive metallurgy of copper* Yannopoulos J. C. and Agarwal J. C. eds (New York: AIME, 1976), vol. 2, 825–48.
16. Demarthe J. M. and Georgeaux A. Hydrometallurgical treatment of complex sulphides. In *Complex metallurgy '78* Jones M. J. ed. (London: IMM, 1978), 113–20.
17. Miöen T. Verfahren zur Verarbeitung komplexer Sulfidkonzentrate. *Erzmetall*, **36**, May 1983, 224–6.
18. Fern J. H. and Shaw R. W. Copper separation and recovery at the B.H.A.S. lead smelter, Port Pirie, South Australia. Paper presented to Joint AIMM–MMIJ meeting, Sandi City, September 1983.
19. Peters E. Applications of chloride hydrometallurgy to treatment of sulphide minerals. In *Chloride hydrometallurgy: proceedings symposium, Brussels, September 1977* (Brussels: Benelux Métallurgie, 1977), 1–36.
20. McClean D. C. Chloride leaching of copper concentrates: practical operational aspects. Paper presented to 111th AIME annual meeting, Dallas, 1982.
21. Price R. Quan P. M. and Townson B. Novel solvent extractants for copper from chloride media: their application in the processing of complex base metal concentrates. Reference 1, paper Q1.
22. Haver F. P. and Wong M. M. Recovering elemental sulfur from nonferrous minerals: ferric chloride leaching of chalcopyrite concentrate. *Rep. Invest. U.S. Bur. Mines* 7474, 1971, 20 p.
23. Haver F. P. and Wong M. M. Recovery of copper, iron and sulfur from chalcopyrite concentrate using a ferric chloride leach. *J. Metals, N. Y.*, **23**, Feb. 1971, 25–9.
24. Haver F. P. Baker R. D. and Wong M. M. Improvements in ferric chloride leaching of chalcopyrite concentrate. *Rep. Invest. U.S. Bur. Mines* 8007, 1975, 16 p.
25. Atwood G. E. and Curtis C. H. U.S. Patent 3 787 944, 1974.
26. Atwood G. E. and Curtis C. H. U.S. Patent 3 879 272, 1975.
27. Schweitzer F. W. and Livingston R. Duval's CLEAR hydrometallurgical process. Paper presented to 111th AIME annual meeting, Dallas, 1982.
28. Goens D. A. and Kruesi P. R. U.S. Patent 3 972 711, 1976.
29. Hazen W. C. for Cyprus Metallurgical Processes Corporation, U.S.A. Canadian Patent 1 012 089, 1977.
30. Hazen W. C. for Cyprus Metallurgical Processes Corporation, U.S.A. Canadian Patent 1 028 651, 1978.
31. McNamara J. H. Ahrens W. A. and Franek J. G. A hydrometallurgical process for the extraction of copper. Paper presented to 1978 AIME annual meeting, Denver, 1978.
32. McNamara J. H. Ahrens W. A. and Franek J. G. A hydrometallurgical process for the extraction of copper. *CIM Bull.*, **73**, March 1980, 201–4.
33. Demarthe J. M. Sonntag A. and Georgeaux A. for Société Minière et Métallurgique de Pennaroya. U.S. Patent 4 016 056, 1977.
34. Demarthe J. M. Sonntag A. and Georgeaux A. for Société Minière et Métallurgique de Pennaroya. U.S. Patent 4 023 964, 1977.
35. Everett P. K. for Dextec Metallurgical Proprietary, Ltd., Sydney, Australia. German Patent 2 605 887, 1976.
36. Everett P. K. Single step conversion of chalcopyrite to copper, iron oxide and elemental sulphur. Paper presented to Extractive metallurgy symposium, University of New South Wales, November 8, 1977.
37. Cathro K. J. Recovery of copper from chalcopyrite concentrate by means of sulphur activation, cupric chloride leach, and electrolysis. *Proc. Australas. Inst. Min. Metall.* no. 252, Dec. 1974, 1–11.
38. Cathro K. J. Recovery of copper from chalcopyrite by means of a cupric chloride leach. Reference 15, vol. 2, 776–92.
39. Dalton R. F. Price R. and Quan P. M. Novel solvent extractants for chloride leach systems. Paper presented to ISEC '83: international solvent extraction conference, Denver, August 1983.
40. Danielssen T. *et al.* Extraction of cupric chloride from iron chloride leach liquors. As reference 39.
41. Price R. and Tumilty J. A. An interpretation of some aspects of solvent extraction as related to the extraction of copper using o-hydroxyaryloximes. In *Hydrometallurgy* Davies G. A. and Scuffham J. B. eds (London: Institution of Chemical Engineers, 1975), 18.1–8. (*Symp. Series* 42)
42. Elkem A/S. Private communication to the authors.
43. Muir D. M. *et al.* Removal of iron and formation of copper(I) from solutions containing iron(II) and copper(II) by addition of chloride ion or acetonitrile. *Hydrometall.*, **9**, 1983, 257–75.

Correlation of collecting power of functionalized organic molecules and their molecular structure by quantitative chemical and statistical methods of calculation

R. Scordamaglia, L. Barino, F. M. Carlini, G. Bornengo and G. Bottaccio

Synopsis

The action of ethyl xanthate in the flotation of sulphides and that of N-octyl-anthranilate in the flotation of cerussite, pretreated with sodium sulphide and after oxidation in neutral solutions, have been compared. A unique mechanism of reaction for collector molecules with the mineral surface was assumed in both cases. The most probable conformations, in terms of Boltzmann distribution, for the two compounds were selected by our computation procedure CSD (Conformations Statistical Distribution).

The two molecules, separately, were put in contact with an oxidized surface (100) of galena, the electrostatic energy interactions between molecule and surface being calculated by the point-charge approximation for a large number of relative positions.

Behavioural differences between the two molecules in regard to surface interaction energy, preferred relative surface positions and features of their polar groups are reported.

The action of thiol-type collectors on sulphide minerals has long been investigated, but controversy on the subject continues. Of considerable importance is the nature of chemical products at the interface between crystal surface and solution—the compounds that can render the surface hydrophobic to bring about the flotation process.

For the flotation of galena with xanthates as collectors many hypotheses have been put forward—for example, the formation of lead ethyl xanthate (which precipitates on the surface), of ethyl dixanthogen[1] (physisorbed film), of some mixture of the two species, of ethyl xanthic acid, of elemental sulphur, dixanthate, etc.

The role of oxygen in the process has also been pointed out. The common conclusion[2-5] is that oxygen is a necessary reagent for sulphides: for a few minerals (pyrite, pyrrhotite and molybdenite) it appears to act electrochemically as a cathodic reactant, but it does not play the same role in all thiol collector–sulphide interactions. Oxygen is mostly considered to enable chemisorption of collector on sulphide surfaces to proceed far enough to allow floatability by alteration of the chemical nature of the sulphide surface to make metal–thiolate formation easier.

We have carried out a quantitative study of thiol collector–sulphide interactions on the assumption that the outermost S^{2-}, S_2^{2-}, SH^-, etc., ions of the lattice are oxidized to S^0[6] or generically to S_xO_y ions, which may be displaced by thiol collector anions. This oxidation mechanism exposes metal atoms or cations at the surface and permits thiolate formation; it also reduces the degree of hydration of surface and thereby facilitates collector adsorption.

ESCA spectra[6] confirmed that the first step is the oxidation of Pb to PbO and S^{2-} to S, in neutral or acid solution, followed by the principal oxidation to $PbSO_4$. We can conclude that, at the beginning of the oxidation process, some poorly oxidized surface zones characterized by the properties noted in our assumed interaction mechanism are formed that are, partly or wholly, responsible for flotation.

Assumed interaction mechanisms in sulphide flotation process

It would be realistic to assume that, after grinding, minerals show as their external faces those which are typical of the crystals together with the cleaved faces. Statistical distributions of face types indicates, however, that we can choose as a model of the surface one face of the elementary cell. We also assume that the oxidation process can easily reach the sulphur ions 'exposed' on the surface to yield some oxidized, generally hydrophobic, product. In Table 1 sulphides are divided into two classes: (A) contains all those with sulphur anions (S^{2-}, SH^-, S_2^{2-}, etc.) lying on the external faces and (B) contains those with sulphur anions not exposed or inside the elementary cell as well as those sulphides the atomic positions of which in the cell are not well defined by X-ray investigation or are of dubious stoichiometry.[7,8]

Table 1 Subdivision of sulphides most widely used in flotation: class (A), sulphur ions 'exposed' on surfaces of crystals, and class (B), sulphur ions 'unexposed'

(A)	(B)
Pyrrhotite	Wurtzite
Marcasite	Blende
Arsenopyrite	Niccolite
Pyrite	Bismuthinite
Cinnabar	Stibnite
Molybdenite	Tetrahedrite
Covelline	
Chalcocite	
Bornite	
Acanthite	
Galena	
Chalcopyrite	
Realgar	

Sulphides that are floatable under normal operating conditions belong to the first class, whereas those which are unfloatable, such as blende, or scarcely floatable belong to the second. It therefore appears to be necessary, for blende flotation, to remove from the ground crystals surface one layer of Zn atoms to expose the sulphur anions to oxidation: this displacement probably occurs when ZnS is treated with $CuSO_4$. We have considered as a class of sulphide collectors the alkyl xanthates. It is well known that they exist predominantly as anions in the neutral and basic pH ranges of greatest practical interest in the form

$$R-O-C{\overset{\displaystyle S}{\underset{\displaystyle S^{(-)}}{}}} \quad \text{or} \quad R-O-C{\overset{\displaystyle S}{\underset{\displaystyle S^{(-)}}{}}}$$

They are, in addition, relatively insoluble in water, but soluble in certain organic solvents, which reveals their hydrophobic nature.

It is assumed that the hydrophobic products of the oxidation reaction with oxygen are adsorbed on the mineral surface and occupy the positions that were previously occupied by the sulphur anions. The atomic arrangement of surface is therefore preserved, but its electrical behaviour is little changed. In our model we accept the hypothesis of the production and deposition of elemental sulphur and consider a surface that is unbalanced with respect to positive and negative charges. Consequently, in line with Pauling's principle of ion charge saturation in crystals,[9] there is a decrease for each cation of the surrounding negative ions and an increase in the fractional positive charge. Thus, on an unoxidized galena surface a positive charge of 0.333 is attributed to a Pb cation in the centre of the 100 face and 1.0 to Pb on the vertices and edges. An increase in oxidation gives rise to charge increases to 0.666 and 1.26, respectively, for the two Pb types.

Theoretical model for quantification of thiol collector–sulphide interactions

The action of xanthates on sulphides was compared with that of N-alkyl derivatives of anthranilic acid (I)

$$R_1 = CH_3, H$$
$$R_2 = C_2H_4OR, CH_3, C_2H_5, \text{etc.(I)}$$
$$X = K, Na$$

in the selective flotation of cerussite and smithsonite minerals (the two flotation processes are based on the same reaction mechanism). Carbonates are pretreated with sodium sulphide and afterwards oxidized with oxygen, such treatment leading, first, to the formation of PbS and ZnS films and the formation of elemental sulphur and a variety of lead hydrates and oxides on the surface, as detected by the ESCA technique.[6,10]

One of the most important hydrophobic species on the surface seems to be elemental sulphur and it must be stressed that compounds such as that shown in (I) exhibit a lower flotation power than that of xanthates.

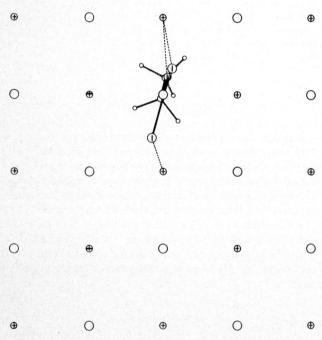

Fig. 1 Lowest energy perpendicular position of (II) to galena surface (energy ≈961 kJ/mole; minus signs placed on sulphur and oxygen atoms of (II))

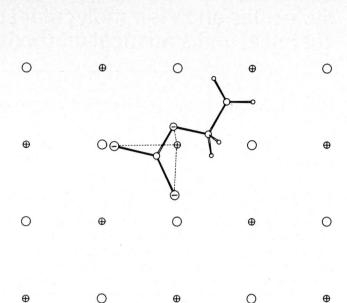

Fig. 2 Lowest energy parallel position of (II) to galena surface (energy ≈920 kJ/mole)

The model of the oxidized surface has been taken as an expansion of the 100 face of galena, corresponding to four elementary cell faces, S^{2-} anions being replaced by uncharged S^0 atoms (in Figs. 1–5 lead atoms are characterized by the plus signs).

The whole conformational surfaces of ethyl xanthate (II) and N-octyl-anthranilate (III) were studied separately by the CSD computational procedure.[11] Each conformation was generated by

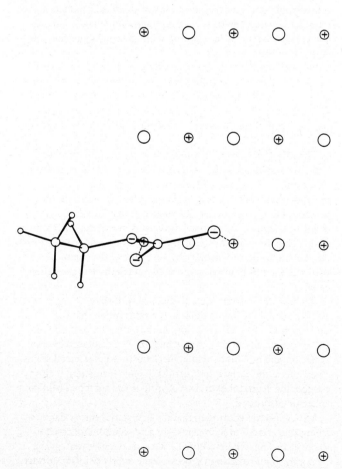

Fig. 3 Another perspective view of (II) in same position as in Fig. 1

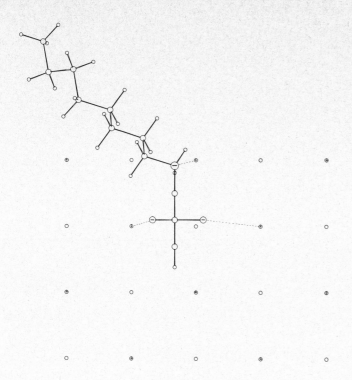

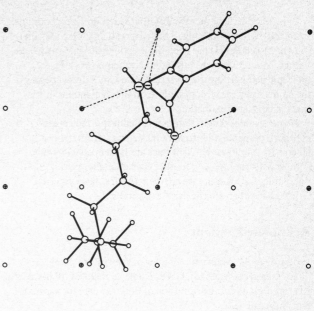

Fig. 5 Lowest energy parallel position of (III) to galena surface (energy ≈752 kJ/mole)

Fig. 4 Lowest energy perpendicular position of (III) to galena surface (energy ≈418 kJ/mole; minus signs placed on oxygen and nitrogen atoms of (III)*)

rotation around all the free single bonds in steps of 30°, its energy being calculated by summation of the non-bonded interactions between atoms according to Lennard–Jones formalism:

$$e_i = \sum_j \sum_k - \frac{A_{jk}}{r_{jk}^6} + \frac{B_{jk}}{rjk^{12}}$$

where i refers to a generic conformation, j refers to a j-type atom, which interacts with a k-type atom. Also, a coulombic interaction term was computed for non-bonded atoms pairs:

$$u_i = \sum_j \sum_k \frac{q_i q_k}{r_{jk}}$$

Hence, the total energy for each conformation is

$$E_i = e_i + u_i$$

The net atomic charges[9] were calculated with the semi-empirical program CNDO/2[12] and A_{jk} and B_{jk} values used were those assumed by Hopfinger.[13] From the Bolzmann distributions[11] of conformations at a temperature of 25°C the most probable *in vacuo* of (II) and (III), respectively, were selected. Since the environment around the crystal surface was taken as being highly hydrophobic it seems sensible to assume such conformations to be those which are most representative in regard to simulation of the reaction at the surfaces. Computational methods[14] were developed that permitted the calculation of the total coulombic energy between the molecule under examination and the surface for a number of relative positions obtained by moving the molecule along the perpendiculars to the surface through the atoms on the crystal. In each position the molecule is free to rotate rigidly around a fixed internal point according to Euler's angles with a pre-

* In this position ring plane forms an angle of 90° with mineral surface.

determined rotation step. Thus, different parts of a molecule can face the crystal surface. We have limited the surface–molecule approach distance to a minimum value given by the sum of the ionic radii of both collector and crystal species. The energy values of about 5000 positions were calculated for each case.

Results and conclusions

Global energies of interaction with the crystal surface are, on average, greater for (II) than for (III), ≈ 961 kJ/mole being the maximum value for xanthate interaction and ≈752 kJ/mole that for anthranilate. The most important energy contributions come from the interactions of Pb cations with S groups (≈125 kJ/mole) and O(≈84 kJ/mole) for (II) and N(≈84 kJ/mole) for (III). In both cases the statistical distribution of the low-energy positions shows that the above groups mostly interact with only one cation (60%) rather than with two separate cations (40%). As expected, the same distribution gives a great statistical weight to those low-energy positions in which the collector molecule interacts with cations on the edges and vertices of the mineral face because of increased local charge due to unsaturation of metal valence change. This is, however, of no significance in regard to microcrystals with dimensions that are larger than those of our model.

There is a marked difference between the two cases when the position of the molecules is compared with respect to the surface, i.e. orientation of the molecules with respect to the mineral surface in low-energy situations. These energies depend on molecule–surface distance, but for each distance chosen they depend on the angle formed by the direction of the molecule elongation with respect to the direction surface. In the distribution of (II) about 80% of low-energy situations give surface–molecule angles within a range 45–90° and only in 20% of cases is the molecule approximately parallel to the surface, but for (III) only 1% of situations give a maximum angular value of 60°, the others showing angles in the range 0–45°. Thus, 'polar group' features (steric hindrances and charge distribution) appear to be responsible both for the preferred attachment position and the 'hydrophobic chain' directionality.

Figs. 1 and 2 show the two different situations (perpendicular and parallel) for (II); in Fig. 3 the perpendicular case is again shown. Molecule (II) has been drawn above the galena surface.

Figs. 4 and 5 show the analogous situations for (III), the molecule being below the surface. Dotted lines drawn between the atoms show the strongest electrostatic interactions in the point-charge approximation.

If one assumes that in flotation the collector molecules approach perpendicular to mineral surfaces, from the results given here it follows that xanthates are better collectors than anthranilates, as has been found experimentally, because the perpendicular positions are energetically less favourable for anthranilates than are the parallel positions.

Acknowledgement

Professor A. M. Marabini, director of the Istituto per il Trattamento dei Minerali, CNR, Rome, is thanked for her useful suggestions and for the provision of flotation data for xanthates and anthranilates.

References
1. Nixon J. C. Discussion of (Cook M. A. and Wadsworth M. E. Hydrolytic and ion pair adsorption processes in flotation, ion exchange and corrosion. In *Proceedings second international congress of surface activity* (London: Butterworths, 1957), vol. 3, 228–42.) 369–70.
2. Sutherland K. L. and Wark I. W. *Principles of flotation* (Melbourne: Australasian Institute of Mining and Metallurgy, 1955), 489 p.
3. Gaudin A. M. *Flotation, 2nd edn* (New York: McGraw-Hill, 1957), 573 p.
4. Taggart A. F. Taylor T. C. and Knoll A. F. Chemical reactions in flotation. *Trans. Am. Inst. Min. Engrs*, **87**, 1930, 217–60.
5. Plaksin I. N. Interaction of minerals with gases and reagents in flotation. *Trans. Am. Inst. Min. Engrs*, **214**, 1959, 319–24.
6. Manocha A. S. and Park R. L. Flotation related studies on PbS surfaces. *Appl. Surface Sci.*, **1**, 1977, 129–41.
7. Gardner J. R. and Woods R. The use of a particulate bed electrode for the electrochemical investigation of metal and sulphide flotation. *Aust. J. Chem.*, **26**, 1973, 1635–44.
8. Bragg W. L. and Claringbull G. F. *Crystal structures of minerals* (London: Bell, 1965), 409 p.
9. Pauling L. The principles determining the structure of complex ionic crystals. *J. Am. chem. Soc.*, **51**, 1929, 1010–26.
10. Garbassi F. and Marabini A. M. Unpublished data.
11. Scordamaglia R. and Barino L. Paper in preparation.
12. Pople J. A. and Beveridge D. L. *Approximate molecular orbital theory* (New York: McGraw-Hill, 1970), 224 p.
13. Hopfinger A. J. *Conformational properties of macromolecules* (New York: Academic Press, 1973), 47–8.
14. Barino L. Internal report.

New flotation reagents—frothers

V. A. Shcherbakov and S. M. Gurvich

Synopsis
Together with methylisobutylcarbinol (MIBC), ethers of polyalkylene glycols and other widely used reagents, semi-products and conditioned by-products from large-tonnage chemical plants with fairly high flotation properties and of lower cost have also been used in the U.S.S.R. Oxal T-80 frother, which is a semi-product of the synthesis isoprene, contains dioxane, pyrane alcohols, diols and triols, as well as their ethers of methanol and trimethylcarbinol. The Oxal T-81 frother has a similar composition to that of Oxal T-80, but differs in its larger average molecular mass.

Tests at non-ferrous metal concentrators and in other industries have confirmed the effectiveness of this reagent in the flotation of a wide variety of non-ferrous metal ores and native sulphur, MIBC, cyclohexanole and other reagents being preferred only for the treatment of, for example, complex Cu–Ni and Cu–Pb–Zn ores.

Production technology has recently been developed and tests on saturated and unsaturated alcohols produced by the oxy-synthesis method on petroleum chemical raw material have been carried out. Synthesized hexenoles and hexanoles are not inferior to MIBC.

In the production of propylene oxide a by-product that contains methylphenylcarbinol and acetophenone is obtained that is water-soluble and shows good organoleptic properties.

The reagents have shown high selective action in tests on Cu–Ni and polymetallic ores.

Such reagents as methylisobutylcarbinol, polypropylene glycol ethers and triethoxybutane are widely used as frothers worldwide for the flotation of non-ferrous metal ores and other minerals. To reduce reagent costs and increase the use of wastes from the chemical industry in the U.S.S.R. middlings and by-products from several chemical plants have been used as frothers directly or after appropriate conditioning.

The Oxal T-80 reagent, a by-product of dimethyldioxane, is obtained by the condensation of isobutylene and formaldehyde in the presence of an oxalic acid. The oxal is a multicomponent product of constant composition; it contains dioxane and pyrane alcohols, diols and triols of the fatty acid series, their esters and methanols and trimethylcarbinol and oxalic acid ethers.

Oxal is a transparent, non-separating oily liquid, aromatic in odour and yellow to brown in colour (density at 20°C, 1.05–1.08 g/cm³; boiling point, 153°C; auto-ignition temperature, 272°C; flash point, 90°C; ester number, 1.5–4.0 mg KOH/g; fraction of total mass of hydroxyl groups, 23–36%; fraction of total mass of dimethyldioxane, <1.0%; and water solubility, ~2%).

Oxal T-80 is used for flotation of non-ferrous metal ores, coal and other types of raw mineral, and is currently used for the beneficiation of some 90% of Soviet non-ferrous metal ores.

Hexenol—a product of the liquid-phase oxidation of hexenes—is a transparent liquid of weak odour and limited water solubility; it is a mixture of non-saturated hexyl alcohols and 20% α-oxides of methylpentenes. The initial propylene is a by-product of many petroleum chemical processes. The technology of hexanol synthesis includes propylene dimerization and oxidation of the dimer. The process of reagent creation is simplified by the ready availability of stock-produced dimers.

Propylene dimer oxidation is carried out in air at atmospheric pressure and a temperature of 60–70°C and requires the use of no special equipment.

A mixture of propylene dimers is subjected to liquid-phase oxidation

$$\text{2-Methylpentene-1} \quad \text{CH}_2\text{=C-CH}_2\text{-CH}_2\text{-CH}_3 \qquad \text{(I)}$$
$$|$$
$$\text{CH}_3$$

$$\text{2-Methylpentene-2} \quad \text{CH}_3\text{-C=CH-CH}_2\text{-CH}_3 \qquad \text{(II)}$$
$$|$$
$$\text{CH}_3$$

or individual hexenes (methylpentenes).

On oxidation the following are produced:

$$\text{2-Methylpentene-1-ol-3} \quad \text{CH}_2\text{=C-CH-CH}_2\text{-CH}_3 \qquad \text{(III)}$$
$$| \quad |$$
$$\text{CH}_3 \ \text{OH}$$

$$\text{2-Methylpentene-2-ol-1} \quad \text{CH}_2\text{-C=CH-CH}_2\text{-CH}_3 \qquad \text{(IV)}$$
$$| \quad |$$
$$\text{OH} \ \text{CH}_3$$

as well as small quantities of the α-oxides of methylpentenes.

Table 1   Hexenol composition

Compound	Content, % by mass
2-Methylpentene-1-ol-3	49.0
2-Methylpentene-2-ol-4	7.5
2-Methylpentene-2-ol-1	8.6
Oxides of methylpentene isomers	22.3
Mesityl oxide	10.5
	1.5
Acetone	0.6

Hexenol has good foaming properties and yields a stable water emulsion; it has a low temperature of solidification, possesses no irritating odour and is stable on storage.

In propylene oxide and styrene production the propylene oxide and methylphenylcarbinol fraction are separated in the propylene epoxidation. The fraction consists of methylphenylcarbinol and acetophenone and is used in the production of styrene. The methylphenylcarbinol fraction, termed 'epoxol', is a transparent liquid with a pleasantly sharp odour. It has limited water-solubility, the solidification temperature is 20.3°C, the boiling point is about 200°C and density is 1.013 g/cm³. The fraction of the total mass of methylphenylcarbinol is not less than 70%, that of the total mass of acetophenone is not greater than 30% and that of the total mass of ethylbenzene is not greater than 1%.

Reagent PF is a product of piperylene condensation with a formaldehyde. Piperylene ($\text{CH}_3\text{-CH=CH-CH=CH}_2$) is a by-product of isoprene production and is formed in large quantities. The condensation reaction proceeds with the formation of a mixture of esters, polyols, dioxalanes and others. It is a light yellow liquid with a pleasant odour and is moderately water-soluble.

The above-mentioned reagents were tested on the flotation of various types of ores under laboratory and commercial conditions.

Table 2 Composition of oxal samples

| Sample | Content, % | |
	Dioxane alcohols	Heavy residue
A	31.8	50.6
B	42.6	30.1
C	46.1	23.2

Tests with oxal of variable composition (Table 2) on a copper–molybdenum ore showed that foaming is mainly

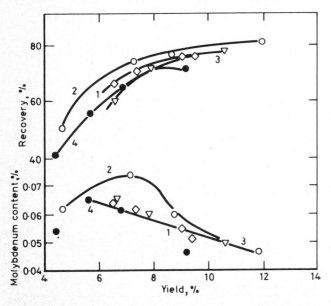

Fig. 1 Relationship between concentrate yield, molybdenum content and recovery in flotation of copper–molybdenum ore: 1, MIBC; 2, Oxal-A; 3, Oxal-B; 4, Oxal-C

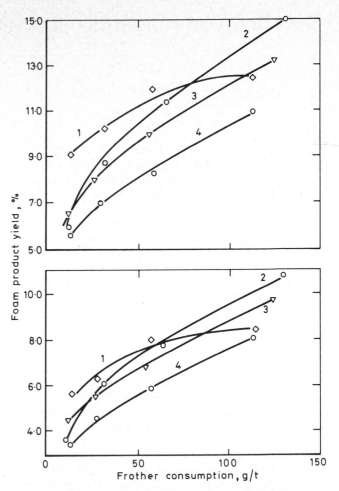

Fig. 2 Variation in yield of foam product of copper–molybdenum ore flotation as a function of frother consumption: 1, MIBC; 2, Oxal-A; 3, Oxal-B; 4, Oxal-C

determined by the heavy residue content. At relatively low consumptions oxal is inferior to MIBC (Fig. 1) in its foaming action, but it is superior to MIBC at consumptions of 80 g/t and above. Better molybdenum recovery has been obtained with Oxal A than with MIBC (Fig. 2), and similar results are obtained for copper.

Oxal T-80 has been tested satisfactorily on various ores. In the flotation of two types of copper–molybdenum ore under laboratory and industrial conditions oxal gave results that are at least equal to those of MIBC (Tables 3 and 4).

Hexenol and epoxol were tested in the flotation of copper–nickel, copper–molybdenum (Table 3) and polymetallic ores, and compared with cyclohexanol in the copper–zinc flotation of polymetallic ores and with Aerofloat in the zinc–pyrite cycle (Fig. 3).

Semi-commercial tests of hexenol and epoxol in the copper–lead and zinc–pyrite stages have established that these reagents reduce metal losses in tailings with some redistribution of metals in the concentrates (Table 5). Epoxol feed to a copper–lead cycle leads to improved lead concentrate quality and recovery, and it is advisable to use epoxol in the zinc–pyrite cycle.

Table 3 Copper–molybdenum ore flotation under laboratory conditions

| Frother type (consumption g/t) | Products | Yield, % | Content, % | | Recovery, % | |
			Cu	Mo	Cu	Mo
MIBC (20)	Cu–Mo concentrate	6.55	9.79	0.083	83.4	71.2
	Middlings	1.43	1.50	0.025	2.8	4.7
	Total concentrate	7.98	8.30	0.073	86.2	75.9
	Tailings	92.02	0.115	0.002	13.8	24.1
	Ore	100.00	0.77	0.0076	100.0	100.0
Oxal (22)	Cu–Mo concentrate	6.50	9.57	0.105	84.7	75.6
	Middlings	1.10	1.33	0.031	2.0	3.8
	Total concentrate	7.60	8.38	0.094	86.7	79.4
	Tailings	92.40	0.105	0.002	13.3	20.6
	Ore	100.00	0.73	0.009	100.0	100.0
Hexanol-M (27)	Cu–Mo concentrate	6.67	9.41	0.092	84.5	73.0
	Middlings	1.33	1.22	0.028	2.2	4.4
	Total concentrate	8.00	8.04	0.082	86.7	77.4
	Tailings	92.00	0.107	0.0021	13.3	22.6
	Ore	100.00	0.74	0.0084	100.0	100.0

Table 4 Commercial tests with Oxal T-80 and MIBC on copper–molybdenum ore

| | Frother type | |
	MIBC	Oxal T-80
Content in ore, %		
Copper	0.321	0.316
Molybdenum	0.0522	0.0525
Content in tailings, %		
Copper	0.070	0.068
Molybdenum	0.0089	0.0087
Content in copper concentrate, %		
Copper	19.4	19.17
Molybdenum	0.041	0.052
Content in molybdenum concentrate, %		
Copper	0.53	0.55
Molybdenum	50.87	50.96
Recovery, %		
Copper	77.84	77.94
Molybdenum	82.40	82.40

Table 5 Semi-commercial tests with hexenol and epoxol in flotation of polymetallic ore

Type of frother (consumption, g/t)		Product	Content, %			Recovery, %		
Cu–Pb flotation	Zn–Py flotation		Pb	Zn	Cu	Pb	Zn	Cu
Cyclohexanol (48)	Butyl Aero-float (60)	Pb concentrate	77.8	2.26	1.48	87.25	1.43	7.32
		Zn concentrate	0.69	60.6	0.22	1.87	92.84	2.63
		Cu concentrate	1.76	1.31	29.9	1.11	0.47	83.41
		Tailings	0.09	0.085	0.013	9.77	5.26	6.64
Hexenol (54)	Hexenol (90)	Pb concentrate	73.06	4.54	1.36	89.65	3.15	8.59
		Zn concentrate	0.66	62.4	0.15	1.71	91.41	1.89
		Cu concentrate	1.33	1.1	29.35	0.81	0.38	84.02
		Tailings	0.07	0.08	0.01	7.83	5.06	5.50
Epoxol (29)	Butyl Aero-float (60)	Pb concentrate	79.5	1.63	1.48	88.8	1.0	7.5
		Zn concentrate	0.32	61.8	0.09	0.9	92.4	1.1
		Cu concentrate	1.37	0.93	31.3	0.8	0.3	82.8
		Tailings	0.085	0.1	0.017	9.5	6.3	8.6
Epoxol (29)	Epoxol (24)	Pb concentrate	79.1	1.42	1.56	87.1	0.9	7.8
		Zn concentrate	0.58	60.5	0.16	1.6	93.1	2.0
		Cu concentrate	1.31	1.59	30.9	0.8	0.5	83.7
		Tailings	0.095	0.087	0.013	10.5	5.5	6.5

Butyl xanthate consumption in Cu–Pb flotation, 10 g/t; in Zn–Py flotation, 40 g/t.

Table 6 Test results for epoxol with various contents of acetophenone

Type of frother (consumption, g/t)	Product	Yield, %	Content, %			Recovery, %		
			Cu	Pb	Zn	Cu	Pb	Zn
Cyclohexanol (40 + 10)	Cu–Pb concentrate	5.0	3.78	19.3	9.70	84.6	84.4	26.0
	Middlings	2.1	0.84	2.67	4.70	7.9	5.0	5.3
	Total concentrate	7.1	2.91	14.38	8.22	92.5	92.4	31.3
	Tailings of Cu–Pb cycle	92.9	0.018	0.09	1.38	7.5	7.6	68.7
	Ore	100.0	0.22	1.10	1.87	100.0	100.0	100.0
DMFC (30% ketone) (38 + 12)	Cu–Pb concentrate	4.0	5.40	24.0	10.7	88.6	87.6	22.3
	Middlings	4.7	0.39	2.26	7.4	7.5	9.7	18.2
	Total concentrate	8.7	2.69	12.26	8.92	96.1	97.3	40.5
	Tailings of Cu–Pb cycle	91.3	0.01	0.032	1.25	3.9	2.7	59.5
	Ore	100.0	0.24	1.10	1.92	100.0	100.0	100.0
DMFC (5% ketone) (38 + 12)	Cu–Pb concentrate	3.9	5.20	24.8	10.6	88.6	89.7	22.0
	Middlings	4.6	0.37	1.8	6.0	7.4	7.7	14.7
	Total concentrate	8.5	2.59	12.35	8.11	96.0	97.4	36.7
	Tailings of Cu–Pb cycle	91.5	0.01	0.031	1.30	4.0	2.6	63.3
	Ore	100.0	0.23	1.08	1.88	100.0	100.0	100.0

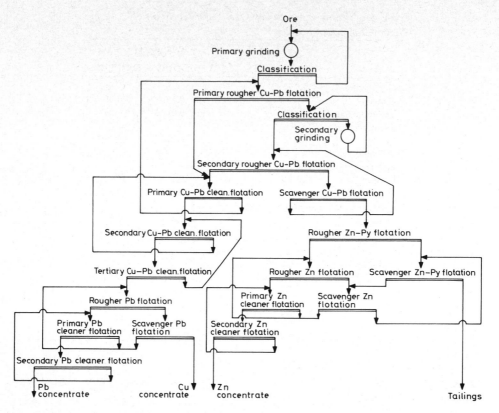

Fig. 3   Flowsheet for copper–lead–zinc ores

Table 7   Polymetallic ore flotation with PF reagent

Frother type	Product	Yield, %	Content, %			Recovery, %		
			Cu	Pb	Zn	Cu	Pb	Zn
Cyclohexanol	Cu–Pb concentrate	4.8	5.9	24.2	11.5	83.3	82.5	24.6
	Middlings	3.6	0.91	4.3	8.8	9.7	11.0	14.1
	Total concentrate	8.4	3.76	15.67	19.34	93.0	93.5	38.7
	Tailings of Cu–Pb cycle	91.6	0.026	0.10	1.50	7.0	6.5	61.3
	Ore	100.0	0.34	1.41	2.24	100.0	100.0	100.0
PF reagent	Cu–Pb concentrate	5.7	5.2	22.0	9.85	88.5	87.7	24.8
	Middlings	5.5	0.44	1.85	5.05	7.2	7.1	12.3
	Total concentrate	11.2	2.86	12.10	7.49	95.7	94.8	37.1
	Tailings of Cu–Pb cycle	88.8	0.016	0.084	1.60	4.3	5.2	62.9
	Ore	100.0	0.33	1.43	2.26	100.0	100.0	100.0

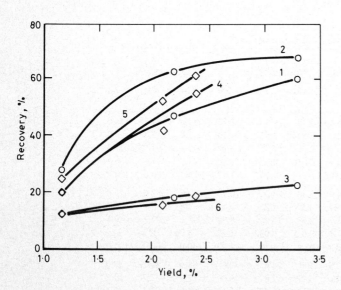

Tests on the flotation of a polymetallic ore without collector have shown (Fig. 4) that epoxol and cyclohexanol possess similar collecting action.

The content of acetophenone in epoxol has little influence on the foaming action or metal recovery of epoxol. Other tests indicate improvements of 2.8–2.9% for copper recovery and 2.3–2.4% for zinc.

Reagent PF is also an effective frother for the flotation of polymetallic ores (Table 7).

Fig 4.   Copper–lead–zinc flotation with use of cyclohexanol (1,2,3) and epoxol (4,5,6): 1, 4, copper recovery; 2, 5, lead recovery; 3, 6, zinc recovery

Zeolites for increased selectivity and recovery in flotation processes

W. von Rybinski, M. J. Schwuger, P. A. Schulz and B. Dobiás

Synopsis

The selective flotation of minerals is influenced by the presence of multivalent ions, which enter the flotation pulp with the process water or by soluble components from salt-type minerals. The adsorption of multivalent ions at the mineral surfaces may lead to an undesirable activation of the gangue minerals and to an increased consumption, especially of anionic collectors. Insoluble inorganic ion exchangers, such as zeolite A, may exchange sodium for multivalent cations in their pore structure and remove them from the flotation pulp. By addition of zeolite A the separation of such minerals as fluorite, baryte and scheelite from silica-containing gangue minerals can be improved and the consumption of collector reduced. Measurements of the ion-exchange isotherms of zeolite A and of the electrophoretic mobilities of minerals confirm that by its addition the activation of quartz by multivalent ions is reduced. Thus, selectivity and recovery of the flotation process can be increased by zeolite A.

Multivalent ions may have a strong influence on the flotation process.[1-5] In many cases their mode of action is based on an adsorption at the mineral surfaces, which leads to a change of flotation properties of the minerals. Multivalent cations are adsorbed at the negatively charged quartz surfaces, so quartz can be floated with anionic collectors under these conditions.[6] This activating effect of multivalent cations is desirable in some separation problems and will even be enhanced by the addition of electrolytes, e.g. activation of sphalerite by Cu^{2+} ions for flotation with xanthogenates.[7] In many cases, however, selectivity and recovery are reduced significantly by adsorption of multivalent ions on mineral surfaces, e.g. flotation of salt-type minerals with anionic collectors for the separation from quartz as gangue mineral.[8] In addition to the adsorption of ions at the mineral surface one reason for these effects is the formation of precipitates of anionic collectors and multivalent ions, which leads to an increased consumption of the collector. The presence of multivalent ions during the flotation process frequently cannot be avoided because these ions enter the flotation pulp with the process water or via sparingly soluble salt-type minerals (for example, CaF_2 and $CaCO_3$). Inorganic or organic complexing agents may be added to the flotation pulp to prevent undesirable activation effects by multivalent ions.[9] The drawbacks to the use of complexing agents are that the selectivity in complexing of multivalent ions is low and that these substances are adsorbed themselves at the mineral surface and therefore influence the grade of hydrophobicity induced by the collector.[10] Because of these effects flotation process control becomes more complex. Insoluble inorganic ion exchangers, such as zeolite A, do not have these undesirable properties. Multivalent ions are exchanged for sodium ions by these compounds[11,12] in their pore structure and are therefore removed from aqueous solutions. Because of the insolubility of zeolites only small interactions occur with the individual mineral components in the flotation pulp.

Experimental

Substances

For the physical chemical measurements and for the flotation experiments in the micro-flotation cell mineral concentrates with a grade of >95% were used. In the experiments on the laboratory scale a phosphate ore was floated that contained magnetite, calcite and magnesium silicates as the gangue minerals. Prior to flotation magnetite was removed from the ore by magnetic separation. Sodium oleate, sodium cetylsulphate (SCS), sodium silicate and zeolite A (SASIL, registered trademark of Henkel KGaA, Düsseldorf) were investigated as flotation reagents. Zeolite A is insoluble in the alkaline pH region and has an average particle diameter of ~4 μm. The exchange capacity is 175 mg CaO/g. The water content of the zeolite sample was about 20 wt%.

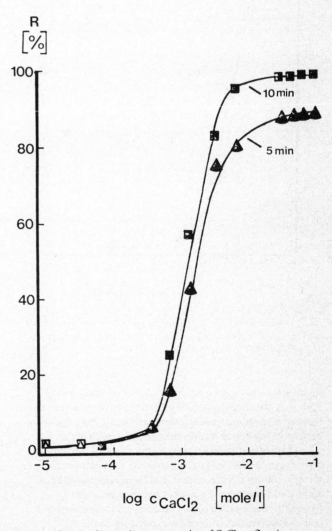

Fig. 1   Influence of increasing concentration of $CaCl_2$ on flotation recovery, R, of quartz in SCS solutions with different flotation times (c_{SCS}, 1.10^{-4} mole/l; pH 10.5–11.0; T, 25°C)

Methods

Surfactant adsorption at the minerals was calculated from measurements of the solution concentration before and after adsorption by two-phase titration. The amounts of multivalent ions adsorbed by the minerals were measured by atomic absorption spectrophotometry. The flotation experiments with mineral concentrates were carried out in a special micro-flotation cell[13] and the phosphate ore was floated in a laboratory cell (volume, 2.4 l).

Results and discussion

The influence of multivalent ions on the flotation of quartz with SCS is shown in Fig. 1. Whereas quartz is not floated with anionic surfactants in distilled water, the addition of a certain amount of calcium ions leads to a high recovery of quartz during flotation. The opposite behaviour results from flotation with cationic surfactants (Fig. 2). In this case the addition of

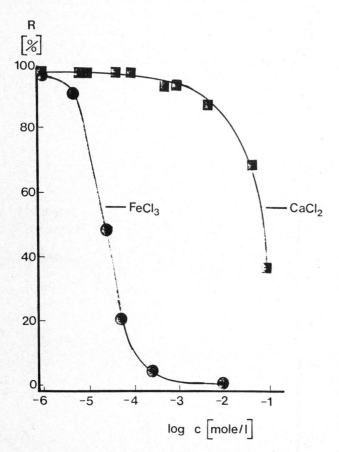

Fig. 2   Flotation recovery, R, of quartz in presence of cationic collector as a function of electrolyte concentration (c (collector), 1×10^{-2} g/l; pH 3.5–5.2; T, 25°C; t (flotation), 5 min)

multivalent ions causes a significant reduction in the good flotation characteristics in distilled water. Recovery is even more reduced in the presence of trivalent ions than in the presence of corresponding amounts of divalent ions as a result of the adsorption of multivalent cations on the negatively charged quartz surface (Fig. 3). As a consequence, the negative charge on the quartz surface is diminished, and therefore adsorption of anionic surfactants by the quartz particles is possible. Competitive adsorption occurs between multivalent ions and collector on flotation with cationic collectors, so the hydrophobicity of the mineral surfaces is not sufficient for flotation. It is assumed that the primary hydroxy complexes of the cations are the species that activate the quartz surface.[8]

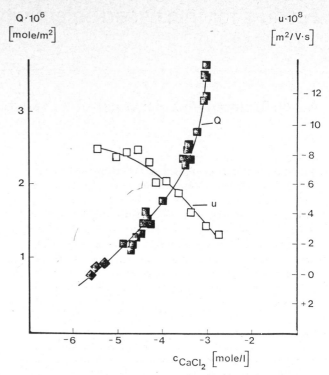

Fig. 3   Adsorption density, Q, of calcium ions on quartz compared with electrophoretic mobility, u, of quartz as a function of calcium ion concentration (pH 10.5; T, 25°C)

Therefore, the following equations for the adsorption of anionic surfactant can be written:[7]

$$- \underset{|}{\overset{|}{Si}} - O^{\ominus} + Ca(OH)^{\oplus} \rightleftarrows - \underset{|}{\overset{|}{Si}} - O^{\ominus} \dots Ca(OH)^{\oplus}$$

$$- \underset{|}{\overset{|}{Si}} - O^{\ominus} \dots Ca(OH)^{\oplus} + {}^{\ominus}\text{\small —} \rightleftarrows - \underset{|}{\overset{|}{Si}} - O^{\ominus} \dots \underset{\underset{H}{\overset{|}{O}}}{Ca}{}^{\oplus} \dots {}^{\ominus}\text{\small —}$$

The bond formation of anionic collectors on quartz and silicates via adsorption bridges of multivalent cations is important for practical flotation. In particular, in the separation of salt-type minerals, such as fluorite, baryte and scheelite from silicate-containing gangue minerals, this effect plays a significant role, a relatively high concentration of multivalent ions in the solution resulting from the marked solubility of these minerals in water. Table 1 shows the results of the flotation experiments with quartz and anionic collectors in saturated solutions of different minerals. From the multivalent ions in solution a significant increase in recovery is observed on the flotation of quartz, which in technical flotation may lead to a reduction in

Table 1   Flotation of quartz in saturated solutions of different salt-type minerals in micro-flotation cell (flotation time, t, 10 min; T 25°C)

Mineral	Collector	$c$collector, mole/l	pH	Quartz recovery, %
—	SCS	1×10^{-4}	10.5	1
CaF$_2$	SCS	1×10^{-4}	10.5	25
CaCO$_3$	Na oleate	2×10^{-4}	7.5	12
CaWO$_4$	Na oleate	2×10^{-4}	8.0	10
BaSO$_4$	Na oleate	2×10^{-4}	6.5	7
BaSO$_4$	Na oleate	2×10^{-4}	10.0	13

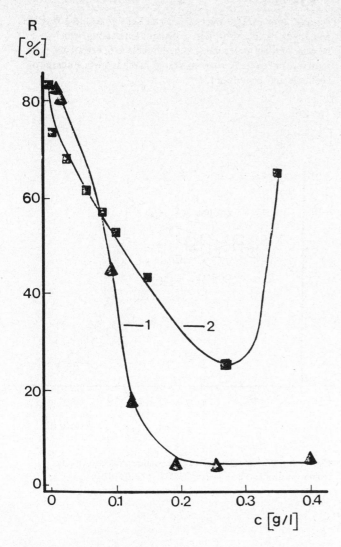

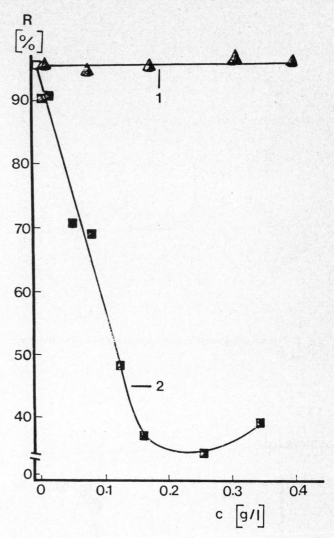

Fig. 4 Flotation recovery, R, of quartz with SCS (c, 1 x 10^{-4} mole/l) at constant concentration of $CaCl_2$ (c, 8 x 10^{-3} mole/l) as a function of zeolite A (1) and sodium silicate (2) concentration (t (flotation), 10 min; T, 25°C; pH 10.5–11.0)

Fig. 5 Flotation recovery, R, of CaF_2 with SCS (c, 1 x 10^{-4} mole/l) as a function of zeolite A (1) and sodium silicate (2) concentration (t (flotation), 10 min; T, 25°C; pH 10.5–11.0)

selectivity. The observed effects depend on the solubility of the mineral and the type of collector used. Usually, sodium silicate is added to depress quartz and silicate-containing minerals.

By the reaction of silicate ions with the activated quartz surface the negative surface charge of quartz particles is increased and the recovery of quartz on flotation is reduced.[9] In Fig. 4 the influence of sodium silicate on the flotation of quartz with anionic collector in the presence of calcium ions is compared with that of the water-insoluble ion exchanger zeolite A. By addition of sodium silicate the recovery of quartz is reduced, whereas at high sodium silicate concentrations the recovery increases again. This corresponds to observations in technical flotation processes, in which the choice of a suitable sodium silicate concentration is very critical.[9] Zeolite A has a better depressing effect towards quartz than sodium silicate at equal dosages. At certain concentrations of zeolite A it is possible to prevent flotation of quartz in the presence of multivalent cations, whereas above this limit flotation is independent of zeolite concentration. The flotation of salt-type minerals with anionic collectors is not affected by the addition of zeolite A, as can be seen in Fig. 5 for the flotation of fluorite. Water-soluble sodium silicate, however, also reduces the recovery of fluorite. As this depressing effect towards fluorite is smaller than that towards quartz (Fig. 4), it is possible to separate fluorite from silicate-containing gangue minerals by use of sodium silicate, but the differences in selectivity are much higher with zeolite A. The effectiveness of zeolite A is based on an exchange of calcium ions

in the solution for sodium ions. Zeolite A has a negatively charged aluminium silicate structure, the excess charge of which is neutralized by sodium ions. The general formula of sodium–aluminium silicates is

$$x\mathrm{Na_2O} \cdot \mathrm{Al_2O_3} \cdot y\mathrm{SiO_2} \cdot z\mathrm{H_2O}$$

For zeolite A in the ideal structure the parameters should be $x \sim 1$, $y \sim 2$ and z = variable.

The aluminium silicate structure encloses a pore structure with a pore diameter of 0.42 nm (Fig. 6), into which multivalent cations—for example, calcium ions—may penetrate. Aluminium silicates of the zeolite A type have a high exchange capacity versus calcium ions (Fig. 7). The exchange capacity amounts to about 175 mg CaO/g zeolite A and, therefore, is comparable with that of water-soluble complexing agents.[14] According to the same mechanism, magnesium and iron ions are also exchanged for sodium ions of zeolite A. The large binding capacity of calcium ions is one of the reasons why zeolite A is used as a builder in detergents.[15,16] Zeolite A has been available in large quantities since 1979.

The negative surface charge of zeolite A is not altered by the exchange of the sodium ions by calcium ions (Fig. 8). At a quartz surface, chosen for purposes of comparison, the negative charge decreases by the adsorption of calcium ions, so at higher concentrations the sign of the surface charge may be changed. At the zeolite surface this effect is observed only when the ion

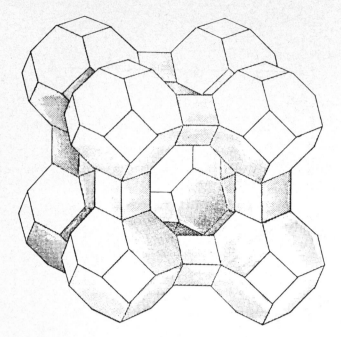

Fig. 6 Schematic diagram of ideal structure of zeolite A (pore diameter, ~0.42 nm)

concentration exceeds the exchange capacity of zeolite A (Fig. 7). Moreover, by the adsorption of cationic surfactants, which because of their molecular size are not able to penetrate the pore structure of zeolite A, such an alteration of the surface charge of zeolite A may be induced.[17]

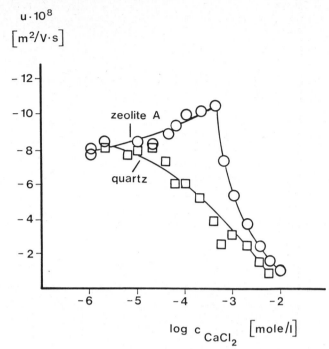

Fig. 8 Influence of calcium ion concentration on electrophoretic mobility of zeolite A and quartz (T, 25°C; pH 10.5–11.0)

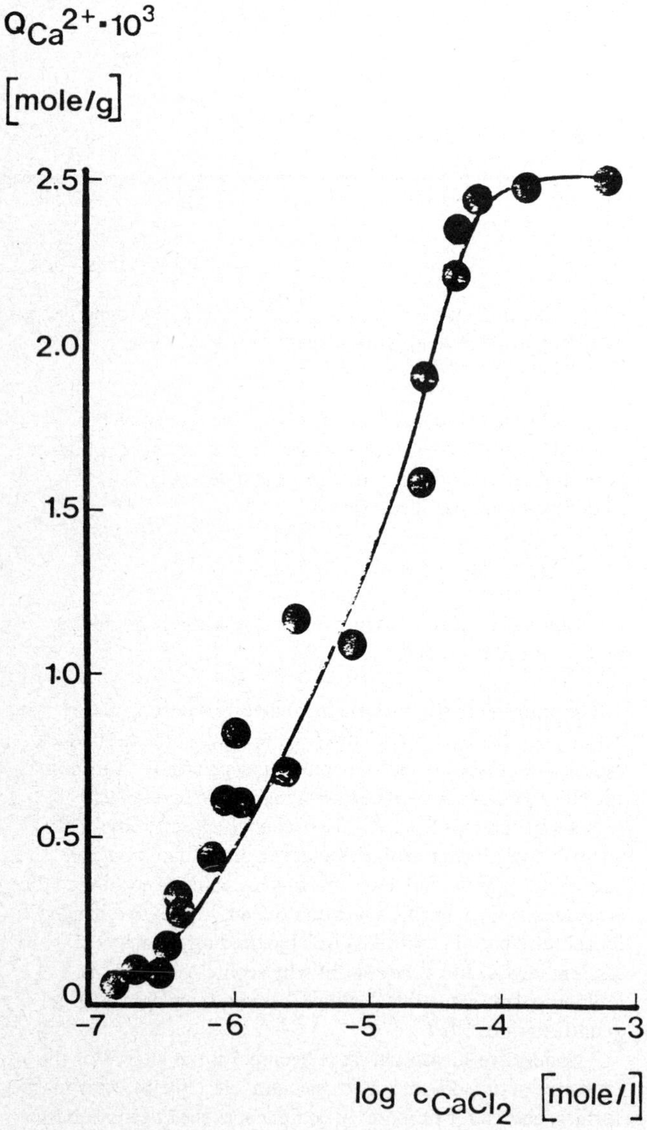

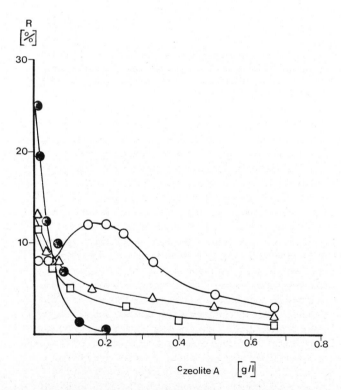

Fig. 9 Flotation recovery, R, of quartz in saturated solutions of different salt-type minerals as a function of zeolite A concentration (t (flotation), 10 min; T, 25°C)

Mineral	Collector	c, mole/l	pH
□ $CaCO_3$	Na oleate	2.10^{-4}	7.3– 9.8
△ $BaSO_4$	Na oleate	2.10^{-4}	9.5–10.0
○ $CaWO_4$	Na oleate	2.10^{-4}	6.4–10.8
● CaF_2	SCS	1.10^{-4}	10.5–11.0

Fig. 7 Calcium ion exchange of zeolite A as a function of calcium ion concentration (T, 25°C)

The depressing effect of zeolite A towards quartz in technical flotation is decisive: zeolite A has this effect on the flotation of quartz in the presence of the sparingly soluble salt-type minerals. For this reason the flotation of quartz in saturated solutions of various minerals was investigated as a function of the amounts of zeolite A added (Fig. 9). The addition of zeolite A reduced significantly the recovery of activated quartz. The effect of zeolite A is related to the collector used and the type of mineral. The most significant effect was observed with SCS as collector and fluorite as mineral. The maximum flotation recovery of quartz in saturated solutions of scheelite at low zeolite concentrations results from a change in the pH value by the addition of zeolite A, the aluminium silicate having a certain alkalinity because of its process of manufacture. At high concentrations of zeolite A the pH value may vary from 9.5 to 10.5.

$c\,(SCS)\cdot 10^6$

$\left[\text{mole}/l\right]$

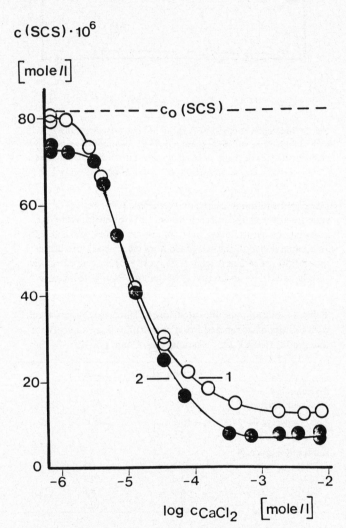

Fig. 10 Influence of addition of $CaCl_2$ on solution concentration of SCS in absence (1) and presence (2) of quartz (initial concentration of SCS: c_0, 82 x 10^{-6} mole/l; T, 25°C)

The advantages of zeolite A in flotation processes are not confined to the deactivation of quartz and silicates—the dosage of anionic collectors may also be reduced. Anionic collectors form insoluble precipitates with calcium ions.[18] This leads to a reduction in the collector concentration in solution (see Fig. 10 for SCS). At high calcium ion concentrations almost the whole of the collector precipitates. The presence of quartz causes a further reduction in the solution concentration of SCS by the adsorption of collector at quartz surface activated by calcium ions. The adsorbed collector at the quartz surface can be estimated from the difference between curves 1 and 2 in Fig. 10. Collector

$c\,(SCS)\cdot 10^6$

$\left[\text{mole}/l\right]$

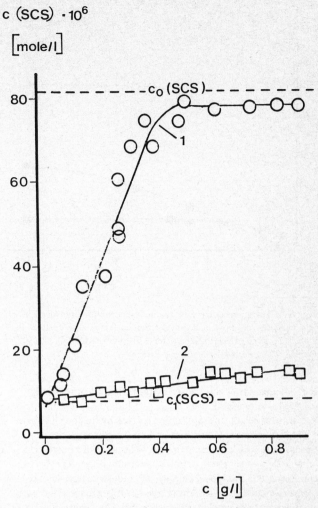

$c\,\left[g/l\right]$

Fig. 11 Influence of addition of zeolite A (1) and sodium silicate (2) on solution concentration of SCS at constant concentration of $CaCl_2$ (c=3.5 x 10^{-4} mole/l) (initial solution concentration of SCS: c_0, 82 x 10^{-6} mole/l; solution concentration of SCS in presence of 3.5 x 10^{-4} mole/l $CaCl_2$: c_1, 8.10^{-6} mole/l; T, 25°C)

consumption in flotation with anionic surfactants is strongly increased by these effects, the major portion of the collector forming insoluble calcium salts and being unable to adsorb at the mineral surface.

Fig. 11 shows the influence of zeolite A on the precipitation of SCS with calcium ions. In the absence of zeolite A the concentration of dissolved collector decreases to a value of c_1 by the addition of 3.5 x 10^{-4} mole/l calcium ions. When the solution is equilibrated with different amounts of zeolite A prior to the addition of collector the precipitation of insoluble $Ca(CS)_2$ may be prevented almost completely with sufficient dosage of zeolite A. If, instead of zeolite A, equal amounts of sodium silicate are added, the effectiveness is only minor. It may be expected from the results obtained that in ore flotation with calcium ions in the pulp zeolite A would reduce the consumption of anionic collector.

This effect was verified by flotation experiments of the model system apatite—calcite with an anionic collector. In the flotation of apatite with sodium oleate as collector recovery clearly depends on the calcium ion concentration in solution (Fig. 12). When floated in distilled water the recovery of apatite is high (curve 1). The addition of calcium ions causes a strong decrease in the recovery of apatite at an identical collector concentration (curve 2). If apatite is floated in a saturated solution of calcite, the most important gangue mineral of phosphate ores, a reduction in recovery is also observed (curve 3). This deterioration in the floatability of apatite in the presence of

201

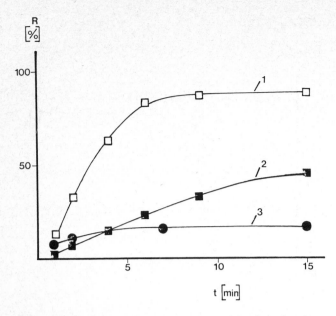

Fig. 12   Flotation recovery, R, of apatite floated with sodium oleate in micro-flotation cell as a function of flotation time, t ($c_{Na\ oleate}$, 2×10^{-5} mole/l; T, 25°C; pH 10; distilled water (1); addition of $CaCl_2$ (c, 1×10^{-3} mole/l) (2); in saturated solution of calcite (3))

calcium ions is probably caused by the formation of sparingly soluble calcium oleate.

Confirmation of this assumption is given by the the results in Fig. 13. A mixture of apatite and calcite (weight ratio 1:1) was floated, sodium oleate being used as collector with a polymeric organic depressant based on maleic acid anhydride. At collector concentrations commonly employed in industrial flotation the recovery of apatite is very low (curve 1). Only a marked increase in collector concentration leads to a sufficient recovery of apatite (curve 2). The selectivity towards apatite of the reagent system selected is very good (85–90%), but the amounts of collector used are too high for practical application because of the formation of insoluble calcium oleate.

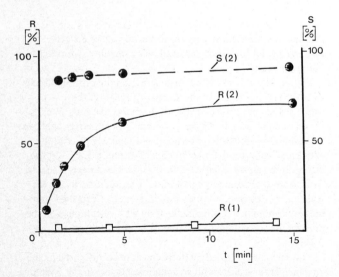

Fig. 13   Flotation of mixture of apatite and calcite (weight ratio 1:1) with sodium oleate and depressant: recovery, R, and selectivity, S, of apatite at different sodium oleate concentrations as a function of flotation time, t (T, 25°C; $c_{depressant}$, 2×10^{-3} g/l; pH 10; 1, $c_{Na\ oleate}$, 2×10^{-5} and 5×10^{-5} mole/l; 2, $c_{Na\ oleate}$, 1×10^{-4} mole/l)

By the addition of zeolite A it is possible to reduce the collector concentration for the same recovery and selectivity of apatite (Fig. 14), the formation of sparingly soluble calcium

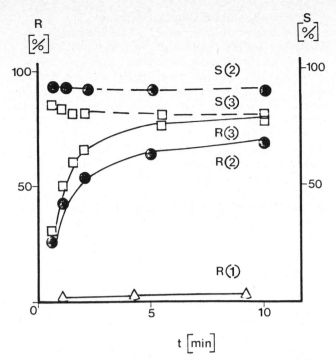

Fig. 14   Flotation of mixture of apatite and calcite (weight ratio 1:1) with sodium oleate and depressant: influence of addition of zeolite A on recovery, R, and selectivity, S, of apatite as a function of flotation time, t (1, $c_{zeolite\ A}$, 0 g/l; 2, $c_{zeolite\ A}$, 0.08 g/l; 3, $c_{zeolite\ A}$, 0.12 g/l)

oleate in the flotation pulp being reduced. These results of the experiments with the micro-flotation cell are confirmed by the flotation of a natural phosphate ore in a laboratory cell (Table 2). In comparison with the system sodium oleate–sodium silicate the addition of zeolite A leads to reduced reagent concentrations and the selectivity and recovery of flotation of apatite increase.

Table 2   Flotation of phosphate ore in laboratory flotation cell with sodium oleate and addition of sodium silicate or zeolite A (ore grade, 16.0% P_2O_5; flotation time, 4 min; pH 11)

	Sodium silicate	Zeolite A
Collector, g/t	300	100
Modifying agent, g/t	2000	1000
Total recovery, %	15.6	20
Apatite recovery, %	22.5	31
Concentrate grade, %		
P_2O_5	23.1	24.3
CO_2	13.6	9.1
SiO_2	6.5	8.6
MgO	7.7	10.6

The results show the positive effect of zeolite A for the separation of salt-type minerals by flotation.

References
1.   Gaudin A. M. and Fuerstenau D. W. Streaming potential studies: 1, quartz flotation with anionic collectors. *Trans. Am. Inst. Min. Engrs*, **202**, 1955, 66–72.
2.   Fuerstenau M. C. Martin C. C. and Bhappu R. B. The role of hydrolysis in sulfonate flotation of quartz. *Trans. Am. Inst. Min. Engrs*, **226**, 1963, 449–54.
3.   Bibawy T. A. and Yousef A. Die Rolle von anorganischen Elektrolyten in der Flotation von α–Fe_2O_3. *Tenside Detergents*, **19**, 1982, 2.
4.   Mercade V. Effect of polyvalent metal-silicate hydrosols on the flotation of calcite. *Trans. Am. Inst. Min. Engrs*, **268**, 1980, 1842–6.
5.   Mishra S. K. The electrokinetics of apatite and calcite in inorganic electrolyte environment. *Int. J. Mineral Process.*, **5**, 1978, 69–83.

6. Iwasaki I. Cooke S. R. B. and Choi H. S. Flotation characteristics of hematite, goethite and activated quartz with 18-carbon aliphatic acids and related compounds. *Trans. Am. Inst. Min. Engrs*, **217**, 1960, 237–44.

7. Schubert H. *Aufbereitung fester mineralischer Rohstoffe, 2. Auflage, Band II* (Leipzig: VEB Verlag für Grundstoffe, 1977), 491 p.

8. Fuerstenau M. C. and Palmer B. R. Anionic flotation of oxides and silicates. In *Flotation: A. M. Gaudin memorial volume* Fuerstenau M. C. ed. (New York: AIME, 1976), 148–96.

9. Leja J. *Surface chemistry of froth flotation* (New York, London: Plenum Press, 1982), 758 p.

10. Röttig G. and Breuer H. Oberflächenreaktionen von Komplexbildnern mit Feststoffen und ihre Bedeutung in der chemischen Technik. *Tenside Detergents*, **17**, 1980, 191–3.

11. Schwuger M. J. and Smolka H. G. Sodium–aluminium–silicates in the washing process, part 1: physico-chemical aspects of phosphate substitution in detergents. *Colloid Polymer Sci.*, **254**, 1976, 1062–9.

12. Smolka H. G. and Schwuger M. J. Sodium–aluminium–silicates in the washing process, part 2: cleansing action of natural zeolites. *Colloid Polymer Sci.*, **256**, 1978, 270–7.

13. Dobiás B. Modified Hallimond tube for the study of the flotability and kinetics of minerals. *Colloid Polymer Sci.*, **259**, 1981, 775–6.

14. Schwuger M. J. and Smolka H. G. Zur Verwendung von Natrium–Aluminium–Silikaten in Waschmitteln, Teil 7: Gegenioneneffekte. *Tenside Detergents*, **16**, 1979, 233–9.

15. Krings P. and Verbeek H. Erfahrungen mit Zeolith-haltigen Waschmitteln. *Tenside Detergents*, **18**, 1981, 260–1.

16. Schwuger M. J. Physico-chemical aspects of phosphate substitution in detergents. *Ber. Bunsenges. phys. Chem.*, in press.

17. Schwuger M. J. von Rybinski W. and Krings P. Adsorption of cationic surfactants on zeolite A. In *Adsorption from solution* Ottewell R. H. Rochester C. H. and Smith A. L. eds (London, etc: Academic Press, 1983), 185–96.

18. Somasundaran P. and Celik M. Precipitation, redissolution and reprecipitation of sulfonates. Paper presented to Fifth Yugoslav symposium on surface-active substances, 1981.

Collectors for barite and oxidized ores

N. V. Selivanova

Synopsis
Effective collectors for the flotation of oxidized ores have been developed by the Institute 'VNIITSVETMET'. Reagents VC-2 and VC-4 are prepared from cotton soapstock fats and comprise mixtures of saponified fatty acids (60-70%), neutral fat (2-5%) and water (20-35%). The reagents dissolved well in water at temperatures of 25–40°C and do not require saponification and emulsification.

The flotation properties of VC-2 and VC-4 were tested on some ores containing non-sulphide minerals—barite, fluorite, beryl, spodumene, scheelite, cassiterite, tantalite and others. Under laboratory and pilot-plant conditions significant improvements resulted in terms of increased recovery and improved concentrate quality.

An intermediate product of the production of synthetic fatty acids (C-3) was proposed as an effective substitute for oleinic acid. Laboratory and pilot-plant tests have shown that this reagent can be used as a collector for barite. Its usage led to increased barite recovery (3.2%) and barite content in the concentrate.

The flotation of barite from complex polymetallic ores and that of oxides and aluminosilicates from rare-metal ores is generally carried out with anionic collectors of the fatty acid type. Oleinic acid, technical fatty acids, tall oils and their treatment products, as well as combinations of fatty acid collectors with different alkylsulphates and other flotation reagents are those which are most widely used in benefication.[1]

These reagents are normally highly selective, but they show insufficient selectivity towards gangue minerals.

VC-2 and VC-4

Investigations at the Institute 'VNIITSVETMET' have shown the usefulness of the application of the products of the sulphurization of raw cotton soapstocks—in particular, the reagents conventionally named VC-2 and VC-4—as collectors for non-sulphide minerals.[2,3,4]

saponified unsaturated (oleinic and linoleic) acids (up to 35%), saturated fatty acids (up to 18%), fatty hydroperoxides and oxyacids (up to 19%) and neutral fat (up to 7%), plus water.

The reagents VC-2 and VC-4 dissolve well in water at 25–40°C and do not require saponification and emulsification. The different components determine their flotation activity and greater selectivity in comparison with the known reagents.

The hydrophobic properties of the new reagents were investigated in the flotation of pure mineral fractions of barite, calcite and quartz in terms of the pH of the pulp and the concentration of the reagents. The results shown in Fig. 1 indicate that VC-2 and VC-4 in alkaline media possess flotation properties similar to those of sodium oleate in regard to barite, but calcite and quartz are floated better by use of sodium oleate—hence the better selectivity of the VC reagents in the flotation of barite from quartz- and calcite-bearing ores.

Eigeles,[5] among others, also noted that mixtures of organic acids are more effective in the concentration of barite than pure individual organic acids. Adsorption isotherms show that with increased concentrations of VC reagents in solution, the quantity of the collector that adheres to the surface of the mineral is increased (Fig. 2), and in this case flotation activity is also increased (Fig. 3).

The extent of increased flotation activity in different minerals is not the same. Maximum flotation of barite with an initial concentration of VC-2 of 25 mg/l is observed when VC-2 adheres to its surface in an amount equal to 1.4 mg/g; in this case the yield of barite was 97%. Further increase in VC-2 concentration has no real effect on barite flotation. Under similar conditions 0.6 mg/g of the reagent adheres to the surface of calcite (89% floatability) and 0.14 mg/g of VC-2 (20% floatability) adheres to the quartz surface. The strength of adhesion of the collectors differs, however: investigations with the use of infrared spectroscopy and washing the reagents with water and hexane have shown that the main part of the reagent adheres to the surface of barite and calcite as a result of physical and chemical sorption, whereas for quartz physical properties are mainly responsible.

The critical micelle concentration (cmc) of the new reagents was determined by measuring the surface tension and the

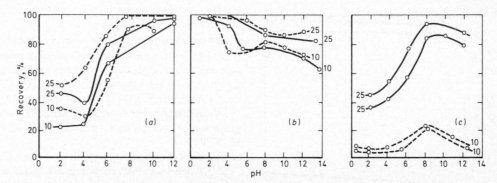

Fig. 1 Influence of pH on recovery of barite (a), calcite (b), and quartz (c) at different concentrations of sodium oleate (solid curve) and of VC (dotted) (numbers on curves are concentrations of reagent solutions, mg/l)

The composition and flotation properties of the reagents depend on the conditions of their preparation. The composition of VC-2, for example, is a complex mixture of, *inter alia*,

specific electrical conductivity of their solutions at different concentrations: that of VC-2 is 270 mg/l, whereas that of VC-4 (290 mg/l) is slightly lower than that of sodium oleate (304

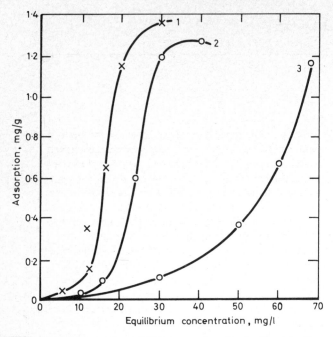

Fig. 2   Adsorption isotherms of VC-2 on surface of barite (1), calcite (2) and quartz (3)

Table 1   Results of comparative tests on collectors for barite flotation

Ore	Concentrate, %	Content, %	Recovery, %	Collector and consumption, g/t of ore
Oxidized lead–	67.9	95.4	99.3	VC-2 170
barite–quartzite	64.7	93.0	98.1	Fatty acid fraction of tall oil, 350
Copper–barite–	54.3	91.9	67.7	Oleinic acid, 350 plus Alkylsuphate, 150
quartz–carbonate	68.9	90.0	88.0	VC-2, 500
Sulphide lead–	8.3	91.7	68.4	Sodium oleate, 80
zinc–barite–				
quartz–carbonate	10.2	90.7	72.3	VC-2, 80
	7.7	88.6	68.9	Alkylsuphate, 80
	9.2	90.7	75.1	VC-4, 120
	8.8	90.5	72.1	Fatty acid fraction of tall oil, 120
	9.2	90.8	74.7	VC-2, 120

mg/l). Apparently, the presence of saturated carbon acids and neutral fat in the composition of VC-2 and VC-4 lowers the cmc.

The flotation properties of the new reagents were tested on various barite-bearing ores from different deposits. The results of the laboratory tests (Table 1) testify to the high efficiency of the new collectors in barite flotation. The use of VC-2 and VC-4 instead of sodium oleate in the flotation of polymetallic barite-bearing ores made it possible to increase barite recovery by 2.2–2.9% with no loss of quality in the barite concentrate (Table 2) and with significant economic benefit.

The new reagents were also tested for the flotation of ores containing beryl, spodumene, scheelite, tantalite and cassiterite, the results obtained being compared with those from the use of oleinic acid, tall oil, etc. Results similar to or better than those achieved on the barite ores were obtained. For example, in the beneficiation of beryl–spodumene ores the recovery of beryl from a bulk concentrate with oleinic acid is equivalent to that obtained with VC-2, and the recovery of lithium from spodumene and amblygonite with VC-2 is 3–4% higher. Tantalite floats effectively with VC-2 yielding a bulk concentrate of 79%, or 2–3% better than that achieved with oleinic acid.

VC-2 and VC-4 also give improved recoveries for scheelite-bearing ores, that of wolfram oxide being 2–3% higher than that from the use of the mixture of oleinic acid and alkylsulphate paste, though reagent consumption is 25–50% greater.

Table 2   Results of treatment with VC-2 and sodium oleate (polymetallic quartzite ore)

	Sodium oleate	VC-2	VC-4
Barite content of ore, %	11.50	12.40	12.1
Yield of barite concentrate, %	7.05	8.20	8.3
Barite content in concentrate, %	90.9	91.7	92.3
Barite recovery, %	58.1	60.3	61.0

The use of VC-2 and VC-4 in the flotation of barite and some rare-metal ores gave rise to significant economic benefits as a result of increased recoveries and improved concentrate quality, coupled with the relatively low cost of the reagents.

C-3

An effective substitute for oleinic acid and the fatty acid fraction of tall oil is a soap glue that is an intermediate product of synthetic fatty acid production, generally termed reagent C-3. Its composition includes saponified fatty acids, C_7–C_{40} (~30–35%), non saponified fatty acids (~5%) and water.

Its external appearance under normal conditions is that of a yellow-brown solid paste; it dissolves in water on heating to 60–70°C.

The results of laboratory tests on C-3 with different ores (Table 3) demonstrate its effectiveness as a collector for barite.

In the flotation of barite from the ores with a carbonate gangue it is preferable to use C-3 in combination with alkylsulphate pastes.

Use of the C-3 in place of tall oil in floating barite from a polymetallic quartz ore containing barite made it possible to increase barite recovery by 1–2% and the content of barite in the concentrate by 1.6%. When used with tall oil an increase in

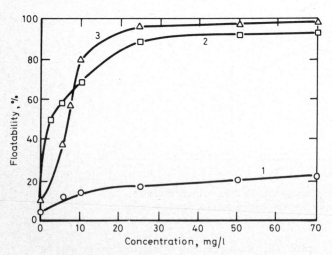

Fig. 3   Influence of concentration of VC-2 on floatability of quartz (1) calcite (2) and barite (3) at pH 7 ± 0.1

Table 3 Results of collector tests in barite flotation

Ore	Barite content % Ore	Concentrate	Barite recovery, %	Collector and consumption, g/t of ore
Sulphide lead–zinc–barite quarzite	42.3	89.0	82.7	Oleinic acid, 270
	41.9	90.5	83.5	C-3, 400
Sulphide poly-metallic barite–quarzite	12.0	82	75.5	Oleinic acid, 100
	12.1	83	76.0	C-3, 100
	11.9	77	75.0	Technical fatty acids, 100
	12.5	86	79.0	C-3, 80 plus Tall oil, 20
Sulphide poly-metallic barite–quartz–carbonate	10.5	90	72	C-3, 100 plus Alkylsulphate, 100
	10.4	80	70	Fatty acid fraction of tall oil, 100 plus Alkylsulphate, 100

barite recovery of 3.2% was achieved. In addition, the use of small quantities (~10%) of tall oil with C-3 improves the rheological properties of the collector water solutions, increases the concentration of its working solutions from 2 to 5%, lowers collector consumption by 30% and improves the structure of the flotation foam. Such a combined usage gave rise to significant economic improvements.

References
1. Klebanov O. B. *et al. Reference book of a technologist for non-ferrous metal ores dressing* (Moscow: Nedra, 1974), 346–54. (Russian text)
2. Russian Patent 345 971, 1972.
3. Russian Patent 352 505, 1973.
4. Russian Patent 760 562, 1980.
5. Eigeles M. A. *Fundamentals of flotation of non-sulphide minerals, 2nd edn* (Moscow: Nedra, 1964), 406 p. (Russian text)

Chemistry and applications of chelating agents in flotation and flocculation

P. Somasundaran and D. R. Nagaraj

Synopsis
Chelating agents, because of their metal specificity or selectivity, can function as good flotaids and selective flocculants. In addition to the metal selectivity, chelating agents offer certain advantages over conventional mineral processing reagents even from the synthesis point of view. With the major donor atoms—S, N, O and, to some extent, P—numerous possibilities exist to tailor-make reagents for specific applications. For polymers the backbone offers further possibilities for the incorporation of the required properties.

In general, the choice of a chelating agent or a group is made on the basis of its function in well-known analytical metal separations. Such a choice is limited in that the number of well-known analytical separations is also limited. In the present work, a new and effective *donor atom* approach is discussed for the design of mineral-specific chelating groups. This generalized approach is focused on the chemical properties of the important donors both in the reagent and on the mineral. Data from many chemical sources have been summarized and applied to systems of relevance to mineral processing. Understanding of the chemical behaviour of donors is of paramount importance in predicting the properties of chelating groups.

Numerous investigations have been made of the application of chelating agents in mineral processing. The various fundamental aspects of the interactions between a mineral and a chelating group are, however, not clearly understood, although there is evidence to suggest that some form of a metal complex is formed at the surface.

The separation of minerals from one another by flotation and flocculation depends mainly on the selective adsorption of surfactants and polymers on them. Although many reagents have long been used in practice for the flotation of minerals, most are not as selective as is required for the efficient separation, in particular, of mineral fines and ultrafines. Reagents with chelating functional groups have received increased attention for this purpose in recent years, being known to exhibit excellent metal selectivity in analytical separations. Many chelating agents have been tried as collectors for various mineral systems and excellent separations have been obtained in certain cases. The mechanisms that involve their collecting action are, however, not adequately understood. In particular, the differences in their mode of action at the mineral surface versus that in the bulk are not fully recognized and, as a result, the development of collectors based on their use in analytical separations is not achieved easily. It is to be noted in this regard that chelating collectors are seldom metal-specific or mineral-specific and the properties of both the chelating agents and the mineral are important in determining their collecting action. The donor atoms on the chelating agents, as well as those associated with the mineral species, play a governing role in their interactions on the surface. In this paper the application of chelating agents in mineral processing systems is reviewed on the basis of the donor properties of the chelating groups and the metal species, and recent approaches to understand chelation are discussed briefly. Emphasis is given to the criteria for selection of chelating agents as collectors for various minerals and the predictability of the behaviour of a chelating agent for a given mineral system.

Chelating agents

Chelating agents are compounds that form metal complexes characterized by ring structures illustrated in Fig. 1.[1,2,3] In type I the metal is coordinated to the four nitrogens of two molecules of ethylene diamine, giving rise to a charged double ringed complex with chloride neutralizing the two charges.[1] Other types of chelating complexes include type II, with an intra-molecular hydrogen bridge, and type III, involving polynuclear halogen bridges.

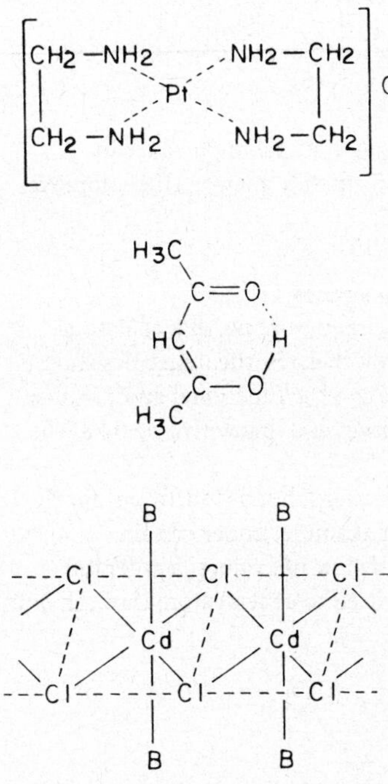

Fig. 1   General structures of chelating agents[1]

Chelating agents can be classified on the basis of donor atoms involved (O-O, N-O, N-N, S-O, S-S, S-N) or ring size (4-, 5- or 6-membered) or charge on the complex (anion, cation, neutral) or number of bonds to the metal for every chelating molecule (bidentate 1:1 ; bidentate 1:2 ; terdentate 1:1)

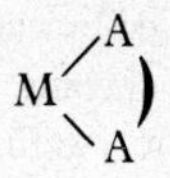

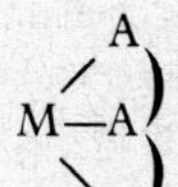

Specificity of chelating agents depends on the interaction

between donor atoms and surface species on the particle. A list of donor atoms and functional groups containing the four major atoms (N, O, P and S) are given in Table 1. Halogen atoms, Cl, Br and I, participate in chelate ring formation in bridged

Table 1 Donor atoms and functional groups containing major donor atoms[3]

C	N	O	H
	P	S	F
	As	Se	Cl
			Br
	Sb	Te	I

Major donor atoms	Functional groups	
	Acidic (lose a proton)	**Basic** (donate electron pair)
N		–NH₂
O	–COOH –OH (enol or phenol) –P(O)(OH)₂	=O –OH (alcohols)
S	–SH	–S–R

polynuclear complexes that are of minimal importance in mineral processing. As and Se form only a few useful complexes and, therefore, are seldom used.

Requirements for chelating agents

There are, essentially, two basic requirements that chelating agents must satisfy to form metal chelates: the molecules should have suitable functional groups and the functional groups must be situated to permit the formation of a ring with a metal as the closing member.

These two conditions are necessary, but not sufficient for the formation of a chelate ring. For example, under certain conditions and under sufficiently low pH values, a potential chelating molecule may attach itself to a metal atom through only one ligand atom:

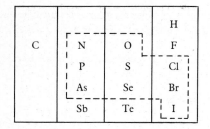

or

$$HOOC.CH_2S-M$$

It has been generally observed that certain additional requirements must be satisfied by chelating agents for mineral processing applications: the chelates should, preferably, be neutral, if the chelating agent is to function as a collector, and the chelates should, preferably, be charged and very hydrophilic if the chelating agent is to function as a depressant. On a polymeric depressant or a flocculant this requirement is not stringent so long as the backbone has other hydrophilic groups (see below).

Requirements for depressants: ionic chelates, e.g. $[Co(DMG)_2(H_2O_2)]^+$, and hydrophilizing groups on molecule

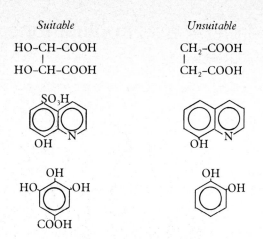

Neutral complexes are usually insoluble in water and, therefore, promote hydrophobicity. For insolubility in water, however, it is not sufficient that the chelate be a neutral complex. A classic example is that of chelates of dimethylglyoximes (DMG) (see Fig. 2). The 1:2 complex of nickel with DMG is insoluble in water. The copper complex is, on the other hand, relatively water-soluble. This results from the subtle differences in the shapes of the two molecules and consequent differences in the mode of packing of the two molecules in their respective crystals (Fig. 2). The nickel compound is planar and the molecules are stacked in the crystal, so the Ni atoms are co-linear and have a weak bond between them. In the copper compound, however, the chelate rings are not co-planar but make a small angle of 28° with one another and there is no metal–metal bonding.[1] The tetragonal pyramidal copper chelate molecules are paired in the crystal in such a way that each copper atom has an O atom from its adjacent molecule as one of its five immediate neighbours. In the Ni complex the –OH and the –O⁻ are strongly internally hydrogen bonded and, hence, less readily solvated. The copper complex actually has a higher stability constant than the Ni complex but, since no internal hydrogen bonding is possible, the complex is easily solvated.

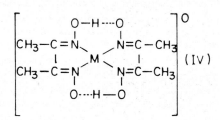

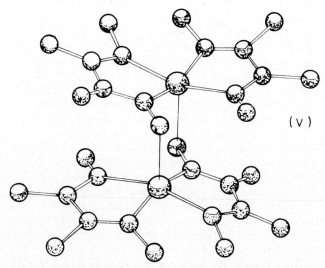

Fig. 2 Geometric structures of DMG chelates of Ni and Cu[1]

210

Specificity and selectivity

Most of the chelating groups form complexes with almost all of the transition and many non-transition metals and, therefore, specificity is not as absolute as is required for their selective adsorption on minerals. In practice selectivity is achieved by making use of differences in stability constants and chelate formation under various solution conditions. As was indicated earlier, contribution from the donors as they are located in the mineral lattice has to be considered in obtaining the selectivity. Also, the solubility of the mineral, in addition to that of the metal chelate, has a pronounced influence on the selectivity and the collection power of the chelating agent.

Stability of complexes

Major factors that determine the stability constant are, in order of decreasing importance, pK_a of the ligand molecule, substituents, nature of donor atoms, central metal atom, and ring size, number of rings.

The first four factors are very important in that they determine the nature and strength of bonds. pK_a of the chelating agent has a direct influence on the chelate formation since it represents the tendency of the donor atoms to donate electrons to metal atoms (or accept from metals, in certain cases) and thus form a chelate. Substitution on the chelating molecule has two important effects:[1] it alters the pK_a and/or it introduces steric factors for the formation of a chelate.

The influence of the nature of donor atom and the central metal atom should be considered together because of the inter-relationship between their behaviour (see later).

Properties of acceptors

Acceptors can be divided conveniently into two main groups based on the unidentate ligands: (a) those which form most stable complexes with N, O and F, and (b) those which form most stable complexes with P, S, and Cl (Table 2).

The stability constants of metal complexes that belong to the two groups follow the general orders N>>P>As>Sb; O>S; F>Cl>Br>I; and for similar ligands N>O>F; differences in the series P>S>Cl are found to be less pronounced.[4] It is seen that a vast majority of elements belong to group (a), i.e. they preferentially complex with O- and N-containing ligands.

A given metal, furthermore, may belong to group (a) or (b), depending on its oxidation state: for example, Cu(I) belongs to group (b), wheras Cu(II) belongs to the overlap region of (a) and (b).

A major shortcoming of the above grouping is that it is based on *unidentate* ligands; the situation is complicated when chelates (or bidentates) are involved. Consideration must be given in this case to chelating agents in which the donor atoms are the same (examples are ethylene diamine, oxalate or thiooxalate) and chelating agents in which the donor atoms are different (examples are *o*-aminothiophenol and *o*-aminophenol). For nickel, thiooxalate ion is believed to form a more stable nickel chelate than the oxalate ion. For zinc, stability constants of the *o*-aminophenol and *o*-aminothiophenol complexes show that the substitution of S for O does have a marked influence on stability.

A more useful grouping is that based on the electronic configuration of the metals. Thus metals can be classified into three groups—those which contain (a) inert-gas type configuration, (b) partially filled d or f orbitals and (c) ions of metals with filled d orbitals (Ag^+, Zn^{2+}, etc).

Metals of group (a) react preferentially with O-containing ligands, such as carboxylate ions and the anions of quinalizarin, and the β-diketones.

Table 2 Classification of acceptors based on unidentate ligands

CLASS A: Form stable complexes with N,O,F

BORDER REGION

Class B: Form stable complexes with P,S,Cl

Transition-metal ions form more stable complexes with ligands that contain polarizable portions, such as amino groups and heterocyclic nitrogen atoms.

Metals in group (c) also prefer highly polarizable ligands, especially if the latter have suitable vacant orbitals into which some of the d electrons from metals can be 'back-bonded'. Examples of such ligands are those which contain S as the donor which is highly polarizable and has vacant 3d orbitals. Thus, thioanalide forms insoluble complexes with Cu, Ag, Cd, Hg(II), Tl, Sn(II), Pb, As, Sb, Bi, Pt and Pd.

Thioanalide

A reagent, such as dithizone, which contains N and S donors therefore reacts with a large part of the transition metal and filled d orbital series. To achieve the degree of selectivity that is desirable in practical applications it is usually necessary to arrive at the appropriate combinations of donors.

Donor–acceptor relationships

A useful classification of acceptors as well as donors is that based on Pearson's concept of *hard* and *soft acids* and *bases* (Table 3).[5,6,7] The acids (or electrophiles) are mostly (metal) cations. This group also includes such electrophiles as CO_2, O, Cl and N and metals in the zero oxidation state. The bases (or nucleophiles) are non-metal anions, neutral atoms and molecules. It should be noted that the donors O and N are hard bases and donor S and P are soft bases.

Table 3 Characteristics of hard and soft acids and bases

Hard (acid or base)	Soft (acid or base)
Small size	Large size
Orbitals involved far apart in energy	Orbitals close in energy
Ionic bonding coulombic attraction	Covalent bonding
High charge ions	High charge ions
Non-polarizable	Polarizable
	Bases have low proton affinity
Hard likes hard	Soft likes soft
High electronegativity	Low electronegativity

The bonding characteristics of these groups are given in Table 3. In general, hard bases preferentially react with hard acids, and similarly for soft bases. The former interaction is characterized by ionic bonding since the orbitals involved are far apart in energy, thereby promoting coulombic attraction. On the other hand, the interaction between soft bases and soft acids is characterized by covalent bonding since the orbitals involved are close in energy.

It is questionable whether this sort of classification will be valid for mineral species, although there is some evidence in the literature that the metal cations that prefer to react with O donors also tend to preferentially adsorb O-containing

collectors on their mineral surfaces.[7] Similarly, S donors react preferentially with sulphide minerals. It has been pointed out that a bond between metal ions and soft bases makes the metal ions soft acids and vice versa.[8] This is especially important to borderline cations. From this viewpoint sulphidization of oxidized minerals should lead to an increase in the capacity of their reactive centres to react with sulphhydryl collectors.[7] Thus, the important contribution of donors on the mineral surfaces to interactions between minerals and chelating agents must be noted. Oxide minerals (which have O donors) of soft-acid metal ions would preferentially adsorb O⁻ and N-containing collectors, whereas their corresponding sulphides would preferentially adsorb S-containing collectors.

Properties of donor atoms

The donors O and N belong to the first row of elements in the periodic table and follow the octet rule[1–4,6,9,10,11] with valencies 2 and 3. The donors P and S belong to the second row, and these also follow the octet rule with valencies 3 and 2; however, P and S can exhibit higher valence states also since they have easily accessible vacant 3d orbitals. It is the electrons at or near the surface of atoms and ions that are the most important in determining their chemical and physical properties. This is especially true of donors P and S and transition metal ions. The latter have incompletely filled d orbitals, which have quite large fractions of their total volumes near the outsides of the ions, so they are easily accessible for bond formation. Additionally, the d orbitals are much more easily polarized, promoting a much more favourable orbital overlapping.

The important properties of the four donors O, N, S and P are summarized in Table 4.

O and N have 2p electrons and no accessible vacant d orbitals. S and P have 3p electrons in their outermost shells, but they have, in addition, easily accessible vacant 3d orbitals. The electronegativities decrease in the order

$$O > N > S > P$$
$$(3.5) \quad (3.07) \quad (2.44) \quad (2.06)$$

Consequently, O invariably forms ionic bonds with a majority of elements in the periodic table. Thus, chelating agents with O–O donors often form chelates with a large number of metals and are, therefore, less selective. The selectivity in general should increase from O to P.

The normal valencies are 2, 3, 2 and 3 for O, N, S and P, respectively. O has two unpaired electrons or two electron pairs to donate, but it seldom donates both pairs; only one pair is active. It can form a maximum of four bonds, but seldom attains all four (three bonds are common). O forms multiple bonds. N has five valence electrons, but only four orbitals and, therefore, a maximum of four bonds can be formed. It has one lone pair of electrons to donate when three electron-pair bonds are formed. Like its neighbours C and O, N also readily forms multiple bonds. In this respect N differs from P, S, As, Sb and Bi. S has two valence electrons and its normal valency is 2. But it has four orbitals and easily accessible d orbitals. Consequently, S can form two to six bonds. Similarly, P forms three to six bonds, although its normal valency is 3 and it has five valence electrons. All four donors have one active lone pair of electrons. Although O and N show strong $p\pi$–$p\pi$ bonding (because of the p outer orbitals and no d orbitals), S and P show very little or no tendency for $p\pi$–$p\pi$. On the other hand, only S and P show strong $d\pi$–$d\pi$ bonding. In addition, S and P show $d\pi$–$p\pi$ bonding (or back-bonding) since they can accommodate electrons from metals in their vacant d orbitals. This ability for back-bonding for P and S, indeed, is an important distinction that puts these donors in a special class. The polarizability of the lone-pair electrons on these donors follows an almost reverse

Table 4 Major properties of donor atoms O, N, S and P

	O	N	S	P
CONFIGURATION	$1S^22S^22P^4$	$1S^22S^22P^3$	$[N_E]\ 3S^23P^43D^0$	$[N_E]\ 3S^23P^33D^0$
ELECTRONEGATIVITY	3.5	3.07	2.44	2.06
VALENCE ELECTRONS	2	5	2	5
NORMAL VALENCY	2	3	2	3
# OF ORBITALS	4	4	4 + D	4 + D
# OF BONDS (VALENCY EXPANSION)	3	4	2-6	3-6
LONE PAIRS	2	1	1	1
$P\pi$–$P\pi$	STRONG	STRONG	POOR	NONE
$D\pi$–$P\pi$ (BACK-BONDING)	NONE	NONE	STRONG	STRONG
POLARIZABILITY	NIL	GOOD	STRONG	GOOD
H-BONDS	STRONG	STRONG	VERY WEAK	NONE
BONDS	MORE IONIC	LESS IONIC	COVALENT	COVALENT
STERIC ACCESSIBILITY	LOW	LOW	HIGH	HIGH

order of the electronegativities. Thus, for polarizability

$$O<N\ll S\sim P$$

O and N have the distinction of having the ability to form very strong H bonds, whereas S and P show little or no such tendency. Since P and S have d orbitals, and large size, these donors are much more sterically accessible for bond formation than O or N.

S is unique in its ability for catenation (forming bonds with itself); its common occurrence is in the form of an eight-membered ring. S is also known to form higher polymers. This unique feature of S is very important in all its interactions.

O and S can enter into chelation either through the ether or thioether form R–O–R, R–S–R, or the R–OH, R–SH. The –SH group is much more acidic than –OH and is highly polarizable, but not an effective acceptor. The R–S–R group forms pyramidal bonds and is an effective $d\pi$ acceptor. The R–SH shows a strong tendency for unidentate bonds, and the R–S–R shows a strong tendency to form chelate rings. The C=S is more ionizable and has a greater volume than C=O. S is a better donor than O with regard to sharing or donating the lone pair of electrons. Similarly, N is also a better donor than O.

It can be readily seen from the foregoing discussion that each donor has some unique properties. The acceptors also fall into certain well-recognized patterns. A judicial combination of donors for any given acceptor, taking into account the properties of both acceptors and donors (on mineral as well as the chelating agent), should provide the required selectivity in minerals processing applications.

The Molecular Orbital treatment is a powerful tool in understanding the donor–acceptor interactions. In this approach[8,9,10,12,13] the individual atoms with their nuclei are all placed in position and all the electrons concerned in bond formation are allotted to the various molecular orbitals. This treatment, however, has scarcely been used in understanding the mechanism of adsorption on minerals.

Substituent effects

The electron-donating or withdrawing tendencies of organic groups will influence the electron densities on donor atoms and the pK_a of the molecule.[9,11,14–17] The inductive effect results from electronegativity differences. Much stronger changes in electron density and delocalization of electrons arise from the resonance or mesomeric effects. With alkyl amines, for example, the alkyl group exerts an inductive effect on the nitrogen, making its unshared electron pair more available for bonding and thereby increasing the basicity.

$$R\rightarrow \overset{\displaystyle H}{\underset{\displaystyle H}{N}}:+H^+ \rightleftharpoons R\rightarrow \overset{\displaystyle H}{\underset{\displaystyle H}{N}}-H^+$$

In carboxylic acids the inductive effect of an alkyl group decreases the acidity; for formic acid the dissociation constant K_a = 17.7 x 10^{-5}, whereas for acetic acid K_a = 1.75 x 10^{-5}—almost one-tenth of the value for formic acid.

$$R\rightarrow C\langle\substack{O\\O}\ \}\ (-)$$

[K_a decreases]

If, on the other hand, the R group exerts an opposite inductive effect owing to certain substituents on R such as Cl or NO_2, the acid strength of the carboxylic acid increases.

$$R\leftarrow C\langle\substack{O\\O}\ \}\ (-)$$

[K_a increases]

The electronic effects are much stronger in aromatic compounds. A benzene ring could exert both electron-donating and electron-withdrawing effects. In benzoic acid the aromatic ring exerts an electron-withdrawing effect and, hence, it has a much higher K_a than that of acetic acid. An alkyl group in the *para* position on the ring exerts an electron-releasing effect. Groups such as —OH or —OCH$_3$ are electron-releasing owing to resonance, in spite of the electronegative oxygen and the electron-withdrawing inductive effects that the groups can be shown to possess.

The effect of electron-active substituents on an aromatic ring is well exemplified by aromatic hydroxy oximes. For an electron-releasing R group, such as —CH$_3$ or —OCH$_3$, the acid strength decreases, and the K_a increases, the release of electrons destabilizing the phenolate ion (the electron density on N may also increase):

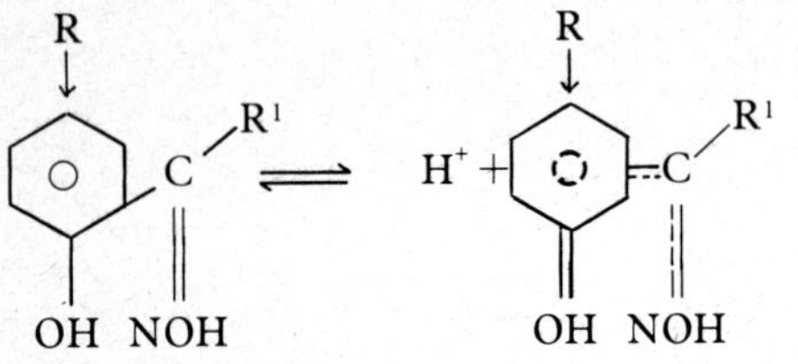

Substituents R = Cl, NO$_2$ etc., have opposite effects. The increase in electron density on donors can (a) enhance basicity and (b) therefore enhance σ bond stability, but (c) it may also decrease π acceptor ability of ligand and (d) therefore decrease donor π-bond stability.

Effects (c) and (d) could be pronounced for donors such as S since the donor–π bond (or dative bond) is formed between the metal and the organic reagent (in addition to the coordinative or s-bond) as a result of transfer of electrons from d orbitals of metal into vacant d orbitals of the donor. The formation of a dative bond, which reinforces the σ bond, is more probable for metals in their lower oxidation state since these would have more electrons than those in the higher oxidation state. Another important requirement is that the donor atom should have easily accessible vacant d orbitals (S). O and N, which do not have these d orbitals, do not form a dative bond. The nitrogen in oximes, however, forms a donor–π bond and, therefore, oximes are an exception. This explains the order of the ligand field stabilization effects observed for the chelates betweeen substituted salicylaldoximes (SALO) and Cu, Ni and Co (Table 5).

Table 5   pK_a of SALO and ligand field stabilizations[18]

pK_a $\pm$0.05	CH$_3$.SALO 11.06	SALO 10.70	Cl.SALO 10.25	NO$_2$.SALO 8.72
Metal $\Delta\beta_2$				
Cu	7.5	8.4	10.1	—
Ni	0.6	1.5	2.6	3.8
Co	0.8	1.1	2.4	3.5

The ligand field stabilization (LFS) increases for each metal as the pK_a decreases, i.e. as the electron density on the donor atoms decreases. This increase in LFS is attributed to the effect of substituents on the π-acceptor capability of the ligands.[18]

The thionocarbonates (Z-200 type) are not only excellent sulphide collectors but also offer an interesting case for study. The molecule contains the three important donors O, N and S. O and N are hard bases and S is a soft base.

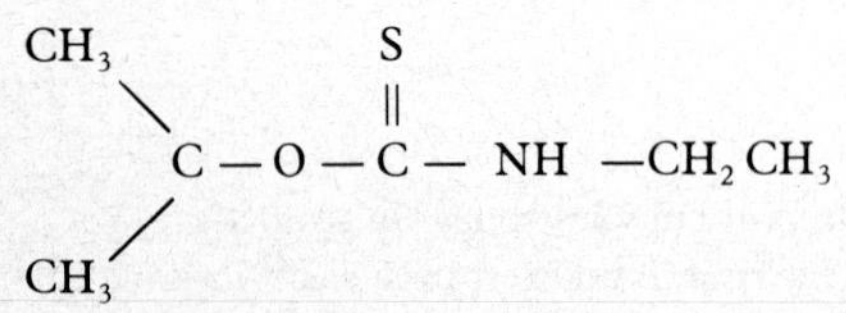

O and N exert an electron-withdrawing inductive effect.

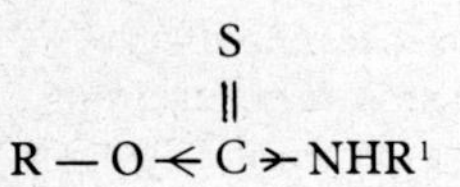

Simultaneously the groups RO and R^{1}NH could exert an electron-donating effect since the C$^+$—S$^-$ is more stable than —C=S. This tautomerism, together with the inductive effect, would delocalize electrons over the entire active group

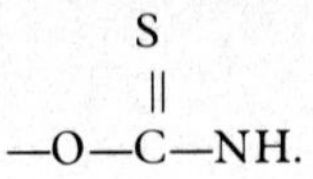

—O—C—NH. Thus,

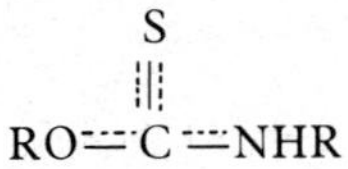

The electron-density order may follow S>O>N and, considering the sizes and polarizability of the donors, the steric accessibility would follow the order S>N,O. S may also show a tendency to bond with S on the sulphide surface. Thus, S is a very active donor in the thionocarbamate molecule.[7]

Substituents introduced into the molecule influence the electron distribution and, therefore, produce some interesting effects. Russian investigators[7,13] have done some extensive study on substituted thionocarbamates—especially phenyl substituents. The N-benzoyl thionocarbamate has been studied the most:

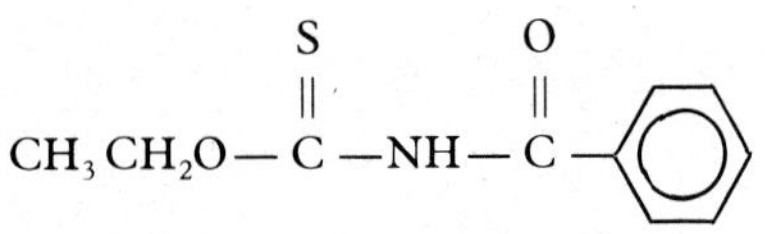

The aromatic ring accentuates the electronic effects compared with an alkyl analogue

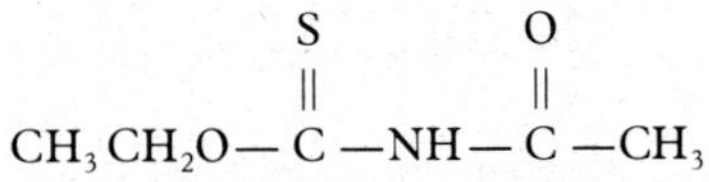

In addition, the O of the C=O exerts some electron-withdrawing effect, being strongly electronegative. The delocalization of electrons is more pronounced. There is a decrease in electron density on S and the pK_a.

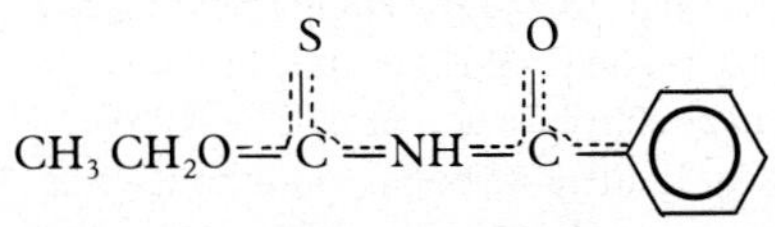

The substitution of a phenyl group instead of a benzoyl group may lead to a different electronic effect, since the phenyl group can either be electron-donating or electron-withdrawing.

For thiol collectors (dithiophosphates, xanthates, and dithiocarbamates) the electron densities on the active S donors depend on the inductive effects in the molecules.

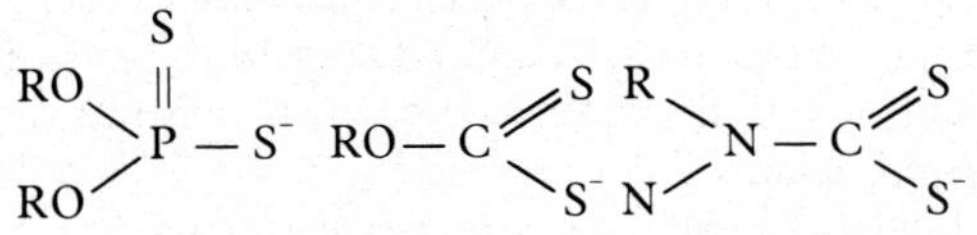

DTP   Xanthate   DTC

In DTP the two RO groups exert an electron-withdrawing inductive effect because of the higher electronegativity of the O atoms. This will delocalize the electron and stabilize the anion. Furthermore, P is more electropositive than C in xanthate. The electron density on S in DTP would be decreased and, consequently, DTP is a stronger acid, weaker collector and more selective than xanthate. These electronic effects are less pronounced in xanthate since there is one less RO group and C is less electropositive than P. In DTC N is less electronegative than

O and has a higher tendency to donate electrons. As a result the DTC would be a stronger collector, weaker acid and less selective than DTP (DTC<X<DTP).

Table 6   Structure and water solubility of various hydroxy oximes[19]

Name	Mol. Wt.	Water Solubility $\underline{M}$	Stock Solution $\underline{M}$
SALO (Salicylaldoxime)	137.1	2×10^{-1}	10^{-2}
OHAPO (O-Hydroxy Acetophenone Oxime)	151.2	4.5×10^{-3}	2×10^{-3}
OHBuPO (O-Hydroxy Butyrophenone Oxime)	179.2	5.0×10^{-4}	3×10^{-4} & 5×10^{-4}
OHBePO (O-Hydroxy Benzophenone Oxime)	213.2	1.5×10^{-4}	1.5×10^{-4} & 2×10^{-4} (1.2% acetone)
2H5MeAPO (2-Hydroxy-5-Methyl Acetophenone Oxime)	166.2	3×10^{-4}	3×10^{-4}
2H5MBAO (2-Hydroxy-5-Methoxy Benzaldoxime)	168.2	5×10^{-3}	5×10^{-3}
2HNAO (2-Hydroxy-1-Naphthaldoxime)	189.2	1×10^{-4}	1.25×10^{-4}
OHCHO (O-Hydroxy Cyclohexanone Oxime)	129.0	~1.0	5×10^{-1}

A recent detailed study with several water-soluble chelating agents (Table 6) of the class of aromatic hydroxy oximes showed several interesting effects of substitution. Flotation results obtained with these chemicals, which can be represented by the general formula

are given in Fig. 3. If R_2=H and R_1=—H, —CH$_3$ or —CH$_2$CH$_2$ CH$_3$, the effect on the collector efficiency was observed to increase in the order —H<<—CH$_3$<—CH$_2$CH$_2$CH$_3$.

The introduction of the first —CH$_2$ in SALO results in a much larger change in polarity of the molecule in comparison with further addition of two —CH$_2$ groups. This is reflected also in the water-solubility of the oximes–SALO, OHAPO and OH–BuPO. Furthermore, the electron-donating tendency of —CH$_2$ group may also favour chelation reaction.

Substitution of a phenyl group on R_1 (R_2=H) will make the molecule much less polar than SALO, as reflected in the water-solubility. On this basis OHBePO can be predicted to have a higher collector efficiency than SALO. The actual finding was, however, contrary to the prediction, suggested as being due to the possible steric hindrance to chelation offered by the second

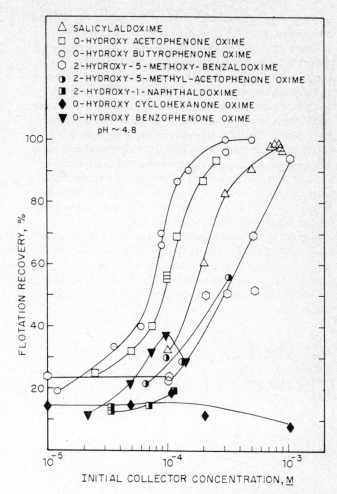

Fig. 3   Flotation of chrysocolla with salicylaldoxime and various substituted oximes[19]

benzene ring and the slower kinetics of adsorption of OHBePO. Adsorption tests, however, snowed the adsorption of OHBePO on chrysocolla to be significantly higher than that of SALO at the same oxime concentration, thereby suggesting that steric hindrance or slow chelation kinetics may not be responsible for the lower collector efficiency of OHBePO than that of SALO. Bubble size reduction observed during flotation may be the major factor in this case.

Substitution in R_2 by —CH$_3$(R_1=CH$_3$ or H, respectively) not only decreased the water-solubility of the parent oximes but also decreased the collector efficiency. The decrease in water-solubility is to be expected from the decrease in polarity of the molecule as a result of substitution. The decrease in collector efficiency could be attributed to the decrease in acid strength of the molecule owing to the increase in electron density on the phenolic oxygen caused by the nucleophilic substituents.[20] This can, however, increase the metal–ligand stability, as is generally observed.[3] The effect of electron-releasing groups on the ring is, therefore, generally favourable for chelation. Again, the reduction in bubble size appears to be the major factor in regard to the lower collector efficiency. This appears to hold for the low collector efficiency observed in the case of OHNAO, although the solution concentrations studied were severely limited by its low solubility.

Surface chelation

It is now generally believed that the adsorption of xanthate on galena proceeds by the formation of a chelate compound PbX on the surface of galena — as opposed to PbX$_2$ in the bulk.[21] Thus, the first layer on galena is believed to be PbX (with a high

215

tenacity) over which layers of PbX$_2$ build up by 'sheer physical attachment'.[22]

Taggart and co-workers[23] proposed that surface compounds differ greatly in their properties from normally expected bulk compounds. This is because the lattice ions or atoms on the surface have only a part of their coordination sphere to contribute to the formation of a surface compound. In addition, steric effects assume a particularly significant role for reactions on surface of mineral as opposed to those in the bulk. It is therefore conceivable that the first-layer compound on mineral may be different from the compound formed by a reaction in the bulk. If it proves that the bulk compound is energetically more favourable (even after taking into account the fact that adsorption of collector is, in general, energetically favourable), either the collector molecules or the surface compound comprising the collector molecules and lattice ion or atom will be scaled-off or detached. Of course, contribution to this detachment could also come from physical factors.

It is not known whether there is a direct relationship between surface and bulk compounds. In many studies a 1:1 surface

chelate has been tacitly assumed with little experimental evidence to support the assumption. Often elaborate structures for surface chelates have been proposed[24,25] (two examples are shown in Fig. 4).

The importance of distinguishing between surface and bulk chelates and quantitatively determining them in the same system under flotation conditions was clearly shown by Nagaraj and Somasundaran.[19,26,27] Surface chelate was favoured under certain conditions and these conditions coincided with those in which flotation of tenorite was obtained with SALO (Fig. 5). The bulk chelate formed under a wide range of conditions and this chelate was ineffective in causing flotation when dispersed in the bulk aqueous phase. This chelate, however, could aid flotation when it is still attached to the first layer on the mineral, as for thiol collectors on sulphides. Chander and Fuerstenau[28] discussed the roles of surface reaction and bulk reaction in the system chalcocite–DTP. Ananathapadmanabhan and Somasundaran,[29] based on detailed calculations of relevant mineral–collector equilibria, have clearly shown that much of the flotation results in the literature can be explained on the basis of surface reactions or precipitation (as opposed to bulk reaction or precipitation).

The influence of bulk chelation as opposed to surface chelation has not been taken into consideration in the past for most systems, even when the bulk chelation is very pronounced. For minerals that have finite solubility (or speciation) in water, bulk chelation (or precipitation) is inevitable if the kinetics of metal chelation (or other complex formation) are reasonably rapid. Any collector associated with this chelate can be considered essentially wasted in flotation systems.

Selective flocculation

The use of chelating agents for selective flocculation and dispersion has been clearly illustrated by several

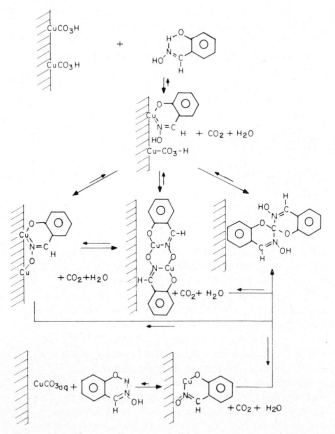

Fig. 4 Schematic illustrations ((a)(*left*)[25] and (b) (*above*)[24]) of surface chelations

216

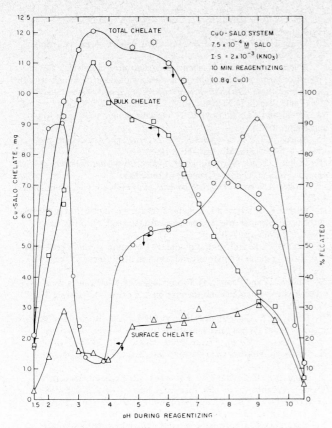

Fig. 5 Correlation of bulk and surface chelation of salicylaldoxime with tenorite and its species with flotation in tenorite-salicylaldoxime system[19]

Table 7 Examples of chelating agents as collectors

Reagents	Minerals
O–O type	
Cupferron	Cassiterite, uraninite, hematite
Salicylaldehyde	Cassiterite
α-Nitroso β-naphthol	Cobaltite
Acetylacetone	Malachite, chrysocolla
Alkylhydroxamic acid (IM50)	Chrysocolla, hematite and minerals containing Ti, Y, La, Nb, Sn and W
Phosphonic acids	Cassiterite
N–O type	
β-Hydroxy oximes	Cu oxide minerals
∝-Hydroxy oximes	Cu oxide minerals
8-Hydroxyquinoline	Cerussite, pyrochlore, chrysocolla
N–N type	
Diphenylguanidine	Cu minerals
Dimethylglyoxime	Ni minerals
Benzotriazole	Cu minerals
S–S type	
Xanthates	
Dithiophosphates	All sulphide minerals
Dithiocarbamates	
N–S type	
Mercaptobenzothiazole	Sulphide and tarnished sulphides
Dithizone	Sulphides
S–O type	
N-benzoyl O-alkyl thionocarbamate	Sulphides

investigators.[30–43] In some of these works chelating groups were incorporated into a polymeric-type molecule, which acted as selective flocculants. For example, Sresty and Somasundaran[32,37] observed hydroxypropyl cellulose xanthate containing an active thiol group to produce good flocculation of chalcopyrite with little effect on quartz (Fig. 6).

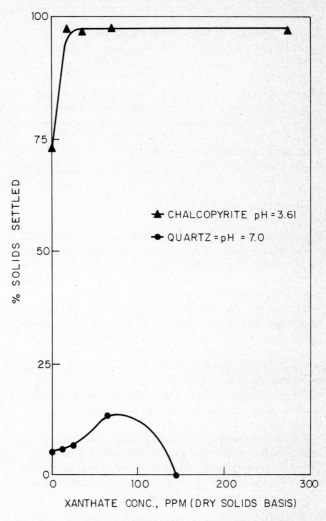

Fig. 6 Flocculation of chalcopyrite and quartz fines in terms of per cent solids settled in 45 s as a function of hydroxypropylcellulose xanthate (reagentizing time, 30 s)[37]

Tests with synthetic mixtures of these minerals showed both grade and recovery of chalcopyrite in the sediment portion to improve with increase in the concentration of the above polymer, but at very high dosages entrapment of the quartz by the bulky chalcopyrite flocs caused a decrease in the grade. This problem can, however, be overcome easily by cleaning the product by redispersion followed by settling.

Applications of chelating agents

Even though the relative proportion of chelating-type reagents among the industrial non-thio collectors is not significant, the actual number of chelating agents that have been tested successfully as collectors, depressants and flocculants for various mineral systems, at least on a laboratory scale, is large (Tables 7, 8 and 9). It is evident that the actual use of these types of reagents in the processing of minerals is likely to undergo a significant rise in the coming decades.

Table 8 Examples of chelating agents as depressants

Reagent	Mineral
Tartaric acid	Fluorite
Gallic acid	Fluorite
Alizarin red S	Siliceous gangue
Starch xanthates	Sulphides
Cellulose xanthates	

Table 9 Polymers containing chelating groups

Reagents	Application
Starch xanthates	
Cellulose xanthates	Selective flocculation and depression of sulphides
Poly (4- and 5-acrylamido salyclic acids)	Cation-exchange polymer for Fe^{3+}, Cu^{2+}, Cr^{3+} and UO_2^{2+}
Resin containing hydroxy oximes group	,, ,, ,,
Polyhydroxamic acids	,, ,, ,,

Concluding remarks

It is clear that although chelating agents can be used effectively for the flotation of ores, they do not possess absolute specificity towards mineral species and it is only the judicious choice of the chelating agents and conditions for selective separation that will make their use possible for the beneficiation of many problematic ores. In this regard a full understanding of the basic mechanisms involved in their chemical interaction with mineral species in the bulk and on the surface becomes essential, even though those in the interfacial region might be understood accurately only by use of new experimental approaches that will permit direct probing of this region.

The role of surface chelation versus bulk chelation has to be taken into account in the development of any mechanism for it to be of significant use in flotation.

Also, more importantly, the role of surface chemical alterations due to either change in oxidation state of surface species or precipitation of various dissolved mineral species will have to be considered for application of the above information in actual mineral processing systems.

Acknowledgement

The authors wish to thank the minerals and primary materials program of the National Science Foundation for the support of this work.

References

1. Dwyer F. P. and Mellor D. P. eds. *Chelating agents and metal chelates* (New York: Academic Press, 1964), 530 p.
2. Chaberek S. and Martell A. E. *Organic sequestering agents* (New York: Wiley, 1959).
3. Martell A. E. and Calvin M. *Chemistry of the metal chelate compounds* (Englewood Cliffs, N.J.: Prentice Hall, 1952).
4. Perrin D. D. *Organic complexing reagents* (New York: Wiley, 1964).
5. Pearson R. A. *J. Am. chem. Soc.*, **85**, 1963, 3533; *J. Am. chem. Soc.*, **89**, 1967, 103; *J. chem. Educ.*, **45**, 1968, 581; 643.
6. Kettle S. F. A. *Co-ordination compounds* (New York: Appleton-Century-Crofts, 1969), 220 p.
7. Glembotskii A. V. Theoretical principles of forecasting and modifying collector properties. *Tsvet. Metally, Mosk.*, **50**, no. 9 1977, 61–4. (Russian text); *Tsvet. Metally, N.Y.*, **18**, no. 9 1977, 68–72.
8. Fleming I. *Frontier orbitals and organic chemical reactions* (London: Wiley, 1976), 258 p.
9. Cotton F. A. and Wilkinson G. *Advanced inorganic chemistry* (London: Interscience, 1966).
10. Orgel L. E. *An introduction to transition metal chemistry* (London: Wiley, 1966).
11. Zolotov Y. A. *Extraction of chelate compounds* (Ann Arbor: Humphrey Science, 1970).
12. Wang T. T. *J. Central-South Inst. Min. Metall.*, **4**, no. 12 1980, 7–14. (Chinese text)
13. Bogdanov O. S. *et al.* Reagents chemisorption on minerals as a process of formation of surface compounds with a coordination bond. In *Proceedings of the 12th international mineral processing congress, 1977* (São Paulo, Brazil: D.N.P.M., M.M.E., 1982), vol. 2, 280–303.
14. Morrison R. T. and Boyd R. N. *Organic chemistry* (Boston: Allyn and Bacon, 1972).
15. March J. *Advanced organic chemistry: reactions, mechanisms and structure* (New York: McGraw-Hill, 1968).
16. Millar I. T. and Springall H. D. *Sidgwick's organic chemistry of nitrogen, 3rd edn* (Oxford: Clarenden Press, 1966).
17. Burger K. *Organic reagents in metal analysis* (New York: Pergamon, 1973).
18. Burger K. and Egyed I. J. Some theoretical and practical problems in the use of organic reagents in chemical analysis, V. *J. inorg. nucl. Chem.*, **27**, 1965, 2361–70.
19. Nagaraj D. R. and Somasundaran P. Chelating agents as collectors in flotation: oximes–copper minerals sytems. *Min. Engng, N.Y.*, **33**, Sept. 1981, 1351–7.
20. Patel R. P. and Patel R. D. Proton ligand stability constants of some ortho-hydroxy phenones and their oximes. *J. inorg. nucl. Chem.*, **32**, 1970, 2591–600.
21. Granville A. Finkelstein N. P. and Allison S. A. Review of reactions in the flotation system galena–xanthate–oxygen. *Trans. Instn Min. Metall. (Sect. C: Mineral Process. Extr. Metall.)*, **81**, 1972, C1–30.
22. Rao S. R. *Xanthates and related compounds* (New York: Marcel Dekker, 1971).
23. Taggart A. F. Taylor T. C. and Ince C. R. Experiments with flotation reagents. *Trans. Am. Inst. Min. Engrs*, **87**, 1930, 285–368.
24. Cecile J. L. Utilisation de réactifs en flotation. Doctoral thesis, Université Orleans, France, 1978.
25. Nagaraj D. R. Chelating agents as flotaids: hydroximes–copper mineral systems. Doctoral dissertation, Columbia University, 1979.
26. Nagaraj D. R. and Somasundaran P. Chelating agents as flotaids: LIX®–copper minerals systems. *Recent Developments in Separation Science*, **5**, 1979, 81–93.
27. Nagaraj D. R. and Somasundaran P. Commercial chelating extractants as collectors: flotation of copper minerals using "LIX" reagents. *Trans. Am. Inst. Min. Engrs*, **266**, 1979, 1892–7.
28. Chander S. and Fuerstenau D. W. On the floatability of sulfide minerals with thiol collectors: the chalcocite/diethyldithiophosphate system. In *Proceedings 11th international mineral processing congress, Cagliari, 1975* (Cagliari: Istituto di Arte Mineraria, 1975), 583–604.
29. Ananthapadmanabhan K. P. and Somasundaran P. Chemical equilibira in hydrolyzable surfactant solutions and their role in flotation. Paper presented to 112th AIME annual meeting, Atlanta, March 1983.
30. Kitchener J. A. Principles of action of polymeric flocculants. *Br. Polymer J.*, **4**, 1972, 217–29.
31. Somasundaran P. Selective flocculation of fines. In *The physical chemistry of mineral–reagent interactions in sulfide flotation: proceedings of symposium, April 6–7 1978* Richardson P. E. Hyde G. R. and Ojalvo M. S. comps. *Inform. Circ. U.S. Bur. Mines* 8818, 1980, 150–67.
32. Sresty G. C. Raja A. and Somasundaran P. Selective flocculation of mineral slimes using polymers. *Recent Developments in Separation Science*, **4**, 1978, 93–105.
33. Somasundaran P. Principles of flocculation, dispersion and selective flocculation. In *Fine particles processing* Somasundaran P. ed. (New York: AIME, 1980), vol. 2, 947–76.
34. Attia Y. A. and Fuerstenau D. W. Principles of separation of ore minerals by selective flocculation. In *Recent Developments in Separation Science*, **4**, 1978, 51–69.
35. Attia Y. A. I. and Kitchener J. A. Development of complexing polymers for selective flocculation of copper minerals. Reference 28, 1233–48.
36. Baudet G. *et al.* Synthèse et caractérisation de flocculants sélectifs à base de dérivés xanthés de la cellulose et de l'amylose. *Industrie minér.-minéralurgie* 1-78, 1978, 19–35.
37. Sresty G. C. and Somasundaran P. Selective flocculation of synthetic mineral mixtures using modified polymers. *Int. J. Mineral Process.*, **6**, 1980, 303–20.
38. Clauss C. R. A. Appleton E. A. and Vink J. J. Selective flocculation of cassiterite in mixtures with quartz using a modified polyacrylamide flocculant. *Int. J. Mineral Process.*, **3**, 1976, 27–34.
39. Attia Y. A. Synthesis of PAMG chelating polymers for the selective flocculation of copper minerals. *Int. J. Mineral Process.*, **4**, 1977, 191–108.
40. Rinelli G. and Marabini A. M. A new reagent system for the selective flocculation of rutile. In *Thirteenth international mineral processing congress, Warsaw, 1979* Laskowski J. ed. (Amsterdam, etc.: Elsevier, 1981), vol. 1, 316–45.

41. Rinelli G. and Marabini A. M. Dispersing properties of tanning agents and possibilities of their use in flotation of fine minerals. Reference 33, 1012–33.

42. Drzymala J. and Laskowski J. Chelating compounds as flotation reagents. *Physico-chemical Problems of Mineral Processing*, **13**, 1981, 39–64.

43. Barbery G. and Cecile J. C. Complexing reagents in flotation and selective flocculation: a review of possibilities and problems. Paper presented to CIM annual meeting, Winnipeg, 1983.

Flotation of a phosphate rock with carbonate–quartz gangue

C. Clerici, A. Frisa Morandini, A. Mancini and R. Mancini

Synopsis
The chemical and mineralogical characteristics of a sedimentary phosphate rock with a calcareous-siliceous gangue from a Syrian deposit are described. Analysis of the composition of the pure phosphate mineral (specific gravity +2.96 and 2.85–2.96) shows that a theoretical maximum grade of 33.0% P_2O_5 can be attained by beneficiation processes.

Enrichment of the phosphate rock by flotation has been obtained according to three different procedures: flotation of the carbonate gangue by use of fatty and fluosilicic acids, followed by separation of the silica by selective flocculation and flotation of the phosphate with an excess of fatty acid; selective flotation of the carbonates and silica in two steps by use of an amphoteric collector (Na salt of n-alkyl-aminopropionic acid); and flotation of the carbonates with the same reagent, followed by selective flocculation and flotation of the phosphate with excess fatty acid.

All three methods yielded a phosphate concentrate with a P_2O_5 grade in excess of 30%, but the best results were obtained with the second and the third techniques, which give better P_2O_5 recoveries.

Phosphate rock with a carbonate or quartz–carbonate gangue has long been a subject of research, interest arising from the present market situation in which phosphate production and supply are centred in a small number of countries and the fact that reserves of these types of ores are very significant.

Some results are given of a study on the beneficiation, by flotation, of a low-grade phosphate rock, with a siliceous carbonate gangue, from the Mediterranean basin (Eastern mine, Syria). Details of the ore composition, grade and physical characteristics were presented previously.[1]

Characteristics of raw mineral

Chemical and mineralogical composition

The mineralogical components of the raw ore are a 'phosphate mineral' (approximately 70%) (see below); a carbonate 'cement' the mechanical strength and crystal grain size of which vary markedly (crystal size ranges between a few millimetres and a few microns), which is composed mostly of calcite with a small amount of magnesian carbonate ('cement' approximately 20%); a siliceous fraction in which three components can be recognized—microcrystalline silica (chert), quartz grains and amorphous silica (opal) (approximately 6%); a clay fraction (hydrosilicates) (approximately 2%); and traces of feldspars, micas (usually very weathered), heavy silicates, opaque iron and titanium–iron oxides.

The chemical composition of the raw ore is 25.6% P_2O_5, 49.7% CaO, 10.4% CO_2 and 6.5% SiO_2.

Types of phosphatic minerals

Broadly speaking, two types of phosphatic minerals—'amorphous' and 'crystalline'—can be recognized, with well-distinguished optical characteristics, which probably relate to the mineral species collophane and francolite (the former is by far the more prevalent). Further differentiation of the phosphate varieties is possible within each general type. Amorphous phosphate occurs as round masses (ooliths) with a smooth surface, usually cloudy because of abundant inclusions of opaque substances and carbonates, which may be randomly scattered in the mass or follow a concentric pattern (the most frequent size of the ooliths ranges between 150 and 400 μm) and irregular shaped, translucent grains in which traces of the original biological structures can sometimes be detected.

Crystalline phosphate occurs as irregular grains, typically larger than the ooliths (up to 1 mm), always with a fibrous structure, reproducing the original biological structure, and microcrystalline, very fine-grained aggregates (crystal size <10 μm), which could be mistaken as a chert, though they are easily recognized as phosphate because of their high refractive index.

Composition of purified phosphatic minerals

It is known that the purified grains of sedimentary phosphate minerals (grains of free phosphate separated from gangues by careful laboratory treatment) do not attain the stoichiometric P_2O_5 grade of pure apatite (45.7%) (they are usually lower than 35% P_2O_5).

The lower grade is usually referred to the so-called 'endo gangue'—micro-inclusions of extraneous minerals that cannot be liberated at the grinding size currently adopted in the beneficiation process. In fact, the lower grade has many causes: in addition to the effect of the micro-inclusions, the anomalous chemical composition of the phosphate mineral and the extraneous molecules retained, with different mechanisms, in the phosphate should be considered.

In studying the beneficiation of a sedimentary phosphate rock it is very important, for the reasons given above, to know the P_2O_5 grade of the 'pure' phosphate mineral (that is, the grade of phosphate grains free from contaminants, apart from the so-called endo gangue). The grade of the pure phosphate mineral can provide a standard against which the results of a beneficiation process can be evaluated.

A 'pure' phosphate fraction was obtained from the raw material by the following treatment of the 74-200 μm material: prolonged scrubbing to obtain grains with surfaces free of contaminants; a three-stage gravity separation (lighter than 2.85, 2.85–2.96 and heavier than 2.96, the fraction lighter than 2.85 being discarded); and mild leaching of the 2.85–2.96 and +2.96 material with dilute (5%) acetic acid solution to eliminate the carbonates, leaving the phosphate unaffected. Microscopic study of the gravity ranges has shown that not all the grains of 'pure' phosphate minerals have a specific gravity higher than 2.96: a number of grains, apparently composed of free phosphate, belong to the immediately lower gravity class. As such, the 'pure phosphate mineral' obtained by purifying the +2.96 class alone could not be fully representative of the average grade of all the phosphate mineral varieties. A 'pure phosphate' product was obtained from both the +2.96 and the 2.85–2.96 ranges to detect any differences in the composition of the two types of phosphatic minerals.

The mineralogical purity of the gravity ranges obtained was checked by microscopic optical examination. Both classes were

Table 1   Chemical composition of purified phosphate fractions obtained from two types of sedimentary phosphate minerals with complex gangue (Conda results[2] given for comparative purposes)

| Mine | Gravity class | Grade, % by mass | | | | | | | | | |
		P_2O_5	CaO	MgO	SiO_2	Fe_2O_3	Al_2O_3	K_2O	Na_2O	F	CO_2
Eastern (Syria)	2.85–2.96	30.3	45.61	0.17	5.09	0.12	0.17	0.11	0.55	5.12	2.58
Eastern (Syria)	+2.96	33.5	50.55	0.20	2.08	0.09	0.10	0.06	0.69	4.40	2.03
Conda (Idaho, U.S.A.)	+2.94	33.6	48.70	0.30	5.87	0.83	0.94	0.30	0.84	3.90	2.11

subjected to careful chemical analysis* (Table 1).

The yields in the two gravity ranges of the phosphate fraction of the run of mine material were 83.5% in the +2.96 class and 16.5% in the 2.85–2.96 class. When the two sets of analyses are compared it can be seen that the lighter class is somewhat lower in P_2O_5 and CaO and richer in silica; the lower grade of the light class was, of course, expected. An upper limit of 33.0% P_2O_5 is suggested as the grade obtainable by a theoretical, perfect beneficiation of the raw material.

Determination of degree of liberation of raw material

Microscopic optical examination of the primary fines of the run of mine (carried out only on grain size classes finer than 833 μm) showed that the degree of liberation is approximately 60% in the coarsest class, increasing gradually in the finer classes: only in the classes finer than 400 μm can a degree of phosphate mineral liberation approaching 95% be observed.

To evaluate the degree of liberation attainable by grinding the +833 μm size of the run of mine the same class has been ground in a rod-mill to –833 μm, the ground material being divided in size ranges for microscopic examination. The liberation of the size classes of the ground rock proved to be lower than that of the same size classes of the primary fines (45% for the 833–589 μm material; approaching 95% only in the classes finer than 300 μm).

To obtain a satisfactory liberation of the phosphate mineral the raw ore has to be ground to –300 μm: in the beneficiation tests described in this paper the grinding size was actually 48 mesh (Tyler) (295 μm).

Evaluation of possible improvement of raw ore grade through attrition scrubbing and desliming

The P_2O_5 distribution is shown in Table 2. An increase in P_2O_5 grade is apparent in the material coarser than 150 mesh, but

Table 2   Distribution of P_2O_5 in size classes of raw rock ground to –48 mesh

Size, μm	% by mass	P_2O_5 grade, %	P_2O_5 distribution, %
295–208	31.3	27.1	33.1
208–147	28.4	27.6	30.6
147–104	13.7	26.7	14.3
104–74	6.9	22.7	6.1
74–53	3.5	22.2	3.0
53–37	3.9	21.0	3.3
37–25	4.1	20.7	3.3
–25	8.2	19.6	6.3
Total	100.0	25.6	100.0

* The authors wish to express their thanks to the Istituto per il Trattamento dei Minerali, Rome, for carrying out the analyses.

very poor results can be expected from a simple desliming process. For example, desliming with suppression of the –150 mesh (104 μm) material can provide a preconcentrated product that assays little more than 27% P_2O_5 (yield, 73.4%). The grade can therefore be improved only marginally, but at the cost of a loss in P_2O_5 recovery of more than 20%.

Poor results are obtained even with a protracted attrition scrubbing followed by desliming, the improvement in grade being insignificant. Tests of this approach consisted of desliming the ground ore, the –37 μm classes being discarded, attrition scrubbing of the +37 μm material (pulp density, 75% solids by mass) and desliming of the attritioned product, again by discarding the –37 μm material. An attrition time of 10 min was selected, preliminary tests having shown that a longer attrition time has no real benefit.

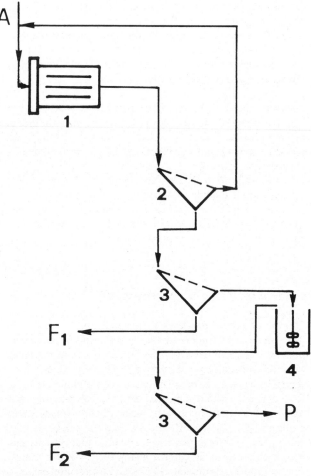

Fig. 1   Process adopted to prepare feed for flotation tests (A, run of mine; F_1, primary and grinding fines; F_2, attrition fines; P, attritioned and deslimed product (flotation feed); 1, rod-mill; 2, 48-mesh screen; 3, 400-mesh screen; 4, attrition cell)

Fig. 1 shows the scheme of the scrubbing plus desliming process adopted to prepare the material for the flotation tests. The results obtained are shown in Table 3. The –37 μm fines obtained by attrition have a composition similar to that of the grinding fines, being somewhat lower in P_2O_5 than the coarser classes; they represent, however, a very small fraction of the raw ore and suppression of these fines therefore has very little effect on the grade of the deslimed product.

Table 3   Distribution of P_2O_5 in size ranges obtained by grinding to 48 mesh, attrition and desliming

Product	Size, μm	% by mass	P_2O_5 grade, %	P_2O_5 distribution, %
F_1	–37	12.4	20.0	9.7
F_2	–37	2.8	21.0	2.3
P	295–208	31.0	27.5	33.1
	208–147	26.4	28.0	28.7
	147–104	12.6	27.1	13.2
	104–74	6.6	23.7	6.0
	74–53	3.6	21.9	3.1
	53–37	4.6	21.2	3.9
Total P	295–37	84.8	26.7	88.0
A	–295	100.0	25.7	100.0

Scrubbing and desliming have only minor effects on the grade, but should be taken into consideration as a preliminary step for a flotation process. The suppression of thin clay and calcite coatings on the grain surface is very beneficial in terms of grain liberation and response to the flotation agents, as well as avoiding the further production of noxious fines in the course of the flotation process.

Flotation

The separation by flotation of the phosphate from a carbonate gangue, already performed successfully on igneous phosphate minerals, cannot easily be applied to the sedimentary phosphates because of their structural complexity and of the simultaneous presence of different amorphous and porous phosphate types.

Various flotation procedures for sedimentary phosphates with calcareous gangue have been tested in laboratories over the last decade, but commercial-scale processes have yet to be introduced. Normally, the processes studied have been of the reverse flotation type, carbonates being recovered in the froth and phosphate in the residue. These methods can be assigned broadly to one of the following: a moderately selective collector (fatty acid) with a phosphate depressant and a selective collector active in regard to the carbonate gangue.

The processes that relate to the first class use of a variety of depressing agents—fluosilicic acid,[2] sulphuric acid,[3] phosphoric acid,[4] etc. For the second two families of collectors are employed—the phosphoric esters[5] and the amphoteric reagents.[6]

Test programme
Because of the overall difficulties the test programme had a comparatively modest target—to obtain P_2O_5 concentrates with a grade of at least 30%. This grade cannot be attained by simple attrition scrubbing and desliming.

The raw rock contains both carbonatic and siliceous gangue so, after a carbonate flotation step, phosphate–silica separation must be envisaged. The latter separation should represent less of a problem as some commercial processes that use it already exist.

Two procedures have therefore been studied. (1) The phosphates are first depressed by use of fluosilicic acid and the carbonates are floated with a fatty acid collector. An excess of fatty acid is then added to yield a selective flocculation and flotation of the phosphate (froth product), the silica remaining in the residue ('A' method). (2) Carbonates are first floated at high pH and silica is then floated at low pH; the reagent used is an amphoteric collector (a salt of the alkyl aminopropionic acid), its behaviour being anionic at high pH values and cationic at low ('B' method).

A third procedure, based on the results of the two already described and representing a combination of both, was then investigated: the carbonates are floated first at high pH with the amphoteric collector, phosphate then being flocculated and floated with an excess of fatty acids ('C' method).

Flotation tests were performed on a previously scrubbed and deslimed feed material (Table 3).

Beneficiation tests according to *A* method
The following parameters were constant in the tests: *carbonate flotation*—pH 6.5, phosphate depression with H_2SiF_6, a 10:1 emulsion of Acintol FA1 ('tall oil') with Emigol (emulsifier) as collector, added in two stages (500 g/t each) to avoid flocculation; *phosphate selective flocculation and flotation*—further addition of 500 g/t of Acintol FA1.

The optimal amount of depressant was found to be 200 g/t (lower amounts provide insufficient selectivity between carbonates and phosphates, higher amounts yield insufficient carbonates in the froth). Results obtained with 200 g/t of H_2SiF_6 are shown in Table 4. With a second addition of collector to improve the yield in the carbonate-bearing froth the carbonate–phosphate selectivity is lost. The effect of a two-stage addition of depressant and collector was therefore investigated. The best results were obtained with 300 g/t H_2SiF_6—200 g/t (before the first collector addition) and then 100 g/t (before the second collector addition) (Table 5).

Comparison of the results shown in Tables 4 and 5 indicates that carbonate–phosphate selectivity is improved markedly by the two-stage addition of the phosphate depressant. This advantage, however, is partly offset by a residual depression of the phosphates in the selective flocculation and flotation stage. Moreover, attempts to improve phosphate recovery in the floccules by a further addition of fatty acid led to a reduction in phosphate–silica selectivity.

The main difficulty in the use of the Acintol FA1 collector lies in its proneness to switch from a collecting action to a flocculating action with the addition of even a small excess of reagent. Considerable disturbances arose both in the first step (flocculation is not selective between phosphates and carbonate) and in the second (flocculation is selective between phosphates and silica only when it is gradual).

Beneficiation tests according to *B* method
The collector used is the Na salt of the *n*-alkyl aminopropionic acid (Cataflot CP1). Its structure encloses two ionic groups of opposite sign (carboxylic and amino); the first is dissociated at high pH values, the second at low, so the collector can exhibit anionic (at high pH) and cationic (at low pH) behaviour.

The amphoteric nature of this class of collectors[7] can be represented thus:

$$R-\overset{\overset{H}{|}}{\underset{\underset{H}{|}}{^+N}}-CH_2-CH_2C\overset{\overset{O}{\parallel}}{-}OH \qquad R-\overset{\overset{H}{|}}{N}-CH_2-CH_2C\overset{\overset{O}{\parallel}}{-}O^-$$

In an acidic environment   In a basic environment

By use of the Cataflot CP1 in an alkaline pulp and then in acidic pulp it is possible (in principle) to float successively the carbonates and the silica from the phosphate mineral. The reagent has been used in an emulsion with diesel oil to enable

Table 4   Flotation results by method A (200 g/t of H_2SiF_6 added initially)

| Product | Yield, % | Grade, % | | Recovery, % | |
		P_2O_5	Insoluble HCl	P_2O_5	Insoluble HCl
First carbonate froth	6.8	15.6	1.6	4.0	1.3
Second carbonate froth	34.8	26.4	1.9	34.5	8.2
Flocculated phosphate	49.3	30.5	5.3	56.4	32.3
Tailings	9.1	14.8	51.8	5.1	58.2
Feed	100.0	26.6	8.1	100.0	100.0

Table 5   Flotation results by method A (H_2SiF_6 added in to stages—200 g/t + 100 g/t)

| Product | Yield, % | Grade, % | | Recovery, % | |
		P_2O_5	Insoluble HCl	P_2O_5	Insoluble HCl
First carbonate froth	6.2	15.0	2.0	3.4	1.4
Second carbonate froth	22.1	24.9	2.3	20.4	5.6
Flocculated phosphate	49.7	30.8	3.9	56.7	21.5
Tailings	22.0	24.0	29.2	19.5	71.5
Feed	100.0	27.0	9.0	100.0	100.0

better froth control to be attained. Different ratios, r, of collector to diesel oil have been tested. Optimum pH and r values established from preliminary testing are, for carbonate flotation, pH 11 and $r = 3$, and for silica flotation pH 4 and $r = 0.5$.

In the first step (carbonate flotation) the range of collector amounts from 700 to 1050 g/t was investigated; carbonate froth yield increases with increase in collector, but the P_2O_5 grade of the froth product also rises correspondingly. In the second step (silica flotation) the collector amount was kept constant throughout at 700 g/t. The best results obtained by the B method are shown in Table 6.

Beneficiation tests according to C method

The C method comprises the combination of the A and B methods, consisting of carbonate flotation with Cataflot CPl, as for method B, and phosphate–silica separation by selective flocculation and flotation of the phosphate with Acintol FA1, as for method A. The main objective was to obtain a higher P_2O_5 recovery in the phosphate concentrate. Carbonate flotation was carried out in the manner described earlier (pH 11, $r=3$), but the amount of Cataflot collector was lowered from 1050 to 700 g/t to reduce the phosphate loss in the carbonate froth (see Table 6). Some changes were also made in the selective flocculation step to

Table 6   Flotation results by method B (carbonate flotation, pH 11, $r=3$, Cataflot CPl, 1050 g/t; silica flotation, pH 4, $r=0.5$, Cataflot CPl, 700 g/t)

| Product | Yield, % | Grade, % | | Recovery, % | |
		P_2O_5	Insoluble HCl	P_2O_5	Insoluble HCl
Carbonate froth	35.5	22.6	6.0	29.8	20.3
Silica froth	8.5	10.9	39.0	3.5	31.6
Phosphate concentrate (residue)	56.0	32.1	9.0	66.7	48.1
Feed	100.0	26.9	10.5	100.0	100.0

Comparison of the data shown in Table 6 with those in Tables 4 and 5 shows that the B method gives better results—higher P_2O_5 grades in the phosphate concentrate and a higher P_2O_5 recovery. This method is, however, more difficult to operate: the pH has to be changed from a very high to a very low value, collector consumption is higher and the collector is much more expensive. It was therefore decided to investigate an intermediate technique (C method).

improve the P_2O_5 recovery—pH adjustment to 6.5, addition of excess Acintol FA1 (1200 g/t), removal of the froth of the first flocculated phosphate concentrate, further addition of Acintol FA1 (240 g/t), recovery of a second phosphate concentrate froth and recleaning of the second phosphate concentrate.

The results obtained are shown in Table 7: as the two phosphate concentrates do not differ greatly in P_2O_5 grade they are combined in a composite phosphate concentrate.

Table 7   Flotation results by method C (carbonate flotation, pH 11, $r=3$, Cataflot CPl, 700 g/t; phosphate selective flocculation and flotation, pH 6.5, Acintol FA1, 1200+240 g/t)

| Product | Yield, % | Grade, % | | Recovery, % | |
		P_2O_5	Insoluble HCl	P_2O_5	Insoluble HCl
Carbonate froth	24.6	19.9	8.5	18.2	19.4
First flocculated phosphate	52.5	31.5	5.4	61.2	26.3
Second flocculated phosphate recleaned	16.4	29.6	9.1	18.1	13.8
Composite phosphate concentrate	68.9	31.0	6.3	79.3	40.1
Cleaner tailings	1.8	13.2	31.3	0.9	9.1
Rougher tailings	4.7	8.9	71.9	1.6	31.4
Feed	100.0	26.9	10.4	100.0	100.0

Table 8   Flotation results by method C (feed not scrubbed; operating conditions as Table 7)

Product	Yield, %	Grade, %		Recovery, %	
		P_2O_5	Insoluble HCl	P_2O_5	Insoluble HCl
Carbonate froth	16.8	19.0	9.0	11.8	16.8
First flocculated phosphate	25.4	29.3	2.8	27.5	7.9
Second flocculated phosphate recleaned	19.2	30.0	2.9	21.3	6.2
Cleaner tailings	0.5	27.9	25.2	0.5	1.5
Rougher tailings	38.1	27.5	16.1	38.9	67.6
Feed	100.0	27.0	8.9	100.0	100.0

Table 9   Comparison of phosphate concentrates obtained by different flotation methods

Method	Phosphate concentrate				
	Yield, %	Grade, %		Recovery, %	
		P_2O_5	Insoluble HCl	P_2O_5	Insoluble HCl
A	49.7	30.8	3.9	56.7	21.5
B	56.0	32.1	9.0	66.7	48.1
C	68.9	31.0	6.3	79.3	40.1

Importance of preliminary attrition of flotation feed

To assess quantitatively the advantages of a preliminary scrubbing of the feed method C was repeated on a sample that had been deslimed (to 37 μm) but *not* subjected to attrition scrubbing (Table 8). Attrition scrubbing improves both the carbonate floatability and (very markedly) the selective flocculation and flotation of the phosphate. The importance of the preliminary attrition of the flotation feed is therefore confirmed.

Concluding remarks

Table 9 shows the results of the different flotation procedures tested; the target of a commercial concentrate with a P_2O_5 grade $\geqslant$30% is attained by use of the methods described.

Method A, however, is less capable of yielding both high grade and high recovery. Methods B and C are decidedly superior, B being more suitable for obtaining high grades in the concentrate and C high recovery.

References

1. Clerici C. *et al.* Studio sull'arricchimento di un grezzo fosfatico a ganga complessa; nota preliminare. *Boll. Ass. Min. Subalpina*, **20**, no. 3–4 1983.
2. Rule A. R. Clark C. W. and Butler M. O. Flotation of carbonate minerals from unaltered phosphate ores of the Phosphoria Formation. In *Seminar on beneficiation of lean phosphates with carbonate gangue: 11th international mineral processing congress, Cagliari, 1975* (Cagliari: Istituto di Arte Mineraria, 1975), 167–86.
3. Alfano G. *et al.* La valorisation des rejets du traitement industriel du minerai phosphaté à gangue carbonatée de la mine de Djebel Onk. *Industrie minér. – les Techniques* 3-84, March 1984, 169–78.
4. Ratobylskaya L. D. *et al.* Development and industrial introduction of new concentration processes for phosphorites of complex mineral composition. Reference 2, 17–39.
5. Baudet G. *et al.* Enrichissement des minerais sédimentaires à gangue carbonatée par flottation inverse et double flottation utilisant un ester phosphorique comme collecteur. *Industrie minér. – les Techniques* 2-84, Feb. 1984, 125–49.
6. Blazy P. *et al.* French Patent Application 81/00052, Jan 5 1981.
7. Gupta S. C. and Smith R.W. Amphoteric collector–mineral charge interaction and flotation. In *Advances in interfacial phenomena of particulate/solution/gas systems; applications to flotation research* Somasundaran P. and Grieves R. B. eds (New York: American Institute of Chemical Engineers, 1975), 94–9. (*AIChE Symp. Series* no. 150, vol. 71)

Use of polyoxyethylene compounds in flotation of fluorite with fatty acids

E. W. Giesekke and P. J. Harris

Synopsis

The influence of commercial polyoxyethylene compounds (POEC) on the flotation recoveries of fluorite from an ore from the western Transvaal, South Africa, was investigated in bench-scale flotation tests. The flotation procedure included a pre-flotation stage for the removal of the sulphides. The pulp was then heated to 60°C and conditioned with sodium carbonate (for pH control) and wattle-bark extract (for the depression of calcite–dolomite). If used, the POEC was added with the fatty acid collector, and the fluorite concentrate (95% CaF_2 or more) was recovered after five or six cleaning stages.

A number of commercial POEC were used in the investigation—Triton X-100, Triton X-405, Brij-35, TWEEN-80, NPX (a series of oxyethylated nonyl phenols, $X = 2, 4, 6, 8, 10$ and 12) and TFX (a series of oxyethylated tall oil fatty acids, $X = 2, 5, 8, 11, 14, 17$ and 20). In the last two series X represents the average number of oxyethylene units per molecule. A dosage of 50 g of POEC per tonne was generally used.

For the series NPX and TFX and others mentioned above all POEC were beneficial to the flotation recoveries of fluorite, improving the recovery for a fixed fatty acid addition, but not necessarily the selectivity of the flotation process. POEC reduce the consumption of fatty acid collector. This collector–extender action of POEC is not influenced greatly by the average length of oxyethylene chain.

The addition of POEC to fatty acid collectors improves the lower grades and recoveries observed at lower pulp temperatures, e.g. 40 and 25°C.

The influence of excess Mg^{2+} and Ca^{2+} in solution and their effect on the flotation recoveries of fluorite with and without POEC are reported.

The presence of POEC prevents the multilayer adsorption of the calcium salts of fatty acids on the mineral surfaces. Under such circumstances the particles of fluorite are more uniformly covered with collector, minimizing the adsorption of the depressant, i.e. improving the hydrophobicity and floatability of the fluorite particles.

The use of polyoxyethylene compounds (POEC) in the processing of non-sulphide minerals has been rather limited. Doren and co-workers[1] reported on the successful use of Triton X-100 in combination with sulphosuccinate in the flotation of cassiterite. An oxyethylated nonyl phenol with an average of four oxyethylene groups per molecule (NP4) has been used in the selective flotation of apatite from calcite–dolomite.[2] Adsorption studies with NP4 have shown that it reduces the multilayer adsorption of fatty acid on both apatite and gangue minerals.[3,4] In flotation plants it has always been thought that NP4 acts mainly as a gangue depressant and emulsifier for the fatty acid, but studies on pure minerals[4] suggest that it improves the flotation of apatite. It is not clear how this specific POEC with an average of four oxyethylene units can promote the flotation of apatite.

Guest[5] reported on the use of Emigol—a product manufactured by Hoechst, South Africa, as a fatty acid emulsifier in the flotation of fluorite. The exact composition of Emigol is not known, but it contains a significant amount of POEC.

The study described here was conducted in two stages. The first involved a general survey to establish the extent to which POEC can be used to promote the flotation, with a fatty acid collector and wattle-bark extract (WBE)[5,6] as a depressant, of fluorite in the presence of calcite and dolomite. A wide range of POEC was used with considerable variation in average length of oxyethylene chain and nature of the alkyl group. This was done with the aim of establishing whether any structural features of the POEC are important in producing improved flotation recoveries. In the second stage of the investigation a compound was chosen that was fairly representative of most POEC for more detailed study. Attention was given to the extent to which POEC can eliminate the need for heating up of the pulp and to the way in which Ca^{2+} and Mg^{2+} ions, with POEC, affect the flotation recoveries of CaF_2.

The flotation process for the fluorite-bearing ore was developed in the Ore-dressing Division of the Council for Mineral Technology (Mintek)[7] and was used in the present investigation with minor alterations.

Experimental

Characteristics of ore

The ore, which emanated from the western Transvaal, South Africa, had a fluorite content of between 20 and 30%. The main gangue minerals were dolomite and, to a lesser extent, calcite. The other minerals present, amounting to a few per cent, were sulphides (pyrite, pyrrhotite, chalcopyrite and sphalerite), pyrophyllite and quartz.

During the initial stages of the survey on the effects of the various POEC on the selective recovery of fluorite, samples of the ore were removed in small batches from the ore feed to pilot-plant tests that were being conducted at Mintek.[7]

For the second phase of the study a much larger sample of the ore was obtained and crushed to less than 1.7 mm and blended fully. The fluorite content of this sample was 22.7%.

Flotation procedure

The tests were conducted in a Denver D-12 laboratory flotation machine in a 2-1 flotation cell. The conditioning was done at an air-impeller speed of 2100 rev/min and all the floats at 1500 rev/min. The following procedure was adopted.

(1) 1 kg of ore was ground with 1 l of water in a rod-mill. For the initial stages of the survey, i.e. when small samples from the feed to the pilot plant were being used, the ore was ground for 12 min. It was found, however, that slightly lower recoveries than expected were obtained and, for the blended sample, the grinding time was increased to 20 min. The sieve analyses for the 12- and 20-min grinds were 48% and 79% smaller than 75 μm and 28% and 46% smaller than 38 μm, respectively

(2) Sulphide minerals were removed in a pre-float. The ore was conditioned for 2 min with 3 g of potassium amyl xanthate per

tonne and 15 g of Dowfroth 200/t, and then floated for 2 min. A further 15 g/t of Dowfroth 200 was then added and the flotation was continued for a further 8 min.

(3) The pulp (density, 1.45 kg l^{-1}) was heated to the required temperature (usually 60°C).

(4) 1.5 kg of sodium carbonate (pH control at pH 9) and 600 g of WBE (depressant) were added per tonne, and the pulp was conditioned for 5 min.

(5) 50–60 g/t of POEC (if used) and varying amounts (150–500 g/t) of Priolene were added, and the pulp was conditioned for a further 5 min. It should be noted that the POEC was always added before the fatty acid.

(6) A rougher float was done for 10 min.

(7) The concentrate was then cleaned in the same cell at least six times. The pulp was conditioned for 2 min each time and then floated to completion. In the fourth, fifth and sixth cleaning stages 10, 10 and 25 g/t of WBE, respectively, were added before the conditioning.

Description of reagents

The fatty acid collector commercially known as Priolene 6921 (kindly supplied by Silicate and Chemical Industries, Wadeville, South Africa) was used without further purification. The collector consisted of a mixture of fatty acids with 63.6% oleic acid and 11.8% linoleic acid (analysis by manufacturer). The iodine value[8] was measured and found to be 92.

WBE in the bisulphited form is a mimosa extract[9] and was used as supplied by the Wattle Bark Industry of South Africa.

The different commercial POEC used are detailed in Table 1. Each POEC consists of a mixture of different polyoxyethylene homologues, i.e. molecules with the same organic hydrophobic portion but different oxyethylene chain lengths, distributed about some mean value (Table 1).

Results

Flotation of fluorite with POEC at 60°C

Pilot-plant tests[7] had indicated that a temperature of 60°C was necessary in the rougher stage for sufficiently high recovery to be achieved at the required grade of 95% fluorite. Consequently, this temperature was used in all the floats in this general survey (i.e. the first stage of the investigation). In addition, only the final grade and recovery after six stages of cleaning were analysed for each test. The grade–recovery curve for tests with only fatty acid is shown in Fig. 1 by the solid line (the influence of the series of nonyl phenol POEC (NPX) on the grade–recovery curve is also shown). Each point represents the grade and recovery of the final concentrate for a constant addition of NPX and varying amounts of fatty acid.

The influence of the other POEC is shown in Fig. 2. Again, the solid line represents the grade–recovery curve when only fatty acid is used, and the individual points represent the grade and recovery when the concentration of POEC was constant at 50 g/t and varying additions of fatty acid were made. In all cases it was found that within the scatter caused by the variations in feed grade very similar grade–recovery behaviour was obtained with all the POEC. For an equivalent grade and recovery, however, the amount of fatty acid required in the presence of the POEC would be reduced by between 20 and 45% of the amount required in the absence of POEC. The POEC appear to extend the collector action of the fatty acid and can be termed collector–extenders. This action does not appear to show any specific variation with the average length of oxyethylene chain or with the type of structure of the POEC used. It was also shown that the POEC themselves did not exhibit any collector action in the absence of the fatty acid.

The possibility that the POEC were acting as emulsifying

Table 1   Characterization of polyoxyethylene compounds used as collector–extenders

Commercial name	Supplier	Abbreviation in text	Composition	Average number of OE group
None	ICI	TFX	VANTAL Al-55 tall oil fatty acid ethoxylated to various degrees	$X = 2, 5, 8, 11, 14, 17, 20$
None	Berol-Kemi	NPX	Polyoxyethylated p-nonyl phenol	$X = 2, 4, 6, 8, 10, 12$
Triton X-100	BDH (Rohm and Haas)	Triton X-100	Polyoxyethylated, $p,tert$-octyl phenol	9-10
Triton X-405	BDH (Rohm and Haas)	Triton X-405	Polyoxyethylated $p,tert$-octyl phenol	40
Brij-35	BDH (Atlas)	Brij-35	Polyoxyethylated lauryl alcohol	23
TWEEN 80	BDH (Atlas)	TWEEN 80	Polyoxyethylated sorbital mono-oleate	20

The saponified fatty acid was prepared from the neutralization of Priolene 6921 with caustic soda in ethyl alcohol by use of a drop of 1% phenol phthalein indicator dissolved in ethyl alcohol. The saponified acid was dried and stored in a vacuum dessicator at room temperature.

The corresponding calcium or magnesium salts of the fatty acid were prepared from an aqueous solution of the saponified fatty acid by the addition of an excess (5 ml) of 1 M calcium chloride or magnesium chloride. So that this insoluble precipitate would be distributed throughout the pulp the solution that contained the precipitate was added to the pulp. In this way an excess of Ca^{2+} or Mg^{2+} was also added to the pulp.

Unless stated otherwise, all the other reagents used were of analytical grade.

agents and so increasing the saponification rate of the fatty acid was also investigated by the use of saponified fatty acid as the collector. No difference in the grade and recovery behaviour was observed, however, which indicates that it was not the improved emulsification behaviour of the POEC that was influencing the amount of fatty acid required.

The collector-extender action of POEC in the flotation of fluorite with fatty acid seems to be generally observed for such compounds. The effect is best observed when the fatty acid content is reduced to yield a poor recovery. The addition of POEC in a ratio of 1 to 4 to fatty acid drastically improves the recovery of fluorite, with almost no decrease in grade. When higher amounts of POEC were used a sharp decrease in grade was observed without any further increase in recovery.

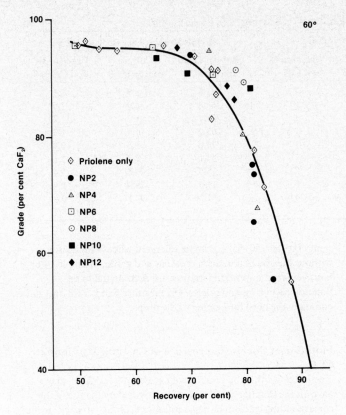

Fig. 1 Flotation of fluorite with fatty acid and polyoxyethylated nonyl phenols (NPX) at 60°C

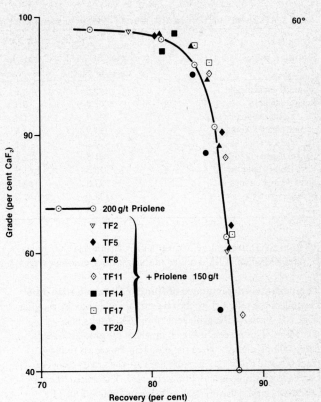

Fig. 3 Flotation of fluorite with fatty acid and with different polyoxyethylated tall oil fatty acids (TFX) at 60°C

In the first stage of the investigation the ore that had been ground for 12 min was used. Grades of 90% CaF$_2$ were achieved at a recovery of about 75%. As indicated by the sieve analysis, the CaF$_2$ in this ground material was insufficiently liberated, and the grinding time was increased for the later study. The ore ground for 20 min yielded grades of 90% CaF$_2$ at a recovery of about 85% (Fig. 3).

The series of ethoxylated tall oil fatty acids was chosen as the best series of POEC for further study under more controlled conditions because of the indications in Fig. 2 for TF5 that an improvement in the grade–recovery behaviour may be possible with this type of POEC. The average oxyethylene chain length varied from 2, 5, 8, 11, 14 and 17 to 20. Because these floats were conducted on reproducible feed material with a constant CaF$_2$ content the points shown in Fig. 3 were obtained from an analysis of the various cleaner tailings and the final concentrate of a single test. Variations of the average oxyethylene chain length had hardly any influence on the selective recovery of fluorite. The best grade–recovery curves were found for TF11 and TF17 when compared with the solid line that represents the values in the absence of TFX. It was felt, however, that the improvements in the selectivity of TF11 and TF17, and to some extent TF8, are too small to be significant and do not justify any further discussion. The collector-extender action of TFX is clearly demonstrated. The values plotted in Fig. 3 were obtained for a 25% reduction in fatty acid in the presence of TFX.

The TFX chosen for further study was TF8: there was no particular reason for this choice, though in the TFX series an X of 14 or more represents waxes. TF8 is a liquid and is easy to handle and gave results fairly representative of most of the POEC used in this investigation.

Table 2 shows the distribution of CaF$_2$ in the different stages for two floats at 60°C—one with only Priolene (200 g/t) and the other in which Priolene (150 g/t) was used with TF8 (50 g/t). Both the valuable and the gangue material apparently interact with the collector because approximately 90% of the ore floated in the rougher stage. The separation between CaF$_2$ and dolomite occurred primarily in the first three cleaner stages. In the fifth and sixth cleaner stages (when additional WBE was used) the concentrate was cleaned at the expense of a loss of fluorite. What Table 2 clearly shows is that the addition of TF8 reduces the CaF$_2$ lost in the cleaner stages, particularly in the last three stages, in comparison with those in the absence of TF8, i.e. only Priolene. These results indicate that the POEC make the

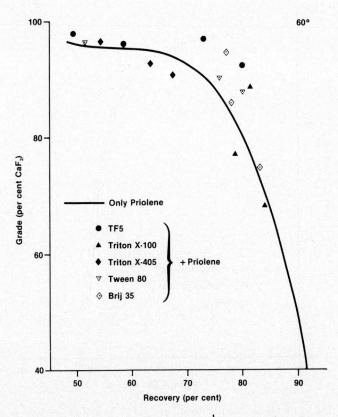

Fig. 2 Flotation of fluorite with fatty acid and different POEC at 60°C

Table 2　Influence of TF8 on distribution of CaF_2 in various flotation stages (head grade, 22.71% CaF_2; 60°C)

Flotation stages	Priolene 6921, 200 g/t; no TF8			Priolene 6921, 150 g/t; 50 g/t TF8		
	Mass of dried material, g	CaF_2 in material, %	Fraction of total CaF_2, %	Mass of dried material, g	CaF_2 in material, %	Fraction of total CaF_2, %
Sulphide concentrate	193.0	8.9	7.6	181.3	8.8	7.1
Rougher tailings	63.6	8.8	2.5	63.8	4.9	1.4
First cleaner tailings	242.9	1.8	1.9	225.1	1.7	1.7
Second cleaner tailings	181.9	1.6	1.3	203.0	1.4	1.3
Third cleaner tailings	74.2	3.1	1.0	74.0	2.8	0.9
Fourth cleaner tailings	31.3	12.4	1.7	34.1	7.3	1.1
Fifth cleaner tailings	16.3	41.5	3.0	15.8	20.1	1.4
Sixth cleaner tailings	17.8	80.8	6.4	11.0	59.9	2.9
Final concentrate	171.6	97.8	74.5	187.7	97.1	80.6
Total	992.6		99.9	995.8		98.4

flotation concentrate more hydrophobic, causing less fluorite to be removed when WBE is added in the last three cleaning stages.

Temperature-dependence of fluorite flotation with TF8
Heating of the pulp before the reagents are added to the rougher stage is essential to the achievement of good grades and recoveries. This is seen in Fig. 4, in which the grade-recovery curve falls off sharply when the pulp temperature is reduced from 60 to 40 to 25°C. The solid lines are the grade-recovery curves when Priolene and TF8 were used. The dotted lines are the curves for the use of Priolene alone (without TF8). The recoveries and grades at 60°C correspond to data already shown in Fig. 3 and Table 2. When only Priolene was used (dotted lines in Fig. 4) the grades and recoveries decreased sharply from 60 to 40°C. When the temperature was further reduced to 25°C very little difference was observed between the grade-recovery curves at 40 and at 25°C. The dosage of collector at lower temperatures needs to be increased more than twofold for any fluorite to be recovered.

The addition of TF8 with collector improves the selectivity of the flotation process at 40°C, but not at 60 or 25°C. Lower bulk

temperatures (50–55°C) can be tolerated when TF8 is used without the loss of too much recovery and grade. Without TF8, however, such lower temperatures are detrimental to the flotation recoveries and grades. On the other hand, TF8 does not eliminate the need for heating of the pulp.

Flotation of fluorite in presence of Ca^{2+} and Mg^{2+} ions at 60°C
The influence that the presence of excess Ca^{2+} and Mg^{2+} may have on the flotation process was investigated by the use of the corresponding calcium or magnesium salts of the fatty acid as the collector. The flotation response with the calcium salt of the fatty acid is shown by the broken line in Fig. 5. The solid line depicts the flotation response when the calcium salt of the fatty acid and TF8 are used as collector and collector–extender, respectively. The calcium salt of the collector acts as a good collector (86% recovery at a grade of 90%); in fact, it is slightly better than that shown in Fig. 3 for the fatty acid float. The TF8 has no effect on the selectivity of the process, but reduces the consumption of collector to the same extent as is shown in Fig. 3.

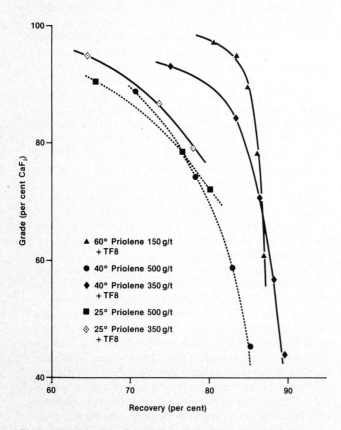

Fig. 4　Flotation of fluorite with fatty acid in absence (---) and presence of TF8 (——) at different temperatures

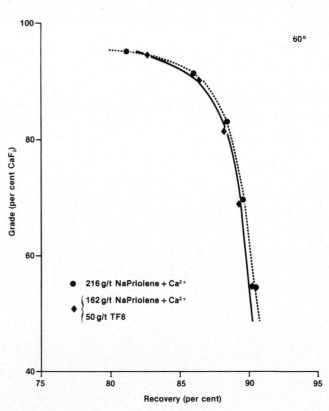

Fig. 5　Flotation of fluorite with fatty acid and Ca^{2+} in absence (---) and presence of TF8 (——) at 60°C

The improved recoveries with the calcium salt of Priolene (over those with unsaponified Priolene) are partly due to a slight variation in the technique for the removal of the sulphide concentrate. By more careful scraping the percentage fluorite lost in the sulphide float could be reduced by between 3 and 4%. This fluorite was now available for recovery in the final concentrate.

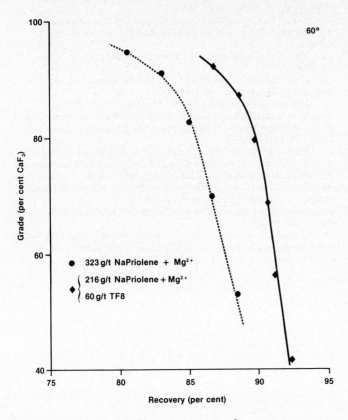

Fig. 6   Flotation of fluorite with fatty acid and Mg^{2+} in absence (---) and presence of TF8 (——) at 60°C

The grade–recovery curve for the magnesium salt of the fatty acid is shown by the broken line in Fig. 6. More fatty acid (33%) was needed to achieve the same grade and recovery as with the unsaponified fatty acid (Fig. 3) or its corresponding calcium salt (Fig. 5). The addition of TF8 with the magnesium salt of the fatty acid significantly improved the recoveries and grades (solid line in Fig. 6). The distributions of fluorite between the different flotation stages for the flotation of fluorite with the magnesium salt of the fatty acid with and without TF8 are shown in Table 3.

In the presence of Mg^{2+} ions the whole character of the flotation process changed, the amount of solids recovered in the rougher stages decreasing from about 90 to 80% or less. In the absence of TF8 the fluorite content of the rougher tailings increased and the amount of fluorite present in the tailings of the last three cleaning stages increased dramatically, which indicates that both the fluorite and the dolomite were very much less hydrophobic. TF8 significantly enhanced the floatability of the fluorite, however, without a corresponding increase in the floatability of the dolomite. Thus, a very much more selective rougher float was obtained, and very little fluorite was found in the tailings of the final cleaning stages. This change in character was not observed when the calcium salt of the fatty acid was used. The behaviour in the presence of Ca^{2+} ions was very similar to that observed when the unsaponified fatty acid was used. Although the Mg^{2+} salt gave better selectivity, it was apparently not as efficient a collector, particularly in the absence of TF8, as the corresponding Ca^{2+} salt since higher addition levels were required. The addition of POEC to fatty acid fluorite floats that use water with a high magnesium content would therefore be beneficial.

Discussion

Role of insoluble fatty acid salts in flotation of fluorite

The fatty acid collector, Priolene 6921, consists primarily of oleic acid, which is saponified in the alkaline medium of the bulk. The extent to which the saponified fatty acid reacts with alkali-earth cations to produce insoluble precipitates depends on the concentration of these ions in the medium of flotation and the solubility product of the precipitates. A number of values are quoted in the literature for the solubility product of calcium oleate: Yoke[10] gave a value of 9.62×10^{-15} and Fuerstenau and Palmer[11] 2.51×10^{-16} for the solubility product of magnesium oleate. These values suggest that, for calcium and magnesium values greater than 10 ppm, calcium and magnesium oleates must form in solution. The presence of these ions in solution arises from the dissolution of the minerals present. The amount depends on the solubility product and the particle size of the fluorite, calcite and dolomite. In the present work it was found that the Ca^{2+} concentration exceeded 14 ppm even after the addition of the fatty acid, and very often, owing to the recyling of the water, the concentrations of Ca^{2+} and Mg^{2+} greatly exceeded this value. Thus, in most salt-type flotation processes it is highly probable that a significant precipitation of the acid occurs in solution. From the results (Figs. 5 and 6) it is evident that, at 60°C, these precipitates themselves can act as collectors. The presence of high concentrations of Mg^{2+} ions may, however, be detrimental to the flotation. Under these circumstances the presence of POEC appears to be necessary for selective recoveries to be achieved (Fig. 6).

The possibility that POEC can form complexes with the alkaline-earth cations is well known.[12] These interactions are assumed to be weak in comparison with the formation of the

Table 3   Influence of TF8 on distribution of fluorite in flotation stages when magnesium salt of fatty acid used (head grade, 22.71% CaF_2; 60°C)

Flotation stages	323 g/t Mg^{2+}–Priolene; no TF8			216 g/t Mg^{2+}–Priolene; 60 g/t TF8		
	Mass of dried material, g	CaF_2, %	Fraction of total CaF_2, %	Mass of dried material, g	CaF_2, %	Fraction of total CaF_2, %
Sulphide concentrate	121.7	4.8	2.3	113.6	5.0	2.5
Rougher tailings	155.5	4.7	3.2	213.0	2.3	2.2
First cleaner tailings	182.3	3.7	3.0	164.7	2.1	1.5
Second cleaner tailings	155.9	2.9	2.0	134.2	2.0	1.2
Third cleaner tailings	96.6	4.1	1.8	67.6	1.9	0.6
Fourth cleaner tailings	47.0	7.7	1.6	42.8	4.4	0.8
Fifth cleaner tailings	26.6	17.1	2.0	25.5	9.8	1.1
Sixth cleaner tailings	13.5	40.9	2.5	17.1	25.2	1.9
Final concentrate	192.1	94.5	80.6	212.0	92.1	86.8
Total	991.2		99.0	990.5		98.6

calcium and magnesium salts of the fatty acids, and will not prevent the formation of these salts.

Role of temperature in flotation of fluorite

The necessity to heat the pulp to yield the required recoveries and grades in the flotation of fluorite is demonstrated in Fig. 4. Although the addition of TF8 improved the recoveries and grades, especially at 40°C, heating of the pulps seems more beneficial than the addition of POEC.

The role of temperature in mineral-oleate systems has been discussed by Fuerstenau.[13] He suggested that at elevated temperatures the adsorption process is activated from physisorption to chemisorption. The adsorption of insoluble precipitates on minerals is neither well documented nor clearly understood. According to Fuerstenau's suggestion, it seems feasible that, at low temperatures, these precipitates are adsorbed physically or are weakly held on all minerals. At higher temperatures, however, a reaction takes place that ensures a more firmly held adsorbate, which is not easily removed by the dispersive action of depressants. This reaction appears to take place only on fluorite and not on the gangue minerals dolomite and calcite. Details of this reaction are not available.

Co-adsorption of oleates and POEC on minerals

The adsorption of sodium oleate (as calcium oleate) on fluorite and calcite occurs as multilayers.[14,15] (Van der Linde[3] drew similar conclusions regarding the adsorption of sodium oleate on apatite and calcite.) Photomicrographs showed that the multilayers of calcium oleate occur as large blisters or islands on the mineral surface[14]—to a greater extent on fluorite than on calcite. The co-adsorbed POEC reduces the build-up of multilayers of calcium oleate on the mineral surface, which causes the adsorbed calcium oleate to form a more uniform coating on the fluorite surface and so to prevent the dissolution of mineral.[15] On calcite the dissolution of the mineral is not prevented by co-adsorbed POEC.

This spreading or smoothing action of co-adsorbed POEC on adsorbed calcium oleate (and presumably magnesium oleate) makes the fluorite surface more hydrophobic (this action being independent of the length of the oxyethylene chain). It is less likely that WBE could be co-adsorbed on such a hydrophobic mineral surface. All this leads to a more efficient use of adsorbed collector as the flotation results have indicated. The inherent difference at 60°C between calcium oleate adsorbed on fluorite from that on calcite is, however, the primary cause for the separation of these minerals by flotation. The addition of POEC only enhances this difference but, of itself, is unable to promote any collector action.

Acknowledgement

This paper is published by permission of the Council for Mineral Technology (Mintek). The authors express their gratitude to Messrs E. L. Benjamin and R. van Gemert for their assistance in the experiments.

References

1. Doren A. van Lierde A. and de Cuyper J. A. Influence of non-ionic surfactants on the flotation of cassiterite. In *Thirteenth international mineral processing congress, Warsaw, 1979* Laskowski J. ed. (Amsterdam, etc.: Elsevier, 1981) vol. 1 86–106.
2. Lovell V. M. Froth characteristics in phosphate flotation. In *Flotation: A.M. Gaudin memorial volume* Fuerstenau M. C. ed. (New York: AIME, 1976), vol. 1, 597–621.
3. Van der Linde G. J. A study of the reactions between reagents and minerals in the flotation of apatite. Ph.D. thesis, Rand Afrikaans University, 1980. (Afrikaans text)
4. Harris P. J. and Coetzee A. J. Private communication.
5. Guest R. N. Laboratory and pilot-plant tests on ore from the Witkop fluorspar mine. *Rep. natn. Inst. Metall.* no. 2004, 1979, 26 p.
6. Ryan P. J. A review of the fluorspar-mining industry in South Africa. In *Proceedings twelfth CMMI Congress, Johannesburg, 1982* Glen H. W. ed. (Johannesburg: South African Institute of Mining and Metallurgy, 1982), vol. 1, 229–47.
7. Loo J. P. *et al.* Private communication.
8. Siggia S. *Quantitative organic analysis via functional groups, 3rd edn* (New York, etc.: Wiley, 1963), 316–8.
9. African Territories Wattle Industry Fund Ltd. The properties, composition, reactions and industrial applications of mimosa extract, 1980.
10. Yoke J. T. The solubility of calcium oleate soaps. *J. phys. Chem.*, **62**, 1958, 753–5.
11. Fuerstenau M. C. and Palmer B. R. Anionic flotation of oxides and silicates. Reference 2, vol. 1, 148–96.
12. Jarber A. M. Y. Moody G. J. and Thomas J. D. R. Cationic complexes of nonyl phenoxypoly (ethylene oxy) ethanol: extraction into dichloromethane and its ion selective electrode properties. *J. inorg. nucl. Chem.*, **39**, 1977, 1689–96.
13. Fuerstenau D. W. Thermodynamics of surface adsorption and wetting. In *Principles of flotation* King R. P. ed. (Johannesburg: South African Institute of Mining and Metallurgy, 1982), 31–51.
14. Giesekke E. W. and Harris P. J. A study of the selective flotation of fluorite from calcite by the use of a single-bubble-stream microflotation cell. Paper presented at Mintek 50, Sandton, South Africa, March 1984.
15. Giesekke E. W. and Harris P. J. The influence of polyoxyethylated nonyl phenols on the adsorption of sodium oleate on calcite in fluorite. Paper submitted to *S. Afr. J. Chem.*, 1984.

Use of solvents for Zn, Mn and H_2SO_4 recovery in the electrolytic zinc industry

D. Buttinelli, C. Giavarini and A. Mercanti

Synopsis
Three solvents (TBP, DEHPA and naphthenic acid) were used to selectively recover zinc from industrial waste liquors from the zinc industry. Sulphuric acid was also recovered from the same liquors by extraction with isobutyl alcohol.

The resulting processes are compared from the technical and economic points of view to enable the advantages and disadvantages of each solvent to be evaluated.

Taking a broad view of 'reagents', the organic solvents that are employed for metal recovery and purification probably constitute one of the fastest-growing classes of reagents in the mineral and metallurgical industries at the present time. It would seem reasonable to predict that future hydrometallurgical processing techniques may recover metals to a greater extent by selective solvent extraction, thereby eliminating many of the purification stages. The benefits in terms of energy saving, absence of pollution, high quality and high yields and simplicity are well known.

The present work considers an application of solvents that, at present, seems to be of the greatest interest and usefulness—the recovery of metals from waste liquors from the metallurgical industries.[1,2,3]

As such liquors are usually acidic, the recovery of the acid has been considered as well. Solvents with good selective properties must be used for recovery because of the high content of impurities in the liquors.

Origin and characteristics of waste liquor considered

Zinc industry spent electrolytes were used for the study. The electrolytic process for zinc production consists of the following main stages: concentrate roasting to yield ZnO calcine plus SO_2, which is converted to sulphuric acid; calcine leaching with H_2SO_4 to yield an impure $ZnSO_4$ solution; solution purification; and electrolysis to yield zinc metal, together with a H_2SO_4 solution (spent electrolyte), which is recirculated to the leaching stage.

Part of the H_2SO_4 solution is purged to avoid the build-up of too high concentrations of impurities, especially manganese, cadmium and magnesium.[3,4] The average composition (g/l) of such waste electrolytes is 230–250 H_2SO_4, 12–17 Zn, 15–20 Mg, 1–3 Mn and 4–10 mg/l Fe, together with Cl^- and minor amounts of Cu, Cd, Ni, Co, etc.

For a plant that produces 100 000 t of zinc annually the purge electrolyte is at least in the range 50–100 m^3/day, depending on the concentration of the impurities. Normally, lime-treatment plants with adequate sludge settling and disposal capability are employed to treat these spent electrolytes.

By recovering metal ions, such as Zn, the treatment costs could be reduced significantly and Zn could be recycled to the electrowinning plant. In addition, the recovery of manganese could be considered if direct recycle of the recovered Zn solution to the electrolytic cells is provided.

Because of its low value, H_2SO_4 recovery would probably be of no interest without consideration of the problem of its neutralization prior to discharge, together with the consequential aspects of chemical consumption, sludge formation and disposal, and its reuse in zinc stripping from the organic solvent.

Reagents and recovery processes

Separation of zinc from cadmium in chloride solution has been studied with use of tri-*n*-butyl-phosphate (TBP) and naphthenic acid.[5] The extraction of zinc from sulphate and chloride solutions with di-2-ethyl-hexyl-phosphoric acid (DEHPA) has also been described.[1,6,7] Earlier laboratory investigations had shown that selective extraction of zinc from acidic sulphate solutions was possible with all these solvents[8,9,10]

The problem of acid extraction has been considered in both the nuclear (extraction of nitric acid by TBP) and in the chemical industries, many processes having been proposed for the extraction and purification of phosphoric acid with solvents.[11,12,13] In regard to H_2SO_4, as well as amines and alcohols, TBP also seems suitable for extraction, but only for extremely concentrated solutions.[14,15] Isobutyl alcohol is suitable for H_2SO_4 extraction from electrolytes.[16]

On the basis of both literature data and previous experimental work three possible routes for zinc or for zinc, manganese and sulphuric acid recovery from waste electrolytes were investigated (Fig. 1).

The first route recovers zinc as chloride owing to the need to use a salting agent (NaCl) to permit solvent extraction with TBP. The recovery solution cannot be recycled to the electrolytic cell because of the presence of chloride ions. The advantage of this route is that no neutralization stage is necessary prior to zinc extraction and TBP is a very selective solvent.

The second possible route requires neutralization to pH $\geqslant$ 2 prior to extraction with DEHPA. Zinc is recovered as sulphate and can be recycled to the electrolytic cells. Like TBP, DEHPA is very selective. Partial neutralization of a highly acidic liquor, such as the spent electrolyte, is, however, an expensive operation with significant drawbacks in regard to sludge formation and zinc losses.

After laboratory experiments this route was modified. The third route can be divided into two 'sub-routes'. In the first stage H_2SO_4 is extracted with alcohol (IBA); only a partial extraction is possible,[16] a minimum residual content of 15–20 g/l being left in the electrolyte.

After this first step it is possible to follow the previous route, i.e. neutralization at pH $\geqslant$ 2 and zinc extraction with DEHPA; it would also be possible to avoid the neutralization step and extract the zinc directly by virtue of the reduced acidity of the solution.[9] Yields, however, would be quite low and a large number of extraction steps, plus high organic/aqueous (O/A) ratios, would be required.

Following acid extraction there is also the possibility of extracting zinc and manganese with naphthenic acid (NA) (neutralization to pH 5.0–5.5 and pH control at each extraction stage are necessary). NA has advantages over DEHPA in terms of low cost and the possibility of recovering Mn as well. Its

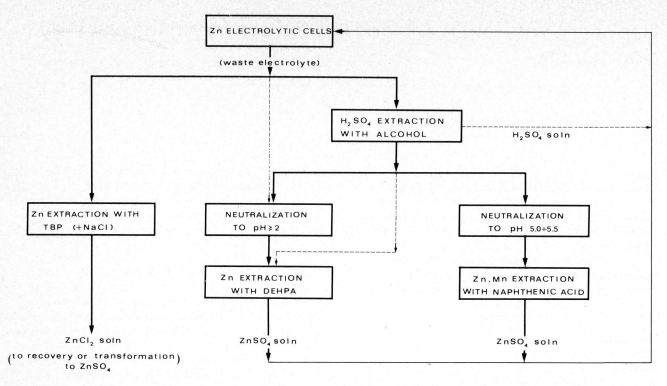

Fig. 1   Schematic diagram of alternative processes for zinc recovery from spent electrolyte

disadvantages are the need for more accurate pH control and the poorer selectivity. In both cases zinc is recovered as a $ZnSO_4$ solution that can be recycled to the electrolytic cells.

The sulphuric acid recovered is used to strip zinc (or zinc and Mn) from the solvents. Neutralization can probably be provided by calcined blende and calcium hydroxide or limestone. Calcined blende could raise the zinc content of the electrolyte, producing minor quantities of sludges.

Experimental

The proposed processes were tested experimentally on two laboratory-scale pilot plants; the simplified flowsheet of the zinc extraction process with TBP and that for acid and zinc extraction with DEHPA or NA are illustrated in Figs. 2 and 3.

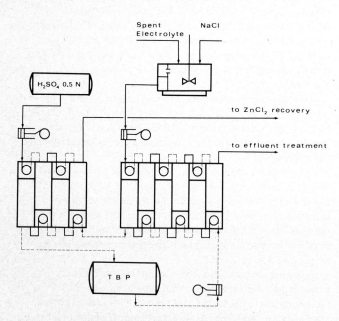

Fig. 2   Pilot-plant flowsheet for Zn extraction with TBP

The extraction sections of the plants were batteries of mixer-settlers (ERIES AT-1). With the use of naphthenic acid careful pH control was also provided at the extraction stages. The zinc was stripped with dilute sulphuric acid. The flow rate for each phase was 1–2 l/h. All experiments were conducted at room temperature for several months. The composition of the industrial electrolyte (g/l) was 230–235 H_2SO_4, 12.5–14.5 Zn and 1.2–1.8 Mn. Technical grade isobutyl alcohol, TBP, DEHPA and naphthenic acid were used (Table 1). The diluent for DEHPA, TBP and NA was a commercial grade kerosene (boiling range 173–250°C). Other reagents were technical grade sodium chloride, calcium hydroxide, calcium carbonate and industrial calcined blende (ZnO 80% by weight).

Table 1

Solvent	Producer	Purity, wt %	Acid value	Conc. in kerosene
IBA	Carlo Erba	97	—	—
TBP	Carlo Erba	98	—	80% by wt
DEHPA	Bayer	96	—	1 M
NA	Fluka	—	230	1 M

Zinc, manganese and impurities in the electrolyte were determined by atomic absorption before and after solvent extraction in the manner described previously.[9,10] H_2SO_4 was titrated potentiometrically by NaOH.[10] Solvent losses were determined by gas chromatography (IBA), X-ray fluorescence (DEHPA and TBP) and ultraviolet spectroscopy (NA).

Extraction with TBP

In the extraction of zinc with TBP a salting agent was added (30–40 g/l NaCl). The extraction was very effective, 90% yields being reached after three or four extraction stages. After five stages extraction was virtually complete, leaving 0.5–1 g/l residual zinc, i.e. a concentration from which further extraction was impossible in the raffinate. Maximum yields were therefore of the order of 95%.

234

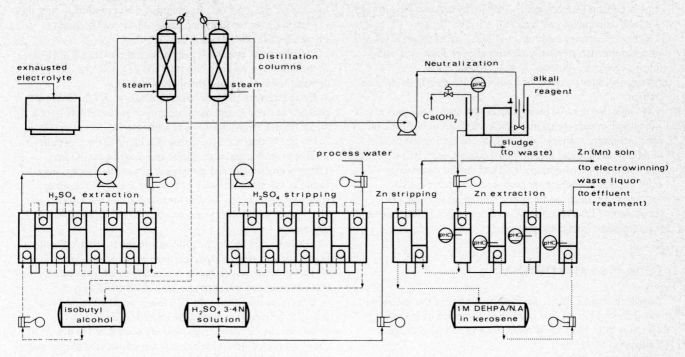

Fig. 3   Pilot-plant flowsheet for Zn extraction with DEHPA or NA

Two indicative extraction profiles are shown in Fig. 4. When concentrations of zinc higher than that in the starting electrolyte were required in the stripping solutions, yields decreased progressively; it was possible to double the zinc concentration by using O/A ratios of two, thus reducing the extraction yields to

85%. The extraction selectivity of TBP towards zinc was high: major impurities normally contained in industrial electrolytes were, in reality, not extracted. Only iron, which is generally contained in small amounts in zinc spent electrolytes, was partially extracted by TBP (one-quarter to one-half of the

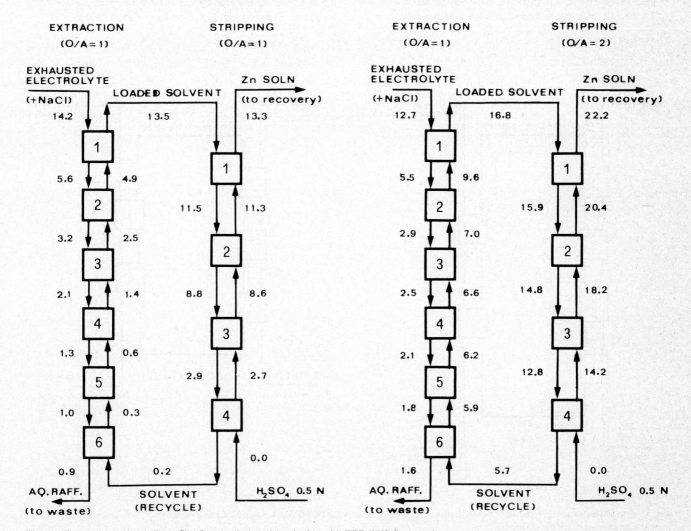

Fig. 4   Zinc concentration (g/l) profile of two typical runs (extraction with TBP (80%)–kerosene)

original content was recovered). TBP losses in the aqueous phase were low, ranging from 0.06 to 0.08 g/l.

Zinc was extracted in the form of $ZnCl_2.nHCl$, where n has a value between 0.5 and 2. Considering the possibilities of using the recovered zinc solution, its direct recycle to the electrowinning plant does not seem feasible owing to its chlorine content.

Possible uses are zinc precipitation with lime or caustic soda and recycle of the precipitate to the leaching section of the zinc plant; solution concentration, $ZnCl_2$ crystallization and recovery of the zinc as chloride; and fractional distillation of HCl after the addition of H_2SO_4: azeotropic HCl and residue containing H_2SO_4 and zinc sulphate are produced—the latter can be recycled to the electrowinning plant (a similar solution was proposed by MX–Processor AG to treat the $FeCl_2$–HCl liquors that originated from metal pickling.[17]

Extraction with DEHPA

As was mentioned above, direct neutralization of the electrolyte was abandoned in the first phase of this research owing to operating difficulties, costs and losses and excessive sludge formation.

A different approach was then tried — preliminary partial extraction of H_2SO_4 to lower the acidity of the electrolyte followed by zinc recovery by DEHPA. Isobutyl alcohol (IBA), a low-cost, easily recoverable, solvent was selected for H_2SO_4 extraction.[16] Sulphuric acid could be extracted with yields of 85–90%, leaving a minimum residual content in the electrolyte of 20–30 g/l with use of a high O/A ratio; however, the corresponding H_2SO_4 concentration in the solvent was low.

To obtain a sufficient acid concentration, which is necessary

for reuse of the recovered acid solution—for example, to strip the extracted zinc in the following phase—lower yields of acid extraction had to be planned.

In the present case it was decided to leave 30–35 g/l of H_2SO_4 in the electrolyte and to recover a 3 N H_2SO_4 solution (more detailed results were presented elsewhere[16]).

By operating in this way zinc extraction with DEHPA was possible without further neutralization,[9] but to achieve better yields limited neutralization was advantageous.

In spite of the fact that alcohol should not extract metallic ions, appreciable amounts of zinc and magnesium (about 120 ppm on average) and manganese (about 10–20 ppm) were found in the recovered acid solution, probably as a result of transport phenomena. When this solution was used to strip the zinc in the succeeding extraction stage no purification was necessary.

Alcohol losses due to the solubility in the aqueous raffinate and in the acid stripped solution were quite high (3–4 and 5.5–6.5 g/100 g, respectively). A recovery step for the alcohol was necessary—it was carried out by batch distillation.[16]

In an industrial plant total IBA losses would be in the range 0.5–1.0% by weight of electrolyte treated. After H_2SO_4 extraction the electrolyte was partially neutralized to pH 4.5 by use of powdered limestone or a mixture of calcined blende and limestone. Calcined blende was used as an alternative to raise the zinc content of the electrolyte and to produce minor amounts of sludge. The final pH level was reached with controlled quantities of milk of lime. The small quantities of sludge produced during neutralization were removed periodically and discarded.

In zinc extraction with DEHPA the O/A ratio ranged from 2.5 to 3.5 during the extraction and from 3 to 6 during the stripping. Typical runs (Fig. 5) relate to $CaCO_3$ and to

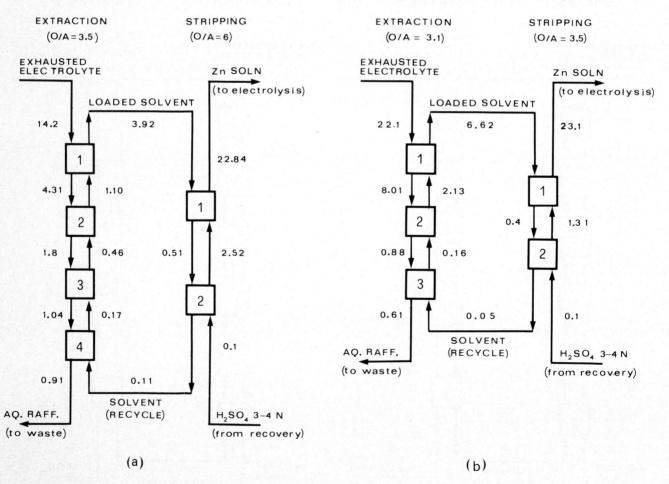

(a)

(b)

Fig. 5   Zinc concentration (g/l) profile of two indicative runs (extraction with 1 M DEHPA in kerosene after neutralization (a) with limestone only and (b) with limestone–calcined blende mixture)

blende–CaCO₃ neutralization, respectively. For the former yields of 93% were achieved after three extraction stages: no pH adjustment was necessary after the initial neutralization. For the blende–CaCO₃ mixtures a 96% yield was achieved in only two steps, albeit with pH control in the second.

After stripping with H_2SO_4 solution (two stages), zinc was recovered completely and at a higher concentration than in the original electrolyte. The solubility of DEHPA in the residual electrolyte and in the recovered zinc solution was in the range 4–6 ppm. Less than 30 ppm Mg and Mn, <5 ppm of Fe and negligible amounts of other ions were obtained in the recovered zinc solution.

Extraction with naphthenic acid

When naphthenic acid was used the acidity of the electrolyte was also lowered by the extraction in a first phase of H_2SO_4 with IBA. Subsequent neutralization to pH 5.2 was accomplished with CaCO₃ and CaCO₃-blende mixtures as for the extraction with DEHPA.

A relatively pure calcined blende had to be used owing to the limited selectivity of NA, which partially extracted any copper and iron contained in the calcined blende. DEHPA, being very selective, did not cause this kind of problem. Some difficulty was encountered in pH control, which had to be carried out very carefully; production of sludge (mainly calcium sulphate) was appreciable and the settlers had to be cleaned daily. The sludge, which contained about 4–5% Zn, was recycled to the preliminary neutralization step.

Extraction yields were high (up to 99%) in only three steps. The amount of co-extracted manganese was controlled by the pH of each step. Mn yields were usually in the range 60–90%. Other metallic ions, such as Fe and Cu, were partially extracted, depending on the lower selectivity of NA than that of DEHPA.

Fig. 6 shows typical runs of the extraction with NA, the experimental conditions being similar to those which were adopted for DEHPA. Naphthenic acid concentration in the aqueous phase was 10–20 ppm. In this case, and probably also for DEHPA, to obtain a zinc solution appropriate for electrowinning an active-carbon treatment can be considered to decrease the organic solvent content.

Process cost estimates

It should be recalled that if zinc and acid are not recovered, the cost of treating the spent electrolyte prior to discharge must be taken into consideration. This cost is reduced markedly if Zn and H_2SO_4 are recovered previously.

Table 2 shows a comparison of the costs of the various processes based on a hypothetical plant suitable for the treatment of 150 m³/day of a waste electrolyte containing 15 g/l Zn and 230 g/l H_2SO_4 (plus other impurities); the plant is assumed to run for 8 h per day. Capital and interest charges are based on a five-year useful plant life and a discount rate of 20% per annum.

Gains in effluent treatment cost are based on raw material requirements and sludge disposal costs at similar plants. Raw materials, utilities and operating labour costs are calculated on the basis of actual (January, 1984) charges in Italy. Maintenance costs are estimated at 8% of the total plant cost. The estimate is based on 1 t of zinc recovered in the form of chloride (TBP) or pure sulphate (DEHPA and NA) solution.

The credits arise from the recovered products other than zinc (H_2SO_4) and from the saving in effluent treatment.

From Table 2 it is apparent that the TBP process is the most expensive in terms of recovered zinc. Moreover, the zinc is not recyclable to the electrowinning cell and must be further processed or recovered as solid $ZnCl_2$ at an additional cost. There is very little cost difference between the other two processes and that selected will probably depend on local and other relevant factors.

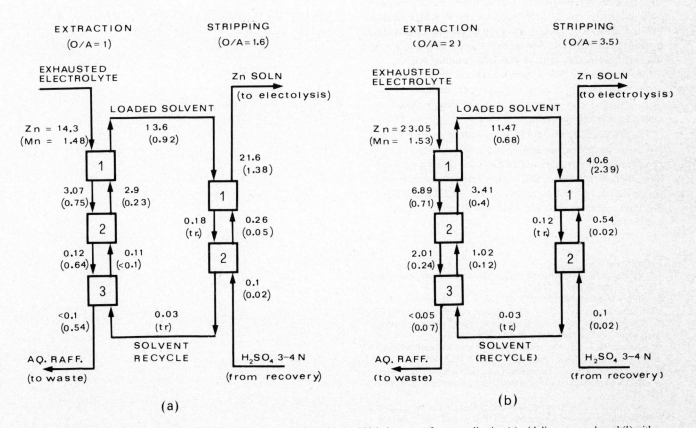

Fig. 6   Zinc concentration (g/l) profile of two typical runs (extraction with 1 M NA in kerosene after neutralization (*a*) with limestone only and (*b*) with limestone–calcined blende mixture)

Table 2 Estimated costs ($U.S.) (1 t zinc recovered in form of ZnCl$_2$ or ZnSO$_4$ solution)

Process	TBP	DEHPA	NA
Operating cost			
Solvent A loss*	—	225.0	225.0
Solvent B loss†	18.2	4.2	1.8
NaCl	74.0	—	—
CaCO$_3$,Ca(OH)$_2$	—	32.6	57.0
H$_2$SO$_4$	103.0	—	—
Electricity, kWh	14.7	19.8	19.8
Steam, 3–4 kg/cm^2	—	82.3	82.3
Process and cooling water	8.5	24.7	24.7
Maintenance	14.6	26.1	29.2
Operating labour	12.0	48.0	48.0
Capital cost			
Investment amortization and interest	74.2	129.8	148.4
Total	319.2	592.5	636.2
Credits‡			
H$_2$SO$_4$	—	234.0	234.0
Effluent treatment	—	137.0	149.0
Net cost/t zinc	319.2	221.0	253.2

* Isobutyl alcohol
† TBP or DEHPA or NA.
‡ Derived from recovered products other than zinc and from saving in effluent treatment.

DEHPA is more selective and enables industrial calcined blende to be used as neutralizing agent. Naphthenic acid is cheaper and recovers manganese as well, but it is less selective than DEHPA and effectively prevents the use of calcined blende as neutralizing agent.

Conclusions

All the processes that have been investigated can remove zinc from exhausted electrolytes or similar effluent liquors, but some basic differences do exist. TBP recovers zinc with high yields, but in a form (zinc chloride) that probably necessitates further treatment. DEHPA and NA, on the other hand, produce a zinc solution directly recyclable to the electrowinning cell.

The selectivity of NA is inferior to that of the other two solvents and plant operation is slightly more difficult, necessitating careful pH control, frequent mixer–settler cleaning and sludge recycling.

The process that uses TBP is very simple; with DEHPA and NA certain complications arise in the H$_2$SO$_4$ extraction section because of the need to recover the dissolved isobutyl alcohol by distillation. Nevertheless, acid recovery reduces the treatment cost of the final effluent significantly. The DEHPA and NA processes look interesting and feasible both technically and economically.

References

1. Reinhardt H. Solvent extraction for recovery of metal waste. *Chemy Ind.*, no. 5, March 1 1975, 210–3.
2. Ritcey G. M. and Ashbrook A. W. *Solvent extraction: principles and applications to process metallurgy* (Amsterdam, etc: Elsevier, 1979), 737 p.
3. Robbins L. A. Liquid–liquid extraction: a pretreatment process for wastewater. *Chem. Engng Prog.*, **76**, Oct. 1980, 58–61.
4. Barbour A. K. Environmental aspects of zinc, lead and cadmium production and use. *Chemy Ind.*, no. 11, June 6 1983, 409–15.
5. Fletcher A. W. *et al.* Separation of zinc and cadmium by solvent extraction. In *Advances in extractive metallurgy* (London: IMM, 1968), 686–711.
6. Sato T. *et al.* The extraction of divalent Mn, Fe, Co, Ni, Cu and Zn from hydrochloric acid solutions by DEHPA. *J. appl. Chem. Biotech.*, **28**, 1978, 85–94.
7. Nogueira E. D. Regife J. M. and Blythe P. M. Zincex — the development of a secondary zinc process. *Chemy Ind.*, no. 2, Jan. 19 1980, 63–7.
8. Bressa M. Buttinelli D. and Giavarini C. Estrazione selettiva dello zinco con TBP da soluzioni acide industriali. *Chimica Ind.*, Milano, **61**, 1979, 893–7.
9. Buttinelli D. and Giavarini C. Recupero dell'acido solforico e dello zinco per estrazione con solventi. *Chimica Ind.*, Milano, **68**, 1981, 563–8.
10. Buttinelli D. Capotorto C. and Mercanti A. Estrazione dello zinco con acido naftenico da effluenti industriali acidi. *Industria min.*, Roma, series III, **3**, no. 4, July /Aug. 1982, 11–16.
11. Baniel A. Blumberg R. and Alon A. French Patent 1 396 077, 1965.
12. Bergdorf J. and Fischer R. Extractive phosphoric acid purification. *Chem. Engng Prog.*, **74**, Nov. 1978, 41–5.
13. Davister A. and Peeterbroeck M. The Prayon process for wet acid purification. *Chem. Engng Prog.*, **78**, March 1982, 35–9.
14. Agers D. W. *et al.* The purification of inorganic acids by the amine liquid ion exchange process. In *Unit processes in hydrometallurgy* Wadsworth M. E. and Davis F. T. eds (New York, London: Gordon and Breach, 1964), 515–27. (*Metall. Soc. Conf.* vol. 24)
15. Sekine T. and Hasegara Y. S. E. *Solvent extraction chemistry: fundamentals and applications* (New York: Dekker, 1977), 260–9.
16. Buttinelli D. Giavarini C. and Mercanti A. Pilot-plant investigation on H$_2$SO$_4$ extraction by alcohols from spent electrolytes. Paper presented to ISEC '83: international solvent extraction conference, Denver, August 1983.
17. Hydrometallurgische Prozesse für die Wiedergewinnung von Metallen. *Stahl Eisen*, **99**, no. 4, Feb. 26 1979, 169.

Reagents in electric separation of minerals

G. Alfano, C. Del Fà, R. Peretti and A. Zucca

Synopsis
First, from a theoretical standpoint the effects that are produced by conditioning solid mineral surfaces and the changes that are induced in their electrophysical properties are examined. On the basis, additionally, of experimental evidence, a model is proposed to represent the behaviour of the crude ores under the influence of particular reagents and the role that the latter can play by differentiation in the behaviour of the various types of mineral during electric separation.

The results of separation tests on pure components, mixtures and crude ores with the use of electrodynamic drum and triboelectric cyclone separators of the authors' design are then presented. These tests, performed on ores refractory to electric separation, revealed the positive effects that some reagents show and a satisfactory separation was achieved. In particular, the results that were obtained with a barite–fluorite pre-concentrate and a kainite–halite mineral are discussed. In both cases surface conditioning was fundamental.

Knowledge of the electrophysical parameters of minerals can result, as previous work has show,[1-15] in a greater understanding of the phenomena that underlie separation processes that rely on the surface characteristics of solid substances. This is of particular importance in the study of the phenomena involved in electric separation processes that result from energy exchanges between the solid phase and the surrounding liquid phase.

Clearly, all other conditions being equal, such exchanges depend on the surface energy structure of the phases in contact, involving, for instance, the electron transfer from one phase to the other in triboelectric charging and electron and ion transfer between the solid and gaseous phases in charging by ionization. Many different techniques have been shown, theoretically and experimentally, to be capable of inducing modifications in the mineral surface energy structure to create the most favourable conditions required by the various beneficiation processes based on surface properties. Among those examined to date in the field of electric separation, the use of reagents that in specific cases can modify the surface characteristics of mineral solids merits special attention.

Fundamentals

A model that adequately described the energy exchange processes at the interface was first defined to provide an explanation of the charge phenomena by contact between mineral solid and surface. In the framework of the more general objective of interpreting the mechanisms involved in beneficiation processes that rely on surface characteristics, representation by means of energy bands was chosen[5,6]

To verify the applicability of the energy band model special techniques to measure the electrophysical parameters had to be devised. Despite its simplicity, for the objectives proposed the model adopted is satisfactory for the derivation of useful correlations to explain the behaviour exhibited by the minerals in both electric separation and flotation. Moreover, the information supplied by the model enabled possible separation results of two or more minerals to be predicted and the most suitable external

actions for enhancing those results to be identified. In fact, the model was also verified for the case of artificially modified surface electronic structures (X- and γ-irradiation, ion bombardment, type of grinding, heat-treatment, conditioning with reagents, humidity, etc).

In charging by ionization or by contact, the conductivity of a mineral particle can be considered as the sum of two terms, dependent on conductivity of volume and solid surface, respectively. It has been ascertained that, in principle, conductivity in the bands of the surface layers is possible, but mobility is so low in comparison with that of the free charge carriers as to determine a predominance of the latter.

The reverse can also happen when, for example, there exists a layer adsorbed at the surface of a solid consisting of several molecular layers: in this case a new substance appears with its own surface energy structure, which will put itself in equilibrium with the semiconductor body, giving rise to zones of spatial charge and to a modification in charge carrier concentration in the various layers, with resultant influence on the surface conductivity of the mineral. This is true of water adsorbed at the mineral surface, the function of the nature of the solid, ambient temperature and humidity, surface state of the mineral, etc. As is well known, water in the atmosphere is easily adsorbed on the surfaces of hydrophilic substances: the mechanism of adsorption lies in the attraction of dipoles of water by the free valences on the surface, followed by capillary condensation. At equilibrium a correspondence exists between the amount of water adsorbed and the ambient humidity: the maximum is reached for 100% relative humidity of air. In some instances, by acting simultaneously on temperature and humidity the most suitable conditions can be found for modification of the surface energy structure of two or more minerals to achieve optimum separation by charging by ionization or triboelectrification.

In other cases this is not so and to achieve the differentiation in behaviour of the mineral solids in the charging phase and, subsequently, in separation the surface of the mineral particles must be treated with reagents that absorb selectively.

Heteropolar organic substances, both adsorbed and adhering chemically to the mineral surface, can render the surface hydrophobic, so the amount of water adsorbed is reduced and, hence, the surface conductivity. Inorganic reagents can have different effects. They may react chemically with the solid surface, forming a layer of a new compound that exhibits electrophysical characteristics different from those of the original solid. On the other hand, inorganic reagents can selectively prevent the adsorption of organic reagents on the surface of certain minerals without hindering their adhesion on the surface of others. Clearly, the reagent used must be selective over the minerals to be separated.

Experience gained in the field of flotation can be of considerable assistance in the choice of the most suitable reagent combination. Several studies have been published on the effect that conditioning of mineral surfaces has on their charge phenomena and on the possibilities of electrostatic separation by such means. In this paper some interesting recent results are discussed that well explain the effect of surface conditioning prior to electric separation. In particular, a barite, fluorite, calcite and quartz pre-concentrate, as well as a kainite and halite mineral, were examined. In both cases the object was to determine optimum separation conditions for the various species after conditioning of the surface, without which the process would not have been applicable or, at least, entirely unsatisfactory results would have been obtained.

Results and discussion

Fluorite–barite pre-concentrate

The behaviour of fluorite, barite, calcite and quartz in electric separation was studied systematically by use of an electrodynamic drum separator under different experimental conditions. To examine the influence of temperature and relative humidity of the air on electric separation with charging by ionization the apparatus was housed in an acclimatized chamber.

The findings indicate that fluorite can be separated from the other mineral species, even at room temperature and high relative humidity (the latter is normal in Sardinia). By contrast, barite proved refractory to separation from quartz (at least at temperatures below 80°C), whereas calcite can be eliminated from the other two species even at room temperature, but under controlled conditions of relative air humidity and not exceeding 75%.

In practice the surface structure of fluorite is not altered to any appreciable extent by the adsorption on the surface of water molecules and this species therefore maintains its characteristics of non-conducting mineral on charging by ionization. Conversely, the effect of humidity and temperature brings about a complete change in behaviour of the other three species, which acquire the characteristic of conductor minerals. Specifically, whereas barite and quartz exhibit, under all experimental conditions, similar behaviour, calcite attains maximum conductivity at high relative humidity values (above 75%).

On the basis of the above considerations the separation of a sample that reproduced with good approximation the granulometric and mineralogical characteristics of a gravity pre-concentrate of fluorite and barite in calcite and quartz gangues was studied. Experiments were conducted under normal ambient conditions at a temperature of 20°C and relative humidity of air of 80% and from a feed assaying 49% CaF_2 a 94.84% grade fluorite concentrate was obtained with a yield of 84.87% after two passes in the electrodynamic separator and with scavenging of the middlings.

Separation of the tailings to recover a high-grade barite concentrate, however, proved unsuccessful. In fact, despite operating under the most favourable conditions, only an appreciable reduction in the calcite content was achieved, the $BaSO_4/SiO_2$ ratio remaining practically the same without significant losses in $BaSO_4$.

In the light of the above, to separate the two minerals reagents were used that are capable of selectively adsorbing on the surface of a certain species, rendering it hydrophobic and thereby reducing the surface conductivity.

In practice, barite maintains its non-conductive characteristic under these experimental conditions, whereas quartz and calcite, under normal separation conditions (room temperature and relative humidity of air above 75%) behave as conductors. Optimum amounts of reagents, varying between 1000 and 1500 g/t of mineral, were added to an aqueous solution of 10-15% by weight of lauryl sulphonate alcohol. This procedure was applied to the barite pre-concentrate obtained after removal of the calcite in the tailings of the fluorite recovery process. This product was conditioned with 1200 g/t lauryl sulphonate alcohol and then subjected to a two-stage electrostatic process with scavenging of the middlings according to a previously described method.[16]

The results of this stage (Table 1) confirm that electrostatic separation of barite from quartz with charging by ionization is only possible after conditioning of these minerals.

The overall electrostatic separation results of the entire fluorite and barite pre-concentrate are given in Table 2.

Halite and kainite mineral

The investigation was concerned with assessing the possibilities of separating electrically a halite–kainite mineral. In particular, the pure constituents of the mineral, their mixtures and industrial minerals were examined. The pure components were obtained by comminution and classification in closed circuit to –2 mm from hand-sorted blocks of halite and kainite. The size class –1.2 +0.6 mm, which represented the most abundant fraction for both minerals (kainite 43.35%, halite 44.14%), was used throughout the tests.

Three distinct series of experiments were conducted in the electrodynamic drum separator with charging both by conductance and by ionization of the particles. The first series was aimed at evaluating the effect of heating the solids in the temperature range 20–110°C. The results obtained (Figs. 1 and 2) show that no practical possibility of separation exists. The adsorption effect of a surface active anionic reagent was the object of the second series of tests. Particular use was made of a

Table 1 Electrostatic separation of barite after conditioning with lauryl sulphonate alcohol (1200 g/t)

| Product | Grade, % | | | | Recovery, % | | | |
	Wt %	CaF_2	$BaSO_4$	$CaCO_3$	SiO_2	CaF_2	$BaSO_4$	$CaCO_3$	SiO_2
Concentrate	49.9	0.35	95.80	0.70	3.15	11.9	90.2	10.8	3.6
Tailings	50.51	2.55	10.17	5.67	81.61	88.1	9.8	89.2	96.4
Total	100.00	1.46	52.55	3.21	42.78	100.00	100.00	100.00	100.00

Table 2 Electrostatic separation of fluorite and barite pre-concentrate

| Product | Grade, % | | | | Recovery, % | | | |
	Wt %	CaF_2	$BaSO_4$	$CaCO_3$	SiO_2	CaF_2	$BaSO_4$	$CaCO_3$	SiO_2
Fluorite concentrate	43.86	94.84	2.14	2.24	0.78	84.87	5.21	8.20	1.63
Barite concentrate	15.54	0.35	95.80	0.70	3.15	0.11	82.70	0.90	2.33
Tailings	40.60	18.13	5.36	26.84	49.67	15.02	12.09	90.90	96.04
Total	100.00	49.01	18.00	11.99	21.00	100.00	100.00	100.00	100.00

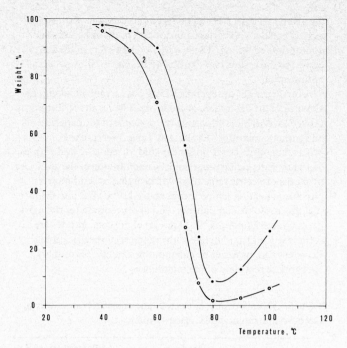

Fig. 1   Weight of 'conductor' mineral as a function of temperature (1, kainite; 2, halite; charging by ionization, Carpco high-tension separator)

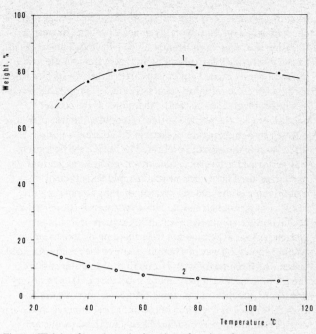

Fig. 3   Weight of 'conductor' mineral as a function of temperature (1, kainite; 2, halite; charging by ionization, mineral conditioned with Pamak 4; Carpco high-tension separator)

commercial reagent of the carboxylate class (Pamak 4). The pure mineral (halite and kainite) was conditioned with varying amounts of reagent (from 100 to 500 g/t), filtered and dried at 75°C. The behaviour of the two mineral species in the sample in regard both to charging by ionization and by conductance was studied as a function of heating temperature of the mineral (range 20–110°C). In the third series of tests a cationic reagent (dodecylamine) was used, the same procedure as that outlined above being used.

The results of conductance charging in the tests with Pamak 4 and dodecylamine as modulating agents were totally negative, despite the similar behaviour of the two species in the separator. Figs. 3 and 4 show the results of the response of both species, charged by ionization, as a function of heating temperature after conditioning with anionic and cationic reagents, respectively.

Concrete separation possibilities exist in both cases. In particular, by use of Pamak 4 (Fig. 3) separation should be accomplished throughout the temperature range examined, whereas dodecylamine tends to give better results at temperatures below 60°C.

Unfortunately, the results of separation tests on synthetic mixtures of the two minerals were totally negative in the presence of both reagents. In this regard it should be noted that conditioning of the kainite and halite was carried out in saturated solutions of one or the other mineral owing to their high solubility in water and conditioning of kainite–halite mixture was done with a saturated solution of the two salts. In both cases, after filtration and drying, the minerals were subjected to electric separation.

The failure of the tests performed on synthetic

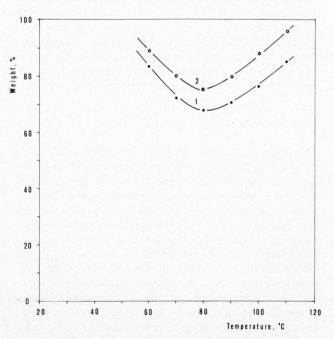

Fig. 2   Weight of 'conductor' mineral as a function of temperature (1, kainite; 2, halite; charging by conductance; Carpco high-tension separator)

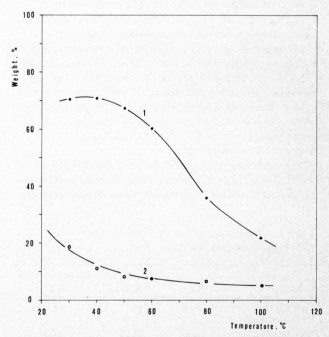

Fig. 4   Weight of 'conductor' mineral as a function of temperature (1, kainite; 2, halite; charging by ionization, mineral conditioned with dodecylamine; Carpco high-tension separator)

mixtures—contrary to expectations—was probably due to the deposition of a mixed salt on the mineral particles during filtration and, more significantly, during drying. This seems to be the most plausible explanation in that systematic electric separation tests carried out on mixtures of the two species where each had been conditioned separately yielded favourable results.

The problem seems to reside, therefore, in the correct conditioning of the particle surface. Conditioning was therefore effected by nebulizing the reagent in 5% aqueous solution directly on to the mixture preheated to 140°C: the operation was performed in a vertical tube traversed by an ascending current of air. This device ensured a rapid and efficient conditioning of the mineral surface, thereby eliminating the drawbacks mentioned above. This hypothesis is supported by the favourable results achieved in subsequent tests in the electrodynamic separator and with charging by ionization. Table 3 shows, by way of example, some of the results obtained: these, which refer to one pass through the separator and are therefore subject to improvement, especially as far as recovery is concerned, are most encouraging. Moreover, bearing in mind the high degree of liberation of the industrial minerals at the size classes examined, it seems quite likely that these results are reproducible in an industrial operation.

Table 3 Electrostatic separation of kainite–halite mixture (temperature, 60°C; tension applied to electrodes, 30 kV; reagent consumption, 400 g/t Pamak 4)

| Product | Wt % | Grade, % | | Distribution, % | |
		Mg	K₂O	Mg	K₂O
Concentrate	44.63	8.70	16.32	78.1	77.8
Reject	55.37	1.97	3.76	21.9	22.2
Total	100.00	4.97	9.37	100.00	100.00

Apart from the use of reagents, another field open to investigation is that of the effect of temperatures in excess of 110°C. A series of experiments was conducted on the pure species with the object of providing some guidelines, the following procedure being drawn up: heating of the dry solid to about 160–170°C; air cooling of the solid to temperatures below 100°C; and separation by use of an electrodynamic apparatus with charging by ionization. With this procedure the kainite, in contrast to the halite, is rendered 'conductor'.

Systematic experiments on synthetic mixtures corroborated the results obtained with the pure minerals. In particular, this behaviour is a function of the temperature at which separation takes place. Operating at around 100°C yields a high-grade kainite concentrate, but recovery is poor; at temperatures below 60°C tailings with a high halite content and an impure kainite concentrate are obtained; at 60–100°C behaviour is intermediate between the two.

Appropriate recycling should therefore make the process remarkably versatile. The overall results of separation tests on a kainite–halite mixture following the procedure outlined above

Table 4 Overall results of electrostatic separation of kainite–halite mixture (size class, –2 mm)

| Product | Wt % | Grade, % | Distribution, % |
		K₂O	K₂O
Concentrate	36.22	17.17	65.7
–0.1 mm not treated	1.16	9.46	1.2
Middlings	22.94	11.25	27.3
Tailings	39.68	1.38	5.8
Feed	100.00	9.46	100.00

are given in Table 4. It should be emphasized that the results were obtained with certain adjustments of the apparatus and appropriate recycling. These were not, however, studied in depth, so the results could probably be improved by process optimization.

A further series of separation tests was carried out along the above lines on a commercial crude ore. The results of these tests proved favourable, supporting the outcome of the experiments on synthetic mixtures. The data in Table 5 refer to the processing of the crude ore under study sized to –2 mm with use of a suitable recycling programme. Concentration of the crude ore by means of electric separation with charging by ionization is possible at heating temperatures above 110°C. Despite the fact that the insoluble components tend to concentrate for the most part with the kainite, the K₂O grades of the concentrates are sufficiently high and in line with commercial specifications. Recovery can, however be enhanced to around 75% or more by appropriate recycling of the middlings.

Table 5 Overall results of electrostatic separation of industrial kainite–halite mineral (size class, –2 mm)

| Product | Wt % | Grade, % | | Distribution, % | |
		K₂O	Insoluble	K₂O	Insoluble
Concentrate	46.48	16.70	2.44	62.6	70.2
	53.96	16.15	2.32	70.3	77.4
–0.1 mm not treated	7.48	12.76	1.55	7.7	7.2
Middlings	19.88	10.82	1.05	17.4	12.9
Tailings	26.16	5.85	0.60	12.3	9.7
Total	100.00	12.40	1.62	100.00	100.00

Further research is presently under way into the possibilities of separating halite from kainite by triboelectric charging of the mineral particles and the 'triboelectric cyclone'. For this purpose a series of experiments is being conducted to measure the electric charge acquired by the particles of the two minerals inside the microcyclone constructed of various materials. The charge is measured by use of a Faraday well and a high-sensitivity electrometer. The first results obtained (Table 6) highlight the fundamental influence that the nature of the charging surface has on the sign and entity of the charge. Temperature also has an effect on charge phenomena. Conditioning of the surfaces with Pamak 4 has not, to date, given the results expected, but this does not rule out the possibility that other types of reagents and different conditions could produce more favourable results.

Conclusions

The correlations that exist between electrophysical parameters and results of the electrostatic separation can afford a deeper understanding of the phenomena that underlie the mechanisms involved. In various instances this knowledge enables the behaviour of minerals in electrostatic separation processes to be predicted. In addition, new techniques can be set up that are capable of enhancing separation selectivity. Among these, the joint effect of temperature and humidity as a means of modifying the surface energy structure offers extremely interesting possibilities. The influence of the adsorption of water molecules at the particle surface, which can be modulated by controlling temperature and humidity of the ambient fluid and/or heating temperature of the solid, has been shown in an initial series of systematic tests on various minerals, the results presented highlighting the essential role that it plays.

The favourable effect of conditioning the solid minerals with

Table 6 Measurements of electric charges (Coulomb/g kainite and halite)

Charged surface	60°C Kainite	Halite	140°C Kainite	Halite	Kainite	Halite
(1) Cyclone in chromium-plated bronze	-1.382	+10.66	-2.003	+10.190	-0.779	+5.326
(2) Cyclone in steel	-0.410	+9.646	-1.363	+6.936	-0.658	+1.101
(3) Cyclone in copper	+0.482	+5.794	-0.099	+4.071	+0.134	+1.957
(4) Cyclone in lead	-0.241	+3.607	-1.565	+2.941	-1.118	-0.324
(5) Cyclone in Teflon	+4.118	+10.701	+4.229	+10.691	+4.606	+3.984

reagents has been substantiated. It is clear that the use of organic and inorganic reagents can alter the surface energy structure of the mineral solids, resulting in enhanced selectivity of electrostatic separation.

The results presented point to the significant possibilities that are available for modification of the behaviour of minerals in electric separation processes and to the extreme interest attached to the study of the solids energy bands.

References
1. Carta M. *et al.* Contribution to the electrostatic separation of minerals. In *Seventh international mineral processing congress, New York, 1964* Arbiter N. ed. (New York: Gordon and Breach, 1965), 427–46.
2. Carta M. *et al.* La séparation électrique des minérais en suspension en milieux gazeux étendue aux fines granulometries avec charge ionique ou triboélectrique. In *Eighth international mineral processing congress, Leningrad, 1968* (Leningrad: Institut Mekhanobr, 1969), vol. 1, 115-31. (Russian text); Paper B1, 12 p. (French text).
3. Del Fà C. Sul caricamento triboelettrico di particelle minerali. *Industria min., Roma,* **19**, 1968, 610-4.
4. Ciccu R. and Foreman E. Sul caricamento triboelettrico dei minerali in relazione allo stato elettrico delle loro superfici. *Industria min., Roma,* **19**, 1968, 525-31.
5. Carta M. *et al.* The influence of the surface energy structure of minerals on electric separation and flotation. In *Proceedings ninth international mineral processing congress, Prague, 1970* (Prague: Ústav pro Výzkum Rud, 1970), vol. 1, 47-57.
6. Carta M. *et al.* Improvement in electric separation and flotation by modification of energy levels in surface layers. In *Tenth international mineral processing congress, London, 1973* Jones M. J. ed. (London: IMM, 1974), 349-76.
7. Pope M. I. *et al.* Factors affecting the triboelectric charging on mineral particles. In *Proceedings 11th international mineral processing congress, Cagliari, 1975: special volume* Ente Minerario Sarda ed. (Cagliari: Istituto di Arte Mineraria, 1975), 213-28.
8. Process and apparatus are subject to Italian Patent 814 154, Aug. 1967, available to principal mineral countries of the world.
9. Carta M. *et al.* Technical and economic problems connected with the dry cleaning of raw coal and in particular with pyrite removal by means of electric separation. In *Seventh international coal preparation congress, Sydney, Australia, May 1976,* paper K2, 35 p.
10. Carta M. *et al.* Optimisation pour l'emploi thermoélectrique de la valorisation d'un charbon flambant avec des teneurs inhabituelles de carbonate et de soufre. In *Eighth international coal preparation congress, Donetsk, USSR, May 1979,* vol. 2, 63-73.
11. Carta M. *et al.* Triboelectric phenomena in mineral processing: theoretic fundamentals and applications. In *Electrostatics: 4th international conference on electrostatic phenomena, The Hague, May 1981: J. Electrostatics,* **10**, 1981, 177-82.
12. Carta M. *et al.* Beneficiation method for desulphurization. In *Coal: phoenix of the '80s, symposium, Halifax, Nova Scotia, June 1981* Al Taweel A. M. ed. (Ottawa: Canadian Society of Chemical Engineering, 1982), vol. 1, 164-73.
13. Carta M. *et al.* Purification of sulphurous coals prior to their final utilization. Paper presented to *Ninth international coal preparation congress, New Delhi, Nov. 1982,* paper H3, 19 p.
14. Carbini P. and Del Fà C. La separazione triboelettrica applicata alla epurazione della pirite e dei componenti di ganga di grezzi di carbone. *Atti Facoltà Ingegneria,* **17**, Oct. 1981, 295-34.
15. Alfano G. and Del Fà C. Separazione elettrica e magnetica. *Boll. Ass. Min. Subalpina,* **19**, no. 3-4, Sept.-Dec. 1982. (Seminar Italy-USA on mineral processing and hydrometallurgy, Pallanza, June 1982).
16. Carta M. Ferrara G. and Del Fà C. Trockene Aufbereitung durch Kombination von selektiver Zerkleinerung und Koronascheidung. Paper presented to Kolloquium Trockene und wassersparende Aufbereitungverfahren, Freiberg, DDR, 21-23 April 1964.

Mechanism of action of new functionalized polymers in flocculation and dispersion of chalcocite

R. Barbucci, A. M. Marabini, M. Barbaro, M. Nocentini and S. Corezzi

Synopsis

New selective dispersing or flocculating agents for chalcocite have been studied. A different class of synthetic polymers with a poly-(amido-amino) structure, with different functional groups, has been used.

Sedimentation tests were carried out at various reagent concentrations and pH values to determine the flocculating action of polymers. Adsorption tests were performed by infrared, ultraviolet and plasma emission spectrometry, the results obtained being related to thermodynamic properties (ascertained by potentiometric measurement of the species present in solution after adsorption). A hypothesis is presented to explain the action of these polymers on the basis of their interaction with the mineral surface.

All polymers that are capable of forming stable and selective complexes with Cu^{2+} exert dispersing power on chalcocite. Polymers that cannot form complexes with the Cu^{2+} ion have strong flocculating power.

Dispersing power is explained in terms of charge repulsion between the particles coated with Cu–polymer complex and particles coated with Cu–polymer complex and complex in solution. Flocculating power is explained in terms of a sheltering of the mineral charge attributable to the adsorption of polymer as a compact coil structure.

Selective flocculation can be employed for the recovery of ultrafine minerals both from fine materials tailings or from the overgrinding of complex ores that cannot be treated by flotation. Reagents that are used for this purpose are natural substances, such as starches or tannins,[1,2,3] or high molecular weight synthetic polymers.[4,5] These reagents act mainly by electrostatic attractive forces and, hence, have no specific affinity towards a given metallic mineral. In the present work the possibility has been studied of utilizing new synthetic polymers that contain functional groups with a known chemical affinity for copper cations as agents capable of changing the aggregation state of fine particles of chalcocite. Synthesized polymers are polyamido-amides with carboxylic and sulphonic groups.

$$\left[\begin{array}{c} O \quad\quad O \\ \| \quad\quad\quad \| \\ -C-N\bigcirc N-C-CH_2-CH_2-N-CH_2-CH_2- \\ \qquad\qquad\qquad\qquad\qquad | \\ \qquad\qquad\qquad\qquad\qquad R \end{array} \right]_n$$

$R = (CH_2)_y COOH (Ay) y = 1, 2 \ldots 5$

$R = (CH_2)_2 SO_3 H (S)$

For comparison results obtained previously with polymers N_1 and N_2 of the same class have been reported.[6]

$$\left[\begin{array}{c} O \quad\quad O \\ \| \quad\quad\quad \| \\ -C-N\bigcirc NC-CH_2-CH_2-N-CH_2-CH_2-N-CH_2-CH_2- \\ \qquad\qquad\qquad\quad | \qquad\qquad\qquad\qquad | \\ \qquad\qquad\qquad\quad R \qquad\qquad\qquad\qquad R \end{array} \right]_n$$

$R = CH_3 (N_1)$

$R = CH_2CH_2OH (N_2)$

Sedimentation tests were carried out at various reagent concentrations and pH values to enable the flocculating or dispersing action of each polymer to be examined. The interaction of each polymer with the mineral surface was investigated, the results being related to the thermodynamic properties of protonation and complex formation to yield an interpretation of their mechanism of action.

Experimental

Materials

The mineral (a pure chalcocite from Messina in the Transvaal, South Africa) was wet-ground in a porcelain mill with the use of distilled water, the $+15~\mu m$ fraction being removed by settling. The $-15~\mu m$ material was maintained in slurry form throughout the experimental work.

Characterization of the surface state by XPS analysis of the mineral aged in this way showed only the presence of $Cu(OH)_2$, in line with earlier studies.[7,8] The Ay and S polymers were synthesized as described previously.[9]

The intrinsic viscosity in $CHCl_3$ at $30°C$ for this series of polymer is in the range 0.1–0.2 dl/g; that of the polymer N_2 ($CHCl_3$ at $30°C$) is 0.17 dl/g, whereas that of N_1 is 0.22 dl/g in $CHCl_3$ at $30°C$, which corresponds to a molecular weight of 7800.

Techniques and apparatus

Sedimentation tests were carried out on 2 g of mineral in the same way as has been described earlier.[2] All the tests were run in a set of 100-ml graduated cylinders. Samples were taken from the stocks of ground pulp kept mechanically agitated. After checking the density, enough pulp to contain about 2 g of solids was transferred to one of the cylinders and the volume was made up to about 80 ml. After pH adjustment and addition of the reagents the volume was brought up to 100 ml. Conditioning was carried out in a mechanical shaker for 5 min. The pH was then rechecked and adjusted to the initial value, if necessary. Sedimentation was started after a further 10 min of conditioning.

The mineral was allowed to settle for a given time, which varied from 1 to about 20 min, as required. A fixed volume of supernatant liquid (70 ml) was then siphoned off and dried by slow evaporation, after which the solids content was determined by weighing.

To establish the time required prior to siphoning preliminary sedimentation tests were run on the varous minerals at different pH values without reagent. In each case a sampling time was selected that ensured 1g of solid P_0 in the 70 ml of supernatant liquid. Flocculating and dispersing power has been calculated by the formula[1,2]

$$F_p = \frac{P_0 - P}{P_0} \times 100$$

where P_0 is the weight of the solid in the supernatant without polymer and P is the weight of the solid in the supernatant after the addition of polymer. Positive values of F_p indicated flocculating action, whereas negative values indicate that the reagent exerts dispersing power. The pH and ionic strength were adjusted by use of analytical grade NaOH, HCl and NaCl.

The thermodynamic measurements were carried out with CO_2-free NaOH solutions, stored and standardized as described elsewhere.[10] The absence of CO_2 in the NaOH solution was tested by Gran's method and by K_w measurements. Hydrochloric acid solution was obtained and standardized as described previously.[10]

The copper(II) nitrate solution was prepared with decarbonated water with use of a C. Erba RPE grade product. To prevent hydrolysis the solution was slightly acidified, the acidity being determined potentiometrically. The concentration of copper(II) was established gravimetrically.

Stock solutions of 0.1 NaCl were prepared from sodium chloride (C. Erba ACS grade) without further purification and used as the ionic medium for all the potentiometric measurements. Viscosity measurements were performed at 25°C with a Cannon Ubbelohde 50/E/998 viscometer with a flow time of 210 s for aqueous 0.1 M NaCl, connected to a Wescan viscosity timer. Corrections for kinetic energy and rate of shear were found to be negligible.

Pure CO_2-free water was used throughout and the solutions were used immediately after preparation. The specific viscosities were determined in the concentration range 10^{-3}–10^{-2} M for polymer solutions. Titrations were performed with 0.1 M hydrochloric acid solution.

The amount of polymer that remained in solution after each settling test was determined by measuring the absorbance at 203 nm at pH 7 and at 201 nm at pH 9 with Perkin-Elmer model 330 ultraviolet visible spectrophotometer. The 203-nm wavelength corresponded to the maximum absorbance for the polymer in solution (this wavelength is characteristic of the carbonyl group substituted by auxocromes as amine groups). In the range of concentrations studied the Lambert–Beer law is obeyed.

For the A_1 polymer there is also an adsorption maximum in the visible region (733 nm): this demonstrates the formation of an A_1-copper complex (at this wavelength the Lambert–Beer law is again obeyed).

The copper concentration in solution before and after adsorption was determined by an ICP plasma technique with a model 5500 Perkin-Elmer spectrophotometer. The adsorption of polymers on the chalcocite surface was studied by infrared spectroscopy with a Perkin-Elmer model 580 B spectrophotometer, controlled by data station 3500. The samples were examined in transmission by use of KBr pellets.

Results

Action of polymers on chalcocite as a function of concentration and pH

The flocculating or dispersing power of polymers was examined at pH 7 and 9 for three different concentrations—10, 50 and 100 ppm, the results obtained being given in Figs. 1-6. Figs. 7 and 8 show the results for N_1 and N_2.

The Ay and S polymers act as dispersants or flocculants. A_1 has a maximum dispersing power of 841, whereas A_5 and S have flocculating powers of 81 and 75, respectively. The N_1 and N_2 polymers show dispersing power at both pH values.

Table 1 gives the amounts of polymer and copper adsorbed at a polymer concentration of 100 ppm. For N_1 and N_2 the quantity of polymers and copper in solution is at a maximum, whereas for the others these quantities are at a minimum; at pH 7 N_1, N_2 and A_1 are dispersants, whereas the others are strong

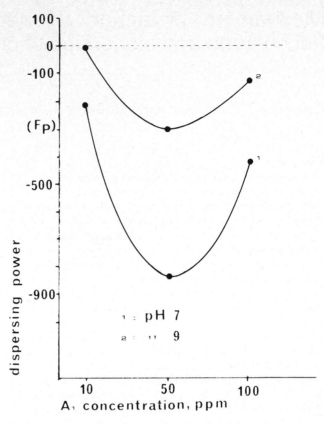

Fig. 1 Flocculating or dispersing power of polymer A_1 as a function of concentration and pH

flocculants; and at pH 9 the dispersing power increases for N_1 and N_2 and falls for A_1. For the other polymers the flocculating power decreases to such an extent that a slight dispersing action is apparent.

Behaviour of polymers in solution
The basicity constants relative to the protonation of the poly

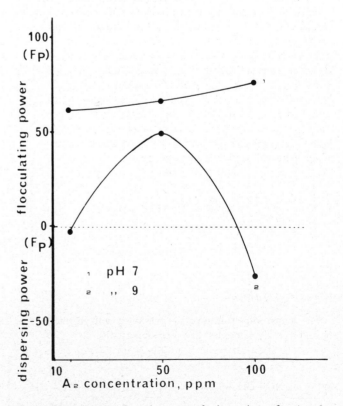

Fig. 2 Flocculating or dispersing power of polymer A_2 as a function of concentration and pH

246

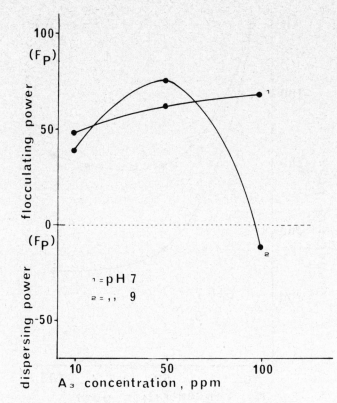

Fig. 3   Flocculating or dispersing power of polymer A_3 as a function of concentration and pH

(amido-amino) acids are reported in Table 2. All these polymers exhibit polyelectrolytic behaviour. The values of their basicity constants have been calculated according to the following equation (obtained by the well-known Henderson–Hesselbach relation):

$$\text{Log } K_i = \log K_i^0 + (n-1) \log (1-\alpha)/\alpha$$

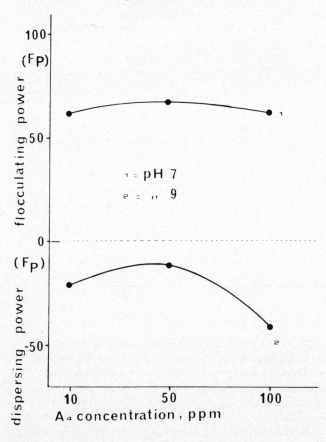

Fig. 4   Flocculating or dispersing power of polymer A_4 as a function of concentration and pH

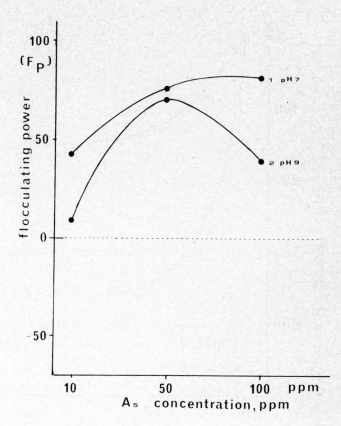

Fig. 5   Flocculating or dispersing power of polymer A_5 as a function of concentration and pH

As is shown in Table 2, the term n_2 is slightly larger than n_1 and increases in passing from A_1 to A_5. Moreover, the basicity of the COO^- group is lower than that of the nitrogen group, but its n_1 value is generally larger. The $\log K_i^0$ value obtained for the tertiary amino group is almost constant throughout, but the basicity constant of the COO^- group gradually increases with

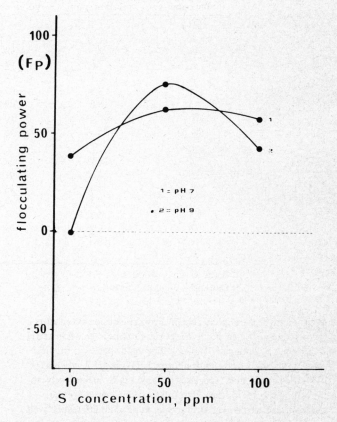

Fig. 6   Flocculating or dispersing power of polymer S as a function of concentration and pH

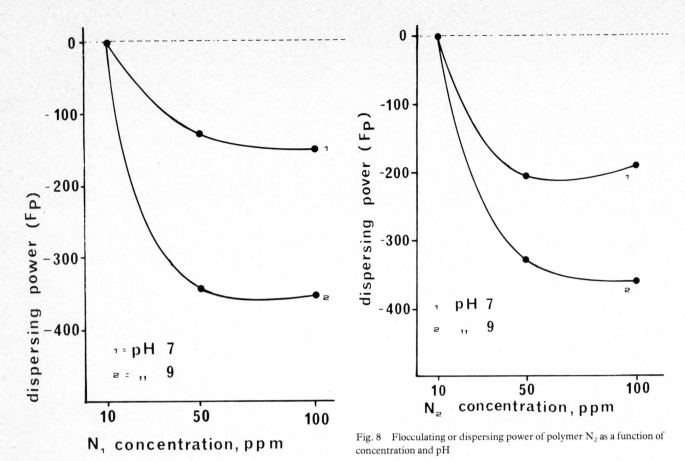

Fig. 7 Flocculating or dispersing power of polymer N_1 as a function of concentration and pH

Fig. 8 Flocculating or dispersing power of polymer N_2 as a function of concentration and pH

Table 1 Action of polymers on chalcocite

Polymers, 100 ppm	Polymer in solution, ppm	Adsorbed polymer, ppm	Cu^{2+}, ppm	Dispersing or flocculating power, Fp, %
pH 7				
A_1	1.4	98.6	0.3	−438
A_2	7.3	92.7	0.0	+ 76
A_3	2.6	97.4	0.0	+ 67
A_4	2.1	97.9	0.0	+ 62
A_5	0.4	99.6	0.2	+ 81
S	18.0	82.0	0.0	+ 57
N_1†	90	10	23.0	−150
N_2†	45	55	11.0	−180
pH 9				
A_1	1.7	98.3	0.2	−134
A_2	8.3	91.7	0.1	− 27
A_3	3.4	96.6	0.0	− 12
A_4	5.4	94.6	0.0	− 42
A_5	3.9	96.1	0.2	+ 38
S	0.7	99.3	0.0	+ 42
N_1*	98	2	16.0	−350
N_2*	22	78	4.0	−360

* Barbucci and co-workers.[6]
† Oestreicher and McGlashan.[8]

lengthening of the aliphatic chain. From the basicity constants the percentages of the different species present in solution at pH 7 and 9 can be obtained (Table 3). The main species of the first class of polymers is the neutral form (L^-H^+) at pH 7, whereas at pH 9 the predominant species is the anionic, L^-. Conversely, the prevailing species for the poly-(amido-amine) series are the mono-protonated and neutral species at pH 7 and 9, respectively.

The polyelectrolytic behaviour of these polymers is also apparent from viscometric titration (Fig. 9).

The viscosity of the A_1 polymer decreases until the formation of the zwitterionic form is complete, then remaining constant until complete protonation of the ligand is established. This behaviour, which is followed by all the polymers of the first series, is probably due to a conformational transition from an expanded to a compact coil. This variation involves a long-range conformational effect that might take place owing to the presence of hanging COO^- groups (the joints between close monomeric units are always very rigid and do not permit of cooperation

Table 2 Protonation constants of poly-(amido-amino)acids

Polymer	$\log K_1^{0*}$ —COO$^-$+H$^+\rightleftharpoons$—COOH	n_1^*	$\log K_2^{0*}$ —N+H$^+\rightleftharpoons$—NH$^+$	n_2^*
A$_1$	2.18	†	8.28	1.03
A$_2$	3.57	1.23	8.52	1.14
A$_3$	3.93	1.12	8.33	1.09
A$_4$	4.21	1.12	8.47	1.10
A$_5$	4.28	1.08	8.50	1.16
A$_6$	1.88	†	7.17	1.15

* Derived from equation $\log K_i = \log K_i + (n-1)\log(1-\alpha)/\alpha$
† Not calculated because of limited data.

between two neighbouring basic groups[11]). The viscometric titrations carried out on the poly(amido-amine)s reveal a different behaviour[11,12] The N$_1$ and N$_2$ polymers show two jumps, which correspond to the neutralization points of the two basic nitrogens (Fig. 9).

The formation of the Cu^{2+} complex has also been observed by drying up the solution that remains after treatment of the mineral with a very high concentration of A$_1$ polymer (2000 ppm).

The infrared spectrum shows the characteristic peaks of the Cu-glycine complex at 3260, 1951 and 1392 cm^{-1}.[13] The same peaks are also evident on the mineral after it has been treated by the polymer solution (50 ppm).

Discussion

At pH 7 the mineral presents a highly positive charge.[7,8] Of the species present at this pH value, only the neutral or negative species can be considered suitable for adsorption, i.e. L$^-$ and L$^-$H$^+$ in the first class of polymers, (Ay, S) and L in the second (N$_1$, N$_2$) (Table 3). Thus, the negative COO$^-$ groups present in both the L$^-$ and L$^-$H$^+$ species are the anchor points to the

Table 3 Percentages of different species present in solution at pH 7 and 9 (per cent referred to L)

Polymer	pH 7			pH 9		
	L$^-$, %	L$^-$H$^+$, %	LH$_2^+$,%	L$^-$, %	L$^-$H$^+$, %	LH$_2^+$, %
A$_1$	10	90	—	85	15	—
A$_2$	3.5	96.5	—	73	27	—
A$_3$	6	94	—	82	18	—
A$_4$	3.3	96.5	0.15	76	24	—
A$_5$	4.5	95	0.3	75	25	—
S	42	58	—	98.5	1.5	—
	L, %	LH$^+$, %	LH$_2^{2+}$, %	L, %	LH$^+$, %	LH$_2^{2+}$, %
N$_1$*	7.0	92.7	0.3	91.3	8.7	
N$_2$*	28.7	71.3	0	95.5	4.5	

* Barbucci and co-workers.[6]

This increase in viscosity arises from the fact that the protonation of the amine nitrogen causes a drastic reduction in the conformational freedom, as has been confirmed by a conformational analysis study.[11]

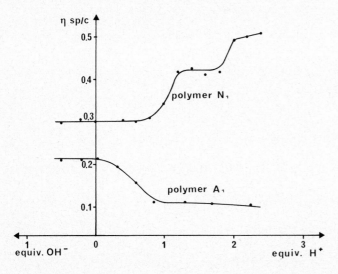

Fig. 9 Viscometric titration of A$_1$ and N$_1$ polymers with HCl in 0.1 M NaCl solution

Of the polymers of the Ay series, only A$_1$ and A$_2$ form complexes with Cu^{2+} in solution. For the A$_1$ polymer the only complex species present in solution is CuL^{2+} with a log β value of about 10.[9] The A$_2$ polymer, on the other hand, gives different complexes in solution. The simple CuL^{2+} species has a log β value of about 5.[9]

positive surface of the mineral. In the second series the amount of L present in solution is low, so adsorption of this type of polymers is lower than that of the first series. Nevertheless, the N$_2$ polymer is more adsorbed than N$_1$, owing to the larger quantity of the neutral species in solution (Table 3) and to the presence of hanging hydroxyethyl groups capable of forming different types of bond with the species on the surface.

The A$_2$-A$_5$ and S polymers, which are not able to form stable Cu^{2+} complexes in solution, show a compact coil structure in the zwitterionic form, which is present to a significant extent at pH 7 (Table 3). The compact form of the polymer induces a self-neutralization of positive and negative charges into the polymer and, when adsorbed, better sheltering of the mineral charges, so they act as flocculant.

The A$_1$ polymer forms a stable complex with Cu^{2+} in solution and can form this type of complex even when Cu is placed on the surface of the mineral. The formation of the complex can occur only with the polymer in the L$^-$ form. The complex formation therefore induces a deprotonation of the —N—H$^+$ groups present in the L$^-$H$^+$ form of A$_1$. A similar mechanism explains the adsorption of poly(acrylic acid) on tribasic calcium phosphate. Infrared spectroscopic studies revealed the ionization of the —COOH groups when adsorbed onto the surface.[14]

The protons released from the repeating units of the polymer involved in the coordination move to protonate the basic groups present in the remaining free part of the molecule, i.e. COO$^-$ groups. Thus, the polymer shows some branches anchored to the mineral in the L$^-$ coordinated form and others free in solution as tails or loops in the LH$_2^+$ form. The presence of these positive branches accounts for the dispersing action of the A$_1$ polymer at pH 7.

The polymers of the second class, N$_1$ and N$_2$, also show a dispersing power. Nevertheless, the proposed mechanism[6] is of a different kind. In fact, the N_1 and N_2 polymers are mainly present as LH$^+$, i.e. in the mono-protonated form, at pH 7. Both polymers provoke a detachment of Cu^{2+}, which, in solution, is coordinated to the polymeric ligand as CuL^{2+} species. Thus, in solution the polymers are always positive charged, either mono-protonated or coordinated to Cu^{2+}, and the surface of the mineral is positive both for its intrinsic charge at this pH and for the presence of some partially adsorbed polymer but with protonated free branches—hence the dispersing power of these two polymers. At pH 9 the mineral surface is slightly positive.[7,8]

The Ay and S polymers are mainly in the anionic form, so they are easily adsorbed on a positive surface. On the other hand, these polymers lose their flocculating power at this pH—to the extent that some become dispersant. The cause can be ascribed to two factors: (1) the lower charge present on the mineral surface and (2) the polymers in the anionic form adopt an extended conformation less suitable for complete adsorption on the mineral surface. This causes poor neutralization of the slightly positive charges of mineral surface and the presence of a large amount of unanchored polymer in the form of tails or loops carrying negative charges. Also, at this pH N_2 is more adsorbed than N_1 and both polymers provoke the detachment of Cu^{2+} from the mineral, albeit to a lesser extent than at pH 7. At pH 9 the Cu^{2+} polymer complex is mainly Cu(OH)L$^+$. From the data in Table 1 it seems that the presence of this species in solution gives rise to a larger dispersing effect than at pH 7, at which only the CuL^{2+} species exists.

Conclusions

From the investigation the following points can be summarized. (1) All polymers that are capable of forming stable and soluble complexes both at neutral and basic pH values with Cu^{2+} exert a dispersing power on chalcocite. (2) Among them, polymer A$_1$ exerts the maximum dispersing power and is completely adsorbed as a complex on the mineral surface. (3) Polymers A$_2$ to A$_5$ and S, in which the number, y, of methylene groups is $y \geqslant 2$, and which cannot form complexes with Cu^{2+} ions, have a strongly flocculating power, which falls with increasing pH. (4) Dispersing power is explained in terms of charge repulsion between particles coated with Cu–polymer complex (A$_1$) and particles coated with Cu–polymer complex and complex in solution (N_1 and N_2). (5) The flocculating power of polymer Ay with $y \geqslant 2$ and S is explained in terms of a sheltering of the mineral charge attributable to the adsorption of polymer as a compact coil structure.

Acknowledgement

The authors are grateful to the Consiglio Nazionale delle Ricerche 'Progetto finalizzato chimica Fine e Secondaria' for financial support and permission to publish this paper. The authors wish to thank B. Passariello, C. Cozza and M. A. Esposito for help in the experimental work.

References

1. Rinelli G. and Marabini A. M. Dispersing properties of tanning agents and possibilities of their use in flotation of fine minerals. In *Fine particles processing* Somasundaran P. ed. (New York: AIME, 1980), vol. 2, 1012–33.
2. Rinelli G. and Marabini A. M. A new reagent system for the selective flocculation of rutile. In *Thirteenth international mineral processing congress, Warsaw, 1979* Laskowski J. ed. (Amsterdam, etc.: Elsevier, 1981), 316–43.
3. Marabini A. M. Goldenberg J. F. and Barbaro M. A new process for the separation of scheelite from gangue minerals by selective flocculation. Paper presented to Pacific region meeting, August 1983.
4. Usoni L. Rinelli G. and Marabini A. M. Selective properties of flocculants and possibilities of their use in flotation of fine minerals. In *Eighth international mineral processing congress, Leningrad, 1968* (Leningrad: Institut Mekhanobr, 1969), 514–33. (Russian text); Paper D13, 14 p. (English text)
5. Lipatov Yu. S. and Sergeeva L. M. *Adsorption of polymers* (New York, etc.: Wiley, 1974), 177p.
6. Barbucci R. Nocentini M. and Marabini A. M. Relationship between the thermodynamic values of two poly(amido-amine)s and their dispersing action on a copper mineral. *Colloids Surfaces*, in press.
7. Healy T. W. and Moignard M. S. A review of electrokinetic studies of metal sulphides. In *Flotation: A. M. Gaudin memorial volume* Fuerstenau M. C. ed. (New York: AIME, 1976), vol. 1, 275–97.
8. Oestreicher C. A. and McGlashan D. W. Surface oxidation of chalcocite. Paper presented to 1972 AIME annual meeting, San Francisco, 1972, Preprint 72-B-1.
9. Barbucci R. *et al.* Paper submitted to *J. phys. Chem.*
10. Barbucci R. *et al.* Thermodynamics of protonation of tetramines with different degrees of n-methycation. *J. phys. Chem.*, **85**, 1981, 64–8.
11. Barbucci R. *et al.* Macroinorganics 7: property–structure relationships for polymer bases whose monomeric units behave independently toward protonation. *Macromolecules*, **14**, 1981, 1203–9.
12. Barbucci R. *et al.* Thermodynamics of protonation and complex formation of multifunctional polymers. *Gazz. chim. ital.*, **112**, 1982, 105–13.
13. Nakamoto K. and McCarthy P. J. *Spectroscopy and structure of metal chelate compounds* (New York: Wiley, 1968), 382 p.
14. Belton D. and Stupp S. I. Adsorption of ionizable polymers on ionic surfaces. *Macromolecules*, **16**, 1983, 1143–50.

Computer-assisted calculations of thermodynamic equilibria in the chalcopyrite–ethyl xanthate system

K. S. Eric Forssberg, Britt-Marie Antti and Bertil I. Pålsson

Synopsis

Calculations show that thermodynamic data can be used to construct pulp chemistry models that satisfactorily describe events in mineral pulps. The usefulness of such models can be enhanced by the insertion of kinetic restrictions derived from analyses of mineral pulps from commercial-scale operations. A number of interesting findings concerning the chalcopyrite–ethyl xanthate system are demonstrated: sulphur is the component that has the strongest influence on the system; grinding with a steel medium does not in itself affect oxidation of chalcopyrite, but the iron introduced into the system will be precipitated as hydroxide, which may adhere to the mineral surfaces; the difference between soda-alkaline and lime–alkaline flotation environments lies in the fact that calcium carbonate and calcium sulphate may be precipitated in the pulp at pH $\geqslant$ 9 if lime is used for pH adjustment; and thiosulphate can interfere with precipitation of cuprous ethyl xanthate on the chalcopyrite surface owing to the formation of a cuprous thiosulphate complex.

As it is possible to calculate an operating line for any given flotation system, the calculation results can be compared at all times with practical experience and measurements of flotation processes.

Chemical reactions on mineral surfaces and in mineral pulps together constitute highly complex chemical systems in the flotation of sulphide minerals. In view of this complexity, manual calculations of equilibrium concentrations in the pulp are necessarily limited by general assumptions as to the activity of various substances present in the pulp liquid. The number of variations in the assumptions on which calculations are based must likewise be limited. Yet it is very important in flotation chemistry research to be able to make theoretical calculations of the influence of such factors as the content of different sulphur anions, iron ions, etc., on the pulp chemistry of the sulphide mineral.

Equilibrium data on simple sulphide mineral systems, investigated with the aid of cyclic voltammetry, have been published by Woods and co-workers.[1,2,3] Manual calculations of pyrite surface chemistry have been presented by Larin et al.[4] General Eh–pH graphs of the chalcocite–xanthate system have been presented by Kuhn.[5] Kielkowska and co-workers[6] reported calculations of the germanium–ethyl xanthate system, and Hepel and Pomianowski[7] presented extensive manual calculations of the copper–ethyl xanthate–water system. Chander and Fuerstenau[8] investigated the copper–diethyl dithiophosphate–sulphur system.

Simple computer-assisted calculations of flotation chemistry processes have recently been reported by Marabini and co-workers[9] with reference to various metal–collector systems in oxide mineral flotation.

The present paper describes computer-assisted calculations of thermodynamic equilibria in the chalcopyrite–ethyl xanthate system under conditions similar to those which prevail in full-scale flotation.

Experimental method

General description

The calculations were performed with the SOLGASWATER computer program developed by the Department of Inorganic Chemistry at the University of Umeå, Sweden. The theory of the calculation of complex chemical equilibria with SOLGASWATER has been described by Eriksson.[10] This program has been used for geochemical calculations by Sjöberg,[11] Pontér[12] and others.

SOLGASWATER offers a new method for calculating equilibrium compositions in multi-phase systems. Each *phase* constitutes a homogeneous part of the system. Homogeneity of a phase means that its chemical and physical properties are the same throughout. The method is applicable to dilute solutions or solutions with an ion medium, which means that the solvent is assumed to have constant unit activity and need not be regarded as an independent component of the system, even though it participates in chemical reactions. The activities of the solutes are assumed to be proportional to their molar concentrations.

The algorithm minimizes the total free energy of the system, which, according to the thermodynamic criterion, has a minimum value at equilibrium, and can be used for systems that contain one or more liquid phases with a variable number of solutes, a gaseous phase of constant volume and a number of *solid* phases.

Solutes are divided into *components* and *complexes*, the components being the smallest number of pure substances required for a rigorous statement of the composition of the system. Every conceivable *species* in the system, both solutes (aq) and solids (s), must be defined before the calculations begin. The version of SOLGASWATER installed at the Computer Centre of Luleå University of Technology can handle systems that comprise up to 98 species, including a maximum of 30 solid phases, based on a maximum of 12 components.

A formation constant, K_f, is stated for each species together with its composition based on the components. The formation constant of the components themselves is set at 1.0, and the formation constant for the species is derived from a combination of known equilibrium relationships with associated equilibrium constants. K_f for $CuS_{(s)}$, for example, is found as follows (cf. Table 1).

Cu^+, e^-, H^+, EtX^-, HS^-, Fe^{3+}, CO_2 and Ca^{2+} have been selected as components of the system. Smith and Martell[13] gave the following equilibrium relationships at 25°C in infinitely dilute solutions:

$$Cu^{2+} + S^{2-} \rightleftharpoons CuS_{(s)} \quad \log K_1 = 36.10 \tag{1}$$

$$HS^- \rightleftharpoons H^+ + S^{2-} \quad \log K_2 = -13.90 \tag{2}$$

251

Table 1   Components and species used in calculation of component variations

SP.NO		LOG KF	KF	FORMULA UNITS							
	FLUID 1										
1	Cu +	.000	1.000E+00	1.00	.00	.00	.00	.00	.00	.00	.00
2	e -	.000	1.000E+00	.00	1.00	.00	.00	.00	.00	.00	.00
3	H +	.000	1.000E+00	.00	.00	1.00	.00	.00	.00	.00	.00
4	EtX -	.000	1.000E+00	.00	.00	.00	1.00	.00	.00	.00	.00
5	HS -	.000	1.000E+00	.00	.00	.00	.00	1.00	.00	.00	.00
6	Fe 3+	.000	1.000E+00	.00	.00	.00	.00	.00	1.00	.00	.00
7	Cu 2+	-2.590	2.570E-03	1.00	-1.00	.00	.00	.00	.00	.00	.00
8	Cu2(OH)2aq	-15.480	3.311E-16	2.00	-2.00	-2.00	.00	.00	.00	.00	.00
9	Cu(OH)2aq	-16.280	5.248E-17	1.00	-1.00	-2.00	.00	.00	.00	.00	.00
10	Cu(OH)3 -	-29.340	4.571E-30	1.00	-1.00	-3.00	.00	.00	.00	.00	.00
11	Cu(OH)4 2-	-42.560	2.754E-43	1.00	-1.00	-4.00	.00	.00	.00	.00	.00
12	(EtX)2(aq)	-2.538	2.897E-03	.00	-2.00	.00	2.00	.00	.00	.00	.00
13	HEtX(aq)	1.520	3.311E+01	.00	.00	1.00	1.00	.00	.00	.00	.00
14	Fe 2+	13.020	1.047E+13	.00	1.00	.00	.00	.00	1.00	.00	.00
15	S2O3 2-	-29.340	4.571E-30	.00	-8.00	-8.00	.00	2.00	.00	.00	.00
16	S4O6 2-	-61.380	4.169E-62	.00	-18.00	-16.00	.00	4.00	.00	.00	.00
17	CuS2O3 -	-18.990	1.023E-19	1.00	-8.00	-8.00	.00	2.00	.00	.00	.00
18	CuS2O32 3-	-46.410	3.890E-47	1.00	-16.00	-16.00	.00	4.00	.00	.00	.00
19	CuS2O33 5-	-74.310	4.898E-75	1.00	-24.00	-24.00	.00	6.00	.00	.00	.00
20	O2(aq)	-85.980	2.709E-76	.00	-4.00	-4.00	.00	.00	.00	.00	.00
21	HS2O3 -	-27.840	1.445E-28	.00	-8.00	-7.00	.00	2.00	.00	.00	.00
22	HSO3 -	-29.970	1.072E-30	.00	-6.00	-6.00	.00	1.00	.00	.00	.00
23	SO3 2-	-37.260	5.495E-38	.00	-6.00	-7.00	.00	1.00	.00	.00	.00
24	FeOH +	3.520	3.311E+03	.00	1.00	-1.00	.00	.00	1.00	.00	.00
25	FeOH 2+	-2.190	6.457E-03	.00	.00	-1.00	.00	.00	1.00	.00	.00
26	Fe(OH)2 +	-5.700	1.995E-06	.00	.00	-2.00	.00	.00	1.00	.00	.00
27	Fe(OH)4 -	-21.600	2.512E-22	.00	.00	-4.00	.00	.00	1.00	.00	.00
28	Fe2O2H2 4+	-2.900	1.259E-03	.00	.00	-2.00	.00	.00	2.00	.00	.00
29	Fe3O4H4 5+	-6.300	5.012E-07	.00	.00	-4.00	.00	.00	3.00	.00	.00
30	H2CO3	.000	1.000E+00	.00	.00	.00	.00	.00	.00	1.00	.00
31	HCO3-	-6.350	4.467E-07	.00	.00	-1.00	.00	.00	.00	1.00	.00
32	CO3 2-	-16.680	2.089E-17	.00	.00	-2.00	.00	.00	.00	1.00	.00
33	CuCO3(aq)	-12.610	2.455E-13	1.00	-1.00	-2.00	.00	.00	.00	1.00	.00
34	CuCO32 2-	-26.120	7.586E-27	1.00	-1.00	-4.00	.00	.00	.00	2.00	.00
35	Ca 2+	.000	1.000E+00	.00	.00	.00	.00	.00	.00	.00	1.00
36	CaOH +	-12.700	1.995E-13	.00	.00	-1.00	.00	.00	.00	.00	1.00
37	CaCO3(aq)	-13.530	2.951E-14	.00	.00	-2.00	.00	.00	.00	1.00	1.00
38	CaHCO3 +	-5.350	4.467E-06	.00	.00	-1.00	.00	.00	.00	1.00	1.00
39	SO4 2- *	-33.970	1.072E-34	.00	-8.00	-9.00	.00	1.00	.00	.00	.00
40	HSO4 - *	-31.980	1.047E-32	.00	-8.00	-8.00	.00	1.00	.00	.00	.00
	SOLIDS										
41	Cu	8.800	6.310E+08	1.00	1.00	.00	.00	.00	.00	.00	.00
42	CuO	-10.950	1.122E-11	1.00	-1.00	-2.00	.00	.00	.00	.00	.00
43	Cu2O	1.620	4.169E+01	2.00	.00	-2.00	.00	.00	.00	.00	.00
44	CuFeS2	46.290	1.950E+46	1.00	.00	-2.00	.00	2.00	1.00	.00	.00
45	CuS	19.520	3.311E+19	1.00	-1.00	.00	.00	1.00	.00	.00	.00
46	Cu2S	34.600	3.981E+34	2.00	.00	-1.00	.00	1.00	.00	.00	.00
47	Fe(OH)2	.120	1.318E+00	.00	1.00	-2.00	.00	.00	1.00	.00	.00
48	Fe(OH)3	-3.200	6.310E-04	.00	.00	-3.00	.00	.00	1.00	.00	.00
49	S	2.230	1.698E+02	.00	-2.00	-1.00	.00	1.00	.00	.00	.00
50	(EtX)2	2.369	2.339E+02	.00	-2.00	.00	2.00	.00	.00	.00	.00
51	CuEtX	19.274	1.879E+19	1.00	.00	.00	1.00	.00	.00	.00	.00
52	Cu(EtX)2	20.407	2.553E+20	1.00	-1.00	.00	2.00	.00	.00	.00	.00
53	FeS	17.220	1.660E+17	.00	1.00	-1.00	.00	1.00	1.00	.00	.00
54	Fe(EtX)3	21.030	1.072E+21	.00	.00	.00	3.00	.00	1.00	.00	.00
55	Fe(EtX)2	20.390	2.455E+20	.00	1.00	.00	2.00	.00	1.00	.00	.00
56	FeCO3	7.020	1.047E+07	.00	1.00	-2.00	.00	.00	1.00	1.00	.00
57	CuCO3	-9.730	1.862E-10	1.00	-1.00	-2.00	.00	.00	.00	1.00	.00
58	Malacite	-16.260	5.495E-17	2.00	-2.00	-4.00	.00	.00	.00	1.00	.00
59	Azurite	-23.440	3.631E-24	3.00	-3.00	-6.00	.00	.00	.00	2.00	.00
60	Ca(OH)2	-22.810	1.549E-23	.00	.00	-2.00	.00	.00	.00	.00	1.00
61	Calcite	-8.330	4.677E-09	.00	.00	-2.00	.00	.00	.00	1.00	1.00
62	CaSO4 *	-29.350	4.467E-30	.00	-8.00	-9.00	.00	1.00	.00	.00	1.00
63	CuOHSO4 *	-15.010	9.772E-16	1.00	-3.00	-3.75	.00	.25	.00	.00	.00

Combining reactions 1 and 2 with the redox equation

$$Cu^{2+} + e^- \rightleftharpoons Cu^+ \quad \log K_3 = 2.68 \tag{3}$$

Equation 1 + equation 2 − equation 3 yields

$$Cu^+ + HS^- \rightleftharpoons CuS_{(s)} + H^+ + e^- \tag{4}$$

which can be written

$$Cu^+ + HS^- - H^+ - e^- \rightleftharpoons CuS_{(s)} \tag{5}$$

i.e. the composition of $CuS_{(s)}$, based on the components Cu^+, e^-, H^+, EtX^-, HS^-, Fe^{3+}, CO_2 and Ca^{2+}, is 1, −1, −1, 0, 1, 0, 0, 0.

The corresponding value of $\log K_f$ is obtained according to

$$\log K_f(CuS) = \log K_1 + \log K_2 - \log K_3 = 19.52 \tag{6}$$

It is also necessary to state the total concentration of each component in the system and how the concentration varies (total concentration here means the sum of the concentrations of all species in which the component is present). Sometimes it may be more advantageous to state the activity of a free component instead of its total concentration, e.g. pH and pe instead of the total concentrations of H^+ and e^- where

$$pH = -\log\{H^+\}$$

$$pe = -\log\{e^-\}$$

SOLGASWATER uses a process of iteration to test which combination of phases gives the minimum free energy in the system. A solid phase is excluded if its substantive quantity is zero or negative. Phases are also excluded if they fail to satisfy Gibbs' phase rule. According to this rule, there is a relationship between the number of independent variables (f = degrees of freedom), components (k) and phases (p) in the system

$$f = k - p + 2 \tag{7}$$

that must always exist at equilibrium. The iteration process is terminated when the phases present at equilibrium have been found and when the equilibrium concentrations of all included species are unchanged and positive in two successive iteration cycles.

In calculations performed on the flotation system the total concentrations of the components were kept constant with the exception of the total concentrations of Ca and CO_2, which both depend on pH. Both pH and pe were varied, pe here being a quantity directly related to the potential of a solution in the proportion

$$\mathrm{p}e = E/g \qquad (8)$$

where E is redox potential and $g = RT(\ln 10)/F$, R is the general gas constant, T is temperature, K, and F is Faraday's constant. The constant $g = 59.16\,\mathrm{mV}$ at $25°\mathrm{C}$ and 1 atm.

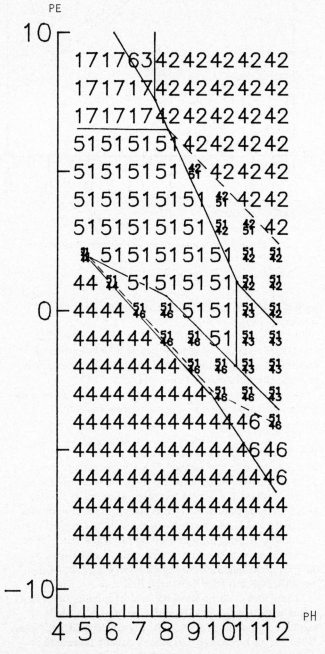

Fig. 1 Raw data plot of Cu predominance diagram for kinetic restriction case: numbers are species numbers according to Tables 1 and 3; lines are manual interpretations of phase boundaries; final plot given in Fig. 14

When the equilibrium composition of the system has been calculated at the specified points (pe–pH), the results can be extracted in the form of tables and graphs. The user can select the contents of the tables, e.g. equilibrium concentration, c, equilibrium activity, a, or their logarithms.

If one opts for results in the form of predominance diagrams, one can select either $+ - \log{(a)}$ or $+ - \log{(Tc)}$ (Tc is total concentration) as axes. A predominance diagram shows which solid phases that contain a given component are present at each pe–pH point; if no solid phase is present, the predominant species in solution is given. In the calculations pe and pH are varied in steps of one unit, i.e. the predominance diagrams are constructed as coordinate matrices in which the equilibrium composition at each point is known (cf. Fig. 1). The boundary lines that divide areas of different phase composition are then drawn on the diagrams by hand.

Assumptions for purposes of computation

Total concentrations are determined partly according to which mineral is present in the system and partly from known concentrations in the pulp liquid. The calculations are performed on the pulp liquid; to calculate the participation of mineral particles in the reactions components that can be regarded as originating from the mineral surfaces are assigned total concentrations equal to their *surface molarity* (defined in Appendix 1).

Studies of commercial-scale flotation processes[14] showed that thiosulphate occurs in much higher concentrations than chemical equilibrium would appear to justify. This was simulated in two ways in the calculations. In the simpler variants sulphur species with an oxidation number of $+\mathrm{vi}$ (sulphate and bisulphate) were excluded;[15] alternatively, adjusted equilibrium constants for the formation of sulphite and sulphate species from thiosulphate were calculated on the basis of known concentrations of thiosulphate, sulphite and sulphate at a given pe–pH point. The adjustments were made to the sulphite and sulphate, as it is the oxidation of thiosulphate that is kinetically restricted. The procedure is described in Appendix 2.

The calculations were performed with the species and components listed in Table 1. Individual species were excluded from or added to the basic list in various specific calculations; these exclusions and additions are discussed under the respective headings. The general principle, starting with a Cu–Fe–EtX–O–S–CO_2–Ca system, was to include all the compounds that might conceivably be present in a flotation pulp. Thermodynamic data on inorganic compounds are taken from Smith and Martell[13] unless otherwise stated. Data at $25°\mathrm{C}$ and ion strength $I = 0$ have been used wherever possible. Electron equilibria are taken from Garrels and Christ.[16] Data on various xanthate compounds were obtained from Hepel and Pomianowski,[7] Du Rietz,[17] Majima,[18] Leja[19] and Pilipenko and co-workers.[20] The formation constant of $O_{2(aq)}$ is derived from the assumption that pure oxygen gas at 1 atm is in contact with water at $20°\mathrm{C}$.

The Ca component is included because it is the predominant cation in alkaline flotation of sulphide ores. Carbon dioxide in the form of carbonate forms water-soluble complexes and solid compounds with copper, e.g. $CuCO_{3(aq)}$, $CuCO_{3(s)}$, $Cu_2(OH)_2CO_{3(s)}$ (malachite) and $Cu_3(OH)_2(CO_3)_{2(s)}$ (azurite). Iron carbonates are also possible products in a flotation pulp. Carbonates originate from the dissolution of carbon dioxide introduced with the air blown into the flotation cells. The determination of actual carbonate activity has been beset by problems; it cannot be assumed that atmospheric carbon dioxide, $CO_{2(g)}$, is in equilibrium with the carbon dioxide dissolved in the pulp, $CO_{2(aq)}$, as this would lead to the absurd conclusion that all the metallic components should be present as carbonate complexes. Instead, one must allow for the fact that the amount of carbon dioxide going into solution is inhibited by the kinetics of reaction[21] and is strongly influenced by pH. Knowing this, one can calculate the total concentration of CO_2 at different pH levels. Unfortunately, a theoretical calculation on this basis gives bicarbonate concentrations about two orders of magnitude higher than those which can actually be measured in flotation circuits.[22] The theoretically calculated total concentrations at various pH levels have therefore been reduced throughout by two orders of magnitude, the resulting figures being used as bases for further calculations. The total concentration figures used are listed in Table 2.

Table 2 Total concentration of CO_2 as a functon of pH (dissolving time, 1 h) (theoretical values $\times 10^{-2}$)

pH	$Tc(CO_2)$
5	1.080×10^{-5} M
6	1.083×10^{-5} M
7	1.111×10^{-5} M
8	1.386×10^{-5} M
9	4.140×10^{-5} M
10	3.168×10^{-4} M
11	3.071×10^{-3} M
12	3.061×10^{-2} M

Results

Normal case
Components and species present in the Cu–Fe–EtX–O–S–CO_2 system are listed in Table 1. Species nos. 35–40 and 60–63 were not included in the calculation. The total concentrations of the components were

$$Tc(Cu) = 2.91 \times 10^{-4} \text{ M}$$
$$Tc(Fe) = 2.91 \times 10^{-4} \text{ M}$$
$$Tc(S) = 5.82 \times 10^{-4} \text{ M}$$
$$Tc(EtX) = 1.00 \times 10^{-4} \text{ M}$$
$$Tc(CO_2) \text{ varies with pH according to Table 2}$$
$$Tc(Ca) = 0$$

The total concentration of ethyl xanthate corresponds to a KEtX dosage of about 30 g/t of ore at a dilution of 40% solids by mass.

System data are given in Figs. 2–6. Solid phases present in the pe–pH range are Cu, $CuFeS_2$, Cu_2S, Cu_2O, CuO, $Cu_2(OH)_2CO_3$, CuEtX, $(EtX)_2$ and $Fe(OH)_3$.

The areas of stability for copper-bearing species are shown in Fig. 2. Chalcopyrite is stable at low redox potentials; when the potential is increased the mineral is successively oxidized to Cu_2S, Cu_2O and CuO. The malachite phase is stable within a very narrow pH interval around pH 6 and above pe 6. Free copper ions dominate at lower pH and potentials above pe 3. The area of stability of CuEtX is marked by broken lines in Fig. 2. This area coincides with the areas of stability of Cu_2S and Cu_2O, and partly with that of CuO.

According to Fig. 3, the dixanthogen $(EtX)_{2(s)}$ is stable at high potentials and EtX^- at low potentials.

Fig. 4 shows the distribution of sulphur-bearing species. SO_4^{2-} and HSO_4^- have not been included in the calculations,

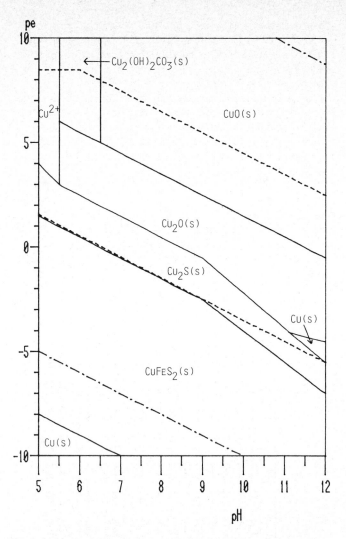

Fig. 2 Cu predominance diagram for normal case (broken lines mark stability area of CuEtX)

so SO_3^{2-} and HSO_3^- predominate among the dissolved species.

The iron predominance diagram in Fig. 5 shows that $Fe(OH)_3$ is stable at potentials that lie above the area of stability of chalcopyrite. A small wedge of Fe^{2+} penetrates between the solid phases below pH 6.

The carbonate diagram in Fig. 6 shows no variation with pe because carbonate does not participate in redox processes.

Variation of EtX concentration
To study the effect of varying EtX concentrations two calculations were made in which $Tc(EtX)$ was changed to 1×10^{-5} M and 1×10^{-3} M, corresponding, respectively, to KEtX dosages of about 3 and 300 g/t. The components and species were otherwise the same as in the normal case.

Changes in EtX concentration do not significantly affect the predominance diagrams of the other components, so only the EtX diagrams are shown here; Fig. 7 shows the low EtX case and Fig. 8 the high EtX case.

At low EtX concentration the area of stability of CuEtX is diminished above pH 10, and an area of free ethyl xanthate ions appears instead. At higher potentials the area of $(EtX)_{2(s)}$ is replaced by an almost equally large area of $(EtX)_{2(aq)}$.

At high EtX concentration the area of stability of CuEtX has the same extent as in the normal case, but as a result of the high total concentration all the available copper in the

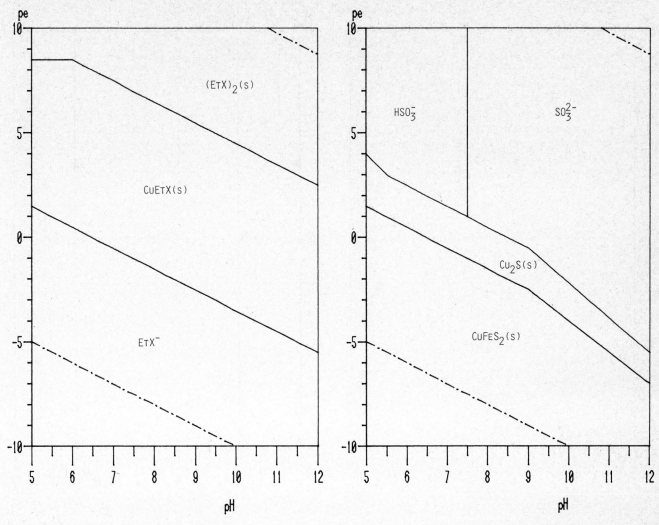

Fig. 3   EtX predominance diagram for normal case

Fig. 4   S predominance diagram for normal case

area is sequestered as cuprous ethyl xanthate. The EtX diagram in Fig. 8 shows that when there is a surplus of EtX, EtX^- is stable below pe 2 and $(EtX)_{2(s)}$ above.

Substitution of butyl xanthate for ethyl xanthate

To investigate the influence of the length of the carbon chain in the xanthate molecule calculations were performed on the normal system, but with the formation constants of n-butyl xanthate substituted for those of ethyl xanthate. The following data were used in the calculations:

$$(BX)_{2(s)} + 2e^- \rightleftharpoons 2BX^- \qquad e^\circ = -0.120\ V^{17}$$

$$HBX \rightleftharpoons H^+ + BX^- \qquad \log K_a = -1.638^{18}$$

$$CuBX_{(s)} \rightleftharpoons Cu^+ + BX^- \qquad \log K_s = -19.33^{19}$$

$$Cu(BX)_{2(s)} \rightleftharpoons Cu^{2+} + 2BX^- \qquad \log K_s = -20.46$$

The last value is calculated according to the difference between the log K_s values of $CuEtX_{(s)}$ and $Cu(EtX)_{2(s)}$. Otherwise, the components and species were the same as in the normal case.

The calculations showed that the area of extension of CuBX agrees with that of CuEtX. Accordingly, no separate diagrams are shown here.

Variation of sulphur concentration

The calculations were performed on the normal system with

$Tc(S) = 5.82 \times 10^{-3}$ M, i.e. an order of magnitude higher than normal. The higher sulphur concentration can be said to correspond to the conditions that prevail when recycled water is supplied to the flotation pulp. The results are shown in Fig. 9 (Cu predominance) and Fig. 10 (S predominance). It will be seen from the latter that the areas of stability of HSO_3^-, SO_3^{2-} and $S_{(s)}$ are increased, and that $CuFeS_2$ coexists with $S_2O_3^{2-}$ and HS^-.

Variation of iron concentration

Grinding with steel rod and ball charges introduces substantial amounts of iron into the flotation pulp. These calculations were based on assumed iron release rates of 100 g/kWh at an energy input of 4 kWh/t for rods and 120 g/kWh at an energy input of 8 kWh/t for balls. This corresponds to an addition of 1360 g Fe per tonne of ore—equivalent to 1.62×10^{-2} M.

Calculations on the normal system with an elevated iron concentration show (Fig. 11) that it is only the areas of extension of iron-bearing species that are affected. The area of stability of $CuFeS_2$ contains the solid phases $Fe(OH)_3$, $FeCO_3$, $Fe(OH)_2$. No Fe–EtX compounds are formed.

pH regulation with soda

In some cases soda, Na_2CO_3, is added to flotation pulps to adjust the pH. Assumed variations in dosage and pH were 300 g/t at pH 9, 1500 g/t at pH 10 and 2500 g/t at pH 11, these being added to the concentrations that arise from dissolved carbon dioxide introduced with blower air.

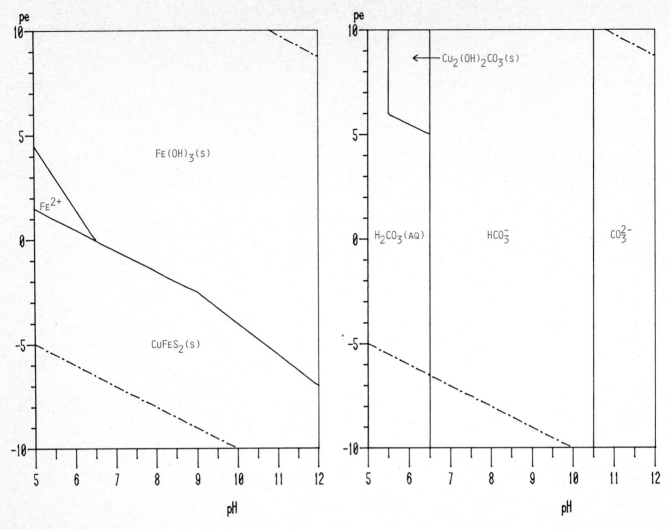

Fig. 5 Fe predominance diagram for normal case

Fig. 6 CO$_2$ predominance diagram for normal case

Components and species were the same as in the normal case.

As the increased carbonate activity had very little effect on the system, only the Cu predominance diagram is shown here (Fig. 12). The only difference from previous findings is that another area of malachite appears inside the area of stability of CuO at pH 9.

pH regulation with lime

Lime is the most common pH-regulating agent in flotation of complex sulphide ores. Lime in the form of CaO was assumed to have been added in the following dosages to obtain given pH levels: 100 g/t at pH 8, 400 g/t at pH 9, 1000 g/t at pH 10, 1700 g/t at pH 11 and 2500 g/t at pH 12. A total concentration of 1×10^{-5} M was assumed for pH ⩽ 7.

Equilibrium calculations on this system took account of the formation of the following calcium-bearing species: Ca^{2+}, $CaOH^+$, $CaCO_{3(aq)}$, $CaHCO_3^+$, $Ca(OH)_{2(s)}$ and $CaCO_{3(s)}$. Sulphate-bearing species (39 and 40 and 62 and 63) were not included. The system is now Cu–Fe–EtX–O–S–CO$_2$–Ca.

The introduction of Ca species into the system does not affect the predominance diagrams of Cu, Fe, EtX or S. Fig. 13 shows the CO$_2$ diagram: comparison with the normal system shows that the area of stability of HCO$_3$ has shrunk because CaCO$_{3(s)}$ is stable at pH levels above 8.5.

Kinetic restrictions

Sulphate species have been excluded from the foregoing

calculations to illustrate the influence of metastable phases. Another way of accomplishing this is to modify the activity coefficients of various species to adapt a theoretical model to actual measured pulp chemistry data. Appendix 2 describes how it is possible to calculate 'adjusted' formation constants on the basis of measured concentrations of sulphur anions. This is equivalent to modifying activity coefficients, but conversion of formation constants is easier to use in computer simulations.

It has thus been possible to include SO_4^{2-}, HSO_4^-, $CaSO_{4(s)}$ and $CuOH_{1.5}(SO_4)_{0.25(s)}$ in the system. The components and species in the system are listed together with their formation constants in Table 3. The total concentration of sulphur has been increased to 7.5×10^{-3} M to enable the results to be compared with the reference data in Appendix 2. As it was not possible to obtain reliable analytical data for tetrathionate, $S_4O_6^{2-}$, in flotation pulps, tetrathionate has been excluded from the calculations of kinetically restricted systems.

The results are shown as predominance diagrams for copper, ethyl xanthate and sulphur in Figs. 14, 15 and 16, respectively. The diagrams of Fe, CO$_2$ and Ca are affected to but a minor degree by the kinetic restrictions.

The area of extension of CuEtX is much smaller, and the (EtX)$_2$–CuEtX boundary line is displaced downward on the pe scale. Cu$_2$O is found only within a narrow pe interval above pH 10.5. The dominating soluble copper species is the cuprous thiosulphate complex.

The previous areas of SO_3^{2-} and HSO_3^- in the S predominance diagram are now replaced by $S_2O_3^{2-}$ and

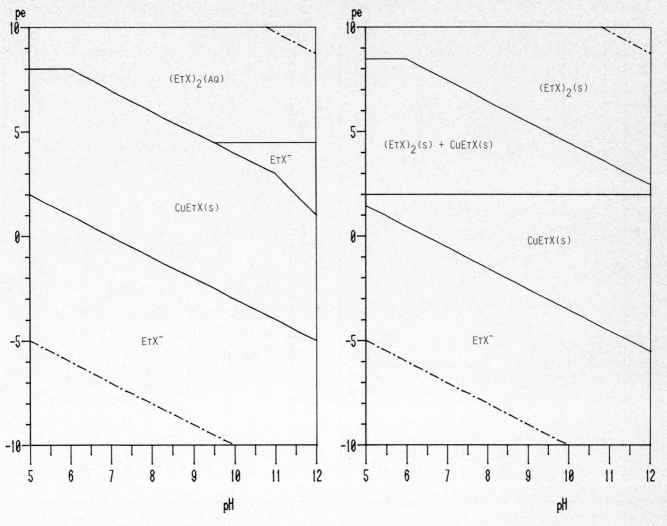

Fig. 7   EtX predominance diagram for low EtX case

Fig. 8   EtX predominance diagram for high EtX case

SO_4^{2-}. The area of extension of $S_{(s)}$ has expanded in the direction of higher pH. The area of extension of SO_4^{2-} contains an area of $CaSO_{4(s)}$.

To further illustrate the complexity of pulp chemistry, SOLGASWATER was used to calculate logarithmic distribution graphs of the various components at pH 11. Figs. 17, 18 and 19 show the resulting graphs for Cu, EtX and S, respectively. Fig. 19 clearly illustrates the relationships between sulphur species at the pH 11–pe 4 point, which is the reference point for calculation of adjusted equilibrium constants. The high concentrations of cuprous thiosulphate complex in the neighbourhood of pe 0 are particularly noteworthy.

Operating line

It is known from previous measurements by Nordström and Pålsson[23] and others that redox potential diminishes with rising pH and that the associated pe–pH values in flotation pulps lie on a line that we can call the operating line. It is of practical interest to learn how the concentrations of various substances vary along the operating line when the pH is altered.

To determine the operating line we proceed from the assumption that no net transfer of electrons out of or into the system takes place. The restriction

$$Tc(e^-) = 0$$

can then be placed on the flotation system, i.e. oxidizing and reducing reactions are constrained to balance out at every point along the operating line. If the pH is then varied, $\{e^-\}$ will represent the free electron concentration (= redox potential) in the system,

$$\{e^-\} \Rightarrow Eh$$

Oxygen saturation of the pulp is assumed. If this should not be the case, the operating line will be displaced downward on the pe–pH graph.

The operating line, calculated in steps of 0.5 pH units, is drawn in on the Cu predominance diagram in Fig. 20. A number of points showing pe–pH values measured during the flotation of Näsliden ore[23] have also been plotted on this diagram. Points that represent copper–lead and zinc flotation middlings lie around the operating line, whereas points for rod-mill discharge lie just below it.

To provide a simple illustration of what happens when the pH changes, concentrations of various substances have been plotted against pH in the logarithmic distribution graphs shown in Figs. 21, 22 and 23 (note that the $\{e^-\}$ line corresponds to pe, but with the sign reversed). The Cu distribution graph in Fig. 21 shows that CuEtX is present up to pH 11.5, but that this compound begins to disappear even at pH 10.5. It further appears that there is a correlation beween electron activity and the Cu^{2+}:Cu^+ ratio. It should, however, be pointed out that the calculations make no allowance for the presence of excess iron ions.

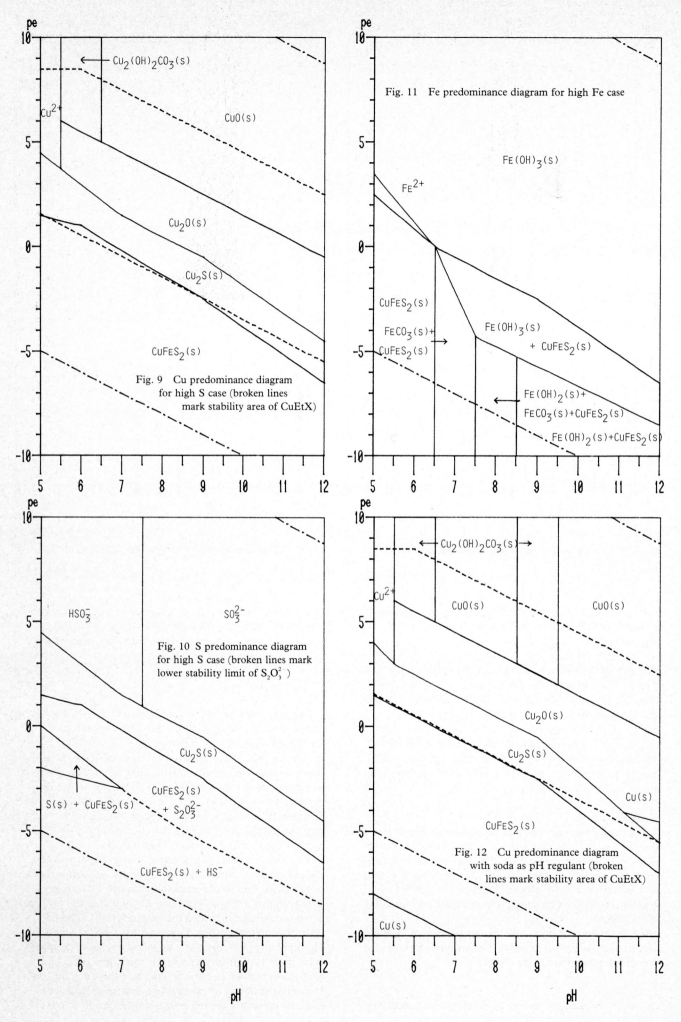

Fig. 9 Cu predominance diagram for high S case (broken lines mark stability area of CuEtX)

Fig. 10 S predominance diagram for high S case (broken lines mark lower stability limit of $S_2O_3^{2-}$)

Fig. 11 Fe predominance diagram for high Fe case

Fig. 12 Cu predominance diagram with soda as pH regulant (broken lines mark stability area of CuEtX)

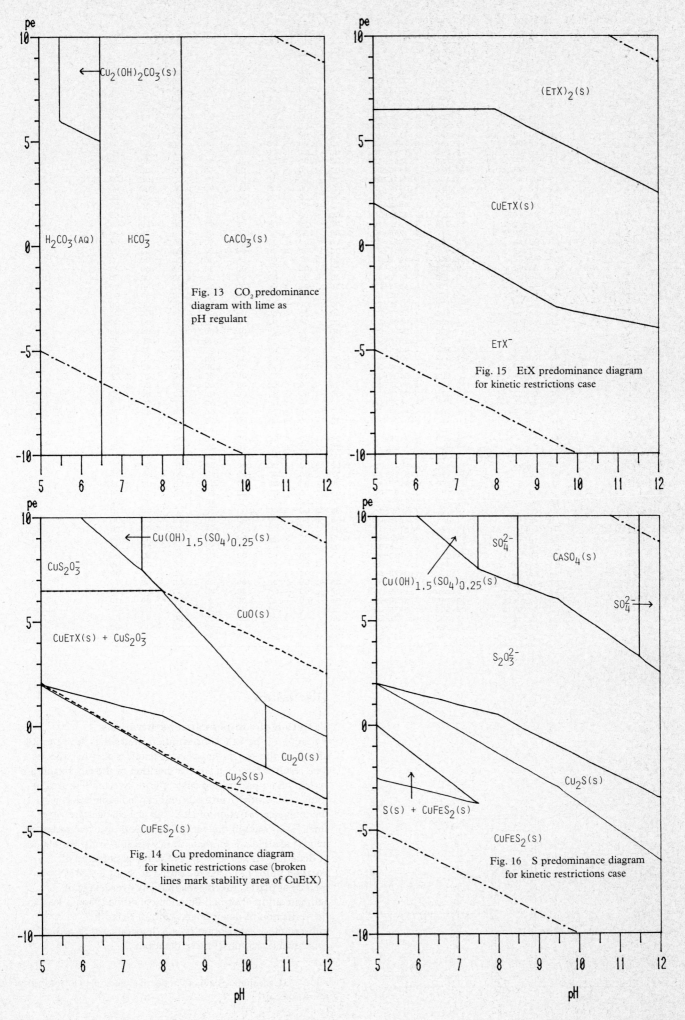

Fig. 13   CO₂ predominance diagram with lime as pH regulant

Fig. 15   EtX predominance diagram for kinetic restrictions case

Fig. 14   Cu predominance diagram for kinetic restrictions case (broken lines mark stability area of CuEtX)

Fig. 16   S predominance diagram for kinetic restrictions case

Table 3 Components and species in kinetically restricted system

SP.NO		LOG KF	KF	FORMULA UNITS							
	FLUID 1										
1	Cu +	.000	1.000E+00	1.00	.00	.00	.00	.00	.00	.00	.00
2	e -	.000	1.000E+00	.00	1.00	.00	.00	.00	.00	.00	.00
3	H +	.000	1.000E+00	.00	.00	1.00	.00	.00	.00	.00	.00
4	EtX -	.000	1.000E+00	.00	.00	.00	1.00	.00	.00	.00	.00
5	HS -	14.670	4.677E+14	.00	4.00	4.00	.00	.50	.00	.00	.00
6	Fe 3+	.000	1.000E+00	.00	.00	.00	.00	.00	1.00	.00	.00
7	Cu 2+	-2.590	2.570E-03	1.00	-1.00	.00	.00	.00	.00	.00	.00
8	Cu2(OH)2aq	-15.480	3.311E-16	2.00	-2.00	-2.00	.00	.00	.00	.00	.00
9	Cu(OH)2aq	-16.280	5.248E-17	1.00	-1.00	-2.00	.00	.00	.00	.00	.00
10	Cu(OH)3 -	-29.340	4.571E-30	1.00	-1.00	-3.00	.00	.00	.00	.00	.00
11	Cu(OH)4 2-	-42.560	2.754E-43	1.00	-1.00	-4.00	.00	.00	.00	.00	.00
12	(EtX)2(aq)	-2.538	2.897E-03	.00	-2.00	.00	2.00	.00	.00	.00	.00
13	HEtX	1.520	3.311E+01	.00	.00	1.00	1.00	.00	.00	.00	.00
14	Fe 2+	13.020	1.047E+13	.00	1.00	.00	.00	.00	1.00	.00	.00
15	S2O3 2-	.000	1.000E+00	.00	.00	.00	.00	1.00	.00	.00	.00
16	S4O6 2- *	-2.700	1.995E-03	.00	-2.00	.00	.00	2.00	.00	.00	.00
17	CuS2O3 -	10.350	2.239E+10	1.00	.00	.00	.00	1.00	.00	.00	.00
18	CuS2O32 3-	12.270	1.862E+12	1.00	.00	.00	.00	2.00	.00	.00	.00
19	CuS2O33 5-	13.710	5.129E+13	1.00	.00	.00	.00	3.00	.00	.00	.00
20	O2(aq)	-85.980	2.709E-76	.00	-4.00	-4.00	.00	.00	.00	.00	.00
21	HS2O3 -	1.600	3.981E+01	.00	.00	1.00	.00	1.00	.00	.00	.00
22	HSO3 -	-36.350	4.467E-37	.00	-2.00	-2.00	.00	.50	.00	.00	.00
23	SO3 2-	-43.530	2.951E-44	.00	-2.00	-3.00	.00	.50	.00	.00	.00
24	FeOH +	3.520	3.311E+03	.00	1.00	-1.00	.00	.00	1.00	.00	.00
25	FeOH 2+	-2.190	6.457E-03	.00	.00	-1.00	.00	.00	1.00	.00	.00
26	Fe(OH)2 +	-5.700	1.995E-06	.00	.00	-2.00	.00	.00	1.00	.00	.00
27	Fe(OH)4 -	-21.600	2.512E-22	.00	.00	-4.00	.00	.00	1.00	.00	.00
28	Fe2OH2 4+	-2.900	1.259E-03	.00	.00	-2.00	.00	.00	2.00	.00	.00
29	Fe3OH4 5+	-6.300	5.012E-07	.00	.00	-4.00	.00	.00	3.00	.00	.00
30	H2CO3(aq)	.000	1.000E+00	.00	.00	.00	.00	.00	.00	1.00	.00
31	HCO3 -	-6.350	4.467E-07	.00	.00	-1.00	.00	.00	.00	1.00	.00
32	CO3 2-	-16.680	2.089E-17	.00	.00	-2.00	.00	.00	.00	1.00	.00
33	CuCO3(aq)	-12.610	2.455E-13	1.00	-1.00	-2.00	.00	.00	.00	1.00	.00
34	CuCO32 2-	-26.120	7.586E-27	1.00	-1.00	-4.00	.00	.00	.00	2.00	.00
35	Ca 2+	.000	1.000E+00	.00	.00	.00	.00	.00	.00	.00	1.00
36	CaOH +	-12.700	1.995E-13	.00	.00	-1.00	.00	.00	.00	.00	1.00
37	CaCO3(aq)	-13.530	2.951E-14	.00	.00	-2.00	.00	.00	.00	1.00	1.00
38	CaHCO3 +	-5.350	4.467E-06	.00	.00	-1.00	.00	.00	.00	1.00	1.00
39	SO4 2-	-72.006	9.863E-73	.00	-4.00	-5.00	.00	.50	.00	.00	.00
40	HSO4 -	-70.016	9.638E-71	.00	-4.00	-4.00	.00	.50	.00	.00	.00
	SOLIDS										
41	Cu	8.800	6.310E+08	1.00	1.00	.00	.00	.00	.00	.00	.00
42	CuO	-10.950	1.122E-11	1.00	-1.00	-2.00	.00	.00	.00	.00	.00
43	Cu2O	1.620	4.169E+01	2.00	.00	-2.00	.00	.00	.00	.00	.00
44	CuFeS2	75.630	3.692E+75	1.00	8.00	6.00	.00	1.00	1.00	.00	.00
45	CuS	34.190	1.549E+34	1.00	3.00	3.00	.00	.50	.00	.00	.00
46	Cu2S	49.270	1.862E+49	2.00	4.00	3.00	.00	.50	.00	.00	.00
47	Fe(OH)2	.120	1.318E+00	.00	1.00	-2.00	.00	.00	1.00	.00	.00
48	Fe(OH)3	-3.200	6.310E-04	.00	.00	-3.00	.00	.00	1.00	.00	.00
49	S	16.900	7.943E+16	.00	2.00	3.00	.00	.50	.00	.00	.00
50	(EtX)2	2.369	2.339E+02	.00	-2.00	.00	2.00	.00	.00	.00	.00
51	CuEtX	19.274	1.879E+19	1.00	.00	.00	1.00	.00	.00	.00	.00
52	Cu(EtX)2	20.407	2.553E+20	1.00	-1.00	.00	2.00	.00	.00	.00	.00
53	FeS	31.890	7.762E+31	.00	5.00	3.00	.00	.50	1.00	.00	.00
54	Fe(EtX)3	21.030	1.072E+21	.00	.00	.00	3.00	.00	1.00	.00	.00
55	Fe(EtX)2	20.390	2.455E+20	.00	1.00	.00	2.00	.00	1.00	.00	.00
56	FeCO3	7.020	1.047E+07	.00	1.00	-2.00	.00	.00	1.00	1.00	.00
57	CuCO3	-9.730	1.862E-10	1.00	-1.00	-2.00	.00	.00	.00	1.00	.00
58	Malacite	-16.260	5.495E-17	2.00	-2.00	-4.00	.00	.00	.00	1.00	.00
59	Azurite	-23.440	3.631E-24	3.00	-3.00	-6.00	.00	.00	.00	2.00	.00
60	Ca(OH)2	-22.810	1.549E-23	.00	.00	-2.00	.00	.00	.00	.00	1.00
61	Calcite	-8.330	4.677E-09	.00	.00	-2.00	.00	.00	.00	1.00	1.00
62	CaSO4	-67.386	4.111E-68	.00	-4.00	-5.00	.00	.50	.00	.00	1.00
63	CuOHSO4*2	-49.044	9.036E-50	2.00	-4.00	-5.50	.00	.25	.00	.00	.00

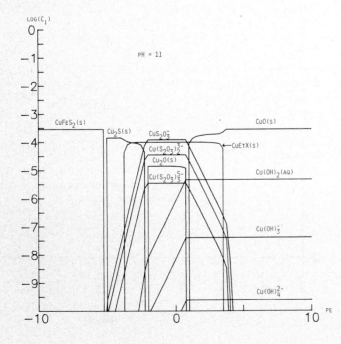

Discussion

Variation of component concentrations

Variation of the EtX concentration shows that the quantity of EtX in the system has very little effect on other species. The result is largely a superimposition of the ethyl xanthate system on an underlying chalcopyrite system. The area of stability of CuEtX contracts and expands somewhat with the total concentration of EtX, but the changes are very small, even though the variations extend over two orders of magnitude. Heavy xanthate dosages result in the formation of dixanthogen above pe 2. As the redox potential of flotation pulps has been measured at about $+200\,mV$ (pe 3.3) at pH 11, this means that any overdosage of xanthate under 'normal' flotation conditions should lead to the formation of dixanthogen, with the risk of indiscriminate adsorption on any mineral surface and, consequently, of unselective flotation.

Fig. 17 Logarithmic graph of Cu distribution at pH 11 for kinetic restrictions case

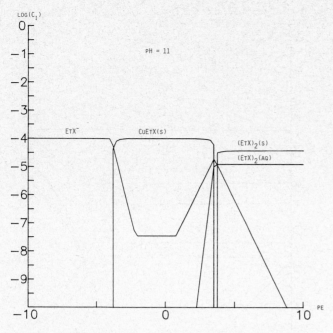

Fig. 18   Logarithmic graph of EtX distribution at pH 11 for kinetic restrictions case

The formation constants of the various butyl xanthate species do not differ significantly from those of their ethyl xanthate counterparts. Therefore it is not surprising to find that the area of extension of CuBX is the same as that of CuEtX. In practical flotation experiments, however, one finds that flotation yield and selectivity are influenced by the length of the hydrocarbon chain. A reasonable interpretation is that the difference in flotation properties between different xanthate homologues is due not to any difference in adsorption on the chalcopyrite surfaces but to the extension of the hydrocarbon chain and its ability to form a hydrophobic boundary layer on the mineral surface.

An order of magnitude increase in sulphur concentration expands the area of extension of elemental sulphur and makes chalcopyrite somewhat more stable at low redox potentials.

The presence of large amounts of iron in a flotation pulp does not affect the areas of extension of copper and sulphur

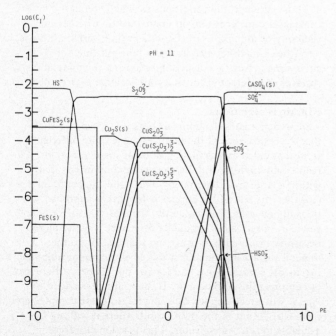

Fig. 19   Logarithmic graph of S distribution at pH 11 for kinetic restrictions case

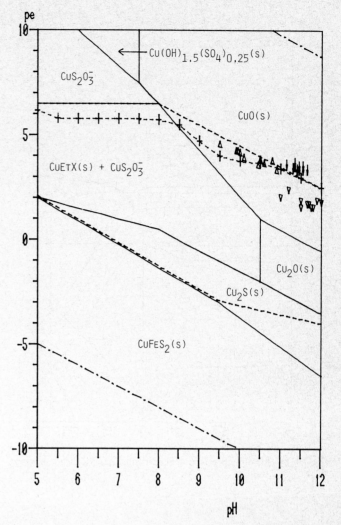

Fig. 20   Cu predominance diagram for kinetic restrictions case (same as Fig. 14) with operating line: + − − + operating line; △ pe–pH in copper flotation tailings; ↓ pe–pH in zinc flotation tailings; ▽ pe–pH in rod-mill discharge

species, but it does affect those of iron-bearing species. The iron predominance diagram shows that almost all the iron in the system is present as ferric hydroxide, i.e. that iron ions or particles dislodged from iron grinding media will form ferric hydroxide. This may then be precipitated on mineral particles and make their surfaces hydrophilic, which will lead to selectivity problems. A further factor is the redox-lowering effect of steel media grinding.

Soda-alkaline flotation is considered in some circumstances to give a better result than lime-alkaline flotation: this applies particularly to sulphide ores with a high content of precious metals and a moderate iron sulphide grade. The theoretical calculations, however, do not support the view that the chalcopyrite–xanthate system is radically affected by a soda-alkaline environment.

Lime-alkaline flotation is regarded as being more 'sluggish' and somewhat less selective. These effects, observed or supposed, are attributed to precipitation of $CaCO_3$ and/or $CaSO_4$ on the mineral surfaces. The theoretical calculations confirm that conditions that favour precipitation of solid calcium species exist at pH levels above 8.5.

The precipitation limit depends mainly on the total concentration of calcium in the system, and should be displaced towards a somewhat higher pH in a 'normal' flotation pulp—the calculated concentration of dissolved calcium species is higher than that actually measured.

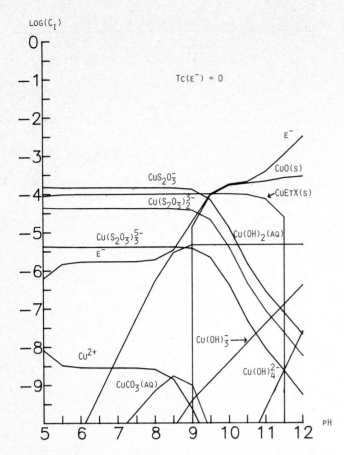

Fig. 21   Operating line in kinetic restrictions case (logarithmic graph of Cu distribution)

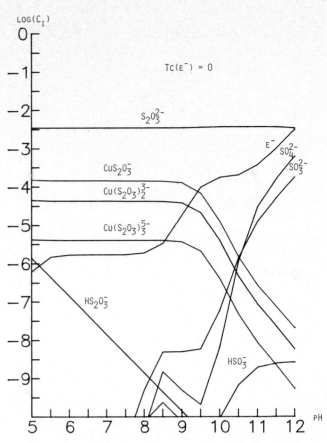

Fig. 23   Operating line in kinetic restrictions case (logarithmic graph of S distribution)

Calcium analyses of flotation pulps at pH 11 give readings of 300–500 mg/l, whereas equilibrium calculations give about 700 mg/l at the same pH. The difference between these figures may indicate that there are other unspecified calcium compounds present in an actual flotation system. Pyrite and arsenopyrite are particularly suspect in this context, both being believed capable of adsorbing calcium in their surface layers.[24] The nature of the compounds concerned is unknown, so it has not been possible to include them in the calculations.

Thus, although the conditions for oxidation of chalcopyrite surfaces remain unaffected by whether the alkalinity of the pulp is of the soda or lime variety, there is, nevertheless, a difference in that a lime-alkaline environment may favour precipitations on the mineral surfaces that do not occur in a soda-alkaline environment.

Kinetic restrictions

The predominance diagrams in Figs. 14, 15 and 16 show that the appearance of the final system is quite different from that given by calculation of component variations. The realistically high thiosulphate concentration means that within a large area there is only one stable copper species—CuEtX. The rest of the copper is present as cuprous thiosulphate ions. Consequently, the mineral surface is not stable in this area but gradually dissolves. It is therefore necessary in practice to bring the xanthate ion to the mineral surface and anchor it there before the thiosulphate breaks the surface down and leaches out copper in the form of cuprous thiosulphate ions. If the xanthate is added too late, it will 'steal' copper from the thiosulphate complex and form CuEtX out in the pulp liquid, where it will not be available to act as a collector. This reaction also frees thiosulphate ions to renew their attacks on the mineral surface.

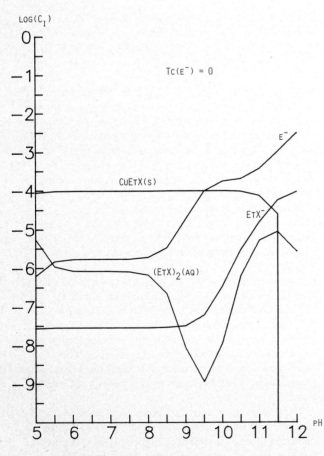

Fig. 22   Operating line in kinetic restrictions case (logarithmic graph of EtX distribution)

We can thus make the theoretical prediction that competition between xanthate and thiosulphate will involve an increased risk of reactions in the pulp liquid, where the xanthate is ineffectual. In practice, one finds, nevertheless, that copper flotation works, even in recycled water.[23] It must be pointed out here that flotation then takes place at $pH \geqslant 11$ where the mineral surface, according to the calculations, is not completely broken down by thiosulphate.

It is possible that the phenomenon described above may explain the belief that flotation results are sometimes better if the collector is added direct to the mill.

A further consequence of the stability of copper thiosulphate is that a high thiosulphate concentration in tailings pond water overflow will mean a higher copper concentration in effluents.

Operating line
The operating line shows how the pe–pH curve of the pulp ought to vary. From distribution graphs illustrating the variation of species along the operating line it can be seen that CuEtX is not thermodynamically stable above pH 11.5. This agrees with data published by Kuhn,[5] who obtained a minimum value for flotation yield with chalcocite–ethyl xanthate at that pH.

Conclusions

The calculations show that thermodynamic data can be used to construct pulp chemistry models that satisfactorily match actual events in mineral pulps. The usefulness of these models can be further enhanced by the insertion of kinetic restrictions derived from analyses of mineral pulps from commercial-scale operations.

As it is possible to calculate an operating line for a given flotation system, the results of calculations can always be compared with practical experience and measurements of flotation processes.

Acknowledgement

The authors wish to convey their thanks, first, to the Swedish Mineral Processing Research Foundation for enabling them to publish results from the project 'Flotation—Theoretical Development'. They would also like to thank Dr. Gunnar Eriksson of the University of Umeå for his advice and help in regard to the implementation of the project.

References
1. Gardner J. R. and Woods R. An electrochemical investigation of the natural floatability of chalcopyrite. *Int. J. Mineral Process.*, **6**, 1979, 1–16.
2. Gardner J. R. and Woods R. A study of the surface oxidation of galena using cyclic voltammetry. *J. electroanalyt. Chem.*, **100**, 1979, 447–59.
3. Hamilton I. C. and Woods R. An investigation of surface oxidation of pyrite and pyrrhotite by linear potential sweep voltammetry. *J. electroanalyt. Chem.*, **118**, 1981, 327–43.
4. Larin W. K. *et al.* Zur thermodynamischen Abschätzung des Zustandes der Pyritoberflächen in Flotationsmedien. *Neue Bergbautechnik*, **13**, Jan. 1983, 35–9.
5. Kuhn M. C. A mechanism of dixanthogen adsorption on sulfide minerals. Doctoral dissertation, Colorado School of Mines, 1969.
6. Kielkowska M. M. Lekki J. and Drzymala J. Flotation of germanium n and p with potassium ethyl xanthate. *Int. J. Mineral Process.*, **9**, 1982, 145–56.
7. Hepel T. and Pomianowski A. Diagrams of electrochemical equilibria of the system copper–potassium ethylxanthate–water at 25°C. *Int. J. Mineral Process.*, **4**, 1977, 345–61.

8. Chander S. and Fuerstenau D. W. On the floatability of sulfide minerals with thiol collectors: the chalcocite/diethyldithiophosphate system. In *Proceedings eleventh international mineral processing congress, Cagliari, 1975* (Cagliari: Istituto di Arte Mineraria, 1975), 583–604.
9. Marabini A. M. Barbaro M. and Ciriachi M. Calculation method for selection of complexing collectors. *Trans. Instn Min. Metall. (Sect. C: Mineral Process. Extr. Metall.)*, **92**, 1983, C20–6.
10. Eriksson G. A. An algorithm for the computation of aqueous multicomponent, multiphase equilibria. *Analyt. chim. Acta*, **112**, 1979, 375–83.
11. Sjöberg S. Chemical modelling of a deep water basin in the Gulf of Bothnia. *Aquilio*, in press.
12. Pontér C. Geochemical studies of a sedimentary profile from the Gulf of Bothnia. Bachelor thesis, Department of Inorganic Chemistry, Umeå University, Sweden. (Swedish text)
13. Smith R. M. and Martell A. E. *Critical stability constants, volume 4* (New York, etc.: Plenum Press, 1976).
14. Sandvik K. L. Die Oxydation in basischen Sulfid-Trüben und die Wirkung der entstehenden Thiosulfate auf die Flotationseigenschaften einiger Sulfide. *Erzmetall*, **30**, Sept. 1977, 391–5.
15. Peters E. Direct leaching of sulfides: chemistry and applications. *Metall. Trans.*, **7B**, 1976, 505–17.
16. Garrels R. M. and Christ C. L. *Solutions, minerals and equilibria* (San Francisco: Freeman, Copper & Co., 1965), 403–29.
17. Du Rietz C. Xanthate analysis by means of potentiometric titration; some chemical properties of the xanthates. *Svensk kem. Tidskr.*, **69**, 1957, 310–27.
18. Majima H. Fundamental studies on the collection of sulphide minerals with xanthic acids, I, on the dissociation and decomposition of xanthic acids. *Sci. Rep. Res. Inst., Tohuku Univ., Series A*, **13**, no. 3 1961, 183–97.
19. Leja J. *Surface chemistry of froth flotation* (New York: Plenum Press, 1982), 247.
20. Pilipenko A. T. Varchenko T. P. Kudelya E. S. and Kostyshina A. P. Chemico-analytical properties of xanthogenates, 4. Solubility products of zinc, nickel, iron and cadmium xanthogenates. *Zh. analit. Khim.*, **12**, 1957, 457–61. (English translation of Russian text)
21. Cotton F. A. and Wilkinson G. *Advanced inorganic chemistry, a comprehensive text, 2nd edn* (London: Interscience Publishers, 1966), 308–9.
22. Jönsson H. *et al.* Test with reuse of tailings pond water, April 1983. *MinFo* 1503. (Stockholm: Swedish Mineral Processing Research Foundation, 1983). (Swedish text)
23. Nordström U. and Pålsson B. Test with reuse of tailings pond water. *MinFo* 1501. (Stockholm: Swedish Mineral Processing Research Foundation, 1982). (Swedish text)
24. Glembotskii V. A. Klassen V. I. and Plaksin I. N. *Flotation* (New York: Primary Sources, 1963), 207–10.

Appendix 1

Definition of 'surface molarity'
Assume an ore having a given metal grade of $x\%$. The ore is ground to pulp with $w\%$ solids by mass and a surface area of S cm²/g. The mineral has a theoretical maximum metal grade of $T\%$.

The unit cell of the mineral has a volume of V cm³ and contains Z formula units. n theoretical cell layers take part in surface reactions. Avogadro's number is 6.0226×10^{23} formula units per mole.

One litre of pulp then contains

$$\frac{\rho_p \times 1000 \times w}{100} \text{ g of solid matter}$$

The solid matter includes

$$\frac{\rho_p \times 1000 \times w}{100} \times \frac{x}{T} \text{ g of mineral}$$

If we disregard any differences in density or in specific surface due to selective comminution in the mill, the mineral has a total surface area of

$$\frac{\rho_p \times 1000 \times w}{100} \times \frac{x}{T} \times S \text{ cm}^2$$

The unit cell has an average edge length of $V^{1/3}$ cm. At a reaction depth of n cell units, we obtain

$$\frac{\rho_p \times 1000 \times w \times x \times S \times n \times Z}{100 \times T \times V^{2/3}}$$

which is the number of formula units in the mineral surface that can be expected to take part in surface and liquid reactions.

Dividing by Avogadro's number, we obtain the number of moles per litre of pulp. Dividing further by the proportional volume of pulp liquid, we obtain the number of moles per litre of pulp liquid. This is called the surface molarity. M_s.

$$M_s = \frac{10 \times \rho_p \times w \times x \times S \times n \times Z}{(1 - v) \times T \times V^{2/3} \times N_0}$$

where

$$\rho_p = \frac{U + 1}{(U + 1/\rho_s)}$$

$$U = \frac{100}{w} - 1$$

and

$$v = \frac{1}{(1 + U \times \rho_s)}$$

Symbols

M_s Surface molarity, mol/l
N_0 Avogadro's number, formula units/mol
n Theoretical number of reacting cell layers
ρ_p Pulp density, g/cm³
ρ_s Ore density, g/cm³
S Surface area, cm²/g
T Theoretical maximum mineral grade, %
U Dilution
V Volume of unit cell, cm³
v Volumetric proportion of solids
w Solids concentration in pulp, mass %
x Metal grade of ore, %
Z Number of formula units per unit cell

Example for chalcopyrite, CuFeS$_2$

x = 1%
ρ_s = 2.7 g/cm³
w = 40%
S = 2000 cm²/g (permeability value acc. to Blaine)
T_{Cu} = 34.62%
V = 292.26 × 10⁻²⁴ cm³
Z = 4
n = 5 (estimated value from Eadington[*])

Inserting these values, we obtain

U = 1.5
ρ_p = 1.337 g/cm³
v = 0.198

which, in turn, gives

M_s = 2.90 × 10⁻⁴ mol CuFeS$_2$ per litre of pulp liquid.

Appendix 2

Conversion of log K_f values for sulphite and sulphate species

A flotation pulp of pH 11 and pe 4 is measured.[*]

$[S_2O_3^{2-}]$ = 200 mg/l = 1.79 × 10⁻³ M
$[SO_3^{2-}]$ = 10 mg/l = 1.25 × 10⁻⁴ M
$[SO_4^{2-}]$ = 400 mg/l = 4.17 × 10⁻³ M

With these data as a guide, 'adjusted' values of K_f can be calculated for SO_3^{2-}, SO_4^{2-}, HSO_3^- and HSO_4^- when these are formed from $S_2O_3^{2-}$, H^+ and e^-.

pH = 11 ; $\{H^+\}$ = 10⁻¹¹ M
pe = 4 ; $\{e^-\}$ = 10⁻⁴ M

The formation of SO_3^{2-} takes place according to

$$0.5\ S_2O_3^{2-} \rightleftharpoons 3H^+ + 2e^- + SO_3^{2-}$$

i.e.

$$K = \frac{\{SO_3^{2-}\} \times \{e^-\}^2 \times \{H^+\}^3}{\{S_2O_3^{2-}\}^{0.5}}$$

With the concentrations as above we obtain

$$K = 10^{-43.53}$$

The value of K_f for HSO_3^- is obtained from the equations

$$0.5\ S_2O_3^{2-} \rightleftharpoons 3H^+ + 2e^- + SO_3^{2-} \qquad \log(K_1) = -43.53 \quad (1)$$

$$H^+ + SO_3^{2-} \rightleftharpoons HSO_3^- \qquad \log(K_2) = 7.18 \quad (2)$$

(1) + (2) ⇒

$$0.5\ S_2O_3^{2-} \rightleftharpoons 2H^+ + 2e^- + HSO_3^- \qquad \log(K_3) =$$

$$\log(K_1) + \log(K_2) = -36.25 \quad (3)$$

A new value of K_f for SO_4^{2-} is likewise obtained from

$$0.5\ S_2O_3^{2-} \rightleftharpoons 5H^+ + 4e^- + SO_4^{2-} \Rightarrow K_f = 10^{-72.006} \quad (4)$$

New values of K_f for HSO_4^- and the respective solid sulphate species can now be calculated on the basis of equilibrium 4.

---

[*]Eadington P. Study of oxidation layers on surfaces of chalcopyrite by use of Auger electron spectroscopy. *Trans. Instn Min. Metall.* (*Sect. C: Mineral Process. Extr. Metall.*), **86**, 1977, C186–9.

[*]Nordström U. and Pålsson B. Test with reuse of tailings pond water. *MinFo* 1501. (Stockholm: Swedish Mineral Processing Research Foundation, 1982). (Swedish text)

Influence of material breakage properties and associated slurry rheology on breakage rates in wet grinding of coal/ores in tumbling media mills

Richard R. Klimpel

Synopsis

Recent work has shown that the wet-grinding rates of minerals and coals in tumbling media mills are influenced strongly by the type of slurry rheology conditions present in the mills. A number of factors—per cent solids, particle size, temperature and use of chemicals—have been identified as having consistent and predictable influence on rheology and, hence, on grinding performance. An additional rheology-related factor that influences grinding rates—the nature in which different materials inherently break in tumbling media mills—is considered.

The industrial-scale practice of wet-grinding minerals and coals in tumbling media mills (ball-, rod-, and pebble-) is well known to operating process engineers and plant designers. Typical factors that influence circuit throughput are mill diameter and length, grinding media size and loading, feed and product particle size, mill power use, and the interaction of classifier type and efficiency with the grinding device, and these have been analysed in some depth.[1,2]

Until recently, knowledge of the importance of slurry rheology on both laboratory-mill and large-scale grinding circuit performance has been limited. A series of papers published in 1981 and 1982 covered slurry rheology influences on the grinding of ores and coals as a function of changes in per cent solids, particle size, temperature and the use of rheological control chemicals.[3,4,5] In addition, several general papers on the related problem of using grinding aid chemicals have appeared.[6-9] To better understand the grinding behaviour involved with rheology changes the work of Klimpel involved two types of experiments run on a variety of materials. The first involved the determination in a batch laboratory mill of the net production of material smaller than some size—for example, kg/h of <75 μm (200 mesh)—as an index of mill production in a standard batch mill test (with a given feed material, feed size, mill and mill conditions, such as constant time of grind[3,4]). This type of experiment led to the type of net production and Brookfield viscosity curves (Fig. 1).

The second type of experiment involved the use of the well-known concepts of first-order breakage rates and primary breakage distributions[2]—also in a batch laboratory mill.

The breakage rate of a given size range of particles (for example, a $\sqrt{2}$ screen interval) is proportional to the amount of that size present when grinding is first-order. Thus, breakage rate of size fraction $j = S_j w_j(t) W$, where S_j is the specific breakage rate (fraction per unit of time) of size j, W is the mill hold-up and $w_j(t)$ is the weight fraction of size j material at grinding time t. If the starting feed contained $w_j(0)$ as the top size

$$\mathrm{d}w_j(t)/\mathrm{d}t = -S_j w_j(t)$$

$$\log w_j(t) = \log w_j(0) - (S_j t/2.3)$$

Measuring the disappearance of material from this size as a function of time, by use of log–linear plots, will directly indicate three important factors. If the plot is linear, the size fraction j is breaking in a first-order manner; the negative slope gives the S_j value. The magnitude of $S_j W$ is a direct indication of grinding throughput. If the plot is not linear but flattens as grinding proceeds (as fines build up and viscosity increases), breakage is slowing down.

The suite of fragments produced by breakage of a given size without further fragment rebreakage is termed primary breakage distribution. Numbering size intervals from 1 for the largest, 2 for the next size, etc., primary breakage distribution is represented by b_{ij}—the fraction of just broken j material that falls into smaller size interval i. $B_{i,j}$ represents the same information put on a cumulative basis of material broken from size j to size i or smaller.

$$B_{i,j} = \sum_{k=n}^{i} b_{k,j}$$

Experimental data on $B_{i,j}$ are fitted to the empirical function

$$B_{i,j} = \phi(x_{i-1}/x_j)^{\gamma} + (1-\phi)\ (x_{i-1}/x_j)^{\beta}$$

Fig. 2 illustrates the nature of the specific rate of breakage, S_j, and primary breakage distribution as a function of the three slurry viscosity regions indicated in Fig. 1. Numerous quantitative examples of Fig. 2 were determined in the study for a variety of ores and coals.[3,4,6]

Regions A, B and B^1 demonstrate first-order breakage, regions B and B^1 give higher breakage rates than regions A and C and regions C and C^1 show slower non-first-order breakage.

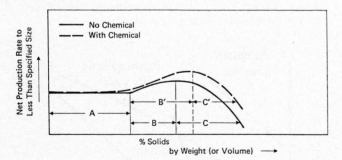

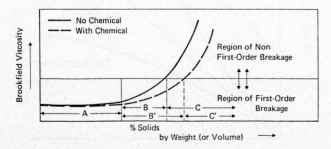

Fig. 1   Illustration of net production and Brookfield viscosity as a function of per cent solids in batch grinding tests run to constant grind time under constant mill and feed conditions

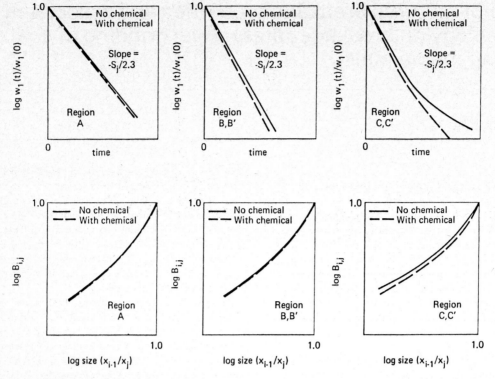

Fig. 2 Illustration of variation in specific rate of breakage parameters, S_j, and primary breakage distribution, $B_{i,j}$, as a function of viscosity region

Grinding with viscosity control chemicals shows no advantage in region A, but an increase over the no chemical case in regions B and C. From a maximum throughput basis tumbling media mills need to operate on a slurry basis that is as thick as possible, yet still offers a low enough viscosity to keep grinding in a first-order manner.

Rheology correlations

In the Klimpel study, it became evident that measurements of the type just presented were not sufficient to explain quantitatively the occurrence and location of regions A, B and C. For example, it is not difficult to show in a batch laboratory test[4] that even for a fixed value of per cent solids rather small changes in particle size make-up (especially of the fines) contributing to the solids can make very large differences in the throughput rate. These throughput differences due to particle size can sometimes overwhelm the influence of changing per cent solids. This problem seriously limits the generality of most plant level per cent solids/throughput correlations that have been developed. With a few ores and coals no region B could be identified; with a few other ores the influence of chemicals was minimal, despite the apparent satisfaction of all desired chemical characteristics.[3]

Part of the answer to a more consistent explanation and prediction of grinding behaviour was provided by accurate measurement of quantitative slurry rheology data (by use of a Haake RV3 rotational viscometer). The data were obtained under sufficiently controlled operating conditions and known geometric configurations to enable plots of shear stress versus rate of shear to be constructed for comparison with the possible types of slurry behaviour shown in Fig. 3.

At a given time all mineral/coal slurries will exhibit one of the shear-strain characteristics outlined in Fig. 3. Pseudo-plastic slurries may or may not have a yield value and when shear stress is plotted versus shear rate a curve results that has a decreasing slope with increasing rate of shear that generally approaches a limiting slope at higher shear rates. Dilatant slurries exhibit the

opposite behaviour—an increasing slope of τ versus Δ. A common method of describing mathematically both of these types is the Ostwald-deWaele or Power law model[10,11,12]

$$\tau = K\Delta^n$$

where K and n are constants for a particular slurry. K is referred to as consistency; the higher the value of K, the more viscous is the slurry. The constant n is called the flow index, which is a measure of the degree of departure from Newtonian behaviour ($n=1$); $n<1$ gives pseudo-plastic behaviour and $n>1$ dilatant behaviour.

Detailed breakage rate tests were carried out on a single size fraction. For each test condition corresponding to the breakage rate tests rheological characterization evaluations were

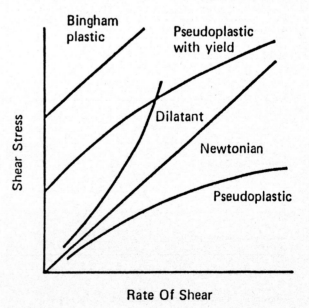

Fig. 3 Shear stress versus shear rate curves for time-independent non-Newtonian slurries

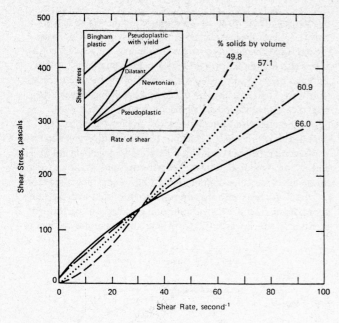

Fig. 4   Variation of slurry rheology for 850 μm $\times$ 600 μm coal in water as a function of slurry density

performed. Controlled changes in per cent solids, fineness of grind and temperature were made during the tests. Figs. 4 and 5 show typical results for this type of testing. Fig. 4 gives the variation of slurry rheology for 850 μm $\times$ 600 μm coal in water as a function of slurry density.[4] This type of data was matched to net production grinding data, such as are given in Fig. 1 for the same conditions of per cent solids. In this manner a grinding

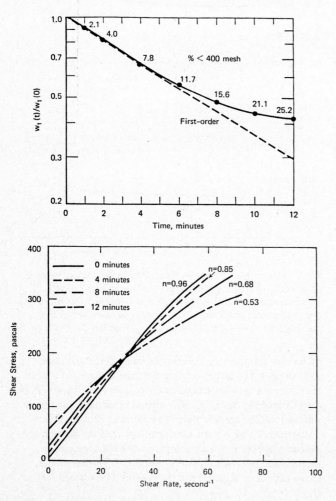

Fig. 5   Variation of slurry rheology with fineness of grinding for starting feed of 300 μm $\times$ 250 μm coal in water [shear stress $\propto$ (shear rate)^n]

rheological correspondence was developed. Fig. 5 demonstrates the variation of slurry rheology with fineness of grinding for a starting feed of 300 μm $\times$ 250 μm coal in water at a fixed per cent solids.[4] The appearance of non-first-order breakage as measured in the mill (see upper portion of Fig. 5), with the occurrence of a significant yield value as measured by the viscometer on the same slurry sampled from the mill, is quite apparent.

This continual matching of laboratory grinding results with a rheological characterization of the corresponding slurries from the mill enables a clear rheological influence on grinding behaviour to be developed. The procedure of using rheological data over a range of shear rates was chosen as a characterization method as the calculation of an average shear rate in the mill was not very meaningful owing to the complexities of motion involved with the mill charge during grinding (mill shear rates were estimated to range from 0 to 60 s^{-1} depending on location). During the study (for example, Klimpel[4]) it became apparent that knowledge of viscosity corresponding to a given shear rate was not as important as knowing whether the slurry was exhibiting a yield value, or was dilatant or pseudo-plastic over a range of shear rates.

Interpreting all the data collected, the following conclusions were drawn.[3]

Many coal and mineral slurries exhibit dilatant character at relatively low slurry densities—less than 40-45% solids volume for typical size distributions. Closely sized solids give more dilatant character than broad distributions.

In this dilatant region grinding is first-order and absolute rates of breakage, SW, do not vary during the grinding or from one slurry density to another (this is region A of Fig. 1 and represents normal wet-grinding practice).

Increasing slurry density causes a trend toward pseudo-plastic behaviour. At a given slurry density more pseudo-plastic character can be developed by increasing the solids packing efficiency (by adding a proportion of fines or controlling the size distribution by use of a bulk thickening agent or by chemicals to modify viscosity[3]).

When a slurry exhibits pseudo-plastic behaviour without a yield stress grinding is first-order with higher absolute rates of breakage, SW, than in corresponding dilatant systems (regions B and B^1 of Fig. 1, representing the most efficient wet-grinding practice).

Grinding aid chemicals that work best in practice are those which maintain pseudo-plastic behaviour in the slurry without associated yield stress, or which reduce the yield stress in a dense pseudo-plastic slurry.

When grinding is performed on a very dense slurry the yield stress increases rapidly and leads to non-first-order breakage with a slowing down of breakage rates (regions C and C^1 of Fig. 1).

Material property influences on rheology

During the test programme summarized above special effort was placed on developing predictions of the location and extent of regions A, B and C for different materials. In particular, the magnitude of region B that corresponds to maximum net production was found to be quite variable when plotted on a per cent solids basis. For example, in a few tests on some materials no region B could be found, whereas in tests on other materials a very distinct region B was identified that was associated with as much as 25% increased net production.

One of the key factors to be identified was the importance of running the mill grinding experiments at a solids mill loading that at least filled the available media void volume.[3] Underfilled mills were found to exhibit breakage characteristics that caused excessive fines to be produced. In batch tests this condition led to an accelerated production of fines, so the slurry transformation from region A to region C occurred rapidly without the existence of a well-defined region B.

The other key factor was the manner in which the different materials produced fines as they were broken in the mill. This property of the material is most easily described and quantified by the $B_{i,j}$ function introduced earlier. In the equation presented for $B_{i,j}$ the γ parameter (the limiting slope of $B_{i,j}$ for fine sizes—see Fig. 2) is particularly important. This is true as it has been shown[13] that the value of γ for a given material dictates the value of the Schuhmann slope of the cumulative log per cent less than size curve versus log size that is typically exhibited by ground products from tumbling media mills. If one material has a small γ— say, $\gamma < 0.5$—the corresponding product size curve resulting from grinding will have a shallow slope, which indicates a large proportion of fine material. On the other hand, with another material with a larger γ—say, >1.0—the ground product will contain relatively fewer fines, even though the grinding conditions, starting feed sizes, etc., may be identical for both materials. In this section some typical data that show the correlation between γ and the associated rheology transformation of that material are given.

Previous experiments[3,4,5] had demonstrated clearly that the controlled change of rheology of a material ground at a constant per cent solids produced significant changes in breakage rates. These changes were performed by the natural creation of fines, the deliberate addition and/or removal of fines, lowering the temperature, the addition of chemical thickeners to low-viscosity slurries and the addition of viscosity control agents to high-viscosity slurries. As might be expected, changing any of the above parameters caused a significant but logical shift in the location and extent of net production associated with regions A, B and C when plotted versus per cent solids.

To demonstrate that the influence of γ of different materials also causes a logical shift in the location of regions A, B and C a large number of special experiments were required. Fig. 6 demonstrates one type of experiment run with an iron ore with $\gamma = 0.72$. In this series of tests the slurry rheology was determined for different product size distributions artificially produced by appropriate sizing, separation and size interval fraction remixing to yield the same approximate upper size but

differing Schuhmann slope. Thus, no grinding was involved, so only the effect of size make-up of the ore is being used to cause the indicated rheological changes with increasing per cent solids. It was also found that the rheological transformations for other common minerals and coals (with different γ values) were very similar in extent and location to the iron ore of Fig. 6 when the same Schuhmann slope distributions were prepared. This observation has also been made by researchers attempting to establish slurry rheology behaviour for pipelining evaluation.[14]

A second type of experiment is exhibited by the data in Fig. 7. The net production of fines versus per cent solids is shown for a limestone ($\gamma = 0.48$), a copper ore ($\gamma = 0.67$) and a quartz-gold ore ($\gamma = 1.16$). All tests with the three materials started with the same approximate feed size distribution and grinding was performed for 20 min, which was sufficiently long for the ground product to

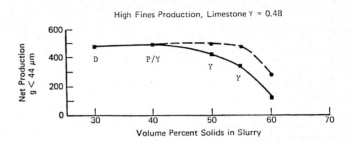

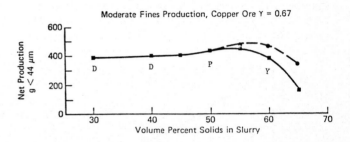

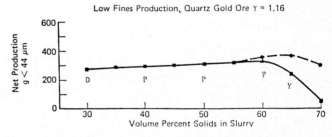

Fig. 7   Influence of primary breakage distribution (indexed by γ) on effectiveness of grinding additive: net production from feed of Schuhmann slope = 1.0 ground for 20 min. D indicates dilatant slurry, P pseudo-plastic, and Y yield value slurry as measured at end of grinding time (——— no additive; ——— with GA-4272* at 1 kg/t)

achieve its characteristic size distribution Schuhmann slope.

At this point it can be seen that the three materials of Fig. 7 exhibit differing locations and extent of regions A, B and C from a net throughput basis. It is also apparent that these differences shift in a similiar pattern to that of iron ore at different size distributions. This is particularly evident when the Schuhmann iron ore slopes of Fig. 6 are compared with the appropriate γ values of the materials represented in Fig. 7. The limestone shows little or no region B and the gold ore a very broad region B.

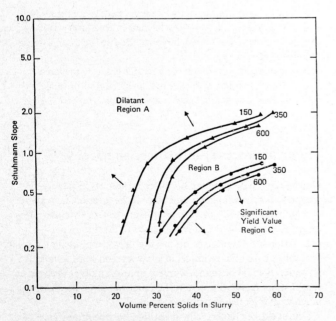

Fig. 6   Influence of particle size distribution on slurry rheology of iron ore where size distributions prepared to follow Schuhmann plot with maximum sizes of 150, 350 and 600 μm ($\blacktriangle$ indicates point of transformation from dilatant to pseudo-plastic; $\bullet$ from pseudo-plastic to pseudo-plastic with significant yield value)

* Dow Chemical Co. patented grinding aid.

Thus, it can be concluded from these and other similar data that the rheological influence of the natural product size distributions produced by grinding different materials (therefore different γ) is the same as that expected from differing size distributions prepared from the same material. This implies that one can then use standard experimental techniques to determine γ[3] and then compare the measured γ with Fig. 6 to indicate approximately the size and location of region B.

Summarizing the data of Figs. 6 and 7, together with other similar test data, gives the following conclusions.
Materials that exhibit low γ values, e.g. <0.5 (high relative fines production), have a small region B that quickly starts to transform to region C at a relatively low per cent solids of 35–40%.
Materials that exhibit intermediate γ values, e.g. $0.5<\gamma<0.9$, have a well-defined region B and, hence, are capable of exhibiting significant increases in net throughput by operating in a well-defined per cent solids region. This region is typically about 8-12% in extent, the last 4-6% being particularly important. Many practical materials (copper ore, medium rank coals, iron ore, etc.) fall in this range. Thus, knowledge and control of rheological parameters in industrial circuits with these materials is quite important.[3]
Materials that exhibit high γ values, e.g. >0.9 (relatively low fines production), have a broad range of region B. This will have the tendency to diminish any dramatic increases in net throughput due to moderate changes in per cent solids. Also, it has been found with some materials with high γ values, e.g. $\gamma>1.2$, that it is very difficult in normal mill operation to generate enough fines to reach region C or even the final portion of region B. The higher the γ, the more important in industrial practice the addition of extra fines becomes.[3] With materials that have increasing γ values the beginning of significant yield value slurries occurs at increasingly higher per cent solids (e.g. 60% with $\gamma>1.1$).

Conclusions

The influence of material breakage properties and associated slurry rheology on breakage rates in the wet grinding of coals/ores in tumbling media mills has been presented. Specifically, it has been shown that the primary breakage distribution of any given material (as indexed by γ) has a direct and predictable effect on the location and extent of the three major rheological regions. Also, it was demonstrated that the rheological influence of the product particle size distributions produced by grinding different materials is similar to that expected from differing product size distributions prepared from the same material. This knowledge helps considerably in explaining some of the conflicting rheological orientated results that have been achieved in which wet-grinding net production tests have been performed on different materials by various research groups.

References

1. Mular A. L. and Jergensen G. V. II. eds. *Design and installation of comminution circuits* (New York: AIME, 1982), 1022 p.
2. Austin L. G. Klimpel R. R. and Luckie P. T. *Process engineering of size reduction* (New York: AIME, 1984), 561 p.
3. Klimpel R. R. Slurry rheology influence on the performance of mineral/coal grinding circuits. *Min. Engng, N.Y.*, **34**, 1982, 1665-8; **35**, 1983, 21-6.
4. Klimpel R. R. Laboratory studies of the grinding and rheology of coal-water slurries. *Powder Technol.*, **32**, 1982, 267–77.
5. Katzer M. Klimpel R. R. and Sewell J. Example of the laboratory characterization of grinding aids in the wet grinding of ores. *Min. Engng, N.Y.*, **33**, 1981, 1471-6.
6. Klimpel R. R. and Austin L. G. Chemical additives for wet grinding of minerals. *Powder Technol.*, **31**, 1982, 239–53.
7. Fuerstenau D. W. Committee on Comminution and Energy Consumption. Report no. NMAB-364, U.S. National Academy of Science, 1981.
8. Somasundaran P. and Lin I. Effect of the nature of environment on comminution processes. *I&EC Process Design Develop.*, **11**, 1972, 321–31.
9. Westwood A. R. C. and Stoloff N. S. eds. *Environment-sensitive mechanical behavior* (New York: Gordon and Breach, 1966), 1–65. (*Metall. Soc. Conf.* vol.35)
10. Van Wazer J. R. *et al. Viscosity and flow measurements: a laboratory hand book of rheology* (New York: Interscience, 1963), 426 p.
11. Wasp E. J. Kenny J. P. and Gandhi R. L. *Solid–liquid flow* (Clausthal: TransTech Publications, 1977), 224 p.
12. Bird R. B. Stewart W. E. and Lightfoot E. N. *Transport phenomena* (New York: Wiley, 1960), 780 p.
13. Austin L. G. Luckie P. T. and Klimpel R. R. Solutions of the batch grinding equation leading to Rosin–Rammler distributions. *Trans. Am. Inst. Min. Engrs*, **252**, 1972, 87–94.
14. Datta S. D. Rheology and stability of mineral suspensions. Ph.D. dissertation, The Pennsylvania State University, 1977.

Effect of polymeric flocculants on solid–liquid separation by dissolved air flotation

J. A. Solari and J. Rubio

Synopsis

The results are presented of the characterization of the effect of polymeric flocculants (polyacrylamide type) on the flocculation settling and dissolved air flotation of suspensions of chromium hydroxide obtained from Cr(III) and Cr(VI). These reagents improved the efficiency of solid–liquid separation of the flocculated precipitates by dissolved air flotation (batch and continuous processes). Flocculation by synthetic polymers was found to be highly dependent on interfacial phenomena, solution chemistry, type of polymer and polymer charge. Finally, the use of other reagents, such as natural polyelectrolytes and surfactant collectors, in the continuous dissolved air flotation of chromium hydroxides is discussed and compared with that of polyacrylamides.

The dissolved air flotation (DAF) process has found widespread application as a solid–liquid separation technique for waste water and industrial effluent treatment.[1,2] In this process micro-bubbles some 50 μm in diameter are generated by saturating air in water under pressure and injecting the water into the flotation cell by use of pressure-reducing devices such as needle valves or orifice plates. Generally, the supersaturated water is obtained by recycling 10–50% of the clarified liquid through packed-bed saturators with air under a gauge pressure of 3–5 kg cm^{-2}.

In industrial practice with DAF hydrolysing metal salts and/or organic polyelectrolytes are usually added prior to the flotation step to aggregate the suspended solids. The addition of surface-active agents is, however, much less common on the industrial scale, although pilot-plant testing[3,4] and basic studies[5,6] showed that hydrophobicity is a prerequisite for the micro-bubbles to float the solids.

The main problems that are associated with industrial DAF operation[7] are those of chemical and pressurization costs, excessive air consumption, inability to handle high feed solids content and low separation efficiency. Conversely, the main advantages of the process over sedimentation techniques are lower capital investment with a similar efficiency, better process control and the production of a sludge of higher solids content.[1,2]

Applications of polymeric flocculants in mineral processing are mainly to the thickening and filtration operations, together with some specialized uses in fine mineral treatment, such as selective flocculation[8] and floc flotation.[9] High molecular weight (surface-active) polymers were used[10] to aggregate dispersed particles and separate them by conventional flotation techniques. Recently, a DAF plant has been reported[11] to treat a coal-washery effluent in which alum, a polymeric flocculant and a surface-active 'collector' are used.

Despite the widespread application of polymer flocculants in solid–liquid separation by DAF, the fundamental aspects of their utilization have not received much attention. The high cost of these reagents requires their usage to be optimized. Moreover, the adsorption behaviour of these reagents has to be determined since their presence in the waste waters is often limited by environmental regulations.

The aim of the work described was to investigate the effect of polymeric flocculants on the efficiency of solid–liquid separation

by settling and dissolved air flotation. Suspensions of chromium hydroxide prepared from Cr(III) and Cr(VI) reagents were used as model solids—mainly because the separation of metal ions from solution is a problem common to many metallurgical and mineral processing operations. Ferrous sulphate and sodium sulphite were used to reduce Cr(VI) before precipitation of the hydroxide.

Experimental

Materials

Solutions of 200 mg l^{-1} Cr(III) or Cr(VI) were prepared from a hydrated chromium nitrate Analar reagent (Riedel) and from potassium dichromate (Merck). The polyacrylamide-based flocculants used were commercial products (Cyanamid Superfloc A100 and N1096, anionic and non-ionic, and Allied Colloids Magnafloc R365, cationic). Brazilian corn starch flocculants were also tested (Prosodene 30 and Acetilex, Refinarias de Milho S.A.). All other reagents used were of analytical grade and, unless otherwise stated, single distilled water was employed.

Methods

Settling and batch DAF tests were carried out with 400-ml solutions by adjustment of the medium pH under high stirring (5 min) followed by a conditioning period under slow stirring (10 min). This was followed by the settling (10 min) or flotation (5 min) stage and by sampling of the residual solution through a side outlet for analysis by nephelometry and atomic absorption spectrophotometry. Flocculants were added during high stirring (2 min) before the settling or flotation stage. When tests with Cr(VI) were performed a reduction step was carried out prior to pH adjustment with ferrous sulphate (1.25×10^{-2} M Fe(II)) or sodium sulphite (8.75×10^{-3} M SO$_3^{-2}$).

Batch DAF studies were carried out in a unit that has been described elsewhere.[6] It is composed of a pressure vessel for water saturation and a 800-ml glass flotation cell connected by a precision release valve and an orifice plate for depressurization. Micro-bubble production was accomplished by the injection through the orifice plate into the flotation cell of 100 ml of water saturated at 4.1 kg cm^{-2}.

Bench continuous DAF tests were carried out with a packed-bed saturator similar to that described by Bratby and Marais,[12] and both column (15-cm diameter) and rectangular (187-cm^2 superficial area) flotation cells. The procedure involved the conditioning at pH 8.5 of the 200 mg l^{-1} Cr(III) solution and feeding of the chromium hydroxide suspension, Q_a, to the flotation cell under a constant flow rate of supersaturated water, Q_s. The flotation effluent was sampled periodically for determination of turbidity and residual chromium.

For simplicity no recycle of the effluent liquid was practised and the micro-bubbles were produced by direct pressurization of tap water. The tests were performed for recycle ratios, Q_s/Q_a, that varied from about 300% to 25% with hydraulic loadings (defined as total flow into unit divided by superficial flotation area) in the range 70–150 m^3 m^{-2} day^{-1} for the rectangular cell and 120–180 m³ m² day⁻¹ for the column cell.

Residual polymer concentration determinations were made in accordance with the method developed by Attia and Rubio.[13] Flotation and settling rates were determined by measuring the height of the solid–liquid interface as a function of time and using the linear section of the curves. Residual chromium concentrations reported in this paper correspond to total (precipitated plus dissolved) Cr concentration. No dissolved Cr was detected in the pH range 7–9, so residual Cr concentrations measured within that pH range should correspond to a measure of effluent suspended solids.

Results and discussion

Flocculation and settling

The settling behaviour of chromium hydroxide precipitated under various conditions is presented in Fig. 1 as a function of pH. The minimum residual concentration (about 5 mg l⁻¹) obtained for Cr(III) and Cr(VI) reduced with sodium sulphite

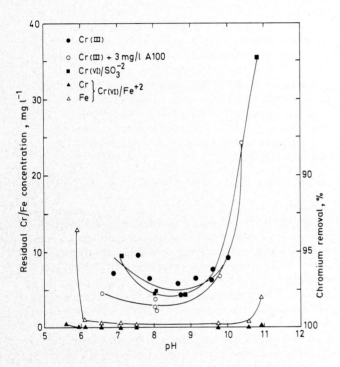

Fig. 1   Settling of chromium hydroxide precipitates as a function of pH

occurred in the pH range 8–9, which corresponds to the isoelectric point of chromium hydroxide (pH 8.5, according to Pourbaix[14]). The addition of 3 mg l⁻¹ Superfloc A100 reduced the Cr residual concentration to about 2.5 mg l⁻¹ and broadened the optimum pH range towards the acid side. This anionic polyacrylamide did not, however, improve the settlement for pH values above 9, at which the surface charge of the precipitates may be controlled by the anionic species $Cr(OH)_4^-$.

For Cr(VI) reduced by ferrous sulphate no Cr was detected in solution in the pH range 6–11 and total Fe concentrations were of the order of 1–2 mg l⁻¹. This behaviour may be explained in terms of the reduction and precipitation reactions of Cr(VI):

$$Cr_2O_7^{-2}+3SO_3^{-2}+8H^+ \rightleftharpoons 2Cr^{+3}+3SO_4^{-2}+4H_2O \qquad (1)$$

$$Cr_2O_7^{-2}+6Fe^{-2}+14H^+ \rightleftharpoons 2Cr^{+3}+6Fe^{+3}+7H_2O \qquad (2)$$

$$Cr^{+3}+3OH^- \rightleftharpoons CrOH_{3(s)} \qquad (3)$$

$$Cr^{+3}+3Fe^{+3}+12OH^- \rightleftharpoons Cr(OH)_{3(s)}+3Fe(OH)_{3(s)} \qquad (4)$$

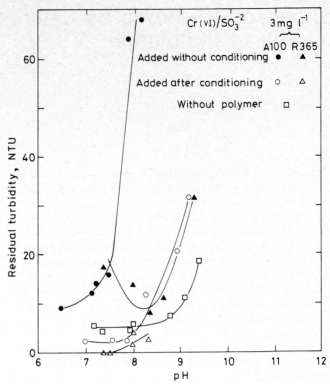

Fig. 2   Effect of polymer addition on settling and flocculation of chromium hydroxide precipitated from Cr(VI) reduced with sodium sulphite as a function of pH

Thus, it is suggested that for Cr(VI) reduced with sulphite the precipitates are only chromium hydroxide, whereas in the presence of ferrous ions co-precipitation of chromium and ferric hydroxide results in better clarification. In the latter case ferric hydroxide represents about 77% of a total suspended solids that amounts to 1.72 g l⁻¹.

The influence of various polymers on the supernatant water clarity of chromium hydroxide (Cr(III)) precipitates by flocculation sedimentation tests was studied at constant pH (8.4 ± 0.3). Best results were obtained with the anionic Superfloc

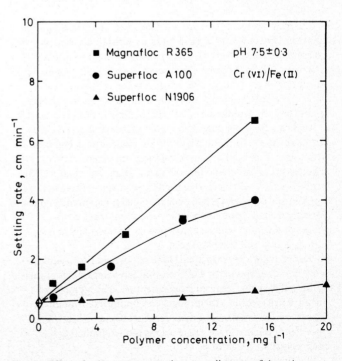

Fig. 3   Effect of polymer concentration on settling rate of chromium hydroxide precipitated from Cr(VI) reduced with ferrous sulphate

A100 at concentrations greater than about 1 mg l⁻¹.

The flocculation and settling behaviour of Cr(VI) reduced by sulphite was studied in the presence of 3 mg l⁻¹ ionic polyacrylamides as a function of pH. Tests were also carried out to determine the influence of precipitate formation on the extent of polymer flocculation, the flocculant being added either after the pH adjustment period or after a subsequent 5-min conditioning period under slow stirring. These two procedures represented the addition of flocculant under conditions of incipient and well pre-formed chromium hydroxide precipitates, respectively. The results presented in Fig. 3 indicate that the addition of flocculant to well-formed precipitates enhanced clarification in comparison with the test without polymer. Conversely, polymer added to incipient precipitates not only led to low flocculation of the suspended solids but also prevented their further nucleation, yielding higher residual turbidities.

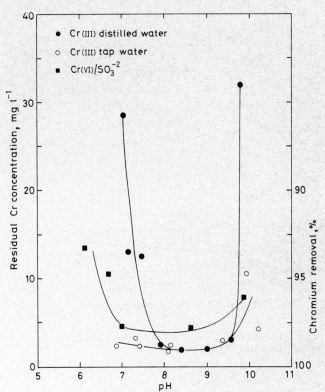

Fig. 5   Dissolved air flotation of chromium hydroxide precipitates as a function of pH

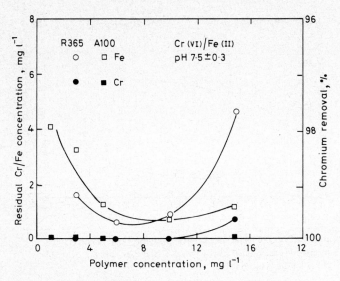

Fig. 4   Effect of polymer concentration on settling of chromium hydroxide precipitated from Cr(VI) reduced with ferrous sulphate

Although the precipitation and settling of Cr(VI) reduced with ferrous sulphate results in 100% chromium removal, the settling rate is very low (~0.5 cm min⁻¹) as a consequence of the suspended solids concentration. In this case the fundamental objective of the addition of polymeric flocculants was to increase the settling rate of the precipitates. Fig. 3 shows the settling rate of the precipitates as a function of polymer concentration and Fig. 4 the process efficiency in terms of residual chromium and iron concentration. The separation kinetics increased for the ionic polymers at a higher rate than that for the cationic. Moreover, the removal of Cr is complete for a wide range of flocculant concentrations, but maximum Fe removal is obtained between 6 and 10 mg l⁻¹ (3.5–5.8 mg g⁻¹ solids). A general trend that was found was the redispersion of the flocs after a critical polymer concentration leading to a slight decrease in the removal of both ions. The non-ionic polymer was not effective as a flocculant for dosages up to 20 mg l⁻¹, even near the isoelectric point of the hydroxide. The ionic polymers may adsorb electrostatically (given the high concentration of sulphate ions in solution) and the A-100 may also show chemical interaction between surface iron hydroxylated complexes and its carboxylic groups.

Batch dissolved air flotation

Fig. 5 shows the dissolved air flotation of chromium hydroxide precipitates formed from Cr(III) and Cr(VI) reduced with sulphite. Optimum chromium removal (~99.0%) was obtained in the pH range 8–9 for Cr(III), but in the presence of tap water this range

was somewhat broader. The residual Cr concentrations obtained by DAF for the Cr(VI)–sulphite system were higher than those for Cr(III) corresponding to about 98% removal. This behaviour was interpreted in terms of the higher concentration of sulphate ions (~8.10⁻³ M) present in the Cr(VI) than in the Cr(III) solution. DAF tests (not shown) on Cr(III) precipitates at pH 8.1 as a function of sulphate (added as Na₂SO₄) concentration indicated that these ions decreased chromium removal efficiency. Probably, sulphate ions adsorb specifically at the chromium hydroxide–solution interface (as has been reported for other hydroxides[15]), generating a net negative surface charge that may interact electrostatically with the micro-bubbles, which are also believed to be negatively charged.

It should be emphasized that no surface-active agents were necessary for flotation to occur. The fact that micro-bubble flotation of metal hydroxide precipitates occurs in the absence of 'collectors' has been investigated by Kitchener and Gochin[5] and Gochin and Solari[6] and explained by the presence of traces of surface-active contaminants in the water utilized. The results obtained with tap water were slightly better in terms of a wider optimum pH—probably because of the presence of a higher amount of surface-active impurities and a higher ionic strength that would reduce the electrostatic repulsion between bubbles and precipitates.

DAF tests with Cr(VI) reduced by ferrous sulphate showed that these precipitates could not be floated by the micro-bubbles. This behaviour was due to the high concentration (1720 mg l⁻¹) of suspended solids in solution resulting from the co-precipitation of ferric hydroxide (equations 2 and 4). Thus, when the initial Cr(VI) concentration was reduced (at constant Cr(VI)/Fe(II) concentration ratio) to give a total suspended solids concentration of 690 mg l⁻¹, total flotation removal of the precipitates was obtained.

The addition of 10 mg l⁻¹ (5.8 mg g⁻¹ solids) of the polymeric flocculant Magnafloc R365 or Superfloc A100 at pH 7.4, however, gave complete flotation of the precipitates formed from the 200 mg l⁻¹ Cr(VI) solution. These studies showed that

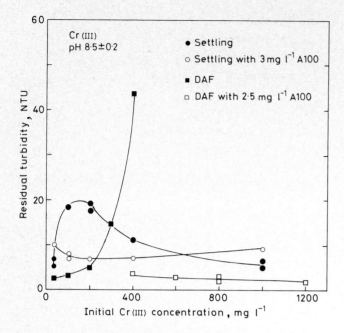

Fig. 6 Settling and DAF of chromium hydroxide precipitates as a function of initial Cr(III) concentration

the limitation imposed by the feed solids concentration on micro-bubble flotation could be solved by the addition of polymeric flocculants. Also, it was found that the addition of 10^{-4} M sodium oleate gave a clarified liquid of good quality.

The influence of the initial Cr(III) concentration on solid–liquid separation by settling and DAF in the presence and absence of flocculant is shown in Fig. 6. According to the stoichiometry of the $Cr(OH)_3$ precipitation reactions, the suspended solids concentrations are approximately double that of the initial Cr(III). These results show that in the absence of polymers sedimentation techniques give a residual solution of better quality than DAF for initial Cr(III) concentrations above 300 mg l^{-1}. Nevertheless, the addition of 2.5 mg l^{-1} A100 gave optimum clarification by DAF even for suspended solids concentrations of 2400 mg l^{-1}.

The parameter that is used in industrial DAF operations to evaluate air consumption efficiency is the air/solids mass ratio (A/S). A literature survey of DAF plants[7,16] indicated that A/S values vary between 0.01 and 0.6. The use of a polymeric flocculant reagent allows the processing of 2.4 g l^{-1} suspended effluent at an A/S value of 0.01 with an efficiency better than a 0.6 g l^{-1} effluent without polymer and with a 0.04 A/S value (Fig. 6).

One advantage of DAF over sedimentation, already mentioned, is the process rate. Table 1 summarizes the results obtained under optimum conditions for flotation and flocculation. DAF shows a higher rate of solid–liquid separation in most cases and the choice of flocculant must be determined not only by its clarification efficiency but also by its separation rate.

From an environmental viewpoint the use of certain polymeric flocculants may represent a potential hazard and so the relationship between initial dosage and residual flocculant concentration must be determined precisely. In these studies tests were carried out for DAF on Cr(III) precipitates flocculated with A100 concentration between 1 and 5 mg l^{-1} and the residual polymer concentration was determined. The results showed that for initial dosages of less than 1 mg l^{-1} A100 no residual flocculant was detected and that for 5 mg l^{-1} A100 0.25 mg l^{-1} was found in the residual liquid. These values are considered within the permissible concentration limits of the Environmental Protection Agency for polyacrylamides.[17]

Continuous dissolved air flotation

Continuous bench DAF tests were carried out with a 4-l rectangular cell at various feed flow rates of Cr(III), the supersaturated water flow rate being kept constant at 1.2 l min⁻¹. Fig 7 shows that the addition of 0.8 mg l^{-1} A 100 gave about 96% chromium removal for a feed flow rate of 1.0 l min⁻¹, corresponding to a recycle ratio of about 120%. The presence of the polymer gave an effluent of better and more constant quality from DAF than its absence. Nevertheless, in both cases the effluent was below the 30 mg l^{-1} suspended solids for the range of recycle ratios tested. Feed flow rates greater than 1.0 l min⁻¹ could not be tested because the hydraulic loading (~11.8 cm min⁻¹) in the cell caused bubble–particle aggregates to be swept out with the effluent.

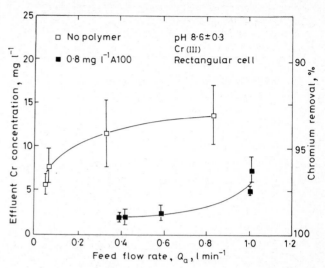

Fig. 7 Effect of feed flow rate on continuous DAF of chromium hydroxide precipitated from Cr(III) (vertical bars indicate standard deviation from mean value)

Also, continuous bench DAF tests with Cr(III) hydroxide were performed in a column cell for a constant recycle ratio of 0.5 and total flow rates of 2.25 and 1.5 l min⁻¹. Superfloc A100, corn starch flocculant and sodium oleate were tested (Table 2).

The results obtained in the column cell showed that for the low feed flow rate (corresponding to a hydraulic loading of 120 m³ m⁻² day⁻¹) both sodium oleate and the Superfloc A100 enabled the production of an effluent below 30 mg l^{-1} suspended solids. At the higher feed flow rate (180 m³ m⁻² day⁻¹ hydraulic loading), however, sodium oleate performed much better than the polymeric flocculant. This is probably due to the flotation rate of the polymer-flocculated chromium hydroxide being close to the hydraulic loading of the unit (12.7 cm min⁻¹) and implies that the addition of the flotation 'collector' sodium oleate allows a higher process rate than that of flocculating agents. The use of the micro-bubbles is therefore optimized by the provision of more hydrophobic sites, the probability of micro-bubble–particle attachment after collision thereby being increased. Nevertheless, a review of various operating DAF units[16] indicated that most of them are run at hydraulic loadings below 120 m³ m⁻² day⁻¹, and polymer and collector may work in a similar manner. On the other hand, the use of natural, starch-based, flocculants which would be competitive in cost with surface-active reagents has not shown to be very promising, at least with the reagents tested in this work.

One question that is to be answered is why industry uses coagulants and/or organic polyelectrolytes instead of surface-active reagents. From an environmental viewpoint biodegradable surface-active agents will be less hazardous than the various extensively used polymeric flocculants. There is always sufficient

Table 1 Comparative results of solid–liquid separations by settling and DAF (batch)

| System | Residual turbidity, NTU | Residual ionic concentration, mg l⁻¹ | | Chromium removal, % | Settling/ flotation rate, cm min⁻¹ |
		Cr	Fe		
Cr(III) (pH 8.5)					
Settling					
Without flocculant	8.5	6.5	—	96.8	2.7
With 3 mg l⁻¹ A100	4	2.5	—	98.7	10.0
DAF	5	2.0	—	99.0	12.3
Cr(VI)/Na$_2$SO$_3$ (pH 7.5)					
Settling					
Without flocculant	5	5.2	—	97.4	1.8
With 3 mg l⁻¹ A100	3	2.4	—	98.8	10.0
With 3 mg l⁻¹ R365	0	3.5	—	98.3	—
DAF	8	3.5	—	98.3	3.6
Cr(VI)/FeSO$_4$ (pH 7.4)					
Settling					
Without flocculant	0	ND	0.6	100	0.5
With 10 mg l⁻¹ A100	0	ND	1.1	100	2.8
With 10 mg l⁻¹ R365	0	ND	0.8	100	3.8
DAF					
With 10 mg l⁻¹ A100	2	ND	0.4	100	5.1
With 10 mg l⁻¹ R365	0	ND	0.3	100	3.6

ND, not detected (<0.1 mg l⁻¹).

Table 2 Summary of bench continuous DAF studies of Cr(III) in column cell*

Reagent	Feed flow rate, l min⁻¹	Effluent Cr, mg l⁻¹	Cr removal, %
(A)			
None	1.0	120	40
1.7 mg l⁻¹ A100	1.0	110	45
2.9 mg l⁻¹ A100	1.0	14	93
5 x 10⁻⁵ M sodium oleate	1.0	10	95
(B)			
1.6 mg l⁻¹ A100	1.5	24	88
3.0 mg l⁻¹ A100	1.5	26	87
5 x 10⁻⁵ M sodium oleate	1.5	7	96.5
9.9 x 10⁻⁵ M sodium oleate	1.5	5	97.5
1.6 mg l⁻¹ Acetilex	1.5	78	61
4.4 mg l⁻¹ Acetilex	1.5	54	73
12.3 mg l⁻¹ Acetilex	1.5	38	81

* 200 mg l⁻¹ Cr(III) initial concentration; pH 8.5 ± 0.2; 4.1 kg cm⁻² saturation pressure; recycle ratio, 0.5; calculated A/S ratio, 0.12. Tests with Prosodene 30 gave less than 50% removal.

concentration of surface-active impurities in those waste-waters (as has been already reported[5]) to make the suspended particles hydrophobic enough and the aggregating reagents are only intended to improve the probability of bubble–particle collision by concentrating the suspended solids in a lesser number of units.

Conclusions

Studies on the flocculation, settling and dissolved air flotation of chromium hydroxide precipitates prepared from Cr(III) and Cr(VI) reagents showed that polymeric reagents contribute substantially to the improvement of solid–liquid separation by DAF. Those reagents gave rise to savings in air consumption, the treatment of higher feed solids concentrations, high process rate and liquid clarification within effluent limits with better process control. The surface properties of the precipitates, the solution chemistry, the type of addition and the charge of the polymers affected the flocculation characteristics of the precipitates.

Batch DAF studies showed that the micro-bubble could separate these precipitates without the need to resort to the use of surface-active reagents and that polymeric flocculants would increase flotation capacity by allowing the processing of higher feed suspended solids. Generally, maximum flotation corresponded with the pH region of good precipitate formation and of high polymer flocculation. Continuous bench DAF studies in a column cell indicated that for low hydraulic loadings the addition of a flotation 'collector' or a polymeric flocculant gave comparable results, but for higher processing rates the collector performed better, probably because of a more efficient use of the available micro-bubbles for collision and attachment.

Acknowledgement

The authors are grateful to the Brazilian National Council for Scientific and Technological Research (CNPq) for financial support and to Sônia Bencke, who carried out most of the experimental work.

References

1. Lundgren H. Theory and practice of dissolved air flotation. *Filtr. Sepn*, **13**, 1976, 24–8.
2. Rees A. J. Rodman D. J. and Zabel T. F. Dissolved air flotation for solid/liquid separation. *J. Sepn Process Technol.*, **1**, 1980, 19–23.
3. Grieves R. D. and Brattachavyya. Ion, colloid and precipitate flotation of inorganic anions. In *Adsorptive bubble separation techniques* Lemlich R.ed. (New York: Academic Press, 1972), 183–9.
4. Pearson D. and Shirley J. M. Precipitate flotation in the treatment of metal-bearing effluents. *J. appl. Chem. Biotechnol.*, **23**, 1973, 101–9.
5. Kitchener J. A. and Gochin R. J. The mechanism of dissolved air flotation for potable water: basic analysis and a proposal. *Water Res.*, **15**, 1981, 585–90.
6. Gochin R. J. and Solari J. A. The role of hydrophobicity in dissolved air flotation. *Water Res.*, **17**, 1983, 651–7.
7. Roberts K. L. Weeter D. W. and Ball R. O. Dissolved air flotation performance. *Proc. 33 Ind. Waste Conf., Purdue Univ.*, 1978, 194–9.
8. Kitchener J. A. Flocculation in mineral processing. In *The scientific basis of flocculation* Ives K. J. ed. (Alphen aan de Rijn, The Netherlands: Sijthoff and Noordhoff, 1978), 283–328.
9. Fuerstenau D. W. Fine particle flotation. In *Fine particles processing*

Somasundaran P. ed. (New York: AIME, 1980), vol. 1, 669–705.

10. Khavski N. N. *et al.* Clarification of water and aqueous solutions by the floto-flocculation method. In *Proceedings 11th international mineral processing congress, Cagliari, 1975* (Cagliari: Istituto di Arte Mineraria, 1975), 1345–69.

11. Kato I. Application of pressure flotation for waste water treatment at Mitsui Ashi–Bet Su coal mine. Paper presented to 5th international conference on coal research '80, Düsseldorf, September 1980.

12. Bratby J. and Marais G. V. R. Flotation. In *Solid/liquid separation equipment scale-up* Purchas D. B. ed. (Croydon, England: Upland Press, 1977), 155–98.

13. Attia Y. A. and Rubio J. Determination of very low concentrations of polyacrylamide and polyethyleneoxide flocculants by nephelometry. *Br. Polymer J.*, **7**, 1975, 135–8.

14. Pourbaix M. *Atlas of electrochemical equilibria in aqueous solution* (Oxford, etc.: Pergamon, 1966), 644 p.

15. Letterman R. D. and Sricharoenchaikit P. Interaction of hydrolized Al and polyelectrolyte coagulants. *J. Envirnm. Engng Div., ASCE*, **108 (EES)**, 1982, 883–900.

16. Solari J. A. Selective dissolved air flotation of fine mineral particles. Ph.D. thesis, University of London, 1980.

17. Bratby J. *Coagulation and flocculation* (Croydon, England: Upland Press, 1980), 89 and 296.

Use of starch in selective flocculation of low-grade hematite ore and high ash content coal

Mario Zuleta, Luis V. Gutierrez and José A. Matar

Synopsis

The results that were obtained in the selective flocculation of two low-grade ores are described—hematite ore with 42.4% iron and coal middling with 56.0% ash with different modified and unmodified starches. With selective flocculation the grade was increased from 44.4 to 50% Fe with a 69% recovery in the –20 μm fraction (almost 30%) in the iron ore and ash contents was decreased to 30.5% with a 52.5% coal recovery.

The flocculation technique employed is based on the determination of the appropriate dispersion state and use of a suitable flocculant. To obtain these conditions the mineral electrokinetic potentials involved in flocculation are measured, account being taken of their pH and the dispersant used. The flocculation reagents are characterized by measurement of the electrophoretic mobilities with respect to pH.

Techniques that lead to the recovery of the fine fraction normally discarded by other processes combine selective flocculation with high-intensity magnetic separation to yield a 53.7% Fe concentrate with a 77% recovery. In regard to coal, the recovery of fines in the washery water increases total coal recovery and decreases the contamination of the river in which these fines were previously deposited.

Starch[1,20] is a polymeric carbohydrate $(C_6H_{10}O_5)_n$ produced by certain plants as a food reserve during their growth period. Although the only material obtained from the overall starch hydrolysis is D-glucose, the term 'starch' covers a number of substances with different structures and molecular weights. Most starches have from 22 to 26% amylose and about 74-78% amylopectin. The former is a linear polymer of D-glucose units, joined by $(1\rightarrow4)$-α-D (molecular weights, about 100000 and 200000); the latter is a branched polymer with linear $(1\rightarrow4)$-α-D links and branching $(1\rightarrow6)$-α-D links of about 1 000 000-6 000 000 molecular weight.

Starches are used in drilling fluids, pharmaceuticals, detergents, coatings, resins and in the metallurgical industry, among others. Chemical modification yields cationic and ionic starches.[8] Electrical variations give rise to compounds that can be ionized in solution in the structure (coals at positions 2 and 6 may cause this substitution). Two groups can be included: (a) The Na^+ cation in solution is separated and the structure is negatively charged, leading to anionic behaviour $(O-CH_2COO-Na^+)$ and (b) under the same conditions the structure is positively charged and it behaves as a cation $(O-CH_2-CHOH-CH_2N(CH_3)_3 + Cl^-)$

The molecular structure and composition of the starches in aqueous solutions is complicated by their association through hydrogen bonding. The infrared spectra indicate that the hydroxyl groups are strongly hydrogen-bonded.

Altos Hornos de Zapla ore

The sample studied was taken from the underflow of the sink–float concentration plant, mineralogical and chemical analyses being presented in Table 1.

Table 1   Size, chemical and mineralogical analyses

Size, ASTM mesh	Wt%	Chemical analyses, %		Mineralogical distribution, wt%	
– 3	4.9	Fe total	43.1	Hematite, Fe_2O_3	53
– 3 + 6	59.4	Fe^{++}	5.5	Siderite, $FeCO_3$	7
– 6 + 10	19.8	SiO_2	21.9	Chlorite (thuringite*)	10
– 10 + 14	2.8	MgO	0.7	Calcite, $CaCO_3$	3
– 14 + 20	1.9	CaO	1.9	Quartz, SiO_2	12
– 20	11.2	Al_2O_3	7.8	Kaolinite, $(Al_4(Si_4O_{10})(OH)_8)$	8
	100.0	ppc	6.3	Muscovite, $(KAl_2(AlSi_3O_{10})(OH,F)_2)$	
		Others	0.7	Biotite $(K(Mg,Fe)_3(AlSi_3O_{10})(OH,F)_2)$ and others	7

* Thuringite $((Fe^{++}, Fe^{+++})_3(Al_2Si_2O_{10})(OH)_2(Mg,Fe)_3(O.OH)_6)$.

Microscopically, hematite is found in irregular oolitic forms of about 0.15 and 0.25 mm in size. Originally, the oolites come from thuringite and alter into hematite.

Río Turbio middling sample

The sample studied comes from the overflow system of the Río Turbio coal-washing circuit; Fig. 1 gives cumulative values and size grades versus distribution.

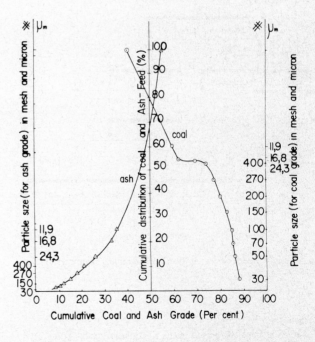

Fig. 1   Grade-cumulative distribution of coal and ash on feed sample as a function of particle size

The fraction –37 + 12.4 μm has a high ash content, but a concentration of about 12%; below 12.4 μm the ash content is about 68.7% and has a concentration of about 60.6%.

Samples and experimental methods

Iron ore

The iron ore samples were obtained from the underflow of the sink-float concentration plant. Grinding tests on these samples

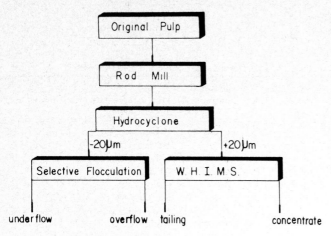

Fig. 2   Simplified flowsheet of Zapla ore treatment

showed that a rod-mill reduction at –50 mesh was the most suitable. The ground pulp was classified in the –20 μm fraction,[4,13,16,17,19] which is flocculated. The +20 μm fraction is concentrated by wet high-intensity magnetic separation[23] (Fig. 2).

Coal middling

Preparation of the pulp for selective flocculation involved extraction of the middling pulp by sampling, others being classified by sizing and hydrocyclone (Fig. 3).

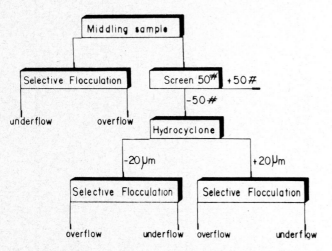

Fig. 3   Simplified flowsheet of Río Turbio middling sample treatment

Reagents

The reagents that were used in the flocculation tests (Table 2) were natural flocculants (supplied by Refinerías de Maíz as unmodified, cationic and anionic starches[2,8,9]) and synthetic flocculants (recognized brands of commercial flocculants used for total flocculation[5,6,12]).

Starch was prepared in a caustic solution in line with published recommendations.[3] The flocculant solution was prepared before each test to prevent biological and chemical alteration. All the reagents were prepared in an aqueous solution

Table 2   Flocculants and other reagents used in laboratory test

Natural flocculants: starches	Synthetic flocculants
Globe pearl starch (G.P.S.)	Praestol (P 3000)
Lock Quik 4 (L.Q.4)	Separan AP 30 (SAP 30)
Cationic, of high-grade substitution (5*)	Magnafloc (M)
Cationic 036 410 (410)	Aerofloc 31 (A 31)
Cationic 036 310 (310)	Praestol 2935 (P 2935)
Cationic 036 210 (210)	

Analytical grade sodium silicate (Na_2SiO_3)
Analytical grade sodium pyrophosphate $Na_4P_2O_7$)
Analytical grade sodium hydroxide (NaOH)

at a concentration of 1%, distilled water being used throughout.

Experimental

The electrophoretic mobility measurements were carried out by use of a zeta-meter equipped with a plexiglass electrophoresis cell.[24] Tests were conducted on separate hematite and coal ore pulps. After conditioning, the coarse particles were allowed to settle out from the suspension and the supernatant containing the fine particles was transferred into the electrophoretic cell. The same procedure was followed for measurements on the mineralogical constituents.

Experimental results

Electrophoretic studies

To determine the appropriate conditions for selective flocculation measurements of the electrophoretic mobilities[13,25,26] of different starches and different mineralogical constituents of the Altos Hornos de Zapla ore and Río Turbio middling were made (in aqueous suspensions).

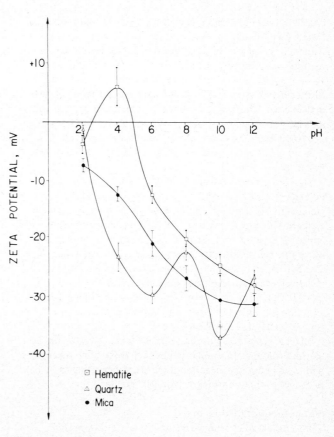

Fig. 4   Zeta-potential of hematite, quartz and mica in water as a function of pH

Zeta-potential measurement of Zapla sample
The results obtained in the zeta-potential measurements of the different mineralogical constituents of the Zapla ore as a function of pH are presented in Fig. 4 (pH regulation by addition of sodium hydroxide and sulphuric acid). Zeta-potential values for different additions of sodium silicate to the original pulp at pH 9 and 10 are shown in Fig. 5 (these pH values ensure a good state of dispersion and greater zeta-potential difference between quartz and hematite (see Fig. 4)).

Zeta-potential values measured in suspensions of the original pulp as a function of the sodium pyrophosphate at pH 9 and 10

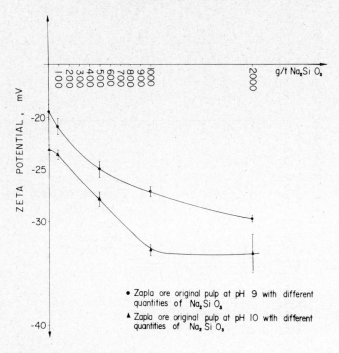

Fig. 5   Relationship between zeta-potential of original pulp and different quantities of dispersant reagent at pH 9 and 10

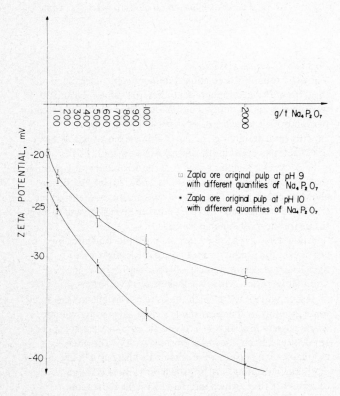

Fig. 6   Relationship between zeta-potential of original pulp and different quantities of dispersant reagents at pH 9 and 10

are shown in Fig. 6. The most suitable dispersion effect is obtained with the use of sodium pyrophosphate.

Zeta-potential measurements of Río Turbio sample
Various measurements of the suspension middling sample and the principal mineralogical constituent electrokinetic potentials of the pulps, coal and clay were carried out.[27,28] Fig. 7 shows zeta-

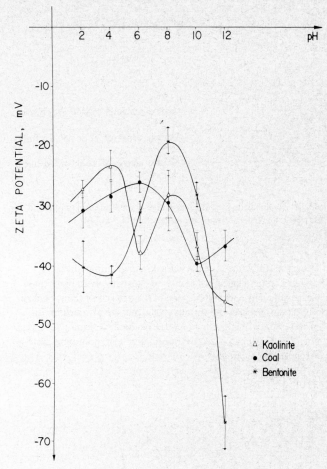

Fig. 7   Zeta-potential of kaolinite, coal and bentonite in water as a function of pH

potential values as a function of pH for coal, bentonite and kaolinite,[37] and Fig. 8 middling sample zeta-potential values as a function of different sodium silicate additions at pH 8 and 10. All the measured values were compared with those obtained in the settling tests. No potential difference was found between pH 9 and 10. At pH 8 and at pH 10, with an addition of 500 g/t sodium silicate, a high dispersion was obtained, so these conditions were selected for the present study.

At pH values higher than 6 the middling sample has adequate dispersion; at pH >9 hydroxide consumption is too high. The pH range 8–9 was chosen for the different flocculation tests. Increased additions of sodium silicate at low pH values raised the zeta-potential. At high pH values higher sodium silicate additions produced a decrease in zeta-potential.

Electrophoretic measurements of starches
Electrophoretic mobility measurements at different pH values were carried out on the starches[8] (Figs. 9 and 10).

Flocculation studies
Lien and Morrow[3] gave a generalized flowsheet for the beneficiation of a low grade ore by selective flocculation—a technique that requires the electrostatic conditioning of

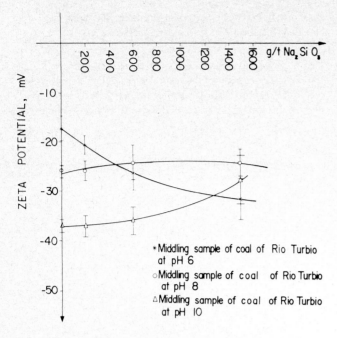

Fig. 8   Relationship between zeta-potential middling coal sample and different quantities of dispersant reagents at pH 8 and 10

mineralogically liberated particles. Good grinding liberates particles mineralogically and effective dispersion liberates them electrostatically (pH and dispersion reagents control dispersion). Fig. 11 summarizes the various stages that are involved in this process. Once the flocculant has been added, desliming is carried out. The dispersion–selective flocculation test–desliming cycle is repeated three times.

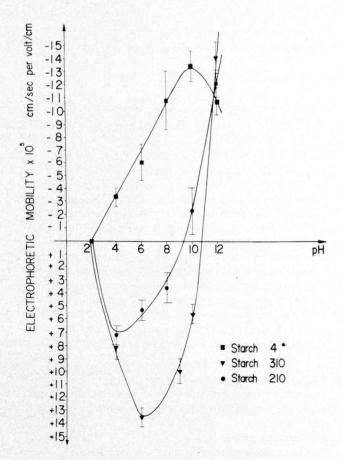

Fig. 9   Electrophoretic mobilities of various corn starches as a function of pH

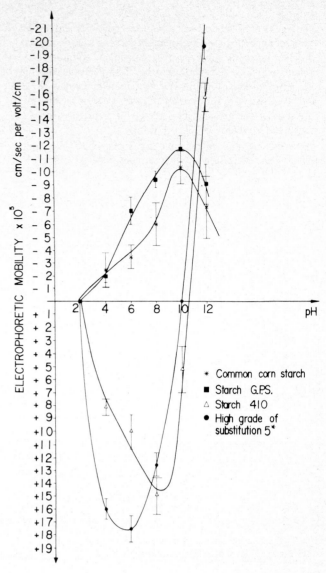

Fig. 10   Electrophoretic mobilities of various corn starches as a function of pH

Zapla ore flocculation studies
The most suitable flocculation conditions were determined on the basis of the electrophoretic studies. pH values of 8 and 10 were chosen and various quantities of sodium silicate and sodium pyrophosphate were tested as dispersant reagents. An experimental design was used to enable the most suitable range of variables involved in the process to be selected.[11,15,30-33]

Selective flocculation[7,10,11,18,21] of the ore under study permits the successful beneficiation of solids below 20 μm. As the ore shows an appropriate liberation of constituents at that size, the tests were designed to yield the optimum dispersion and to allow the use of the most suitable flocculant.

A flowsheet was adopted that included rod-mill grinding, attrition of the product to clean the particle surface and hydrocyclone classification at –20 μm. Fig 12 shows the flocculation results with dispersion reagent variations.

Test conditions for the high-intensity wet-magnetic separation[22] were: grinding, –50 mesh; sample weight, 60 g; water volume, 60 ml; current intensity, 3–4 A; and air gap flux density, approx. 18 000 gauss. Each test was performed with two or three cleanings. Good results were obtained with a particle size of –50 mesh; finer grinding (–70 or –100 mesh) produced large quantities of fines, which interfered with the separation.

The product combination permitted the production of concentrates with grades and recoveries equivalent to those

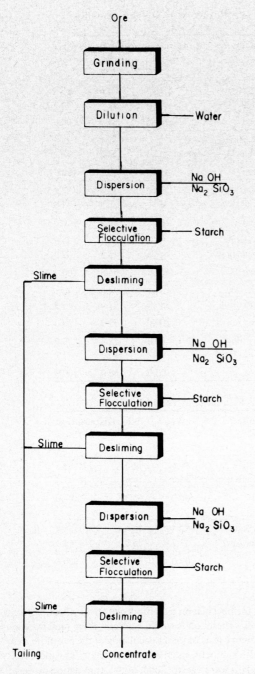

Fig. 11   Flowsheet of laboratory tests

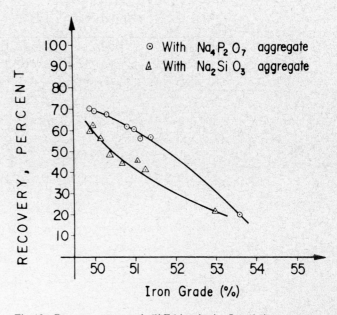

Fig. 12   Recovery versus grade (% Fe) in selective flocculation tests

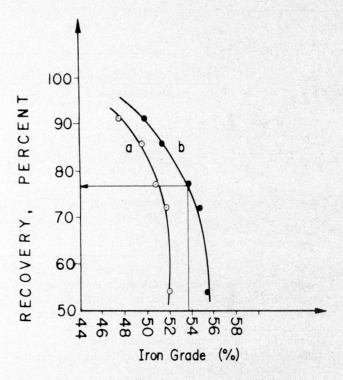

Fig. 13   Recovery–grade (%Fe) of (a) concentrate and middling combination and (b) roasting at 600°C, concentrate and middling combination

obtained by Altos Hornos de Zapla with reduction roasting and wet low-intensity magnetic separation (see Table 3).

Fig. 13 shows the grade recovery curves for selective flocculation and wet high-intensity magnetic separation applied to samples without previous treatment and roasted at 600°C.

Río Turbio slime flocculation study
To study the effect of certain variables under established pH

Table 3   Results of product combination (These results are not plotted)

Product	Wt %	Grade of Fe, %	Distri-bution, %	Product combination	Cumula-tive wt %	Grade, %	Distri-bution, %
Magnetic concentrate	44.6	50.8	53.5	M.C.	44.6	50.8	53.5
Overflow	15.3	50.0	18.1	M.C. + Ov	59.9	50.6	71.6
Middling 3	5.7	39.8	5.3	M.C. + Ov + M$_3$	65.6	49.7	76.9
Underflow	9.7	35.7	8.2	M.C. + Ov + M$_3$ + Un	75.3	47.9	85.1
Middling 2	7.1	34.8	5.8	M.C. + Ov + M$_3$ + Un + M$_2$	82.4	46.7	94.7
Middling 1	6.6	24.7	3.8		6.6	24.7	5.3
Tailing	11.0	20.3	5.3		11.0	20.3	
Feed	100.0	42.4	100.0				

Table 4 Selective flocculation tests at different pH values with varying additions of sodium silicate

Dilution, no.	pH	Dispersion OH⁻, g/t	Na₂SiO₃, g/t	Flocculant starch LQ4, g/t	Product	Concentration, %	Ash grade, %	Distribution, %
			100		Overflow	39.5	74.6	16.5
					Underflow	60.5	43.5	83.5
19	8	350		400	Feed	100.0	55.9	100.0
			1000		Overflow	57	72.1	27.4
					Underflow	43	34.2	72.1
					Feed	100	55.8	100.0
			100		Overflow	55	72.7	27.2
					Underflow	45	35.6	72.8
19	9	750		400	Feed	100	56.1	100.0
			1000		Overflow	55.4	65.7	30.8
					Underflow	44.5	43.5	69.2
					Feed	100.0	55.8	100.0
			100		Overflow	44.1	74.0	20.1
					Underflow	55.9	41.6	74.4
19	10	2700		400	Feed	100.0	55.9	100.0
			1000		Overflow	56.8	72.3	28.9
					Underflow	43.2	34.3	71.1
					Feed	100.0	56.0	100.0

Table 5 Selective flocculation results and test conditions with pulps at 5 and 10% solids

Working conditions	Solids, %	Product	Wt %	Ash grade, %	Distribution of fines, %
Original pulp Dispersion		Overflow	55.4	72.0	32.6
		Underflow	44.6	35.8	67.4
350 g/t NaOH 600 g/t Na₂SiO₃	5	Feed	100.0	55.9	100.0
Flocculant 300 g/t 410*		Overflow	57.3	70.6	35.9
		Underflow	42.7	36.5	64.1
pH 8 Dilution, 10 and 19	10	Feed	100.0	56.0	100.0

conditions[29,34] previous tests were reviewed. A comparison of the results obtained with unclassified pulps at pH 8, 9 and 10 was made. At the same pH values comparisons were made for sodium silicate additions of 100 and 1000 g/t, flocculant additions to the system remaining constant (Table 4).

Sodium silicate has a greater influence on flocculation selectivity than on dispersion of the middling sample.

Pulps of 5 and 10% solids were used, but no significant variation in the selective flocculation of both pulps was apparent (Table 5).

As there is no significant electrostatic difference in the mineralogical constituent at the selected pH values, it was decided to test cationic and anionic starches. Tests were carried out at pH 8, 9 and 10 with identical quantities of sodium silicate as a dispersant (Table 6). Flocculant quantity varies because the higher the pH values, the greater is the reagent consumption required to bring about flocculation.

In all cases the non-modified or anionic flocculants form larger flocs more quickly. As regards selectivity, they were more suitable than the cationic flocculants at pH 8 and 9.

Various selective flocculation tests were carried out in line with a previously designed programme (Table 7). The acceptable results obtained at pH 8 are compatible with a reasonable sodium hydroxide consumption.

Fig. 2 shows that sizing and hydrocyclone classification were used to obtain –50 mesh +20 μm and –20 μm fractions, which were selectively flocculated in separate tests (Table 8 and 9).

All the flocculation tests produced an overflow with some solids content—these solids would be removed by total flocculation.[23] Laboratory tests of total flocculation of the overflow were carried out with synthetic and natural flocculants. The most effective flocculant was Praestol 3000, but a combination of Aerofloc A 31 and a high-grade substitution cationic starch was acceptable (Table 10).

Discussion and conclusions

Altos Hornos de Zapla ore
A combination of wet high-intensity magnetic separation and selective flocculation give better results than those obtained by their individual application. Altos Hornos de Zapla aims to achieve a concentrate grade of 55% Fe with a recovery of 80–85%. Such results are feasible on the basis of studies by Fabricaciones Militares with reduction roasting and wet low-magnetic separation. Our studies show a concentrate with a grade of 54% Fe and a recovery of 77%.

Our technology is simpler and more economical, resulting from optimization of a study of the variables grinding, sizing, dispersion and selective flocculation.

The iron distribution indicates that the –20 μm cyclosizer fraction contains 30% Fe, which could not be recovered by conventional ore dressing methods.

Zeta-potential determinations of the ore mineralogical

Table 6 Representative tests of varying pH and flocculant in selective flocculation

Dilution, no.	pH	Dispersion OH⁻, g/t	Dispersion Na₂SiO₃, g/t	Flocculant, g/t	Product	wt% %	Ash grade, %	Distribution, %
19	8.0	350	500	410* 750	Overflow Underflow	81.5 18.5	60.7 36.3	72.0 28.0
					Feed	100.0	56.2	100.0
19	8.0	350	500	LQ4* 750	Overflow Underflow	77.2 22.8	62.0 35.5	65.2 34.8
					Feed	100.0	56.0	100.0
19	9.0	750	500	410* 1000	Overflow Underflow	51.1 48.9	60.3 42.3	31.4 68.6
					Feed	100.0	56.0	100.0
19	9.0	750	500	LQ4* 1000	Overflow Underflow	65.9 34.1	67.6 36.2	47.4 52.6
					Feed	100.0	56.9	100.0
19	10.0	2700	500	LQ4* 1500	Overflow Underflow	52.1 47.9	71.1 41.6	32.4 67.6
					Feed	100.0	57.0	100.0
19	10.0	2700	500	410* 1500	Overflow Underflow	43.8 56.2	71.5 44.8	26.5 73.5
					Feed	100.0	56.5	100.0

Table 7 Selective flocculation tests on unclassified pulps: reagents consumptions and results

Dispersion OH⁻	Dispersion Na₂SiO₃	Flocculants 410	Flocculants LQ4	pH Natural	pH Initial	Product	Wt %	Ash grade, %	Distribution, %
(a) 350	750	800		7.5	8	Overflow Underflow	70.5 29.5	67.8 30.5	47.5 52.5
						Feed	100.0	56.8	100.0
(b) 350	1800	350		7.5	8	Overflow Underflow	66.3 33.7	67.9 32.9	44.1 55.9
						Feed	100.0	56.1	100.0
(c) 350	600	350		7.5	8	Overflow Underflow	60.8 39.2	71.1 33.4	37.4 62.6
						Feed	100.0	56.0	100.0
(d) 750	1600	700		7.5	9	Overflow Underflow	63.3 36.7	69.4 34.3	41.6 58.4
						Feed	100.00	56.8	100.00
(e) 350	850		400	7.5	8	Overflow Underflow	57.0 43.0	72.1 34.1	27.9 72.1
						Feed	100.00	55.8	100.00
(f) 2700	850		400	7.5	10	Overflow Underflow	56.8 43.2	72.3 34.3	28.9 71.1
						Feed	100.0	56.0	100.0

Table 8 Combination of selective flocculation products obtained from −50 mesh +20 μm and −20 μm fractions

Product	Wt %	Ash grade, %	Distribution, %	Product combination	Cumulative wt %	Grade, %	Distribution, %
+50 mesh	8.5	12.0	18.5	+50 mesh	8.5	12.0	18.5
Underflow −20 μm	9.8	38.0	14.6	+50 mesh +(Un-20 μm)	18.3	25.9	33.1
Underflow +20 μm	21.8	38.3	32.4	+50 mesh +(Un-20 μm) +(Un+20 μm)	40.1	32.7	65.5
Overflow −20 μm	51.3	73.1	29.4		91.4	55.5	94.4
Overflow +20 μm	8.6	72.7	5.1		100.00	57.0	100.0
Feed	100.0	57.0	100.0				

Table 9 Selective flocculation test conditions and reagent consumption from –50 mesh +20 μm and –20 μm fractions

Dilution, no.	Dispersion OH⁻, g/t	Dispersion Na₂SiO₃, g/t	Flocculation 210, g/t	Flocculation 410, g/t	pH Initial	Test	Test
19	200	600	80	—	7.2	8.5	–50 mesh +20 μm
19	600	750	—	770	7.6	8.0	–20 μm

Table 10 Flocculant consumption, technical specifications and results

	Test Flocculant used	Flocculant consumption, g/m³	Settling rate, m/h	Solids content in overflow, g/l	pH	Dilution, no.	Ash content, % Initial	Final
1	P.3000	10	12.7	0.75	8	30	83	90
2	P.3000	4	3.3	1.8	8	30		
	5*	20						
3	P.3000	2	2.3	0.8	8	30	83	93
	5*	40					83	95
4	P.3000	1	1.8	1.5	8	30	83	97
	5*	40				80		
5	P.3000	4	5.9	1.4	8	30	83	92
	5*	20					68	
6	SAP 30	2	2.6	1.2	8	30	83	95
	5*	40						
7	M	2	1.4	0.6	8	30	83	96
	5*	40						
8	A31	4	9.6	3.0	8	30	83	96
	5*	40						

constituents and electrophoretic mobility values recorded during the characterizing starch preparation showed the most effective and selective starch to be the cationic one with a 036 410 degree of substitution. Logically, these considerations were combined with pH selection and dispersant agents. It is important to note that sodium pyrophosphate was the most suitable dispersant (Fig. 6).

Fig. 4 suggests that the zeta-potentials at pH 10 of the most abundant mineral are –37 mV for quartz and –23 mV for hematite. These values help to define theoretically the use of a certain flocculant. Taking into account the electrical conditions and the greater specific gravity of hematite, the unmodified or anionic flocculant would be that indicated for the selective flocculation tests, but the results were not as expected.

Tests with cationic starches were more successful. Mineralogical studies demonstrated the presence of specular hematite in a laminar form, which explains the anomalous flocculation behaviour.

Fig. 13 shows clearly that grades are increased when the wet high-intensity magnetic separation–selective flocculation concentrates are roasted at 600°C, and gives the grades and recoveries of the unroasted and roasted concentrate combination. The presence of siderite ($FeCO_3$) prevents a higher-grade magnetic concentrate from being obtained, but after roasting there is an increase of 4 or 5 points. Scatter in Fig. 13 is due to the fact that siderite occurs to a greater extent in the +20 μm fraction, affecting the magnetic concentrates.

Río Turbio middling sample

It is possible to obtain an additional coal recovery from the Río Turbio slimes. Electrophoretic studies and settling tests determined that a value of pH 8 gives a suitable dispersion of the pulp. The results obtained in the laboratory test support this.

Size classification showed it was convenient to separate the –20 μm fraction by hydrocyclone. Selective flocculation on the +20 μm and –20 μm fractions gave better recoveries than those obtained in the flocculation of unclassifed pulp, and better results were obtained with cationic starches than with anionic starches, larger and more selective flocs being produced.

The high ash content overflow was tested by total flocculation in order to recover clear water.[35] Synthetic flocculants and a mixture with starch were utilized for these tests. The A31-5* mixture (3.0 g/l) gave results similar to those obtained with 0.75 g/l Praestol 3000—a finding that should be studied further since the coal content at 3.0 g/l is greater than that recorded at 0.75 g/l of Praestol.

The concentrate obtained by selective flocculation of the unclassified fraction has a more suitable grade (30.5% ash and recovery of 52.5%) than that obtained with hydrocyclone classified product (32.7% ash and 65.5% recovery).

Finally, the results show the usefulness of the method in regard to unclassified pulp, the concentrate obtained having a moderate-grade ash content. For use industrially it is necessary not only to combine it with fines but also to briquette it for home consumption.[36]

The selective flocculation concentrate combination with the ore produced at present in Río Turbio would increase the ash content by 1%, but net annual production would increase by 7%.

References

1. Johnson J. C. *Industrial starch technology: recent developments* (Park Ridge, N. J.: Noyes Data Corporation, 1979), 370 p.
2. Iwasaki I. and Lai R. W. Starches and starch products as depressants in soap flotation of activated silica from iron ores. *Trans. Am. Inst. Min. Engrs*, **232**, 1965, 364–71.
3. Lien H. O. and Morrow J. G. Beneficiation of lean iron ores solely by selective flocculation and desliming. *CIM Bull.*, **71**, Oct. 1978, 109–20.
4. Yarar B. and Kitchener J. A. Selective flocculation of minerals. *Trans. Instn Min. Metall. (Sect. C: Mineral Process. Extr. Metall.)*, **79**, 1970, C23–33.
5. Flocculation and suspensions of solids with organic polymers—a literature survey. *Warren Spring Laboratory Mineral Process. Inf. Note* no. 5, 1965, 39 p.
6. Slater R. W. and Kitchener J. A. Characteristics of flocculation of mineral suspensions by polymers. *Disc. Faraday Soc.* no. 42, 1966, 267–75.
7. Dicks M. L. and Morrow J. B. Application of the selective flocculation silica flotation process to the Mesabi Range ores. Paper presented to AIME annual meeting, Denver, Colorado, 1978. Preprint 78-8-6.

8. Balajee S. R. and Iwasaki I. Adsorption mechanism of starches in flotation and flocculation of iron ores. *Trans. Am. Inst. Min. Engrs*, **244**, 1969, 401–6.

9. Iwasaki I. Carlson W. J. Jr. and Parmerter S. M. The use of starches and starch derivatives as depressants and flocculants in iron ore beneficiation. *Trans. Am. Inst. Min. Engrs*, **244**, 1969, 88–98.

10. Werneke M. F. and Van Wyk J. U.S. Patent 4 081 357, 1978.

11. Stoev S. and Kintisheva R. Vibroacoustical methods for improving selective flocculation. In *Proceedings of the 12th international mineral processing congress, 1977* (São Paulo, Brazil: D.N.P.M. M.M.E., 1982), vol 2, 85–105.

12. Linke W. F. and Booth R. B. Physical chemical aspects of flocculation by polymers. *Trans. Am. Inst. Min. Engrs*, **217**, 1960, 364–71.

13. Lyklema J. Surface chemistry of colloids in connection with stability. In *The scientific basis of flocculation* Ives K. J. ed. (Alphen aan den Rijn: Sijthoff & Noordhoff, 1978), 3–36.

14. O'Melia C. R. Coagulation in wastewater treatment. Reference 13, 219–68.

15. Matar J. A. and Rudolph C. G. Estudios sobre causas de contaminación de las aguas de Río Turbio. Contrato de asesoramiento 44/76 y 2/76 del Instituto de Investigaciones Mineras, San Juan (IIM), 1976.

16. Paananen A. D. and Turcotte W. A. Factors influencing selective flocculation desliming practice at the Tilden mine. Paper presented to AIME, 1965.

17. Somasundaran P. and Arbiter N. eds. *Beneficiation of mineral fines; problems and research needs, report of a workshop held at Sterling Forest, August 27 to 29 1978* (New York: AIME, 1979), 406 p.

18. Colombo A. F. Selective flocculation and flotation of iron-bearing materials. In *Fine particle processing* Somasundaran P. ed. (New York: AIME, 1980), vol. 2, 1934–56.

19. Fuerstenau D. W. ed. *Froth flotation, 50th anniversary volume* (New York: AIME, 1962), 677 p.

20. Zappi Enrique V. *Tratado de química orgánica, Vol. 3, 2nd edn* ('El Ateneo', 1952), 1805–19.

21. Sorensen R. T. and Frommer D. W. Laboratory and pilot plant development of flotation procedures for fine-grained hematite ores of Marquette Range, Michigan. *Rep. Invest. U.S. Bur. Mines* 6976, 1967, 34 p.

22. Bartnik J. A. Zabel W. H. and Hopstock D. M. On the production of iron ore superconcentrates by high-intensity wet magnetic separation. *Int. J. Mineral Process.*, **2**, 1975, 117–26.

23. Stone W. D. D. and Kennedy A. J. Commercial application of high intensity wet magnetic separation for iron ores. Paper presented to AIME meeting, 1971.

24. Riddick T. M. Control of colloid stability through zeta potential. Zeta Meter, Inc., U.S.A., 1968.

25. Beam E. I. Campbell S. J. and Anspach F. R. Zeta potential measurement in the control of coagulation chemical doses. Paper presented to A.I.M.E. Pennsylvania Section meeting, June 5 1963.

26. Sennett P. and Olivier J. P. Colloidal dispersion, electrokinetic effects and the concept of zeta potential. *Ind. Engng Chem.*, **57**, Aug. 1965, 32–50.

27. Olivier J. P. and Sennett P. Electrokinetic effects in kaolin water systems, I. The measurement of electrophoretic mobility. Freeport Kaolin Company Research Laboratory, Gordon, Georgia.

28. Parreira H. C. Electrophoresis of carbon black in liquids of low permeability: effect of the chain length of the adsorbate. *J. Colloid Interface Sci.*, **43**, 1973, 382–8.

29. Laskowski J. Surface chemistry aspects of fine coal beneficiation. Paper presented to First meeting of the Southern Hemisphere on mineral technology, Brazil, 1982. Preprints, vol. 1, 59–69.

30. Villas Bôas R. C. La importancia del método en la investigación tecnológica.

31. Duckworth W. E. and Wyatt J. K. Rapid statistical techniques for operational research. *Operational Research Quarterly*, **9**, no. 3, Sept. 1958, 218–33.

32. Cuthbert D. Statistical design of experiments in proces metallurgy. In *Physical chemistry of process metallurgy, part 2* Pierre G. R. St. ed. (New York, London: Interscience, 1961), 1315–26. (*Metall. Soc. Conf.* vol. 8)

33. Finch E. and Yarroll W. Computer methods and applications in extractive metallurgy. *Mineral Ind. Bull. Colo. Sch. Mines*, **12**, Jan. 1969, 15 p.

34. Sarquis P. and Rudolph C. G. Ensayos preliminares de floculación de lamas del circuito de agua de la planta depuradora de carbón Ing. J. Bacigalupo, Río Turbio. *IIM Informe* no. 102, 1975.

35. Snyder G. A. and Gregory M. J. Electrocoagulation of coal preparation plant waters. Society of Mining Engineers of A.I.M.E. Preprint 79-352, 1979.

36. Van den Broek J. J. M. From metallurgical coal tailings to thermal fuel. *Min. Engng, N.Y.*, **34**, Jan. 1982, 49–52.

37. Wen W. W. and Sun S. C. An electrokinetic study on the amine flotation of oxidized coal. *Trans. Am. Inst. Min. Engrs*, **262**, 1977, 174–80.

Novel frother–collector for flotation of sulphide minerals—CEED

Ma Jiwu, Yu Longling and Sun Kuoxiong

Synopsis

A novel reagent, cyanoethyl diethyldithiocarbamate (CEED), for the flotation of sulphide minerals is reviewed. Its structure, properties, mechanism of reaction and industrial application are considered.

The industrial application of CEED has led to improvements in the flotation process, resulting in a concentrate with a higher grade and fewer impurities; even in the absence of cyanide the arsenic content in the concentrate is much lower. Reagent consumption and the number of addition points in the process were reduced and fewer types of reagent were used (e.g. no frother added). Thus, the reagent system was simplified and the flotation process was easier to operate and control.

CEED can be used over a wide alkaline range, so rendering the flotation process more stable. With its use a high alkaline medium is not necessary for the flotation of copper ores, which usually contain some pyrite. As a result, less time is required and conditions for the subsequent pyrite flotation are improved.

CEED's lack of offensive odour and its fairly stable chemical properties benefit environmental control.

The main collectors for sulphide minerals, especially for copper sulphides, with few exceptions, are xanthates, which suffer from such disadvantages as poor selectivity (lower-grade concentrate with higher As content), ease of decomposition, offensive odour and environmental pollution. Non-ferrous sulphide minerals are normally associated with pyrite. To promote Cu–S separation it is necessary to increase the pulp pH to prevent pyrite from floating, which, in turn, consumes a large quantity of lime. Some ores that contain a considerable quantity of arsenic sulphides result in a concentrate with a high content of impurities, including arsenic. To improve the quality of the concentrate it is necessary to add cyanides to depress the arsenic sulphides. Since the 1960s Z-200 has been widely used as a collector for sulphide minerals in the U.S.A. and Chile[1] and has demonstrated some superior properties: for example, its selectivity is better (collector power of pyrite is poor), it requires lower dosages and consumption of lime and the disadvantages of using xanthates have been overcome to some extent. In the 1970s extensive research into, and the application of, ester-type collectors was begun and many new products were developed.

The ester-type collectors (i.e. non-ionic oily polar collectors) reported in the literature are the derivatives of ionic sulphydryl collectors, called divalent thioester collectors. Their main types of structure are alkyl dithiocarbamate,[2] alkyl dithiocarbonate,[3] thionocarbamate and alkyl dithiophosphate.[4,5] All are characterized by better selectivity for sulphide minerals, lower dosage, simple operation, stable chemical properties and little odour. In general, however, their power for collecting sulphide minerals is weaker than that of the corresponding ionic collectors. In practice, they are often used in conjunction with ionic collectors.

Recently, further progress has been made in research into ester-type collectors. To both ends of the molecular structure can be attached various functional groups acceptor electrons, such as the ether bond (R_1–O–R_2–), carboxy ($-\overset{\overset{\displaystyle O}{\displaystyle \|}}{C}$–O–), benzoyl ($C_6H_5\overset{\overset{\displaystyle O}{\displaystyle \|}}{C}O$–) and methoxy carbonyl ($-\overset{\overset{\displaystyle O}{\displaystyle \|}}{C}$–O–R), which would improve the behaviour of the reagents.[5,6,7]

CEED (cyanoethyl diethyl dithiocarbamate) is one oily polar collector. Laboratory and commercial tests have shown that it is a satisfactory frother–collector for non-ferrous metal sulphides, is chemically stable, has a higher ability for frothing and collecting, better selectivity, a faster flotation rate as well as little odour, and requires lower dosages and lower consumption of lime.

Preparation and properties of CEED

The preparation of CEED is based on the reaction of diethylamine with carbon disulphide to produce the ammonium salt of diethylamino dithioformic acid, the latter then being added to vinyl cyanide, thus producing cyanoethyl diethyl dithiocarbamate. The reaction mechanism is[8]

$$(C_2H_5)_2 NH + CS_2 \rightarrow (C_2H_5)_2 NCSSH \cdot HN(C_2H_5)_2$$
$$(C_2H_5)_2 NCSSH \cdot HN(C_2H_5)_2 + CH_2CHCN \rightarrow$$
$$(C_2H_5)_2 NCSSCH_2CH_2CN + (C_2H_5)_2 NH$$

The predominant component of CEED is cyanoethyl diethyl dithiocarbamate, the product of the reactions mentioned above. Purified by molecular distillation, the infrared and ultraviolet spectroscopy and physical constants were determined. The infrared spectrogram shows there is a characteristic absorption peak of cyanide at 2250 cm^{-1} (no free acrylonitrile was found in pure product by GC analysis) and a characteristic absorption peak of cyano-N, N-dialkyl-dithiocarbamate at 1490 cm^{-1}. The latter is due to stretch vibration of the C≡N bond in the structure of $\overset{}{>}$N$-\overset{\overset{\displaystyle S}{\displaystyle \|}}{C}$-S-,[9,10] which proves that the compound contains the $\overset{}{>}$N$-\overset{\overset{\displaystyle S}{\displaystyle \|}}{C}$-S- group and the $-C$≡N group. In the ultraviolet spectrogram there are two absorption peaks at 248 nm and 280 nm, which represent the $\overset{}{>}$N$-\overset{\overset{\displaystyle S}{\displaystyle \|}}{C}$- group and $-\overset{\overset{\displaystyle S}{\displaystyle \|}}{C}$-S group, respectively. Furthermore, its physical constants, such as density, refractive index and molar refraction, fit well with reports in the literature.[11] All these show that the compound is cyanoethyl diethyl dithiocarbamate.

The commercial product of CEED is a brownish-black oily liquid with a slight smell of fish, its density being approximately 1.11, freezing point ~22°C, insoluble in water, but easily soluble in organic solvents, such as alcohol, carbon tetrachloride and ether. It possesses stable chemical properties and contains more than 80% of the predominant component.

Tests on CEED for collecting power and selectivity

The copper ore sample tested came from a mine in northern China. The principal metallic minerals include chalcopyrite, bornite, chalcocite, pyrite and sphalerite; the primary gangue minerals are calcite, quartz and biotite.

A 350-g sample was ground to 68% –200 mesh with lime (1 kg/t), followed by flotation in a cell (1 l) with mechanical agitation. Butyl xanthate was added in three dosages (20+5+5 g/t). The addition points for the two reagents were the same. The time for agitation was 1 min. The froth produced was collected every 2 min. Altogether, nine froth products were taken. Flotation with CEED was as mentioned above, with similar addition points and stage additions (37+7+7 g/t).

The recovery of copper in the products was calculated separately. Regression analysis was made in accordance with the hyperbolic equation

$$\frac{1}{y} = a + \frac{b}{X}$$

$$\frac{1}{\epsilon} = a + \frac{b}{t}$$

Curves of flotation rate and concentrate grade versus Cu recovery are given in Figs. 1 and 2, respectively. Both the

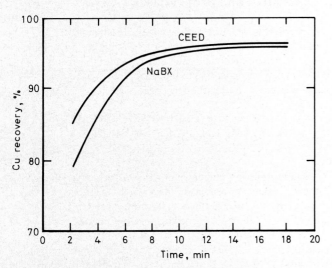

Fig. 1 Rate of flotation

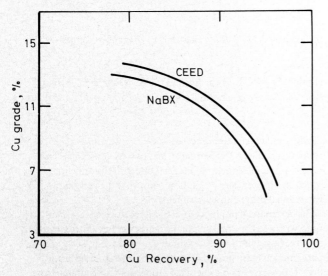

Fig. 2 Concentrate grade–Cu recovery relationship

flotation rate and selectivity of CEED are better than those of butyl xanthate.

Action mechanism of reagent

CEED may be regarded as a derivative of the salts of dithiocarbamic acid—an ionic collector the metal ions of which are substituted by the cyanoethyl group ($-CH_2CH_2CN$). Its structure is

$$C_2H_5{-}\!\!\!\diagdown\!\!\!\underset{C_2H_5{-}\diagup}{}N{-}\overset{\overset{S}{\|}}{C}{-}S{-}CH_2{-}CH_2{-}C\equiv N$$

Because of the asymmetry and the conjugation of the $p\pi$ bond of group $>\!\!\ddot{N}\!\!-\!\!C\!\!=\!\!S$ in the molecular structure the CEED molecule possesses considerable dipolar moment and appears as a strong dipole in aqueous solution. Under the action of Van der Waals forces the CEED molecule expels a hydrated layer from the surface of minerals and is polarized, adsorbing on the active site of the mineral surface;[12] chemical adsorption therefore takes place to produce a coordinate compound.

The structure of the chelate compound formed by the reaction of CEED with metal ions on the mineral surface may be

$$\left(R_2N{-}\overset{\overset{S}{\|}}{\underset{S{-}(CH_2)_2\;\;CN}{C}}\right)_n M$$

In neutral or acidic medium CEED only demonstrates static conjugation and induction effects. As the molecular polarity does not increase under the influence of the environment, CEED in the molecular state reacts with metal ions in flotation, physical adsorption playing a dominant part.

Moreover, in neutal or acidic medium, the selectivity of CEED becomes poor because the natural floatability of pyrite is high. In basic medium, however, CEED shows high selectivity, owing to the $p\pi$ conjugation of p-electrons of the nitrogen atom with π-electrons of the group ($C\!\!=\!\!S$) in its molecular structure, which makes the electron cloud evidently transfer to the sulphur atom, resulting in the nitrogen atom being partially positively charged. Furthermore, under the influence of an external electron field, the dynamic conjugate effect occurs, further

polarizing the molecule to form the ionic bond $=\!\!C\!\!-\!\!S\!\!-$, which reacts with the metal ions of the mineral surface to produce a stable chelate compound.

The action mechanism is as follows:

$$\underset{R\diagup}{\overset{R\diagdown}{}}\ddot{N}{-}\overset{\overset{S^{\delta_\theta}}{\|}}{C}{-}S{-}CH_2{-}CH_2{-}C\equiv\ddot{N} \quad \xrightarrow{OH^-}$$

$$\left[\underset{R\diagup}{\overset{R\diagdown}{}}\underset{OH}{\overset{}{N}}{=}\overset{\overset{S^-}{|}}{C}{-}S{-}CH_2{-}CH_2{-}C\equiv\ddot{N}\right] \xrightarrow{M^{+n}}$$

$$\left(R_2N{=}\underset{OH\;\;S{-}(CH_2)_2\;\;CN}{\overset{\overset{S}{|}}{C}}\right)_n M$$

288

The selectivity of a reagent depends on the different forces of interaction between the reagent molecule and various metal ions, i.e. the different solubilities of the metal complex compounds formed. From the data available in the literature it can be assumed that, for divalent metals, the solubilities of the metal complex compounds, whatever the ligands, increase in the order Pd>Cu>Ni>Pb>Co>Zn>Cd>Fe>Mn>Mg.

Thus, the complexing solubilities of CEED with copper and iron ions are quite different and, thus, copper sulphide minerals can be separated easily from pyrite minerals by use of CEED in basic medium. The higher the basicity of medium, the greater is the ionization of the molecule and the better the selectivity.

In the molecular structure of CEED the diethyl group, being further away from the polarized group, exhibits hydrophobicity to some extent. Both the cyano group at the other end and the super-conjugation effect of its π-bond with the σ-bond of the methane group demonstrate a strong tendency to attract electrons, which strengthens the association (H-bonding association) of nitrogen atoms with water molecules, causing CEED to have frothing ability.

It was proved by measurements of surface tension that the frothing ability of CEED is much higher than that of other ester collectors, such as cyanoacetic isopropyl xanthate, diethyl aminodithioformic propionate and butyl cyanoacetic thioester.[13]

Commercial flotation tests

Several commercial flotation experiments were carried out to compare CEED with other reagents.

Raw ore from a massive copper-containing pyrite deposit in northwest China had as its principal minerals pyrite, chalcopyrite, sphalerite, galena, arsenopyrite and covellite (main gangue minerals, dolomite, calcite, quartz and chlorite). The flotation results are given in Table 1.

Table 1   Flotation results

Reagents			Results		
Name	Dosage, g/t	Addition points	Cu grade, % Feed	Conc.	Cu recovery, %
NaBX	209				
Pine oil	82	5	0.862	15.357	84.71
CEED	59.1	2	0.870	15.988	86.18

CEED is characterized by lower dosages, fewer reagent addition points and improved metallurgy in comparison with butyl xanthate. Since changes in basicity of pulp and the dosage of other reagents have little effect on flotation with CEED, it will favour a stable flotation operation.[14]

Raw ore for the second test came from an impregnation copper deposit in northwest China. The principal metallic minerals include pyrite, chalcopyrite, covellite and sphalerite; the gangue minerals are quartz, sericite with minor amounts of

Table 2   Flotation results

Reagents			Results		
Name	Dosage, g/t	Addition points	Cu grade, % Feed	Conc.	Cu recovery, %
NaBX	80	2			
Pine oil	60	2	0.540	10.98	87.96
CEED	30	1	0.588	12.25	89.34

carbonates and gypsum. Flotation results are listed in Table 2.

The use of CEED to replace NaBX and pine oil would reduce the dosage of reagents by 80% and increase the grade of concentrate and the recovery of copper by about 1.3%. The estimated consumption of lime would decrease by one-half. As CEED may recover copper sulphides at a lower basicity, favourable conditions for further sulphur recovery (as pyrite) could be created.

For the third test the raw ore came from a copper-containing skarn deposit in eastern China. The dominant copper minerals are chalcopyrite with minor amounts of bornite, chalcocite and malachite, as well as pyrite and pyrrhotite; the gangue minerals are garnet, diopside and chlorite.

Flotation results are shown in Table 3. The dosage of CEED accounted for only one-third of the total dosage of NaBX and pine oil, and the recovery of copper improved to some extent.[14]

Table 3   Flotation results

Reagents			Results		
Name	Dosage, g/t	Addition points	Cu grade, % Feed	Conc.	Cu recovery, %
NaBX	60	Rougher	0.644	20.80	95.64
Pine oil	60	Scavenger			
CEED	40	Rougher	0.589	19.93	96.37

The fourth ore tested was mined from a copper-containing quartz vein deposit in northeastern China. The principal metallic minerals are chalcopyrite, pyrite, pyrrhotite and arsenopyrite; non-metallic minerals are feldspar, hornblende, plagioclase, quartz, etc.

The use of CEED (65 g/t) to replace xanthate (70 g/t) and pine oil (60 g/t) would increase the grade of concentrate from 20 to 24.5% Cu, with the recovery of copper maintained constant, the As content in the concentrate would decrease significantly, even without cyanide.

Finally, the raw ore was obtained from a pyrite deposit containing higher-grade copper minerals in northwestern China. Pyrite, chalcopyrite and magnetite are the principal metallic minerals, hematite, limonite, covellite and malachite being present in lesser amounts; the oxidation state of the copper reaches 4–10%; gangue minerals are primarily quartz, chlorite and calcite.

The flotation results are listed in Table 4. The use of CEED in conjunction with NaBX gives results that are better than those with NaBX alone. It is evident that CEED mixed with NaBX would be reasonable for the treatment of copper ores with a relatively high oxidation state.

Table 4   Flotation results

Reagents			Results		
Name	Dosage, g/t	Addition points	Cu grade, % Feed	Conc.	Cu recovery, %
NaBX	58	Rougher Scavenger			
Pine oil	93	Rougher Scavenger	3.305	19.58	92.42
CEED	44	Rougher			
NaBX	12	Scavenger	2.648	20.62	92.75
Pine oil	36	Rougher			

Conclusions

(1) The examples of flotation show that CEED is a good collector, being especially suitable for recovering copper sulphides and characterized by high adaptability, good frothing ability and selectivity. It can reduce the consumption of reagents and lime, and improve flotation performance, providing economic benefits. For ores that contain high levels of As the use of CEED will lower the content of As (as impurities) in the concentrate. For copper ores with a higher oxidation state it is reasonable to use CEED in combination with NaBX to improve its suitability.

(2) CEED is characterized by stable chemical properties, little odour, simple synthesis, low cost and ready availability.

(3) The crystallization temperature of CEED is slightly high, but this can be overcome by heating or mixing with similar reagents in appropriate proportions.

References

1. Huan S. S. Study and application of Z-200 collector abroad. *Metallic Ore Dressing Abroad* no. 5, 1974, 24. (Chinese text)
2. Bikales N. M. U.S. Patent 3 298 520, 1963.
3. Livshits A. K. and Kitaeva N. B. Alkyl esters of alkylatic acids as reagents–collectors in sulfide flotation. *Tsvet. Metally, Mosk.*, no 6 1969, 12–15.
4. *Nonferrous Metals (Mineral Processing Section)*, no. 1, 1974, 45. (Chinese text)
5. Bikales N. M. and Booth R. B. U.S. Patent 3 223 238, 1963.
6. Bogdanov O. S. *et al.* Trends in the search for effective collectors. *Tsvet. Metally, Mosk.*, **49**, no. 4 1976, 72–9, (Russian text); *Tsvet. Metally, N.Y.*, **17**, no. 4 1976, 79–85.
7. Bikales N.M. U.S. Patent 3 226 417, 1965.
8. Turkevich N.M. *et al. Chemistry of heterocyclic compounds*, no. 5, 1967, 845–9. (Russian text)
9. Plaksin I. N. *et al. Infrared spectroscopy of the surface layer of reagent on mineral*, 1966, 44. (Russian text)
10. Kellner R. Beitrag zum Problem der Bandverschiebungen in den I.R.-Spektren von Diäthyl- und Tetramethylendithiocarbamidamen. *Analyt. chim. Acta*, **63**, 1973, 277–84.
11. Ding C. X. *et al.* Studies on the structure of CEED and the analysis methods. *Information of Mining and Metallurgy, Baiyin Res. Inst. Min. Metall.*, no. 1, 1978. (Chinese text)
12. Wang D. Z. *Action mechanism of flotation reagents and its application* (Beijing: Metallurgical Industry Publishing House, 1982), 32. (Chinese text)
13. Li L. G. Study on frothing power of CEED. *Nonferrous Metals*, no. 2 1982, 29. (Chinese text)
14. Ma J. W. *et al.* The preparation and application of CEED. *Nonferrous Metals (Mineral Processing Section)*, no. 1 1977, 18. (Chinese text)

Electrochemical study of sphalerite activation and deactivation in a complexing medium: role of potential

J. Bessière and P. Bernasconi

Synopsis

An electrochemical study of sphalerite activation and deactivation by use of Cu^{2+} ions in the presence of such complexing agents as ammonia, ethylene diamine tetra-acetate (EDTA) and ethylene diamine (EN) has permitted their influence on the Cu(II)–ZnS interaction without oxygen to be determined, as well as the role of potential in the activation and deactivation process (the latter parameter is generally not referred to).

Without oxygen sphalerite activation is thermodynamically possible in the presence of NH_3 and EDTA over the whole pH range. Nevertheless, at pH 10 with EDTA and at pH 11 with EN kinetic factors prevent the reaction from taking place.

In the presence of oxygen and other complexing agents activation does not take place under certain pH conditions. In the same way pretreated sphalerite is deactivated under these conditions because of surface CuS dissolution, this last compound being more reducing towards oxygen in the presence of complexing agents.

Voltamperometric, potentiometric and flotation test results confirm the hypotheses put forward.

The present need to process complex sulphide ores, finely disseminated in their gangue, implies an optimization of flotation operations. Fine grinding enables various metallic cations, potential activators, to be dissolved, which is detrimental to selectivity.[1] A large number of studies have been carried out on the mechanisms of sphalerite activation and depression, as well as their consequences on flotation.[2-6] To the best of our knowledge, however, the influence of potential on these processes has not been examined in detail.

The object of the present study is to assess the combined action of potential and complexing ions on activation and deactivation processes. To facilitate the interpretation of the action of potential the complexing agents that have been tested have no oxidizing or reducing properties. Ammonia (NH_3), ethylenediamine (EN) and ethylenediaminetetraacetic (EDTA) were selected.

Experimental methods

Mineral

The sphalerite used was a natural mineral of fairly high purity (65.36% Zn, 33.47% S, 0.008% Pb, 0.004% Cu and 0.06% Fe). It was dry-ground in an agate mill at a size finer than 60 μm.

Polarography

Intensity–potential curves were obtained via a three-electrode system—a saturated calomel reference electrode, a mercury drop electrode and an auxiliary electrode made up of a platinum wire; 0.1 N sodium nitrate was used as an electrolyte. The experiments were carried out in a 50-ml volume of solution that contained 1 g of ZnS. Cupric ions were added as hydrated copper sulphate at a concentration of 5.10^{-4} M.

Complexing agents were added at various concentrations as a function of the results of thermodynamic calculations.

Concentrations were 1 N for NH_3, 10^{-2} N for EN and 2×10^{-3} N for EDTA. pH control was by addition of caustic soda.

Tests 'without potential effect' were carried out under a nitrogen atmosphere. Oxygen was dissolved in the slurry by bubbling compressed air. Intensity–potential curves were then obtained after degassing with nitrogen.

Activated sphalerite electrode 'ZnS'

For the voltamperometric and potentiometric tests at zero intensity an activated sphalerite electrode was prepared: it was covered with the activation product that resulted from the chemical reaction between Cu^{2+} ions and ZnS. A solid piece of sphalerite, which was obtained by pressing at 200 kg/cm² and sintering at 800°C under vacuum a synthetic ZnS powder, was dipped in a warm (30-40°C) copper sulphate solution at a concentration of 0.01 M. After several hours it was completely covered with a conducting film of copper sulphide ('CuS'). This piece was connected to the instruments by a platinum wire in contact with 'CuS'. The observed electrochemical signal is due to the activation product.

Potentiometry

Potential with respect to a saturated calomel electrode was measured for the 'ZnS' electrode in solutions at pH 12 (NaOH) of ammonia (1 N) ethylenediamine (10^{-2} N) in a carrier electrolyte ($NaNO_3$ 10^{-1} M). Solutions were saturated in oxygen by air bubbling.

Voltamperometry

Curves were obtained for 'ZnS' electrode by use of the three-electrode set-up. The signal for the activation product was thus obtained for the following conditions: absence of oxygen (nitrogen atmosphere), in water ($NaNO_3$ 0.1 M) at pH 12 and in ammonia medium 1 M (pH 12), and then in the presence of dissolved oxygen.

Flotation

The tests were carried out in a glass cell (diameter, 3.5 cm; height, 30 cm; volume 280 ml), the bottom of which is made of fritted glass (porosity, 4) through which air is injected. ZnS (2 g) was conditioned in a 100-ml solution (1 M NH_3 or 10^{-2} M EN or 2×10^{-3} M EDTA) at pH 12 through which air was passed. The collector used was amylxanthate at a concentration of 3×10^{-5} M/l. A 5-min conditioning time was followed by a 2-min flotation. The various flotation tests were carried out without frothing agents.

Results and discussion

Activation under complexing conditions

Thermodynamics

Marsicano et al[6] studied the thermodynamics of CuS dissolution by ethylenediamine and ammonia from the theoretical point of view. Curves of percentage of CuS formed as a function of conditioner concentration showed that EN, like NH_3, exhibits weak deactivation ability.

These theoretical findings were not in agreement with the

experimental results of Gaudin and co-workers.[4] In the absence of more data it has been impossible to reconcile these differing results.[3]

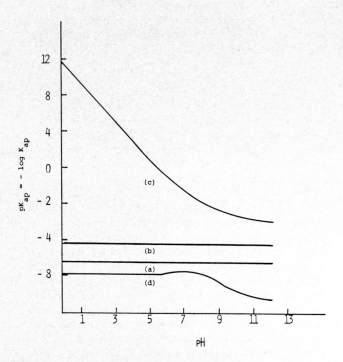

Fig. 1 pK_{ap}-f(pH) diagram for reactions (a) $ZnS + CuY^{-2} \rightleftharpoons CuS + ZnY^{-2}$; (b) $ZnS + Cu(NH_3)_4^{2+} \rightleftharpoons CuS + Zn(NH_3)_4^{2+}$ ($|NH_3| = 1$ M); (c) $ZnS + Cu(EN)_2^{2+} + EN \rightleftharpoons CuS + Zn(EN)_3^{2+}$ ($|EN| = 10^{-2}$ M); and (d) $ZnS + Cu(+II) = CuS + Zn(+II)$ in water

To determine the deactivation role of, for example NH_3, EN and EDTA the thermodynamic aspect of the activation reactions was taken into account in calculating,* as a function of pH and for a given conditioner concentration, the constant K_{ap} values of the following reactions ($pK_{ap} = -\log K_a$) (Fig. 1):

$$ZnS + CuY^{2-} \rightleftharpoons ZnY^{2-} + CuS \qquad (I)$$
$$ZnS + Cu(NH_3)_4^{2+} \rightleftharpoons Zn(NH_3)_4^{2+} + CuS \text{ (for } |NH_3| = 1 \text{ M)} \qquad (II)$$
$$ZnS + Cu(EN)_2^{2+} + EN \rightleftharpoons Zn(EN)_3^{2+} + CuS \text{ (for } |EN| = 10^{-2} \text{ M)} \qquad (III)$$

The choice of such concentrations for NH_3 and EN is again dictated by thermodynamic considerations. It is essential for the zinc and copper complexes that are formed to be more stable than the corresponding hydroxides.

The pK_{ap} of reactions I and II (pH 0-12) and of reaction III (pH>6) are negative, which indicates the preferential formation of CuS. Thermodynamically, ZnS activation by the copper ions is possible, despite the presence of the complexing agents at the stated concentrations and under the pH conditions noted previously.

Polarography
It is possible to demonstrate, by polarographic techniques, the activation of ZnS by metallic cations. Fig. 2 demonstrates the activation of ZnS by Cu^{2+} cations at pH 5. Since the diffusion wave is proportional to the concentration in solution of the compound, it can be seen that, after a few minutes of conditioning, some of the copper in solution has disappeared, whereas an equivalent quantity of Zn^{2+} has appeared in solution, according to a reaction such as

$$Cu^{2+} + ZnS \rightleftharpoons CuS + Zn^{2+} \qquad (IV)$$

* Thermodynamic data taken from Charlot.[10]

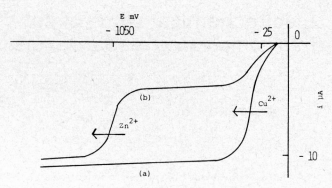

Fig. 2   ZnS activation with Cu^{2+} ions in water at pH 5-6: (a) 5×10^{-4} M Cu^{2+} without ZnS; (b) after 25-min conditioning with 1 g ZnS

It is possible, in the same manner, to characterize sphalerite activation by copper ions in the presence of 1 M NH_3 (Fig. 3), 10^{-2} M EN (Fig. 4) and 2×10^{-3} M EDTA.

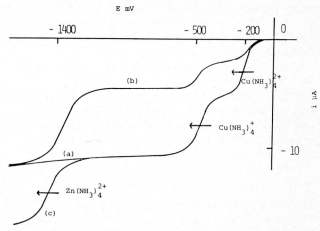

Fig. 3   Activation and deactivation of ZnS in 1 M NH_3 solution: (a) $Cu(NH_3)_4^{2-}$ solution before addition of ZnS; (b) after 20-min *activation* of 1 g ZnS in preceding solution in nitrogen atmosphere; (c) *deactivation* after 20-min oxygen bubbling in preceding slurry

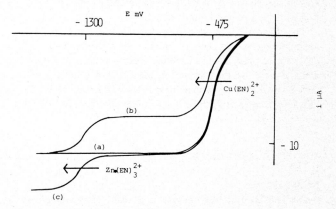

Fig. 4   Activation and deactivation of ZnS in 10^{-2} M EN solution (pH 12): (a) $Cu(EN)_2^{2-}$ solution before ZnS addition; (b) after 40-min *activation* of 1 g ZnS in preceding solution in nitrogen atmosphere; (c) *deactivation* after 20-min oxygen bubbling in preceding slurry

Completion and stoichiometry of the reactions depend on pH (for the pH values investigated between 10 and 12). Activation is efficient (Table 1) in NH_3 medium (1 N) at pH 12, in EDTA medium (2×10^{-3} M) at pH >10 and in EN medium (10^{-2} M) at pH >11. It should also be stressed that at pH 10 with EDTA and at pH 11 with EN ZnS activation by copper ions does not occur for kinetic reasons. This is an interesting result since it can

Table 1 Effect of pH on ZnS activation in complexing solutions

pH	NH₃ Conditioning time, min	NH₃ Cu loss, %	EN Conditioning time, min	EN CU loss, %	EDTA Conditioning time, min	EDTA Cu loss, %
10	—	—	40	0	40	0
11	—	—	40	0	40	19
12	45	35.5	40	26	40	46

provide a method to prevent the unwanted activation of sphalerite—for example, by grinding in a medium of controlled pH and complexing power.

Effect of potential

According to Finkelstein and Allison,[3] the activation product 'CuS' is made up of a mixture of covellite and copper sulphide $Cu(II)S(-II)$ in variable proportions. Deactivation is directly related to the dissolution of this compound. Cyanide ions are commonly used for this purpose. The deactivation mechanism is then probably due to the complexing and reducing properties of these anions with respect to $Cu(II)$. Various authors have studied the role of CN^- ions.[7,8,9] Finkelstein and Allison[3] referred to the reaction

$$CuS + H^+ + 5CN^- \rightarrow Cu(CN)_4^{3-} + SH^- + \tfrac{1}{2}C_2N_2 \qquad (V)$$

Also possible is the oxidizing dissolution of CuS. Oxygen dissolved in the solution is incapable of oxidizing the copper sulphide. In the presence of a complexing agent for copper (II), such as NH_3, EN or EDTA, the reducing ability of CuS increases. Thus, the activation product may be oxidized by oxygen.

Voltamperometry

The mechanism is shown by curves for $i = f(E)$ for a sphalerite-activated electrode ('ZnS') (Fig. 5). The speed of oxygen reduction with this electrode is slow in the absence of complexing agent (exchange current very weak). In the presence of 1 M NH_3 there is a displacement of 150mV towards the reducing media. The exchange current that corresponds to the

chemical reaction

$$CuS + O_2 + 4NH_3 \rightarrow Cu(NH_3)_4^{2+} + S(-II)_{oxidized} \qquad (VI)$$

is important. Conditioner addition increases the kinetic oxidation of 'CuS'. On the other hand, under certain conditions an increase in the speed of dissolution of 'CuS' could be expected if a stronger oxidant were used.

Potentiometry

The finding was confirmed by potentiometric measurement at zero intensity on the 'ZnS' electrode (Fig. 6), immersed in an oxygen-saturated solution (pH 12). With the addition of NH_3 a rapid potential drop of about 150 mV is apparent. With EN a jump of the same magnitude is produced, albeit much more slowly. The phenomena associated with sphalerite activation and deactivation can therefore be controlled in the presence of a copper complexing agent by potential measurement.

In the presence of oxygen NH_3, EN and EDTA permit the deactivation of 'ZnS' and the prevention of its activation by Cu^{2+} ions.

Polarography

By the use of potential it is possible to bring about the deactivation of a 'ZnS' pulp in the presence of a copper (II)

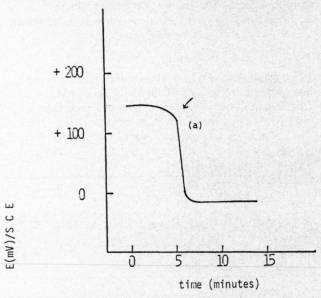

Fig. 6 Activated sphalerite electrode 'ZnS' (zero current potentiometry in oxygen-saturated solution ammonia): (a) addition of 1 M NH_3 (pH controlled at 12)

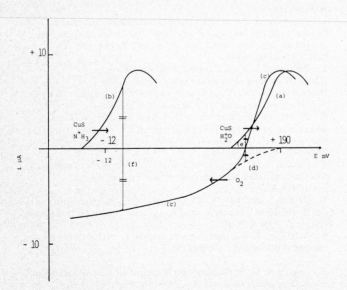

Fig. 5 Activated sphalerite electrode ('ZnS')–effect of oxygen and complexing agent (NH_3): curves $i = f(E)$: (a) 'ZnS' electrode in water at pH 12 in absence of oxygen; (b) 'ZnS' electrode in 1 M NH_3 at pH 12 in the absence of oxygen; (c) 'ZnS' electrode in water at pH 12 in presence of oxygen (O_2 reduction on 'ZnS'); (d) theoretical oxygen reduction curve obtained from (a) and (c); (e) current for O_2 reduction by 'CuS' in water; (f) current for O_2 reduction on 'CuS' in NH_3

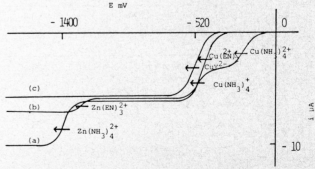

Fig. 7 Deactivation of 'ZnS activated by Cu^{2+} in water' in complexing solution saturated in oxygen. After activation with 5×10^{-4} M $CuSO_4$, filtration and washing solids immersed in solution containing complexing agent and saturated in oxygen. Following curves (pH 12) drawn: (a) after deactivation in 1 M NH_3 solution; (b) after deactivation in 10^{-2} M EN; (c) after deactivation in 2×10^{-3} M EDTA

complexing agent, such as NH_3, EN or EDTA (Figs. 3 and 4). In the first phase the sphalerite was activated in a nitrogen atmosphere according to reactions I, II or III. The slurry was then saturated in oxygen for 15 min. All of the copper that had been adsorbed on sphalerite during the activation period was then released into solution (reaction VI). Sphalerite that, when activated, had turned dark brown in colour, returned to its original light beige colour.

'ZnS' deactivation is efficient even if sphalerite is activated with a solution of copper sulphate in the absence of a complexing agent. After this first-stage activation 'ZnS' was filtered, washed in distilled water and immersed in a solution of NH_3, EN or EDTA, saturated in oxygen, at pH 12. After a 20-min conditioning the slurry polarogram shows that the activation product has been solubilized.

In the presence of oxygen, ammonia, ethylenediamine and EDTA are thus good deactivating agents for sphalerite.

Flotation

Flotation tests were carried out at the same ZnS/Cu^{2+} ratio as that which was used in the electrochemical tests.

Activation prevention

The objective, during conditioning, is to prevent the formation of an activation product on the ZnS surface by use of complexing agents and oxygen. The tests were run by conditioning unactivated sphalerite in the presence of cupric ions, complexing agents (NH_3, EN or EDTA) and oxygen.

Deactivation

In this case the film of copper sulphide that has grown on the ZnS surface during activation is dissolved; 2 g of ZnS is conditioned in a copper sulphate solution for 20 min, the required concentration of complexing agent then being added. The resulting slurry, saturated in oxygen, is agitated for 20 min.

Table 2 Flotation test results

	pH	Conditioning	Recovery, %
Blank test			
ZnS activated by Cu^{2+}	12	pH 4.5, 20 min.	92.7
ZnS activated by Cu^{2+}	12	pH 4.5, 1 min	92.5
Activation prevention			
With NH_3	11.7	ZnS in 1 M NH_3 in presence of Cu^{2+} without O_2, 10 min	15.2
With EDTA	12	ZnS in 2×10^{-3} M EDTA with O_2, 10 min	4.3
With EN	12	ZnS in 10^{-3} M EN with O_2, 10 min	8.0
Deactivation			
With NH_3	11.7	(*a*) ZnS in 5×10^{-4} M, $CuSO_4$ 20 min (activation) (*b*) Addition of 1 M NH_3 with O_2, 20 min.	18.5
With EDTA	12	(*a*) As above (*b*) pH 12, addition of 3×10^{-2} M EDTA with O_2, 20 min	25.5
With EN	12	(*a*) As above (*b*) As above but with 10^{-2} M EN	22.3
Deactivation in presence of EN and strong oxidizing agent			
	12		7.2

A check is made of the non-floatabililty of unactivated sphalerite at pH 12 (recovery below 10%), whereas in the presence of cupric ions >92% of the mineral is recovered (Table 2). The overall results (Table 2) confirm the following hypotheses: activation prevention is complete in the presence of EDTA and ethylenediamine; nevertheless, the deactivation that results from the combined action of a complexing agent and oxygen is not complete: the approximately 20% recovery, although much reduced, is better than the 10% expected. With the use of an oxidant stronger than oxygen deactivation is complete (7.2% recovery).

Conclusions

The investigation described has shown the importance of potential in sphalerite activation and deactivation. The selection of complexing reagents without oxide-reducing properties was intentional. Electrochemical methods enabled the simple mechanisms involved to be demonstrated. Polarographic tests revealed the activation and deactivation reactions. Methods that made use of potentiometry and voltamperometry indicated the role of oxygen, which is unable to oxidize 'CuS' until the reducing power of the latter is increased by the presence of cupric ions.

The flotation tests confirmed the hypotheses. The present study is in line with the experimental results of Gaudin and co-workers[4] and the thermodynamic work of Marsicano *et al.*[6]

ZnS activation by cupric ions in the presence of a complexing agent in a nitrogen atmosphere is thermodynamically possible, as has been shown experimentally. There are, however, exceptions for EDTA and EN at pH 10 and pH 11, respectively.

It is probable that the mechanisms apply equally in regard to sphalerite activation by other metallic cations (Pb^{2+} and Ag^+) and to cases in which complexing agents with oxide-reducing properties are used.

Acknowledgement

The authors wish to thank the Délégation Générale à la Recherche Scientifique for the provision of financial assistance and M. J. J. Prédali, Société Minemet-Recherche, for the interest that he has taken in the investigation described here.

References
1. Bernasconi P. La minéralurgie et la métallurgie extractive des minerais sulfurés complexes d'origine volcanosédimentaire: êtat des travaux de recherche et des procédes en 1982. Rapport IRCHA, C.R.V.M. Nancy, 1983.
2. Pomianowski A. *et al.* Influence of iron content in sphalerite–marmatite on copper ion activation in flotation. In *Proceedings eleventh international mineral processing congress, Cagliari, 1975* (Cagliari: Istituto di Arte Mineraria, 1975), 639–53.
3. Finkelstein N. P. and Allison S. A. The chemistry of activation, deactivation and depression in the flotation of zinc sulfide: a review. In *Flotation: A. M. Gaudin memorial volume* Fuerstenau M. C. ed. (New York: AIME, 1976), 414–57.
4. Gaudin A. M. Fuerstenau D. W. and Mao G. W. Activation and deactivation studies with copper on sphalerite. *Min. Engng, N.Y.*, **11**, April 1959, 430–6.
5. Ralston J. and Healy T. W. Activation of zinc sulphide with Cu(II), Cd(II) and Pb(II): I, activation in weakly acidic media. *Int. J. Mineral Process.*, **7**, 1980, 175–201.
6. Marsicano F. *et al.* Some thermodynamic aspects of systems relevant to the flotation of sphalerite. *Rep. natn. Inst. Metall.* 1785, 1976, 61 p.
7. Gaudin A. M. Effect of xanthates, copper sulfate and cyanides on flotation of sphalerite. *Trans. Am. Inst. Min. Engrs*, **87**, 1930, 417–28.
8. Khin Maung Win. Application of infrared spectroscopy in determining the mechanisms of depression of sphalerite by cyanide. *Union Burma J. Sci. Technol.*, **1**, no. 2 1968, 333–41.
9. Stewart B. V. Goold L. A. and Marsicano F. Deactivation of copper-activated sphalerite with cyanide. *Rep. natn. Inst. Metall.* 1613, 1974, 28 p.
10. Charlot G. *Les réactions chimiques en solution: l'analyse qualitative minérale* (Paris: Masson, Gene Edition).